APPLIED

DIFFERENTIAL EQUATIONS

PRENTICE-HALL MATHEMATICS SERIES

APPLIED

DIFFERENTIAL EQUATIONS

Second Edition

MURRAY R. SPIEGEL

Professor of Mathematics
Rensselaer Polytechnic Institute

PRENTICE-HALL, INC., *Englewood Cliffs, N.J.*

Library of Congress Catalog Card Number 67-10753

Printed in the United States of America

To my mother

PREFACE TO THE SECOND EDITION

In this second edition I have tried to maintain the objectives of the first edition, together with the advantages of brevity, clarity, and flexibility, by introducing a minimum of change. Notable among changes which have been made are:

1. A chapter on Laplace transforms has been added. This chapter is independent of others and thus may either be treated briefly or entirely omitted.

2. The A, B, and C Exercises have been expanded or changed at various places in the book.

3. A brief discussion of the concept of linear dependence and the Wronskian has been introduced in the chapter on linear differential equations.

4. The chapter on numerical solutions of differential equations has been enlarged by the addition of a section on the Runge-Kutta method.

5. A short section on Fourier-Bessel series and orthogonal functions has been added.

I wish to take this opportunity to thank all those who have expressed interest in the book.

M. R. SPIEGEL

PREFACE TO THE FIRST EDITION

This book has been written with the following objectives:

1. To provide in an elementary manner a reasonable understanding of differential equations for students of engineering, physics, and chemistry as well as students of mathematics who are interested in applications of their field. Such aids as Illustrative Examples, Questions, and Problems for Discussion are used throughout to help facilitate understanding. Wherever possible, stress is on motivation rather than following of rules.

2. To demonstrate how differential equations can be useful in solving many types of problems—in particular, to show the student how to: (a) *translate* problems into the language of differential equations, i.e., set up mathematical formulations of problems; (b) *solve* the resulting differential equations subject to given conditions; (c) *interpret* the solutions obtained. Elementary problems from many different and important fields are explained with regard to their mathematical formulation, solution, and interpretation. Their applications are arranged so that topics of major interest to the reader or instructor may be chosen without difficulty. For example, in Chapter 3 there are applications of first-order and simple higher-order differential equations to problems of physics, geometry, chemistry, astronomy, including such topics as rockets, beams, radioactivity, heat flow, and many others.

3. To provide relatively *few* methods of solving differential equations that can be applied to a *large* group of problems. A minimum number of basic methods which the student would normally meet in practice have been emphasized; other methods not of general applicability but of interest are to be found in the Exercises.

4. To give the student who may wish to investigate more advanced methods and ideas, or more complicated problems and techniques, an opportunity to do so. This is done by providing Exercises which are graded in difficulty. The A Exercises are mostly straightforward, requiring little originality and designed for practice purposes. The B Exercises involve more complex algebraic computations or greater originality than the A group. The C Exercises are intended mainly to supplement the text material; they generally require a high degree of originality and background, intended to challenge the student.

5. To unify the presentation of the subject through a logical and orderly approach, the emphasis being on general concepts rather than isolated details.

For example the theory of first-order equations is treated from the general viewpoint of exactness. Thus the methods of separation of variables and solution of a first-order linear equation become special instances in which an equation can be made exact upon multiplication by a suitable integrating factor. Also the general notion of transformation of variables to arrive at simpler equations is emphasized. Thus the Euler differential equation is treated as simply one instance in which a differential equation can be transformed into a linear equation with constant coefficients. Use of the historical approach is also valuable in achieving unity. Thus Fourier series arise quite naturally in attempting to solve a certain boundary-value problem in heat conduction.

6. To separate the theory of differential equations from their application so as to give ample attention to each. This is accomplished by treating theory and applications in separate chapters, particularly in the early chapters of the book. This is done for two reasons. First, from a pedagogical viewpoint it seems inadvisable to mix theory and applications at an early stage since the beginner usually finds applied problems difficult to formulate mathematically and, when he is forced to do this in addition to learning techniques for solution, it generally turns out that he learns neither effectively. By treating theory without applications and then gradually broadening out to applications (at the same time reviewing theory) the student may better master both, since his attention is thereby focused on only one thing at a time. A second reason for separating theory and applications is to enable instructors who may wish to present a minimum of applications to do so conveniently without being in the awkward position of having to "skip around" in chapters.

The author wishes to express thanks to Esther and Meyer Scher for their continued interest and encouragement; to his colleagues for their helpful suggestions; to his students who provided the means whereby particular techniques of instruction were tested and, finally, to the staff of Prentice-Hall for accomplishing successfully a difficult task.

M. R. Spiegel

CONTENTS

Chapter Five

Chapter Six

Chapter Seven

Chapter One

DIFFERENTIAL EQUATIONS IN GENERAL

I. Some Preliminary Review

In analytic geometry and calculus, the concept of function was of fundamental importance. The student is reminded of the fact that, given an equation or relation involving the two variables x and y,

$$f(x,y) = 0 \tag{1}$$

it may be possible* to think of y as a real function of a real variable x. It will be remembered that a variable y is said to be a (real) function of a (real) variable x, if for given (real) values of x, there are corresponding (real) values of y. The student is reminded that the variable which is assigned values (in this case x) is called the *independent variable*, while the variable which takes on values as a result is called the *dependent variable*.† The functional relation between x and y may be *explicit* or *implicit*. If we can express equation (1) in the form $y = g(x)$, we call y an explicit function of x; otherwise it is an implicit function of x.‡ Whenever we speak of functional relation or function we shall think of function in either sense.

The student may remember that, in calculus, he learned methods of finding derivatives of the dependent variable with respect to the independent

---

* We say "may be possible" because we may have an equation involving two variables which does not define a real function. For example, consider the "innocent-looking" equation $x^2 + 4y^2 = 4xy - 1$. Writing it as $(x - 2y)^2 = -1$, we see that it cannot be satisfied for any real values of x and y. It should be mentioned that while functions involving complex numbers are of great importance in advanced mathematics, in this book whenever we speak of function or functional relation we shall assume, unless otherwise stated, that the variables are real.

† The set of values assigned to the independent variable is often called the *domain* of the function. For example in the case of the function defined by $y = \sqrt{x}$, $x \geq 0$, the domain is $x \geq 0$ and y is a real function of x. However if $y = \sqrt{x}$, $x < 0$, the domain is $x < 0$ and y is not a real function of x.

‡ If for each value of x for which a function is defined there corresponds one and only one value of y, we call y a *single-valued* function of x; otherwise it is a *many-valued* function. Thus, if $y^2 = x$, then given a value of $x > 0$ there are two values for y. The functions $y = \sqrt{x}$ and $y = -\sqrt{x}$ are branches of $y^2 = x$.

variable by means of the functional relation. Thus, if x is considered a dependent variable and y an independent variable, the student learned how to find dx/dy, d^2x/dy^2, ... If y is considered dependent and x independent, then the derivatives are with respect to x and one writes dy/dx, d^2y/dx^2, ...* It is understood that when one writes d^3y/dx^3, for example, one *automatically implies* that x is considered the independent and y the dependent variable.

Later in his calculus course, the student found that he could extend the functional concept. For example, given a relation

$$U(x,y,z) = 0 \tag{2}$$

it may be possible to think of z as a function of x and y, or of y as a function of x and z, or of x as a function of y and z.† In this case, two variables are assigned values, and the third may take on values. The variables which are assigned values are the independent variables, and the variable which takes on values is the dependent variable, as before. In equation (2) we would have one dependent and two independent variables. As before, we may speak of explicit and implicit functions. Thus, if (2) can be expressed as $x = R(y,z)$ then, in this form, x is an explicit function of y and z. Again, whenever we speak of function we think of it as either explicit or implicit.‡

The student may remember that he learned methods of finding derivatives of the dependent variable with respect to the independent variables. Thus, given the relation (2), he could compute $\partial z/\partial x$, $\partial z/\partial y$, $\partial^2 z/\partial x\,\partial y$, $\partial^3 z/\partial x^2\,\partial y$, $\partial^4 z/\partial y^4$, ..., in this case considering z a dependent variable and x and y independent variables. Similarly, if he took x as dependent and y and z as independent variables, he could compute $\partial x/\partial y$, $\partial x/\partial z$, $\partial^2 x/\partial y\,\partial z$, $\partial^3 x/\partial y^2\,\partial z$, ... It is understood, when one writes $\partial^3 y/\partial x^2\,\partial z$ for instance, that y is to be considered a dependent variable and x and z as independent variables. When one writes $\partial^4 y/\partial x^4$, one understands that y is a dependent variable, x is an independent variable, and the other independent variables are taken as constant.

---

* We assume that sufficient care has been taken to make sure that one knows what one is doing when computing these derivatives. For example, a student might attempt to determine dy/dx from the relation in the first footnote of page 1 as follows:

$$2x + 8y\frac{dy}{dx} = 4\left(x\frac{dy}{dx} + y\right), \frac{dy}{dx} = \frac{4y - 2x}{8y - 4x} = \frac{2(2y - x)}{4(2y - x)} = \frac{1}{2} \quad \text{if } 2y - x \neq 0$$

He might then "deduce" that the slope of the curve at any point was $\frac{1}{2}$ (except at points where $2y - x = 0$). The student should try to determine the fallacy of such an interpretation.

† This is subject to remarks similar to those in the second footnote of page 1. The set of values assigned to the independent variables is called the *domain* of the function. Thus, for example, if $z = \sqrt{1 - (x^2 + y^2)}$, $x^2 + y^2 \leq 1$, the domain is the set of all pairs of values (x,y) for which $x^2 + y^2 \leq 1$. Geometrically, this defines a region of the xy plane.

‡ We could extend the idea of function by means of simultaneous equations, parametric representations, and so on. The ideas involved are similar to those presented above.

REVIEW EXERCISES

1. Find dy/dx for each of the following functional relations.*

(a) $y = x^4 - 3x^2 + x + 5$.

(b) $y = x^2 + \dfrac{3}{\sqrt{x}} - \sqrt[3]{4x} + \dfrac{2}{x^5}$.

(c) $y = \dfrac{\sin 3x}{\sqrt{x}} - \cos 3x$.

(d) $y = x \sin 4x - \cos^2 2x$.

(e) $y = e^x \ln (x^2 + 1) - e^{-2x}$.

(f) $y = e^{-3x}(A \sin 4x + B \cos 4x)$.

(g) $y = \sqrt{x^2 + 3x} - 2 \csc 4x + 3 \sec 2x$.

(h) $y = \ln (\sec 3x + \tan 3x)$.

(i) $y = \dfrac{x}{2} \sqrt{1 - x^2} + \tfrac{1}{2} \arc \sin x$.

(j) $y = e^{\arc \tan x^2} + 3 \sin (2 \arc \cos x)$.

(k) $x^2 + y^2 = cx$.

(l) $x^3 y - y^4 = 4x^2$.

(m) $x \sin y + y \cos 3x = 5$.

(n) $x^2 \arc \sin 2y - 3xy + 1 = 0$.

(o) $e^{x^2 y} + \arc \tan xy = 2x$.

(p) $x \sqrt{1 - y^2} + y \sqrt{1 - x^2} = a$.

(q) $y \ln (x + y) + 2 \cos (x + y) = 3x^2$.

(r) $y \sin^2 3x - x[\ln y]^3 = 10$.

(s) $x \sec y - y \tan^2 x = \sqrt{2x + 1}$.

(t) $\sqrt{x^2 + y^2} + \arc \sin y/x = 4$.

2. Find d^2y/dx^2 for each of the following.

(a) $y = 3 \sin 2x - 4 \cos 2x$.

(b) $y = e^{-x}(\sin x + \cos x)$.

(c) $x \ln y = x + 1$.

(d) $x^{2/3} + y^{2/3} = 1$.

3. Given the following sets of parametric equations, find dy/dx and d^2y/dx^2.

(a) $x = 2t^2 - t, \ y = t^3 + t$.

(b) $x = 3 \sin t, \ y = 3 \cos t$.

(c) $x = a(\theta - \sin \theta), \ y = a(1 - \cos \theta)$.

(d) $x = \dfrac{e^u - e^{-u}}{2}, \ y = \dfrac{e^u + e^{-u}}{2}$.

4. If $\dfrac{dy}{dx} = 1 + y^2$ show that $\dfrac{d^3y}{dx^3} = 2(1 + y^2)(1 + 3y^2)$.

5. Find each of the indicated partial derivatives.

(a) $V = 2 \sin (x + 3y)$: $\dfrac{\partial V}{\partial x}, \dfrac{\partial V}{\partial y}, \dfrac{\partial^2 V}{\partial x^2}, \dfrac{\partial^2 V}{\partial y^2}, \dfrac{\partial^2 V}{\partial x \, \partial y}, \dfrac{\partial^2 V}{\partial y \, \partial x}, \dfrac{\partial^3 V}{\partial y^2 \, \partial x}$.

(b) $U = e^{-\lambda y} \sin \lambda x, \ \lambda = $ constant: $\dfrac{\partial^2 U}{\partial x^2}, \dfrac{\partial^2 U}{\partial y^2}$.

* In these exercises, as well as in later ones, we shall assume unless otherwise specified, that letters at the beginning of the alphabet represent constants. We shall use the notation "ln" for "log$_e$" where $e = 2.71828 \cdots$ is the base of natural logarithms. Also we shall assume unless otherwise stated that the domain of each function considered will be suitably chosen so that the functions are real, single-valued, continuous, and have continuous derivatives.

(c) $x^2 - yz = 4z^2$: $\dfrac{\partial z}{\partial x}$, $\dfrac{\partial z}{\partial y}$, $\dfrac{\partial^2 z}{\partial y^2}$.   (d) $x^4 y - z = 5z^2$: $\dfrac{\partial x}{\partial z}$, $\dfrac{\partial x}{\partial y}$.

(e) $T = \ln (x^2 + y^2 + z^2)$: $\dfrac{\partial^2 T}{\partial x^2}$, $\dfrac{\partial^2 T}{\partial y^2}$, $\dfrac{\partial^2 T}{\partial z^2}$.

6. Compute each of the indicated derivatives. State which variables are dependent and which are independent.

(a) $y = x^2 + 3x - 2$: $\dfrac{dx}{dy}$, $\dfrac{d^2 x}{dy^2}$.   (b) $V = e^{-3x+y}$: $\dfrac{\partial^2 V}{\partial x^2}$, $\dfrac{\partial^2 V}{\partial x \, \partial y}$.

(c) $yz^3 - x^4 z = y + 2$: $\dfrac{\partial y}{\partial z}$, $\dfrac{\partial y}{\partial x}$.   (d) $r \cos \theta + e^{-r} = \sin 2\theta$: $\dfrac{dr}{d\theta}$.

II. Some Definitions and Some Remarks

DEFINITION 1. A *differential equation* is an equation* which involves derivatives of a dependent variable† with respect to one or more independent variables. This equation may have the variables present only in the derivatives.

Example 1. The equation‡

$$y'' + y = e^x \tag{1}$$

is an equation which involves the dependent variable y, the independent variable x, and derivatives of y with respect to x. Hence, it is a differential equation.

Example 2. The equation

$$\left(\frac{d^4 s}{dt^4}\right)^2 + 2\left(\frac{d^2 s}{dt^2}\right)^5 + \left(\frac{ds}{dt}\right)^2 = 0 \tag{2}$$

is a differential equation because it involves derivatives of the dependent variable s with respect to the independent variable t, even though the variables are present only in the derivatives.

---

* In general, we shall exclude from the class of differential equations, those equations which are identities, such as

$$\frac{d}{dx}(xy) = x\frac{dy}{dx} + y \quad \text{or} \quad \frac{d}{dx}(\sin x) = \cos x$$

We shall also assume that the derivatives exist in some specified domain, such as for example an interval $a \leq x \leq b$ ($a \neq b$) in the case of one independent variable x, or a rectangle $a \leq x \leq b$, $c \leq y \leq d$ ($a \neq b$, $c \neq d$) in the case of two independent variables x and y, etc.

† It is possible for a differential equation to have more than one dependent variable; for example, $d^2x/dt^2 + dy/dt = e^t$ is a differential equation with dependent variables x and y and independent variable t. Such equations will be considered in Chapter 6.

‡ It will be the custom to use primes to denote derivatives with respect to a single independent variable when this variable is evident. Thus, in the given example, $y' \equiv dy/dx$, $y'' \equiv d^2y/dx^2$.

Example 3. The equation

$$\frac{\partial^2 V}{\partial x^2} + \frac{\partial^2 V}{\partial y^2} + \frac{\partial^2 V}{\partial z^2} = 0 \tag{3}$$

is a differential equation because it involves derivatives of the dependent variable V with respect to the independent variables x, y, z.

DEFINITION 2. Any function (whether defined explicitly or implicitly) which is free of derivatives, and which satisfies identically a differential equation, is said to be a *solution* of the differential equation.*

Example 1. The function y defined (implicitly in this case) by

$$y^3 - 3x + 3y = 5 \tag{4}$$

is a solution of the differential equation

$$y'' = -2y(y')^3 \tag{5}$$

because upon differentiation of the relation (4) with respect to x we find

$$y' = \frac{1}{y^2 + 1}, \qquad y'' = \frac{-2y}{(y^2 + 1)^3} \tag{6}$$

so that substitution of the derivatives given by (6) into (5) yields

$$\frac{-2y}{(y^2 + 1)^3} = -2y\left[\frac{1}{(y^2 + 1)}\right]^3$$

which is an identity.

Example 2. The function V defined (explicitly in this case) by

$$V = e^{3x} \sin 2y \tag{7}$$

is a solution of the differential equation

$$\frac{\partial^2 V}{\partial x^2} + 2\frac{\partial^2 V}{\partial y^2} = V \tag{8}$$

because upon differentiation of the relation (7) we find

$$\frac{\partial^2 V}{\partial x^2} = 9e^{3x} \sin 2y, \qquad \frac{\partial^2 V}{\partial y^2} = -4e^{3x} \sin 2y$$

and substituting these together with (7) into (8), we have the identity

$$9e^{3x} \sin 2y + 2(-4e^{3x} \sin 2y) = e^{3x} \sin 2y$$

DEFINITION 3. A differential equation which involves derivatives with respect to a single independent variable is called an *ordinary differential equation.*

* In the case of equations such as those mentioned in the second footnote on page 4, this definition needs appropriate modification.

DEFINITION 4. A differential equation which involves derivatives with respect to two or more independent variables is called a *partial differential equation*.*

Example. The differential equations (1) and (2) are ordinary differential equations, while (3) is a partial differential equation.

DEFINITION 5. The *n*th derivative of a dependent variable with respect to one or more independent variables is called a *derivative of order n* or, simply, an *n*th order derivative.

Example. d^3y/dx^3, $\partial^3z/\partial x\, \partial y^2$ are third-order derivatives;
$\partial^4z/\partial x^4$, $\partial^4V/\partial x^2\, \partial t^2$, d^4s/dt^4 are fourth-order derivatives.

DEFINITION 6. The *order* of a differential equation is the order of the highest-order derivative which is present.

Example 1. Equation (1) is an ordinary differential equation of order *two*. Equation (2) is an ordinary differential equation of order *four*. Equation (3) is a partial differential equation of order *two*.

Example 2. $\dfrac{\partial^4 z}{\partial x^4} + \left(\dfrac{\partial^2 z}{\partial x\, \partial y}\right)^6 = x$ is a fourth-order partial differential equation, while $(y')^2 + y^3 = x$ is a first-order ordinary differential equation.

DEFINITION 7. If a differential equation can be rationalized and cleared of fractions with regard to all derivatives present, the exponent of the highest-order derivative is called the *degree* of the differential equation. Not every differential equation has a degree.

Example 1. The differential equation $(y'')^{2/3} = 1 + y'$ can be rationalized by cubing both sides to obtain $(y'')^2 = (1 + y')^3$. The exponent of the highest-order derivative present (namely y'') is 2. Hence, the differential equation is of degree two. However, note that $y''' = \sqrt{x + y}$ is of degree *one*.

Example 2. The differential equations (1), (3), (5), and (8) are of degree one, or of first degree. Equation (2) is of degree two, or of second degree.

Example 3. $y'' + (y')^2 = \ln y''$ is an example of a differential equation for which a degree is not defined.

The student has now learned how to verify whether a given function is a solution of a given differential equation. One of the main problems in a study of differential equations is the determination of all the functions, if any, which are solutions of a given differential equation. Thus, for example,

---

* There are other classifications of differential equations based on number of variables, but the two given in Definitions 3 and 4 are adequate for the purposes of this book (see second footnote page 4).

we could ask: What functions are solutions of the equation $y'' + xy = 0$? Clearly $y = 0$ is a solution. Are there any others and, if so, can we find them? We could ask the same question about the partial differential equation

$$\frac{\partial^2 V}{\partial x^2} + 2\frac{\partial^2 V}{\partial y^2} = V$$

It has already been shown that $V = e^{3x}\sin 2y$ is a solution. It is also clear that $V = 0$ is a solution. Are there others and, if there are, can we find them?

Not every differential equation has a solution. For example, there cannot be a real function satisfying the differential equation

$$(y')^2 + 1 = 0$$

since, if there were, the left-hand side of the equation would be greater than, or equal to, one and thus could not possibly be zero.* There exist differential equations for which it is less obvious that a (real) solution does not exist.

In many instances, solutions of differential equations must be found which satisfy certain conditions. These conditions (which may arise quite naturally as in a physical problem) are often referred to as *initial* or *boundary conditions* depending on whether they are specified at one or more than one point. The corresponding problems of finding such solutions are then collectively called *boundary-value problems.*

In such cases we must ask not only whether solutions to the differential equations exist but whether they exist subject to the given conditions. As an example, suppose one were given the differential equation

$$xy' - 2y = 0 \tag{9}$$

and desired a solution of this equation such that when $x = 1$, $y = 1$. By methods which we shall later discuss, we can show (and the student may verify) that $y = Ax^2$ is a solution. If $y = 1$ where $x = 1$, we must clearly have $A = 1$. Hence, a solution satisfying the given conditions is $y = x^2$. Whether it is the only solution satisfying the given conditions is a question which we have not answered.

To show that the conditions may play a very important part in answering the question of existence of a solution, consider the case where we wish to determine a solution of (9), such that when $x = 0$, $y = 1$. Considering the solution $y = Ax^2$, it soon becomes clear that there is no value of A satisfying these conditions.

From the remarks above it is realized that there are at least three questions which we could and should ask about differential equations.

* Note, however, that the equation has the non-real solutions $y = \pm ix$, where $i = \sqrt{-1}$.

1. *Question of Existence.* Given a differential equation, does a solution satisfying certain given conditions exist?

2. *Question of Uniqueness.* If one solution satisfying the conditions does exist, can there be a different solution which also satisfies the given conditions?

3. *Question of Determination.* If one or more solutions satisfying the conditions do exist, how do we find them?

In the usual elementary course, the tendency is to emphasize the third question and to avoid even mention of the first and second ones. The reason for this is clear. The mathematics needed to answer the first two questions in a fairly complete manner is beyond that usually acquired in the first two years of college mathematics. Consequently the physicist, engineer, or other scientist may not even be aware of the existence of such questions. It is important for students of applied science, especially those who are going to use some differential equations in their fields, to know about such questions even though they may not have achieved background enough to investigate their answers. To realize this importance, suppose that one has succeeded in obtaining a solution satisfying certain conditions. Then, of course, one has answered in the affirmative the question of *existence*. It would be a good thing to know whether there are different solutions which satisfy the given conditions. It there were different solutions, this would be tantamount to a physical system (if the differential equation arose in an applied problem) behaving in several different ways *under the same conditions.* The mathematics, then, would definitely not agree with science because one of the practical principles of science is that physical systems under the same conditions behave in the same manner. Naturally, in such a case the differential equation would be the thing to revise until it gave results agreeing with physical facts.

Suppose, on the other hand, that one were in a position to realize that a solution definitely did not exist. Clearly then, there would be very little point in wasting time trying to find a method of obtaining the solution.*

In this book we shall study methods of solving differential equations but shall keep in mind the other two questions and, where possible, we shall give indications of their answers.

III. The Purpose of This Book

It has been hinted that differential equations are useful to the student of applied science. Perhaps it may be of interest to list various differential

---

* The author is aware of at least one case where a research worker was trying to solve a differential equation subject to certain conditions. He tried all sorts of techniques, but each one failed. Finally, it was pointed out to him that by use of an advanced *existence theorem*, it could be shown that the differential equation had no solution.

equations which have arisen in various fields of engineering and the sciences. The list is intended to indicate to the student that differential equations can be applied to many "practical fields" even though, it must be emphasized, the subject is of great interest in itself. The differential equations have been compiled from those occurring in advanced textbooks and journals. The student who wishes to convince himself has only to look casually at the various advanced books and journals in his intended field. If he does he may see equations like the following:

$$xy'' + y' + xy = 0 \tag{1}$$

$$\frac{d^2x}{dt^2} = -kx \tag{2}$$

$$\frac{d^2I}{dt^2} + 4\frac{dI}{dt} + 5I = 100 \sin 20t \tag{3}$$

$$EIy^{(IV)} = w(x) \tag{4}$$

$$y'' = \frac{w}{H}\sqrt{1 + (y')^2} \tag{5}$$

$$v + m\frac{dv}{dm} = v^2 \tag{6}$$

$$\frac{\partial^2 V}{\partial x^2} + \frac{\partial^2 V}{\partial y^2} + \frac{\partial^2 V}{\partial z^2} = 0 \tag{7}$$

$$\frac{\partial U}{\partial t} = k\left(\frac{\partial^2 U}{\partial x^2} + \frac{\partial^2 U}{\partial y^2}\right) \tag{8}$$

$$\frac{\partial^2 Y}{\partial t^2} = a^2\frac{\partial^2 Y}{\partial x^2} \tag{9}$$

$$\frac{\partial^4 \phi}{\partial x^4} + 2\frac{\partial^4 \phi}{\partial x^2 \partial y^2} + \frac{\partial^4 \phi}{\partial y^4} = F(x,y) \tag{10}$$

Equation (1) arises in mechanics, heat, electricity, aerodynamics, stress analysis, and many other fields.

Equation (2) is famous in the field of mechanics, in connection with simple harmonic motion, as in small oscillations of a simple pendulum. It could, however, arise in many other connections.

Equation (3) might arise in the determination of the current I as a function of time t in an alternating current electric circuit.

Equation (4) is an important equation in civil engineering in the theory of beam deflections, or bending.

Equation (5) arises in connection with a problem relating to suspended cables.

Equation (6) arose in a problem on rocket flight.

Equation (7) could arise in heat, electricity, aerodynamics, potential theory, and many other fields.

Equation (8) arises in the theory of heat conduction as well as in the diffusion of neutrons in an atomic pile for the production of nuclear energy. It also arises in the theory of Brownian motion.

Equation (9) arises in connection with the vibration of strings, as well as in the propagation of electric signals.

Equation (10) is famous in the theory of stress analysis.

These are but a few of the many equations which could arise and a few of the fields from which they are taken. Examinations of equations such as these by pure mathematicians, applied mathematicians, theoretical and applied physicists, chemists, engineers, and other scientists throughout the years have led to the conclusion that there are certain definite methods by which many of these equations can be solved. The history of these discoveries is, in itself, extremely interesting. There are, however, many unsolved equations; some of them of great importance. Modern giant calculating machines are presently engaged in determining solutions of such equations vital for research involving national defense, as well as many other endeavors.

It is one of the aims of this book to provide an introduction to some of the important problems arising in science and technology with which most scientists should be acquainted. In order to accomplish this aim it will be necessary to demonstrate how one solves the equations which arise as a result of mathematical formulation of these problems. The student should keep in mind that there are three steps in the theoretical solution of scientific problems.

1. *Mathematical Formulation of the Scientific Problem.* Scientific laws, which are of course based on experiment, are translated into mathematical equations.

2. *Solution of the Equations.* These equations need to be solved, subject to conditions arrived at from the physical problem, to determine the unknown, or unknowns, involved. The procedures involved may yield an exact solution or, in cases where exact solutions cannot be obtained, approximate solutions. Often, recourse is made to the use of machinery in numerical computations. In the consideration of solutions, one should naturally keep in mind the questions of existence and uniqueness which were previously raised.

3. *Scientific Interpretations of the Solution.* From the known solution, the scientist may be able to interpret what is going on physically. He may make graphs or tables and compare theory with experiment. He may even base further research on such interpretations.

Every one of these steps is important in the final solution of an applied problem and, for this reason, we shall emphasize all three steps in this book.

A EXERCISES

1. Complete the following table.

	Differential Equation	Ordinary or Partial	Order	Degree	Independent Variables	Dependent Variables
(a)	$y' = x^2 + 5y$					
(b)	$y'' - 4y' - 5y = e^{3x}$					
(c)	$\dfrac{\partial U}{\partial t} = 4\dfrac{\partial^2 U}{\partial x^2} + \dfrac{\partial U}{\partial y}$					
(d)	$\left(\dfrac{d^3 s}{dt^3}\right)^2 + \left(\dfrac{d^2 s}{dt^2}\right)^3 = s - 3t$					
(e)	$\dfrac{dr}{d\theta} = \sqrt{r\theta}$					
(f)	$\dfrac{d^2 x}{dy^2} - 3x = \sin y$					
(g)	$\dfrac{\partial^2 V}{\partial x^2} = \sqrt[3]{\dfrac{\partial V}{\partial y}}$					
(h)	$(2x + y)dx + (x - 3y)dy = 0$					
(i)	$y'' + xy = \sin y''$					
(j)	$\dfrac{\partial^2 T}{\partial x^2} + \dfrac{\partial^2 T}{\partial y^2} + \dfrac{\partial^2 T}{\partial z^2} = 0$					

2. Make a table similar to the one above for the differential equations 1–10 of Section III and complete the table.

3. Show that each of the functions defined in Column I, with one exception, are solutions of the corresponding differential equations in Column II, subject to the given conditions, if any.

I	II
(a) $y = e^{-x} + x - 1.$	$y' + y = x;\ y(0) = 0.$
(b) $y = Ae^{5x} + Be^{-2x} - \frac{1}{2}e^x$	$y'' - 3y' - 10y = 6e^x.$
(c) $s = 8\cos 3t + 6\sin 3t.$	$\dfrac{d^2 s}{dt^2} = -9s;\ s = 8;\ \dfrac{ds}{dt} = 18$ at $t = 0.$

(d) $8x^3 - 27y^2 = 0$.

(e) $Y(x,t) = 4 \sin (2x - 3t)$.

(f) $y = c_1 e^{-2x} + c_2 e^x + c_3 e^{3x}$.

(g) $y = Ax^3 + Bx^{-4} - \dfrac{x^2}{3}$.

(h) $1 + x^2 y + 4y = 0$.

(i) $xy^2 - y^3 = c$.

(j) $V(x,y) = e^{2x-y} \cos (y - 2x)$.

$(y')^3 = y; \; y(0) = 0$.

$9 \dfrac{\partial^2 Y}{\partial x^2} = 4 \dfrac{\partial^2 Y}{\partial t^2} \; ; \; Y(\pi,0) = 0$.

$y''' - 2y'' - 5y' + 6y = 0$.

$x^2 y'' + 2xy' - 12y = 2x^2$.

$y'' = 2x(y')^2; \; y'(0) = 0, \; y'''(0) = \frac{1}{8}$.

$y \, dx + (2x - 3y)dy = 0$.

$\dfrac{\partial^2 V}{\partial x^2} + 4 \dfrac{\partial^2 V}{\partial x \, \partial y} + 4 \dfrac{\partial^2 V}{\partial y^2} = 0$.

B EXERCISES

1. (a) If $y = Y_1(x)$ and $y = Y_2(x)$ are two different solutions of

$$y'' + 3y' - 4y = 0$$

show that $y = c_1 Y_1(x) + c_2 Y_2(x)$ is also a solution, where c_1 and c_2 are any constants. (b) Verify that $y = e^{-4x}$ and $y = e^x$ are solutions of the differential equation in (a) and, hence, that $y = c_1 e^{-4x} + c_2 e^x$ is also a solution. (c) By using the result in (b), find a solution of the differential equation satisfying the conditions $y(0) = 5, \; y'(0) = 0$.

2. For what values of the constant m will $y = e^{mx}$ be a solution of the differential equation

$$2y''' + y'' - 5y' + 2y = 0$$

(a) Use the ideas of the previous exercise to obtain a solution involving three constants: $c_1, c_2,$ and c_3. (b) Find a solution of the given differential equation satisfying the conditions

$$y(0) = 10, \quad y'(0) = 9, \quad y''(0) = 1$$

3. (a) For what values of the constant m is $V = e^{y+mx}$ a solution of

$$\dfrac{\partial^2 V}{\partial x^2} = 4 \dfrac{\partial^2 V}{\partial y^2}$$

(b) Show that $V = f(y + 2x) + g(y - 2x)$ is a solution, where f and g are any functions which are at least twice differentiable.

4. (a) Show that

$$Y(x,t) = 6 \sin (2x - 3t) + 8 \sin (4x - 6t) + 2 \sin (2x + 3t)$$

is a solution of the differential equation $9 \, \partial^2 Y / \partial x^2 = 4 \, \partial^2 Y / \partial t^2$, which satisfies the condition $Y(\pi,0) = 0$. (b) Can other solutions to the boundary-value problem in (a) be found? What can be said about the existence, uniqueness, and determination of solutions in this case?

5. Show that a solution of $y' = 1 + 2xy$ subject to $y(1) = 0$ is

$$y = e^{x^2} \int_1^x e^{-t^2}\, dt$$

6. If $y = Y_1(x)$ and $y = Y_2(x)$ are solutions of $y'' + y^2 = 0$, is $y = Y_1(x) + Y_2(x)$ also a solution? Compare with Exercise 1 and discuss.

C EXERCISES

1. In the equation $dy/dx + dx/dy = 1$, which variable is independent? Which variable is independent in the equation

$$\frac{d^2y}{dx^2} + \frac{d^2x}{dy^2} = 1$$

2. Show that the first-order, second-degree equation

$$xy(y')^2 - (x^2 + y^2)y' + xy = 0$$

is equivalent to two differential equations each of first order and degree. Show that $y = cx$ and $x^2 - y^2 = c$, where c is any constant, are solutions of the second-degree equation.

3. (a) Show that $\dfrac{d^2y}{dx^2} = -\dfrac{d^2x}{dy^2} \bigg/ \left(\dfrac{dx}{dy}\right)^3$ is an identity. (*Hint:* Differentiate both sides of $\dfrac{dy}{dx} = 1 \bigg/ \dfrac{dx}{dy}$ with respect to x.) (b) Use the result in (a) to transform the differential equation

$$\frac{d^2x}{dy^2} + (\sin x) \left(\frac{dx}{dy}\right)^3 = 0$$

with independent variable y, into one with independent variable x.

4. (a) Show that a solution of the first-order differential equation

$$y = xy' + \sqrt{1 + (y')^2}$$

is $y = cx + \sqrt{1 + c^2}$. (b) How would a solution of $y = xy' + f(y')$ be obtained? This equation is called *Clairaut's equation*. Is the method applicable to $y = 2xy' + (y')^3$?

5. Show that $x = a(\theta - \sin \theta)$, $y = a(1 - \cos \theta)$, where a is any constant other than zero, is a solution of $1 + (y')^2 + 2yy'' = 0$.

6. In a footnote to the definition of a differential equation on page 4, we exclude equations such as $(xy)' = xy' + y$. If we revise the definition so as to include such equations, discuss the nature of their solutions.

7. Some textbooks define a differential equation as an equation involving derivatives or differentials. From this viewpoint would (a) $3y\,dx + 2x\,dy = 0$ and (b) $e^{dx} = dy$ be differential equations? Discuss.

8. Show that the differential equation $x\,dx + y\,dy + z\,dz = 0$ has two dependent variables and one independent variable when written $x + y\dfrac{dy}{dx} + z\dfrac{dz}{dx} = 0$, but three dependent and one independent variable when written $x\dfrac{dx}{dt} + y\dfrac{dy}{dt} + z\dfrac{dz}{dt} = 0$. Explain.

9. (a) Show that a solution of $x\,dx + y\,dy + z\,dz = 0$ is $x^2 + y^2 + z^2 = c$, where c is any constant. (b) Show that $x^2 + y^2 = c_1$, $z = c_2$, where c_1 and c_2 are any constants, is also a solution of $x\,dx + y\,dy + z\,dz = 0$. Discuss a possible definition of solution for differential equations with more than one dependent variable, to supplement the definition in the text.

10. Show that $\dfrac{d^2x}{dt^2} + \dfrac{dy}{dt} = 10$ has a solution given by $x = 3t^2 + 2t - 1$, $y = 4t - 3$. Find other solutions.

IV. Some Observations Concerning Solutions of Ordinary Differential Equations

In Section II, a solution of a differential equation was defined. In this section, we investigate some properties of such solutions. To motivate our discussion, let us consider the following simple example. Let

$$x = A \sin 2t + B \cos 2t \tag{1}$$

where A and B are constants. By differentiation, we have

$$\frac{dx}{dt} = 2A \cos 2t - 2B \sin 2t \tag{2}$$

$$\frac{d^2x}{dt^2} = -4A \sin 2t - 4B \cos 2t \tag{3}$$

The right-hand side of (3) is -4 times that of (1). Hence,

$$\frac{d^2x}{dt^2} = -4x \tag{4}$$

which is a differential equation of order 2. It is clear that we obtained equation (4) from (1) by eliminating the constants A and B. It is also clear that (1) is a solution of (4), since it satisfies (4) identically. The constants A and B have no specific value, and (1) is a solution of (4), regardless of the values assigned to A and B. Furthermore, the two constants A and B cannot be replaced by a smaller number of constants. Such constants are called *essential arbitrary constants.** We put this in the form of a

> DEFINITION. If a relation involving a certain set of constants is a solution of a differential equation regardless of the specific values assigned to the constants, and if the set of constants cannot be replaced by a smaller set, then the constants are called *essential arbitrary constants.* Whenever we speak of arbitrary constants, we shall mean *essential* arbitrary constants.

Note that (1) has two arbitrary constants and that elimination of these constants led to the differential equation (4). We ask the

Question. Since a relation containing two arbitrary constants led to a differential equation of order 2 with the constants removed, will it be true that a relation with n arbitrary constants leads to an nth order differential equation with constants removed?

The answer to this question is, in general, *yes.* Mathematicians have been able to prove the following theorem, although we shall not present the proof.

> THEOREM 1. A relation between a dependent and independent variable involving n arbitrary constants may be differentiated so as to give rise to an ordinary differential equation of order n, in which the arbitrary constants are no longer present.

Remark: By virtue of this theorem we refer to a differential equation of order n, obtained by eliminating the n arbitrary constants of a given relation, as the *differential equation of the relation.*

ILLUSTRATIVE EXAMPLE 1

Find the differential equation for the relation

$$y = Ae^{3x} + Be^{-2x} + Ce^{2x}$$

where A, B, and C are arbitrary constants.

Solution. We have

$$y = Ae^{3x} + Be^{-2x} + Ce^{2x} \tag{5}$$

$$y' = 3Ae^{3x} - 2Be^{-2x} + 2Ce^{2x} \tag{6}$$

We may eliminate one arbitrary constant (B for example) by multiplying equation (5) by 2 and adding the result to equation (6), thus obtaining

$$2y + y' = 5Ae^{3x} + 4Ce^{2x} \tag{7}$$

---

* For example, the relation $y = Ae^{2x+B}$ has two constants, A and B. However, they are not essential arbitrary constants since, upon writing the given relation as $y = Ae^B \cdot e^{2x} = Ce^{2x}$, it is evident that A and B have been replaced essentially by one constant, C, which we refer to as one essential arbitrary constant or, briefly, as one arbitrary constant.

Differentiating (7), we have

$$2y' + y'' = 15Ae^{3x} + 8Ce^{2x} \tag{8}$$

Multiplying (7) by 3 and subtracting (8), we find

$$6y + y' - y'' = 4Ce^{2x} \tag{9}$$

having one arbitrary constant. Differentiation of (9) yields

$$6y' + y'' - y''' = 8Ce^{2x} \tag{10}$$

Multiplying (9) by 2 and subtracting (10), we eliminate C and find

$$y''' - 3y'' - 4y' + 12y = 0 \tag{11}$$

which is, indeed, a *third*-order differential equation having solution (5).

It should be noted that a higher-order differential equation could have been found with the given relation as solution. One example is the equation obtained by differentiation of (11). The student should always be on guard to check that the order of the differential equation is equal to the number of (essential) arbitrary constants.

ILLUSTRATIVE EXAMPLE 2

Find a differential equation for the family of all circles which have radius 1 and center anywhere in the xy plane.

Solution. The equation of a circle with center (A,B) and radius 1 is

$$(x - A)^2 + (y - B)^2 = 1 \tag{12}$$

Differentiating (12) with respect to x, we obtain

$$2(x - A) + 2(y - B)y' = 0 \tag{13}$$

Solving for $(x - A)$ and substituting into (12), we have

$$(y - B)^2(y')^2 + (y - B)^2 = 1 \tag{14}$$

so that we have been successful in eliminating A. To eliminate B, solve for $(y - B)$ to obtain

$$y - B = \pm[1 + (y')^2]^{-1/2} \tag{15}$$

Differentiating and simplifying this last equation yields

$$\frac{y''}{[1 + (y')^2]^{3/2}} = \pm 1 \tag{16}$$

which is the required second-order differential equation. The student may remember that the left side of (16) is the curvature of a plane curve. Thus, (16) states that the curvature of a certain plane curve at any point on it is equal to 1 in absolute value. Only circles of radius 1 have this property.

From the examples we have seen that

$$x = A \sin 2t + B \cos 2t \tag{17}$$

containing two arbitrary constants is a solution of the second-order equation

$$\frac{d^2x}{dt^2} = -4x \tag{18}$$

and that

$$y = Ae^{3x} + Be^{-2x} + Ce^{2x} \tag{19}$$

with three arbitrary constants is a solution of the third-order equation

$$y''' - 3y'' - 4y' + 12y = 0 \tag{20}$$

The following question immediately arises.

Question. Is (17) the *only* solution of (18)? Is (19) the only solution of (20), or more generally: given a relation with n arbitrary constants, is it the only solution of its corresponding nth order differential equation?

The answer to this is: not necessarily. There may be solutions other than the given relation (and special cases of it obtained by assigning particular values to the arbitrary constants). Consider

$$y = xy' + (y')^2 \tag{21}$$

It is easy to verify that $y = cx + c^2$ is a solution of (21). Conversely, (21) is the differential equation of the relation $y = cx + c^2$. However, the student may easily show by substitution in (21) that $y = -x^2/4$ is also a solution of (21), but that this solution cannot be obtained as a special case of $y = cx + c^2$ *by any choice of the constant c.* While such cases are relatively rare in practice, they do arise and, hence, consideration must be given to them. However, mathematicians have proved the following very important:

> THEOREM 2. Under certain conditions an nth-order differential equation has a solution with n arbitrary constants, and this is the only (or unique) solution—all others being particular cases.

The "certain conditions" of this theorem are elaborated upon in the next section. For present purposes it suffices to say that when they are satisfied, a solution with the n arbitrary constants is referred to as a *general solution* and all special cases of it are called *particular solutions.*

Thus for example, a general solution of the second-order equation

$$\frac{d^2x}{dt^2} = -4x \tag{22}$$

is

$$x = A \sin 2t + B \cos 2t \tag{23}$$

while particular solutions are

$$x = 3 \sin 2t, \qquad x = B \cos 2t, \qquad x = 2 \sin 2t - 5 \cos 2t$$

We can actually show in this case that *all* solutions are of the type (23) so that the terminology "general" is justified.

Trouble arises when the "certain conditions" of the theorem are not satisfied. Thus for example, as we have seen, the equation (21) has solutions

$$y = cx + c^2 \tag{24}$$

and

$$y = -x^2/4 \tag{25}$$

and it is clear that (25) is not obtained as a special case of (24) for any choice of the constant c.

It has been the custom even in this case to refer to (24) as a general solution or, what is even worse, as *the* general solution. The solution (25), which cannot be obtained from this general solution, is then referred to as a *singular solution*. At first sight, this terminology would appear to be atrocious since the word "general" seems to imply that all solutions are special cases. However, it turns out to be really not so bad for several reasons. First, in many instances which arise in practice, the differential equations and conditions are defined in some suitable region such that there actually is a general solution with all others as special cases. Second, singular solutions as the name implies are rather the exception than the rule, and their possible presence is often indicated through careful examination of the differential equations and conditions. The basis for these reasons will be investigated further in the next section on existence and uniqueness.

V. Some Remarks Concerning Existence and Uniqueness

Let us say at the outset that, for most of the differential equations with which we shall deal, there are unique solutions that satisfy certain prescribed conditions. However, lest the engineer or other scientist become too confident with this knowledge, we show, by means of an example, how important it is to be aware of existence and uniqueness problems. The student who feels that he will get by in 99 per cent of the cases is probably correct, but the author knows of a few who were "trapped" in the remaining 1 per cent category.

We consider the differential equation

$$xy' - 3y = 0 \tag{1}$$

which arose in a certain applied problem, the details of which we will omit. Suffice it to say that an experimental curve obtained appeared as in Fig. 1.

From this curve it appears that $y = 0$ for $x \leq 0$ and that y increases (in some way) for $x \geq 0$. By simple methods which we discuss later, the scientist working the problem deduced that the general solution of (1) is $y = Cx^3$, where C is an arbitrary constant. Theoretical considerations provided the condition $y = 1$ where $x = 1$, which agreed with experiment. Thus, the scientist decided that the required solution was given by $y = x^3$, the graph of

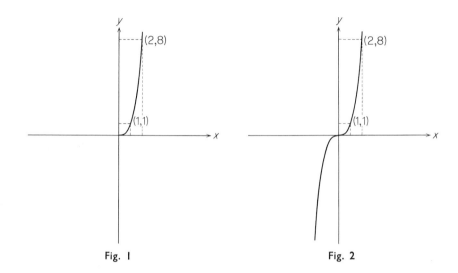

Fig. 1   Fig. 2

which appears as Fig. 2. The theoretical and experimental graphs agreed for $x \geq 0$ but disagreed for $x < 0$. The scientist decided that the mathematics must be wrong. However, it turned out that the *handling* of the mathematics was wrong. The scientist had erroneously assumed, as he had previously always assumed, that a unique solution existed. It is not difficult to show that

$$y = \begin{cases} Ax^3, & x \geq 0 \\ Bx^3, & x \leq 0 \end{cases} \tag{2}$$

where A and B are constants, is an even "more general" solution than is $y = Cx^3$. By choosing $A = 1$ to satisfy $y = 1$ where $x = 1$, and choosing $B = 0$, the solution (2) becomes

$$y = \begin{cases} x^3, & x \geq 0 \\ 0, & x \leq 0 \end{cases}$$

agreeing completely with experiment.

This example shows the need for knowing just when a unique solution does exist. Even though we cannot go into detail concerning proof, we shall not hide our heads from reality like the proverbial ostrich but, instead, shall satisfy our consciences by quoting the following

> THEOREM. Given the first-order differential equation $y' = F(x,y)$, let $F(x,y)$ satisfy the following conditions:
>
> 1. $F(x,y)$ is real, finite, single-valued, and continuous at all points (x,y) within a region R of the xy plane (which may comprise all points).
>
> 2. $\dfrac{\partial F(x,y)}{\partial y}$ is real, finite, single-valued, and continuous in R.
>
> Then there exists one and only one solution $y = g(x)$ in R, which passes through any given point of R.

This theorem provides *sufficient conditions* for the existence and uniqueness of a solution; i.e., if the conditions hold, the existence and uniqueness are guaranteed. However, the conditions are not *necessary*; i.e., if the conditions are not all satisfied, there may *still* be a unique solution. It should be noted that the theorem does not tell us *how* to obtain this solution. Corresponding theorems for higher-order equations are available.*

By using the theorem, the scientist might have avoided difficulty, for his equation is equivalent to the equation

$$y' = \frac{3y}{x}$$

provided $x \neq 0$. Here $F(x,y) \equiv 3y/x$, and $\partial F/\partial y = 3/x$ are real, finite, single-valued, and continuous at all points in the region $x > 0$, and a unique solution is guaranteed to exist in this case. Similarly, for $x < 0$, a unique solution exists. However, there is *no reason* to suppose that a unique solution valid in both regions $x > 0$ and $x < 0$ exists, which explains the seeming dilemma of the scientist.

The existence theorem also provides clues as to the presence of singular solutions and their connections with general solutions. For example, from equation (21) of the last section we find

$$y' = \frac{-x + \sqrt{x^2 + 4y}}{2}, \qquad y' = \frac{-x - \sqrt{x^2 + 4y}}{2} \tag{3}$$

Considering the first equation in (3) we note that the partial derivative of the right-hand side is $1/\sqrt{x^2 + 4y}$ and this is real, single-valued, and continuous if and only if $y > -x^2/4$, which describes geometrically the region above a parabola (Fig. 3). Given a point, say (1,2), in this region we see from the

---

* Such a theorem is considered in C Exercise 14, page 25 and in Chapter 4, page 142. See also reference [10] in the Bibliography, page 365. Henceforth, any reference number in square brackets will refer to this Bibliography. Page numbers after numbers in square brackets refer to specific pages in the given reference.

general solution $y = cx + c^2$ that $c^2 + c - 2 = 0$ or $c = 1, -2$, i.e., $y = x + 1, y = 4 - 2x$. Of these only $y = x + 1, x \geq -2$ satisfies the first equation of (3) in accordance with the existence theorem. Similarly, $y = 4 - 2x, x \leq 4$ is the only solution of the second equation in (3) through (1,2).

It is interesting to note that $y = x + 1, y = 4 - 2x$ and in fact $y = cx + c^2$, are tangents to the parabola $y = -x^2/4$ which is what we have

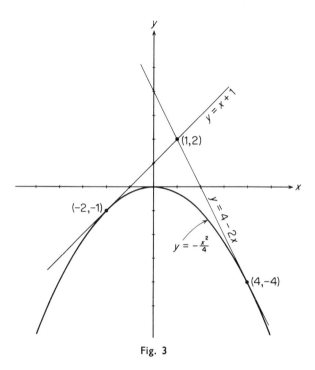

Fig. 3

called a singular solution. This parabola which "envelops" all the tangents (Fig. 4) is for obvious reasons called the *envelope*.*

The examples just given serve to indicate some guiding principles concerning solutions. For first-order, first-degree ordinary differential equations there will usually be a general solution in certain restricted regions as guaranteed by the existence theorem. Singular solutions, if they occur, may manifest themselves at the boundaries of such regions. In some cases they can be seen from certain factors which may become zero or infinite (as for example in B Exercise 7). Extensions of these ideas to other differential equations can be made.

---

* For some further discussion of envelopes and singular solutions, together with related topics, see the advanced exercises and also reference [5].

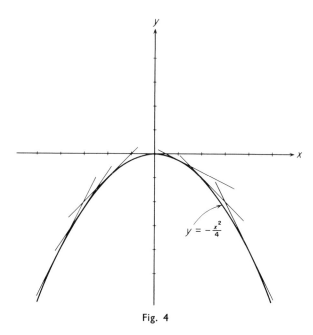

$$y = -\frac{x^2}{4}$$

Fig. 4

A EXERCISES

1. Find a differential equation corresponding to each relation, with indicated arbitrary constants. Verify that each relation is a general solution of the differential equation obtained.

(a) $y = 3x^2 + ce^{-2x}$: c.   (b) $y = x + c \sin x$: c.

(c) $x^2 - ay^2 = 1$: a.   (d) $y \ln x = bx$: b.

(e) $y = c_1 \sin 4x + c_2 \cos 4x + x$: c_1, c_2.

(f) $I = \alpha t e^{-t} + \beta e^{-t} + 2 \sin 3t$: α, β.

(g) $x^2 + y^2 - cx = 0$: c.   (h) $y = ax^3 + bx^2 + cx$: a, b, c.

(i) $y = Ae^{-3x} + Be^{2x} + Ce^{4x}$: A, B, C.

(j) $r = a \ln \theta + b\theta + c$: a, b, c.

2. Show that each relation in Column I is a general solution of the differential equation of Column II. Obtain particular solutions satisfying conditions in Column III.

I	II	III
(a) $y = A \cos x$.	$y' + y \tan x = 0$.	$y(\pi) = 4$.
(b) $y = c_1 e^x + c_2 e^{-x} - 4x$.	$y'' - y = 4x$.	$\begin{cases} y(0) = 2, \\ y'(0) = 0. \end{cases}$
(c) $x^2 - y^2 + 2xy = c$.	$y' = (y + x)/(y - x)$.	$y(-2) = 3$.

(d) $y = c_1 + c_2x + c_3x^2$. $y''' = 0$. $\begin{cases} y(0) = 1, \\ y(1) = 2, \\ y(2) = 9. \end{cases}$

(e) $xy^2 = Ax + B$. $x(y')^2 + 2yy' + xyy'' = 0$. $\begin{cases} y(3) = 1, \\ y'(3) = 2. \end{cases}$

3. Find a differential equation for each of the following families of curves in the xy plane:

(a) All circles with center at the origin and any radius. (b) All parabolas through the origin with x axis as common axis. (c) All circles with centers on $y = x$ and tangent to the y axis. (d) All ellipses with center at the origin and axes on the coordinate axes.

B EXERCISES

1. Find a differential equation of third order having $y = ax \sin x + bx \cos x$, where a and b are arbitrary constants, as a solution. Is this a general or particular solution of the third-order equation?

2. (a) How many arbitrary constants has $y = c_1e^{5x+c_2} + c_3e^{5x}$? (b) Find a differential equation having this as general solution.

3. Show that the general solution of $y'' + y = e^{-x^2}$ is

$$y = A \cos x + B \sin x + \sin x \int_0^x e^{-t^2} \cos t \, dt - \cos x \int_0^t e^{-t^2} \sin t \, dt$$

Find the particular solution satisfying $y(0) = y'(0) = 0$.

4. (a) Show that $f(x)dx + g(y)dy = 0$ has general solution $\int f(x)dx + \int g(y)dy = c$.
(b) Use (a) to solve

$$\frac{dy}{dx} = \frac{x^2 + 1}{y^2 + 4}, \ y(0) = 1.$$

Do you think the name "separation of variables" for this method is appropriate?

5. Solve (a) $y' = xy$, $y(0) = 4$; (b) $(x + xy^2)dx + (y + x^2y)dy = 0$, $y(0) = 1$.

6. Prove that $y = cx + c^2$ is tangent to $y = -x^2/4$.

7. Show that $y' = y^{2/3}$ has solutions $y = 0$ and $y = (x + c)^3/27$. Discuss the relations between these. Investigate similarly $y' = y^{1/3}$.

C EXERCISES

1. (a) Show that the differential equation for $y = c_1u_1(x) + c_2u_2(x)$, where $u_1(x)$ and $u_2(x)$ are functions which are at least twice differentiable, may be written

in determinant form as

$$\begin{vmatrix} y & u_1(x) & u_2(x) \\ y' & u_1'(x) & u_2'(x) \\ y'' & u_1''(x) & u_2''(x) \end{vmatrix} = 0$$

(b) What happens in the case where

$$W = \begin{vmatrix} u_1(x) & u_2(x) \\ u_1'(x) & u_2'(x) \end{vmatrix} \equiv 0$$

The determinant W is called the *Wronskian* of $u_1(x)$ and $u_2(x)$.

2. (a) Make use of the previous exercise to obtain the differential equation having as general solution $y = c_1 e^{3x} + c_2 e^{-2x}$. (b) Generalize the method of Exercise 1 and, thus, obtain a differential equation having general solution $y = c_1 x^4 + c_2 \sin x + c_3 \cos x$.

3. Using the existence and uniqueness theorem, locate graphically those regions of the xy plane in which each of the following differential equations is guaranteed to have unique solutions. In particular determine whether there is a unique solution passing through the indicated point.

(a) $y' = 3x + \sin 2y$; $y(1) = \pi$.   (b) $y' = 1/(x^2 + y^2)$; $y(0) = 1$.
(c) $y' = 1/(x^2 + y^2)$; $y(0) = 0$.   (d) $y' = y \csc x$; $y(\pi/2) = 4$.
(e) $y' = (x - 2y)/(y - 2x)$; $y(1) = 2$.   (f) $y' = 1/(x^2 - y^2)$; $y(1) = 2$.

4. Show that $y = 0$, $y = c^2 x + 2c$, $y = -1/x$ are solutions of

$$y' = \left(\frac{\sqrt{1 + xy} - 1}{x} \right)^2$$

Discuss these solutions and their relation to the existence theorem and to each other.

5. Discuss possible solutions of $(y' - 2x)(y' - 3x^2) = 0$.

6. (a) Show that $|y'| + |y| = 0$ has a solution but not one involving an arbitrary constant. (b) Show that $|y'| + 1 = 0$ has no solution. (c) Discuss (a) and (b) from the viewpoint of the existence theorem.

7. (a) Find a differential equation for the family of tangents to $x^2 + y^2 = 1$. (*Hint:* Let $(\cos c, \sin c)$ be any point on the circle.) (b) Show that a general solution of the differential equation in (a) is defined by the family of tangent lines. (c) Show that $x^2 + y^2 = 1$ is a solution of the differential equation of (a). What kind of solution is it?

8. (a) Show that the differential equation for the family of straight lines $y = cx - c^3$ is $y = xy' - (y')^3$. (b) Show that the envelope of the family $y = cx - c^3$ is also a solution of the differential equation in (a). What kind is it? (*Hint:* The envelope of a one-parameter family $F(x,y,c) = 0$, if it exists, may

be found from the simultaneous solution of $F(x,y,c) = 0$ and $\dfrac{\partial F(x,y,c)}{\partial c} = 0$.)

(c) Can the envelope be obtained directly from the differential equation?

9. Use Exercise 8 to solve (a) $y = xy' + 1 + (y')^2$; (b) $y = xy' + \tan y'$.

10. Solve $y^2 + (x^2 - 1)(y')^2 = 2xyy' + 1$.

11. Let $y' = F(x,y)$ where $F(x,y)$ satisfies the conditions of the existence theorem on page 20. At each point (a,b) of region R, construct a short line, called a *lineal element* having slope $F(a,b)$. Doing this for a large number of points, we obtain a graph as in Fig. 5 called the *direction field* of the differential equa-

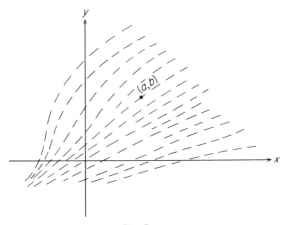

Fig. 5

tion. (a) Obtain the direction field for $y' = 2x - y$. (b) Explain the relationship existing among various solutions of the equation and the direction field. (c) Can you guess the approximate position of that curve passing through $(0,0)$? (d) Show that the general solution of $y' = 2x - y$ is $y = 2x - 2 + ce^{-x}$ and thus compare with your guess in (c).

12. Use the method of Exercise 11 to obtain approximate graphical solutions of each of the following. (a) $y' = 2x$, $y(0) = 1$. (b) $y' = x + y$, $y(0) = 2$. (c) $y' = 1/(x^2 + y^2)$, $y(1) = 0$.

13. (a) Show how the tedium of computation in Exercise 11 can be reduced by setting $y' = 2x - y = m$ and realizing that for any constant m all points on the line $2x - y = m$ have associated lineal elements of slope m. This is sometimes called the *method of isoclines* (constant slope). (b) Use the method of (a) to work Exercise 12.

14. An existence theorem for the second-order differential equation $y'' = F(x,y,y')$, which can be written as two first-order equations $z' = F(x,y,z)$, $y' = z$, states that if $F(x,y,z)$ and its partial derivatives $\partial F/\partial y$, $\partial F/\partial z$ are real, single-valued, and continuous at all points (x,y,z) within a region R of 3-dimensional space, then there exists one and only one solution $y = g(x)$ which passes through any given point of R. Note that if the point is (x_0,y_0,z_0) this is equivalent to $y = y_0$, $y' = z_0$ for $x = x_0$. (a) Using this theorem investigate the existence and uniqueness of solutions to $y'' + x(y')^2 = 1$. (b) Work part (a) for $xy'' + y' + xy = 0$, $y(1) = 2$, $y'(1) = 0$. (c) What difficulties occur in case conditions are prescribed at $x = 0$? (d) Can you think of a generalization of this theorem?

Chapter Two

FIRST-ORDER AND SIMPLE HIGHER-ORDER

ORDINARY DIFFERENTIAL EQUATIONS

I. Some Intuitive Preliminaries—The Idea of Exactness

A differential equation of first order and degree has the form

$$\frac{dy}{dx} = F(x,y) \quad \text{or} \quad M(x,y)dx + N(x,y)dy = 0 \tag{1}$$

For example, the differential equation

$$\frac{dy}{dx} = \frac{x - 3y}{2y - x}$$

may also be written

$$(x - 3y)dx + (x - 2y)dy = 0$$

where $M \equiv x - 3y$, $N \equiv x - 2y$. The whole problem of solving first-order, first-degree differential equations hinges on the solution of either of equations (1).

In Section IV of Chapter 1 we found that under certain conditions an nth order differential equation has a general solution with n arbitrary constants. In our case $n = 1$, so we expect the general solution of (1) to have one arbitrary constant.* If we can solve for this constant, which we shall call c, this solution may be written

$$U(x,y) = c \tag{2}$$

In Section IV of Chapter 1 we also found that, in general, we could obtain an nth order differential equation corresponding to a relation with n arbitrary constants by successive differentiations and elimination of the arbitrary constants. It follows that we ought to be able to obtain a first-order differential

---

* We assume that, in accordance with the existence theorem of page 20, there is a region R in which such a general solution exists.

equation from (2). If we take the differential of both sides of (2) we have

$$dU = \frac{\partial U}{\partial x} dx + \frac{\partial U}{\partial y} dy = 0 \tag{3}$$

so that

$$\frac{\partial U}{\partial x} dx + \frac{\partial U}{\partial y} dy = 0 \quad \text{or} \quad \frac{dy}{dx} = -\frac{\partial U/\partial x}{\partial U/\partial y} \tag{4}$$

is the required differential equation. This equation must be the same equation as the equations (1), the second of which may be written

$$\frac{dy}{dx} = -\frac{M}{N} \tag{5}$$

From (4) and (5) it clearly follows that

$$\frac{\partial U/\partial x}{\partial U/\partial y} = \frac{M}{N} \tag{6}$$

or

$$\frac{\partial U/\partial x}{M} = \frac{\partial U/\partial y}{N} \tag{7}$$

Calling each of these ratios μ, which in the general case may be a function of x and y, we have

$$\frac{\partial U}{\partial x} = \mu M, \quad \frac{\partial U}{\partial y} = \mu N \tag{8}$$

Substituting these values into (3) we find that

$$\mu(M\,dx + N\,dy) = dU = 0 \tag{9}$$

From (9), we see that $\mu(M\,dx + N\,dy)$ is the differential of a function U of x and y. We call this a *perfect* or *exact differential*. If we start with the differential equation

$$M\,dx + N\,dy = 0 \tag{10}$$

and multiply by μ to obtain

$$\mu(M\,dx + N\,dy) = 0 \tag{11}$$

where the left-hand side is an exact differential, we say that we have made equation (10) exact, and call (11) an *exact differential equation*. In such a case, (11) can be written

$$dU(x,y) = 0 \tag{12}$$

from which we may obtain, by integration, the solution

$$U(x,y) = c \tag{13}$$

The function μ, which enables us to go from (10) to (12) and then by an integration to (13), is for obvious reasons called an *integrating factor*. Let us summarize these remarks in three definitions.

DEFINITION 1. The differential of a function of one or more variables is called an *exact differential*.

DEFINITION 2. If $M\,dx + N\,dy = 0$ is multiplied by $\mu(x,y)$ to obtain $\mu(M\,dx + N\,dy) = 0$, whose left-hand side is an exact differential, we say that we have made the differential equation exact.*

DEFINITION 3. The multiplying function μ is called an *integrating factor* of the differential equation $M\,dx + N\,dy = 0$.

Motivation Example. Let it be required to solve the equation

$$(2y + 3x)dx + x\,dy = 0 \tag{14}$$

Suppose we "happen to know" that an integrating factor of this equation is x. Multiplication of (14) by x yields

$$(2xy + 3x^2)dx + x^2\,dy = 0 \tag{15}$$

which, by definition of integrating factor, should be exact. The student can verify that this is so, since we can write (15) as

$$d(x^2y + x^3) = 0 \tag{16}$$

and so, by integration, the general solution is $x^2y + x^3 = c$.

Theoretically, the example is perfectly clear but the student may be asking himself the following:

Questions. 1. How does one "know" that x is an integrating factor? 2. How does one "know" that we can write (15) as (16)?

Question 2 is answered in the next section. Question 1 will form a basis for the rest of this chapter.

II. Exact Differential Equations

If the differential equation $M\,dx + N\,dy = 0$ is exact, then by definition there is a function $U(x,y)$ such that

$$M\,dx + N\,dy = dU \tag{1}$$

But, from elementary calculus,

$$dU = \frac{\partial U}{\partial x}\,dx + \frac{\partial U}{\partial y}\,dy \tag{2}$$

---

* Naturally, we assume $\mu \not\equiv 0$. Also, if $\mu \equiv 1$, the equation is already exact.

and so, upon comparison of (1) and (2), we see that

$$\frac{\partial U}{\partial x} = M, \qquad \frac{\partial U}{\partial y} = N \tag{3}$$

Differentiating the first of equations (3) with respect to y and the second with respect to x, we find*

$$\frac{\partial^2 U}{\partial y\, \partial x} = \frac{\partial M}{\partial y}, \qquad \frac{\partial^2 U}{\partial x\, \partial y} = \frac{\partial N}{\partial x} \tag{4}$$

Under suitable conditions, the order of differentiation is immaterial,† so that equations (4) lead to the condition

$$\frac{\partial M}{\partial y} = \frac{\partial N}{\partial x} \tag{5}$$

This is a *necessary* condition for exactness; i.e., if a differential equation is exact, then of necessity it follows that (5) is true. The converse theorem states that if (5) holds, then $M\, dx + N\, dy$ is an exact differential, i.e., we can find a function U such that $\partial U/\partial x = M$, $\partial U/\partial y = N$. This converse theorem can be proved‡ and shows that (5) is also a sufficient condition for exactness. We summarize these remarks in the following

THEOREM. A necessary and sufficient condition for the exactness of the differential equation $M\, dx + N\, dy = 0$ is $\partial M/\partial y = \partial N/\partial x$. This means that (1) if $M\, dx + N\, dy = dU = 0$ (i.e., the equation is exact), then $\partial M/\partial y = \partial N/\partial x$ (necessity); (2) if $\partial M/\partial y = \partial N/\partial x$, then U exists such that $M\, dx + N\, dy = dU$ or, what is equivalent, U exists such that $\partial U/\partial x = M$ and $\partial U/\partial y = N$ (sufficiency).

To illustrate the theorem, consider equation (15) of the last section, i.e.,

$$(2xy + 3x^2)dx + x^2\, dy = 0$$

Here

$$M = 2xy + 3x^2, \quad N = x^2, \quad \frac{\partial M}{\partial y} = 2x, \quad \frac{\partial N}{\partial x} = 2x$$

Thus, by the sufficiency part of the theorem, we are guaranteed that there does exist a function U so that

$$(2xy + 3x^2)dx + x^2\, dy = dU \tag{6}$$

---

* We are naturally supposing that these derivatives exist; otherwise we have no right to take them.

† A sufficient condition under which the order of differentiation is immaterial is that U and its partial derivatives (of order two at least) be continuous in the region under consideration. We shall assume that this condition is satisfied unless otherwise stated.

‡ See page 31.

or, what amounts to the same thing, there exists a function U so that

$$\frac{\partial U}{\partial x} = 2xy + 3x^2, \qquad \frac{\partial U}{\partial y} = x^2 \qquad (7)$$

It remains for us to determine U. This is not difficult, for the first equation in (7) states merely that the partial derivative of U with respect to x is $2xy + 3x^2$. We should then be able to find U by the *reverse of differentiation* with respect to x, i.e., *integration* with respect to x, keeping y constant. The constant of integration which must be added is independent of x but *might* depend on y; i.e., the arbitrary constant may really be a function of y. Denote this by $f(y)$. Thus, we obtain

$$U = \int (2xy + 3x^2)\partial x + f(y) \qquad (8)$$

the symbol ∂x emphasizing that integration is with respect to x, keeping y constant. Performing this integration, we find

$$U = x^2 y + x^3 + f(y) \qquad (9)$$

To find $f(y)$, substitute (9) into the second of equations (7). Then,

$$\frac{\partial}{\partial y} [x^2 y + x^3 + f(y)] = x^2 \quad \text{or} \quad x^2 + f'(y) = x^2$$

so that

$$f'(y) = 0 \quad \text{or} \quad f(y) = \text{constant} = A$$

Hence,

$$U = x^2 y + x^3 + A$$

Thus, the differential equation may be written

$$d(x^2 y + x^3 + A) = 0$$

and integration yields

$$x^2 y + x^3 + A = B \quad \text{or} \quad x^2 y + x^3 = c$$

where we have written $c = B - A$. It is observed that this is the same solution obtained in the last section. It is also observed that there was really no need to add the constant of integration, A, in finding $f(y)$.

To prove the sufficiency part of the theorem on page 30, it is enough to show that if $\partial M/\partial y = \partial N/\partial x$ then we can actually produce a function $U(x,y)$ such that

$$\frac{\partial U}{\partial x} = M, \qquad \frac{\partial U}{\partial y} = N \qquad (10)$$

There certainly are functions U which will satisfy the first of equations (10); in fact all such functions are given by

$$U = \int M \, \partial x + f(y) \qquad (11)$$

All we have to do now is show that there exists a function $f(y)$ such that (11) will also satisfy the second of equations (10), i.e., we must show that there is a function $f(y)$ such that

$$\frac{\partial}{\partial y}\left[\int M \, \partial x + f(y)\right] = N \quad \text{or} \quad f'(y) = N - \frac{\partial}{\partial y}\int M \, \partial x$$

To show this, we need only prove that

$$N - \frac{\partial}{\partial y}\int M \, \partial x \tag{12}$$

is a function of y alone. This will indeed be true if the partial derivative with respect to x of the expression (12) is zero. But this is easily shown as follows:

$$\frac{\partial}{\partial x}\left[N - \frac{\partial}{\partial y}\int M \, \partial x\right] = \frac{\partial N}{\partial x} - \frac{\partial}{\partial x}\frac{\partial}{\partial y}\int M \, \partial x$$

$$= \frac{\partial N}{\partial x} - \frac{\partial}{\partial y}\frac{\partial}{\partial x}\int M \, \partial x$$

$$= \frac{\partial N}{\partial x} - \frac{\partial M}{\partial y} = 0$$

since $\partial M/\partial y = \partial N/\partial x$ by hypothesis. The sufficiency is therefore proved.

ILLUSTRATIVE EXAMPLE 1

Solve

$$2xy \, dx + (x^2 + \cos y)dy = 0$$

Solution. Here

$$M = 2xy, \quad N = x^2 + \cos y, \quad \frac{\partial M}{\partial y} = 2x = \frac{\partial N}{\partial x}$$

and the equation is exact. Thus U exists such that

$$\frac{\partial U}{\partial x} = 2xy, \quad \frac{\partial U}{\partial y} = x^2 + \cos y \tag{13}$$

Integrating the first equation with respect to x,

$$U = x^2y + f(y)$$

Substituting into the second equation of (13),

$$x^2 + f'(y) = x^2 + \cos y, \quad f'(y) = \cos y, \quad f(y) = \sin y$$

Hence, $U = x^2y + \sin y$ and the required general solution is

$$x^2y + \sin y = c$$

ILLUSTRATIVE EXAMPLE 2

Solve $y' = (xy^2 - 1)/(1 - x^2y)$, given that $y = 1$ where $x = 0$.

Solution. Writing the equation as $(xy^2 - 1)dx + (x^2y - 1)dy = 0$, we have

$$M = xy^2 - 1, \quad N = x^2y - 1, \quad \frac{\partial M}{\partial y} = \frac{\partial N}{\partial x} = 2xy$$

and the equation is exact. Thus, from $\partial U/\partial x = M$ and $\partial U/\partial y = N$ we find the solution

$$U = \frac{x^2y^2}{2} - x - y = c$$

Using the condition that $y = 1$ where $x = 0$, we have finally

$$\tfrac{1}{2}x^2y^2 - x - y = -1$$

The student may find it easier to solve exact equations by a method of inspection known as "grouping of terms." It is based on ability to recognize certain exact differentials.

ILLUSTRATIVE EXAMPLE 3

Solve $2xy\,dx + (x^2 + \cos y)dy = 0$ by "grouping of terms."

Solution. The equation is exact. If we group terms as follows:

$$(2xy\,dx + x^2\,dy) + \cos y\,dy = 0$$

we see that the equation may be written

$$d(x^2y) + d(\sin y) = 0 \quad \text{or} \quad d(x^2y + \sin y) = 0$$

Thus, the general solution is $x^2y + \sin y = c$, which agrees with that obtained in Illustrative Example 1.

ILLUSTRATIVE EXAMPLE 4

Solve $y' = (xy^2 - 1)/(1 - x^2y)$ by "grouping of terms."

Solution. The equation written $(xy^2 - 1)dx + (x^2y - 1)dy = 0$ is exact. By grouping we obtain

$$(xy^2\,dx + x^2y\,dy) - dx - dy = 0$$

or $\qquad d\left(\dfrac{x^2y^2}{2}\right) - dx - dy, \quad$ i.e., $\quad d\left(\dfrac{x^2y^2}{2} - x - y\right) = 0$

Hence, $\qquad \dfrac{x^2y^2}{2} - x - y = c$

In general, the grouping method yields results faster but may require more experience. The general method requires less ingenuity.

A EXERCISES

1. Write each equation in the form $M\,dx + N\,dy = 0$, test for exactness, and solve those equations which are exact.

(a) $3x\,dx + 4y\,dy = 0$.

(b) $y' = \dfrac{x - y}{x + y}$.

(c) $2xyy' = x^2 - y^2$.

(d) $y' = \dfrac{x}{x + y}$.

(e) $\dfrac{dy}{dx} = \dfrac{x - y\cos x}{\sin x + y}$

(f) $\dfrac{dr}{d\theta} = \dfrac{r^2 \sin\theta}{2r\cos\theta - 1}$.

(g) $(ye^{-x} - \sin x)dx - (e^{-x} + 2y)dy = 0$.

(h) $\left(x^2 + \dfrac{y}{x}\right)dx + (\ln x + 2y)dy = 0$.

(i) $y' = \dfrac{y(y - e^x)}{e^x - 2xy}$.

(j) $(x^2 + x)dy + (2xy + 1 + 2\cos x)dx = 0$.

2. Solve each equation subject to the indicated conditions.

(a) $y' = \dfrac{y - 2x}{2y - x}$; $y(1) = 2$.

(b) $2xy\,dx + (x^2 + 1)dy = 0$; $y(1) = -3$.

(c) $y' = \dfrac{2x - \sin y}{x\cos y}$; $y(2) = 0$.

(d) $\dfrac{dx}{dy} = \dfrac{x\sec^2 y}{\sin 2x - \tan y}$; $y(\pi) = \dfrac{\pi}{4}$.

(e) $(x^2 + 2ye^{2x})y' + 2xy + 2y^2 e^{2x} = 0$; $y(0) = 1$.

3. Show that each of the following equations is not exact but becomes exact upon multiplication by the indicated integrating factor. Thus, solve each equation.

(a) $(y^2 + 2x^2)dx + xy\,dy = 0$; x. (b) $y\,dx + (4x - y^2)dy = 0$; y^3.

(c) $\cos x\,dy - (2y\sin x - 3)dx = 0$; $\cos x$.

(d) $(x - y)dx + (x + y)dy = 0$; $\dfrac{1}{(x^2 + y^2)}$.

B EXERCISES

1. Solve the equation

$$\left[\dfrac{y}{(x + y)^2} - 1\right]dx + \left[1 - \dfrac{x}{(x + y)^2}\right]dy = 0$$

2. Prove that a necessary and sufficient condition for the equation

$$f(x)dx + g(x)h(y)dy = 0$$

to be exact is that $g(x)$ be constant.

3. Prove that a necessary and sufficient condition for the equation

$$[f_1(x) + g_1(y)]dx + [f_2(x) + g_2(y)]dy = 0$$

to be exact is that $g_1(y)dx + f_2(x)dy$ be an exact differential.

4. Determine the most general function $N(x,y)$ such that

$$(y \sin x + x^2y - x \sec y)dx + N(x,y)dy = 0$$

is exact, and obtain its solution.

5. Solve

$$\left(2x \sin \frac{y}{x} + 2x \tan \frac{y}{x} - y \cos \frac{y}{x} - y \sec^2 \frac{y}{x}\right) dx + \left(x \cos \frac{y}{x} + x \sec^2 \frac{y}{x}\right) dy = 0$$

6. Show that

$$y = \frac{2 - 2x}{1 + \sqrt{1 + 2x^3 - 2x^2}}$$

is a solution of Illustrative Example 2, page 33 and explain its relation to the solution given there.

C EXERCISES

1. Show that $yf(xy) + xg(xy) = 0$ is not exact in general but becomes exact on multiplying by the integrating factor $\{xy[f(xy) - g(xy)]\}^{-1}$.

2. Use Exercise 1 to solve $(xy^2 + 2y)dx + (3x^2y - 4x)dy = 0$.

3. If $\partial P/\partial x = \partial Q/\partial y$ and $\partial P/\partial y = -\partial Q/\partial x$ show that the equation $P\,dx + Q\,dy = 0$ is not exact in general but becomes exact on multiplying by $1/(P^2 + Q^2)$. Illustrate by considering $P = x^2 - y^2$, $Q = 2xy$.

4. Let $f(z) = P(x,y) + iQ(x,y)$ where $f(z)$ is a polynomial in the complex variable $z = x + iy$ and P and Q are real. (a) Prove that

$$\frac{\partial P}{\partial x} = \frac{\partial Q}{\partial y}, \qquad \frac{\partial P}{\partial y} = -\frac{\partial Q}{\partial x}$$

(b) Discuss the relationship of (a) to Exercise 3. (c) Are the equations in (a), often called the *Cauchy-Riemann equations*, valid for other functions? Explain.

5. (a) Prove that a solution of the partial differential equation

$$\frac{\partial \varphi}{\partial x} + f(x,y) \frac{\partial \varphi}{\partial y} = 0$$

is given by $\varphi = U(x,y)$, where $U(x,y) = c$ is the general solution of $y' = f(x,y)$. (b) By using the result in (a), obtain a solution of

$$x \frac{\partial \varphi}{\partial x} + (2x - y) \frac{\partial \varphi}{\partial y} = 0$$

(c) Show that $\varphi = \psi[U(x,y)]$, where ψ is an arbitrary function, is a more general solution of the partial differential equation in (a). Illustrate by obtaining other solutions of the equation in (b).

III. Equations Made Exact by a Suitable Integrating Factor

If the equation $M\,dx + N\,dy = 0$ is exact, i.e., if $\partial M/\partial y = \partial N/\partial x$ then the equation can be solved by the methods of the last section. In case the equation is not exact, we may be able to make the equation exact by multiplying it by a suitable integrating factor μ, so that the resulting equation

$$\mu M\,dx + \mu N\,dy = 0 \tag{1}$$

will be exact, i.e.,

$$\frac{\partial}{\partial y}(\mu M) = \frac{\partial}{\partial x}(\mu N) \tag{2}$$

Unfortunately there is no single method for obtaining integrating factors. If there were, our task would be greatly simplified. Fortunately, however, there are a few methods, which we shall discuss, which seem to arise often in practice. The first method is so simple that it should always be looked for. The method is known as:

1. The method of separation of variables. We illustrate this method by several illustrative examples.

ILLUSTRATIVE EXAMPLE 1

Solve

$$\frac{dy}{dx} = \frac{y^2}{x^3} \tag{3}$$

Solution. If we write the equation in the form $M\,dx + N\,dy = 0$, i.e.,*

$$y^2\,dx - x^3\,dy = 0$$

it is clear that

$$M = y^2, \qquad N = -x^3, \qquad \frac{\partial M}{\partial y} = 2y, \qquad \frac{\partial N}{\partial x} = -3x^2,$$

so that the equation is not exact. If we divide by x^3y^2, the equation becomes

$$\frac{dx}{x^3} - \frac{dy}{y^2} = 0 \tag{4}$$

for which

$$M = \frac{1}{x^3}, \qquad N = \frac{-1}{y^2}, \qquad \frac{\partial M}{\partial y} = \frac{\partial N}{\partial x} = 0$$

* Note that in doing this we are inherently restricting ourselves to regions in which $x \neq 0$.

so that the equation has been made exact upon multiplying by the integrating factor $1/(x^3y^2)$. Integration of (4) yields

$$\frac{x^{-2}}{-2} - \frac{y^{-1}}{-1} = c \quad \text{or} \quad \frac{1}{y} - \frac{1}{2x^2} = c \tag{5}$$

We say that we have separated the variables in (4) because we have written the equation in the form

$$F(x)dx + G(y)dy = 0$$

(x's together and y's together). Another way to solve (3) is to realize that it can be written $dx/x^3 = dy/y^2$, and integration yields

$$-\frac{1}{2x^2} = -\frac{1}{y} + c \quad \text{or} \quad \frac{1}{y} - \frac{1}{2x^2} = c \tag{6}$$

ILLUSTRATIVE EXAMPLE 2

Given $y(1) = 3$, solve

$$\frac{dy}{dx} = \frac{3x + xy^2}{y + x^2y}$$

Solution. As is, the equation is not obviously "separable." If we write

$$\frac{dy}{dx} = \frac{x(3 + y^2)}{y(1 + x^2)}$$

we see that the variables are separable, to yield

$$\frac{y\,dy}{y^2 + 3} = \frac{x\,dx}{x^2 + 1}$$

Upon integration* we have

$$\tfrac{1}{2} \ln (y^2 + 3) = \tfrac{1}{2} \ln (x^2 + 1) + c_1$$

which may be written in the equivalent forms

$$\ln \left(\frac{y^2 + 3}{x^2 + 1}\right) = c_2 \quad \text{or} \quad y^2 + 3 = c(x^2 + 1)$$

Using the condition $y(1) = 3$ in the last equation we find $c = 6$, so that the required solution is $y^2 + 3 = 6(x^2 + 1)$.

---

* We shall use $\int \dfrac{du}{u} = \ln u$, with the understanding that $u > 0$. Actually, to take care of the cases where $u > 0$ or $u < 0$, one should use $\int \dfrac{du}{u} = \ln |u|$.

A EXERCISES

1. Solve each of the following, subject to conditions where given.

(a) $\dfrac{dy}{dx} = -\dfrac{x}{y}$; $y = 2$ where $x = 1$.   (b) $\dfrac{dy}{dx} = -\dfrac{y}{x}$; $y(1) = 3$.

(c) $3x(y^2 + 1)dx + y(x^2 + 2)dy = 0$.   (d) $2y\,dx + e^{-3x}\,dy = 0$.

(e) $y' = \dfrac{x + xy^2}{4y}$; $y(1) = 0$.   (f) $r\dfrac{d\theta}{dr} = \theta^2 + 1$.

(g) $\sin^2 y\,dx + \cos^2 x\,dy = 0$; $y\left(\dfrac{\pi}{4}\right) = \dfrac{\pi}{4}$.

(h) $x\sqrt{1 + y^2}\,dx - y\sqrt{1 + x^2}\,dy = 0$.

(i) $2y \cos x\,dx + 3 \sin x\,dy = 0$; $y\left(\dfrac{\pi}{2}\right) = 2$.

(j) $y' = 8xy + 3y$.   (k) $\dfrac{dI}{dt} + 5I = 10$; $I(0) = 0$.

(l) $y\,dx + (x^3y^2 + x^3)dy = 0$.

2. The slope of a family of curves at any point (x,y) is given by

$$\frac{dy}{dx} = -\frac{3x + xy^2}{2y + x^2y}$$

Find the equation of that member of the family passing through $(2,1)$.

B EXERCISES

Solve each of the following:

1. $\dfrac{dy}{dx} = \dfrac{(y - 1)(x - 2)(y + 3)}{(x - 1)(y - 2)(x + 3)}$.

2. $\dfrac{dr}{d\theta} = \dfrac{\sin \theta + e^{2r} \sin \theta}{3e^r + e^r \cos 2\theta}$; $r = 0$ where $\theta = \dfrac{\pi}{2}$.

3. $x^3 e^{2x^2 + 3y^2}\,dx - y^3 e^{-x^2 - 2y^2}\,dy = 0$.

C EXERCISES

1. Solve the differential equation $dy/dx = F(y/x)$ by changing the dependent variable from y to v by the substitution $y = vx$.

2. Use the method of the previous exercise to solve:

(a) $y' = \dfrac{y}{x} + \sec^2\dfrac{y}{x}$.   (b) $(x - 4y)dx + (3x - 2y)dy = 0$.

3. Solve the equation $y' = (x + y)^2$ by letting $v = x + y$.

4. Solve (a) $y' = \frac{1}{2}\tan^2(x + 2y)$; (b) $y' = \sqrt{2x + 3y}$.

5. Are the solutions $\ln(y + 2) + \ln(x - 3) = c_1$ and $(y + 2)(x - 3) = c_2$ equivalent for all x and y? Explain.

6. Is the solution $y = 0$ of $y' = \sqrt{y}$ related to the general solution? Explain.

2. Equations made exact by integrating factors involving one variable. Suppose it is desired to solve the differential equation

$$(2y^2x - y)dx + x\,dy = 0 \tag{7}$$

It is easy to show that the equation is not exact and not separable. By suitably grouping the terms in the form

$$(x\,dy - y\,dx) + 2y^2x\,dx = 0$$

and dividing by y^2 we may write the equation as

$$-d\left(\frac{x}{y}\right) + d(x^2) = 0$$

Upon integrating, we obtain the general solution

$$-\frac{x}{y} + x^2 = c$$

The method is commonly known as the *method of inspection* and is based on ingenuity in many cases. The student may observe from the method above that $1/y^2$ is an integrating factor of equation (7). Multiplication by this factor makes equation (7) exact, and we may then use our standard procedure. But how can we tell that $1/y^2$ is an integrating factor? Let us consider this general problem.

Consider the case where $M\,dx + N\,dy = 0$ is not exact or separable. Let us multiply our equation by the integrating factor μ (as yet unknown). By definition of an integrating factor, the equation $\mu M\,dx + \mu N\,dy = 0$ is now exact, so that

$$\frac{\partial}{\partial y}(\mu M) = \frac{\partial}{\partial x}(\mu N) \tag{8}$$

We shall simplify our task by considering two cases:

Case I. μ is a function of x alone.

In this case we may write (8) as

$$\mu\frac{\partial M}{\partial y} = \mu\frac{\partial N}{\partial x} + N\frac{d\mu}{dx} \quad \text{or} \quad \frac{d\mu}{\mu} = \frac{1}{N}\left(\frac{\partial M}{\partial y} - \frac{\partial N}{\partial x}\right)dx \tag{9}$$

If the coefficient of dx on the right side of (9) is a function of x alone [say $f(x)$] then we have $d\mu/\mu = f(x)dx$ and so

$$\ln \mu = \int f(y)dx \quad \text{or} \quad \mu = e^{\int f(x)dx}$$

omitting the constant of integration. We may state this result as follows:

THEOREM. If $\dfrac{1}{N}\left(\dfrac{\partial M}{\partial y} - \dfrac{\partial N}{\partial x}\right) = f(x)$, then $e^{\int f(x)dx}$ is an integrating factor.

Case II. μ is a function of y alone.

In this case, (8) may be written

$$\mu \frac{\partial M}{\partial y} + M \frac{d\mu}{dy} = \mu \frac{\partial N}{\partial y} \quad \text{or} \quad \frac{d\mu}{\mu} = \frac{1}{M}\left(\frac{\partial N}{\partial x} - \frac{\partial M}{\partial y}\right)dy$$

and we may prove the

THEOREM. If $\dfrac{1}{M}\left(\dfrac{\partial N}{\partial x} - \dfrac{\partial M}{\partial y}\right) = g(y)$, then $e^{\int g(y)dy}$ is an integrating factor.

The following is a mnemonic scheme to summarize procedure. Consider

$$M\,dx + N\,dy = 0$$

Compute

$$\frac{\partial M}{\partial y} = (1), \qquad \frac{\partial N}{\partial x} = (2)$$

If (1) $=$ (2), the equation is exact and can easily be solved.
If (1) $\neq$ (2), compute (1) minus (2), divided by N; call the result f.
If f is a function of x alone, then $e^{\int f\,dx}$ is an integrating factor.
If not, compute (2) minus (1), divided by M; call the result g.
If g is a function of y alone, then $e^{\int g\,dy}$ is an integrating factor.

ILLUSTRATIVE EXAMPLE 1

Solve

$$y\,dx + (3 + 3x - y)dy = 0$$

Solution. Here

$$M = y, \qquad N = 3 + 3x - y$$

$$\frac{\partial M}{\partial y} = 1, \qquad \frac{\partial N}{\partial x} = 3$$

Now $\dfrac{1 - 3}{3 + 3x - y}$ is not a function of x alone.

But $\dfrac{3 - 1}{y} = \dfrac{2}{y}$ is a function of y alone.

Hence, $e^{\int(2/y)dy} = e^{2\ln y} = e^{\ln y^2} = y^2$ is an integrating factor.

Multiplying the given equation by y^2, the student may show, indeed, that it becomes exact and the solution is

$$xy^3 + y^3 - \frac{y^4}{4} = c$$

ILLUSTRATIVE EXAMPLE 2

A curve having a slope given by

$$\frac{dy}{dx} = \frac{2xy}{x^2 - y^2}$$

passes through the point (2,1). Find its equation.

Solution. The differential equation may be written

$$2xy\,dx + (y^2 - x^2)dy = 0$$

Thus,

$$M = 2xy, \qquad N = y^2 - x^2$$

$$\frac{\partial M}{\partial y} = 2x, \qquad \frac{\partial N}{\partial x} = -2x$$

so the equation is not exact. Now

$$\frac{2x - (-2x)}{y^2 - x^2} = \frac{4x}{y^2 - x^2}$$

is not a function of x alone, but

$$\frac{-2x - 2x}{2xy} = \frac{-2}{y}$$

is a function of y alone. Hence, an integrating factor is given by

$$e^{\int(-2/y)dy} = e^{-2\ln y} = y^{-2}$$

Using this integrating factor, we find the general solution

$$x^2 + y^2 = cy$$

For the particular curve through (2,1) we find $c = 5$, and the required equation is $x^2 + y^2 = 5y$.

ILLUSTRATIVE EXAMPLE 3

Solve $y' = x - y$, given that $y = 2$ where $x = 0$.

Solution. Writing the differential equation as

$$(x - y)dx - dy = 0$$

we have

$$M = x - y, \qquad N = -1$$

$$\frac{\partial M}{\partial y} = -1, \qquad \frac{\partial N}{\partial x} = 0$$

so the equation is not exact. Now $(-1 - 0)/-1 = 1$ is a function of x. Hence, $e^{\int 1\,dx} = e^x$ is an integrating factor. The required solution is

$$(x - 1)e^x - ye^x = -3$$

as the student may show.

A EXERCISES

1. Solve each of the following:

(a) $(3x + 2y^2)dx + 2xy\,dy = 0$.

(b) $(2x^3 - y)dx + x\,dy = 0$; $y(1) = 1$.

(c) $(y^2 \cos x - y)dx + (x + y^2)dy = 0$.

(d) $(x + x^3 \sin 2y)dy - 2y\,dx = 0$.

(e) $\dfrac{dy}{dx} = \dfrac{\sin y}{x \cos y - \sin^2 y}$; $y(0) = \dfrac{\pi}{2}$.

(f) $(2y \sin x - \cos^3 x)dx + \cos x\,dy = 0$.

(g) $\dfrac{dy}{dx} + \dfrac{4y}{x} = x$.

(h) $\dfrac{dx}{dy} = \dfrac{y^3 - 3x}{y}$.

(i) $\dfrac{dI}{dt} = \dfrac{t - tI}{t^2 + 1}$; $I(0) = 0$.

(j) $(y^3 + 2e^x y)dx + (e^x + 3y^2)dy = 0$.

2. The differential equation of a family is $y' = (x + y)/x$. Find the equation of a curve of this family passing through $(3,0)$.

B EXERCISES

Solve each of the following:

1. $\dfrac{dy}{dx} = \dfrac{3y^2 \cot x + \sin x \cos x}{2y}$.

2. $\dfrac{dy}{dx} = \dfrac{x}{x^2 y + y^3}$.

3. $(3x^2 + y + 3x^3 y)dx + x\,dy = 0$.

4. $(2x + 2xy^2)dx + (x^2 y + 2y + 3y^3)dy = 0$.

C EXERCISES

1. Show that if the equation $M\,dx + N\,dy = 0$ is such that

$$\frac{1}{xM - yN}\left(\frac{\partial N}{\partial x} - \frac{\partial M}{\partial y}\right) = F(xy)$$

i.e., a function of the product xy, then an integrating factor is $e^{\int F(u)\,du}$ where $u = xy$.

2. Use the method of Exercise 1 to solve

$$(y^2 + xy + 1)dx + (x^2 + xy + 1)dy = 0$$

3. Solve $(2y^2 + 4x^2y)dx + (4xy + 3x^3)dy = 0$, given that there exists an integrating factor of the form $x^p y^q$, where p and q are constants.

4. In Exercise 2 of the A Exercises is there a curve belonging to the family and passing through $(0,0)$?

3. An important special case of the previous method—the linear first-order equation. An equation which can be written in the form

$$\frac{dy}{dx} + P(x)y = Q(x) \tag{10}$$

is called a *linear differential equation of first order.** It is easy to verify that the equation has $e^{\int P\,dx}$ as integrating factor, for upon multiplication of both sides of (10) by this factor we obtain

$$e^{\int P\,dx}\frac{dy}{dx} + Pye^{\int P\,dx} = Qe^{\int P\,dx}$$

which is seen to be equivalent to

$$\frac{d}{dx}(ye^{\int P\,dx}) = Qe^{\int P\,dx} \tag{11}$$

From this we obtain by integration

$$ye^{\int P\,dx} = \int Qe^{\int P\,dx}\,dx + c \tag{12}$$

which is the general solution.

There is really no need to consider (10) as a new equation for it falls into a category already considered, namely, the category of equations having an integrating factor which is a function of one variable only. Nevertheless, the form in which (10) appears is of so frequent occurrence in practical applications, and the method of solution is so simple, that it is worthwhile to become acquainted with it. However, should the student fail to recognize that a particular equation has the form (10), he can rest assured that the method of integrating factors of one variable will work. For example, consider the equation

$$y\,dx + (3 + 3x - y)dy = 0$$

---

* An equation which cannot be written in this form, as for example

$$\frac{dy}{dx} + xy^2 = \sin x$$

is called a *non-linear first-order differential equation.*

which we discussed in Illustrative Example 1, page 40. Should we happen to recognize that it can be written as

$$\frac{dx}{dy} + \frac{3x}{y} = \frac{y-3}{y}$$

and is therefore of form (10) with x and y interchanged, we can solve it as a linear equation. Otherwise we may look for an integrating factor involving one variable. To show that this method is applicable we write (10) as

$$[P(x)y - Q(x)]dx + dy = 0$$

Then

$$M = P(x)y - Q(x), \qquad N = 1$$

$$\frac{\partial M}{\partial y} = P(x), \qquad \frac{\partial N}{\partial x} = 0$$

Now $[P(x) - 0]/1 = P(x)$ is a function of x alone, and so $e^{\int P(x)dx}$ is an integrating factor.

ILLUSTRATIVE EXAMPLE 1

Solve

$$\frac{dy}{dx} + 5y = 50$$

Solution. This is of the form (10) with $P = 5$, $Q = 50$. An integrating factor is $e^{\int 5\,dx} = e^{5x}$.

Multiplying by e^{5x}, the equation may be written

$$\frac{dx}{d}(ye^{5x}) = 50e^{5x}$$

and, upon integrating, we have the general solution

$$ye^{5x} = 10e^{5x} + c \quad \text{or} \quad y = 10 + ce^{-5x}$$

ILLUSTRATIVE EXAMPLE 2

Solve $\dfrac{dI}{dt} + \dfrac{10I}{2t+5} = 10$, given that $I = 0$ where $t = 0$.

Solution. The equation has the form (10), with I replacing y and t replacing x. An integrating factor is

$$e^{\int 10\,dt/(2t+5)} = e^{5\ln(2t+5)} = e^{\ln(2t+5)^5} = (2t+5)^5$$

Multiplying by $(2t+5)^5$, the equation may be written

$$\frac{d}{dt}[(2t+5)^5 I] = 10(2t+5)^5$$

and, by integration,

$$I(2t+5)^5 = \tfrac{5}{6}(2t+5)^6 + c$$

Placing $I = 0$ and $t = 0$ in the equation, we have

$$c = -78{,}125/6$$

Thus,

$$I = \frac{5}{6}(2t + 5) - \frac{78{,}125}{6(2t + 5)^5}$$

A EXERCISES

1. Solve each of the following:

(a) $\dfrac{dy}{dx} + \dfrac{y}{x} = 1.$

(b) $xy' + 3y = x^2.$

(c) $y^2 \dfrac{dx}{dy} + xy = 2y^2 + 1.$

(d) $\dfrac{dy}{dx} - \dfrac{2y}{x} = x^2 \sin 3x.$

(e) $I' + 3I = e^{-2t};$ $I(0) = 5.$

(f) $y' + y \cot x = \cos x.$

(g) $y' = \dfrac{1}{x - 3y}.$

(h) $\dfrac{dr}{d\theta} = \theta - \dfrac{r}{3\theta};$ $r = 1, \theta = 1.$

2. The current I, in amperes, in a certain electric circuit satisfies the differential equation

$$\frac{dI}{dt} + 2I = 10e^{-2t}$$

where t is the time. If $I = 0$ where $t = 0$, find I as a function of t.

B EXERCISES

1. The equation $\dfrac{dy}{dx} + Py = Qy^n$, where P and Q are functions of x alone and n is a constant, is called *Bernoulli's differential equation*. Show how to solve it where $n = 0$ or 1.

2. If $n \neq 0, 1$, none of the methods discussed so far applies. Show, however, that by changing the dependent variable from y to v according to the transformation $v = y^{1-n}$ the equation can be solved.

3. Solve $y' - y = xy^2$ by the method of Exercise 2.

4. Solve $y^2\, dx + (xy - x^3)dy = 0.$

5. Solve $xy'' - 3y' = 4x^2.$ (*Hint:* Let $y' = v.$)

6. Solve Exercise 4 by looking for an integrating factor of the form $x^p y^q$, where p and q are suitably chosen constants.

C EXERCISES

1. Show that the differential equation $y' + Py = Qy \ln y$, where P and Q are functions of x, can be solved by letting $\ln y = v$.

2. Solve $xy' = 2x^2y + y \ln y$.

3. Show that a linear equation with independent variable x is transformed into another linear equation when x undergoes the transformation $x = f(u)$, where u is a new independent variable and f is any differentiable function.

4. (a) Discuss the conditions under which a solution to the linear equation (10) exists and is unique by using the existence theorem on page 20. (b) Can a linear equation have singular solutions? Explain.

IV. Other Methods of Solution

Up to now we have considered first-order equations which were exact or could be made exact upon multiplication by a suitable integrating factor. Unfortunately, not every first-order equation can be solved by these methods. In this section we consider methods which should be tried when none of the previous methods appears to work. There are even more specialized techniques which could be given, but these occur so rarely that we shall not devote time to them in the text. A few of them, however, will be given in the B and C exercises.

The most important method of solving equations which do not fall into categories already considered is that of transformation of variables. This process may enable us to change or transform a given equation into one which we can solve by methods already discussed. The general ideas involved in such transformation will be illustrated in this section, both in the text and in the problems.

1. The homogeneous equation. If a differential equation is, or can be put into the form

$$\frac{dy}{dx} = f\left(\frac{y}{x}\right) \tag{1}$$

it is called a *homogeneous differential equation*. The equation may always be solved by the transformation $y/x = v$ or $y = vx$, i.e., by change of the dependent variable from y to v, keeping the same independent variable x. To see this, we differentiate both sides of $y = vx$ with respect to x, remembering that v depends on x. Then

$$\frac{dy}{dx} = v + x\frac{dv}{dx}$$

and equation (1) becomes

$$v + x \frac{dv}{dx} = f(v)$$

so that

$$\frac{dx}{x} = \frac{dv}{f(v) - v} \tag{2}$$

in which the variables have been separated. The solution is easily obtained.

ILLUSTRATIVE EXAMPLE 1

Solve

$$\frac{dy}{dx} = \frac{x - y}{x + y}$$

Solution. We may write the equation as

$$\frac{dy}{dx} = \frac{1 - y/x}{1 + y/x}$$

in which the right-hand side is a function of y/x, so that the equation is homogeneous. Letting $y = vx$, we have

$$v + x\frac{dv}{dx} = \frac{1 - v}{1 + v}, \qquad x\frac{dv}{dx} = \frac{1 - 2v - v^2}{1 + v}, \qquad \frac{dx}{x} = \frac{(1 + v)dv}{1 - 2v - v^2}$$

Thus, by integration,

$$\ln x = -\tfrac{1}{2} \ln (1 - 2v - v^2) + c_1 \quad \text{or} \quad \ln [x^2(1 - 2v - v^2)] = c_2$$

and, therefore,

$$x^2(1 - 2v - v^2) = c$$

Replacing v by y/x and simplifying, we find

$$x^2 - 2xy - y^2 = c$$

The differential equation written as $(y - x)dx + (x + y)dy = 0$ may also be solved as an exact equation.

ILLUSTRATIVE EXAMPLE 2

Solve

$$\frac{dy}{dx} = \frac{ye^{y/x} + y}{x}$$

The right-hand side can be written as $(y/x)e^{y/x} + (y/x)$, a function of y/x, so that the equation is homogeneous. Letting $y = vx$, we obtain

$$v + x\frac{dv}{dx} = ve^v + v \quad \text{or} \quad \frac{e^{-v} dv}{v} = \frac{dx}{x}$$

upon separating the variables. Hence

$$\int \frac{e^{-v}\, dv}{v} = \ln x + c$$

The integration cannot be performed in closed form.

Remark: The student should notice that an equation $y' = f(x,y)$ is homogeneous if upon placing $y = vx$ into the right-hand side of the equation it becomes a function of v alone. Thus, in Illustrative Example 1, for instance, $(x - y)/(x + y)$ becomes $(1 - v)/(1 + v)$.

A EXERCISES

Solve each of the following:

1. $\dfrac{dy}{dx} = 1 + \dfrac{y}{x}.$

2. $\dfrac{dy}{dx} = \dfrac{y}{x} + \dfrac{y^2}{x^2}$; $y(1) = 1.$

3. $xy' = 2x + 3y.$

4. $(x^2 - y^2)dx - 2xy\, dy = 0.$

5. $(x + 2y)dx + (2x + y)dy = 0.$

6. $\dfrac{dy}{dx} = \dfrac{y + x \cos^2(y/x)}{x}$; $y(1) = \dfrac{\pi}{4}.$

7. $xy' = y - \sqrt{x^2 + y^2}.$

8. $y\, dx = (2x + 3y)dy.$

9. $(x^3 + y^3)dx - xy^2\, dy = 0$; $y(1) = 0.$

10. $\dfrac{dy}{dx} = \dfrac{1}{2}\left(\dfrac{x}{y} + \dfrac{y}{x}\right).$

B EXERCISES

Solve:

1. $\dfrac{dy}{dx} = \dfrac{\sqrt{x^2 + y^2}}{x}.$

2. $\dfrac{dy}{dx} = \dfrac{2x + 5y}{2x - y}.$

3. $\dfrac{dy}{dx} = \dfrac{6x^2 - 5xy - 2y^2}{6x^2 - 8xy + y^2}.$

4. Solve the equation $\dfrac{dy}{dx} = \dfrac{2x + 3y + 1}{3x - 2y - 5}$ by letting $x = X + h$ and $y = Y + k$, where X, Y are new variables and h and k are constants. By choosing h and k appropriately, solve the given equation.

5. Solve $(3x - y - 9)y' = (10 - 2x + 2y).$

6. Show that the method of Exercise 4 fails to work for the equation

$$(2x + 3y + 4)dx = (4x + 6y + 1)dy$$

However, show that the substitution $2x + 3y = v$ leads to the solution.

7. Solve $(2x + 2y + 1)dx + (x + y - 1)dy = 0.$

8. Solve

$$\left[2x \sin\frac{y}{x} + 2x \tan\frac{y}{x} - y \cos\frac{y}{x} - y \sec^2\frac{y}{x}\right] dx + \left[x \cos\frac{y}{x} + x \sec^2\frac{y}{x}\right] dy = 0$$

Compare with Exercise 5 of the B exercises, page 35.

9. A function $F(x,y)$ is said to be *homogeneous of degree n* if

$$F(\lambda x, \lambda y) = \lambda^n F(x,y)$$

Determine which of the following functions are homogeneous and the corresponding degree. (a) arc tan $\left(\dfrac{x^2 - xy + y^2}{x^2 + xy + y^2}\right)$. (b) ln $(x + y)$. (c) $xy \sin (y/x)$. (d) $x(x + 2y)^3$. (e) $y^2(3x - y)^{-5}$.

10. Show that if $P(x,y)$ and $Q(x,y)$ are homogeneous of the same degree then the equation $P\,dx + Q\,dy = 0$ can be solved by the transformation $y = vx$.

C EXERCISES

1. Solve $\dfrac{dy}{dx} = \dfrac{\sqrt{x + y} + \sqrt{x - y}}{\sqrt{x + y} - \sqrt{x - y}}$.

2. Solve $\dfrac{dy}{dx} = \dfrac{2y}{x} + \dfrac{x^3}{y} + x \tan\dfrac{y}{x^2}$ by the transformation $y = vx^2$.

3. Solve $\dfrac{dy}{dx} = \dfrac{3x^5 + 3x^2y^2}{2x^3y - 2y^3}$ by letting $x = u^p$, $y = v^q$, and choosing the constants p and q appropriately. Could the equation be solved by letting $y = vx^n$ and choosing the constant n?

4. By letting $y = vx^n$ and choosing the constant n appropriately, solve

$$(2 + 3xy^2)dx - 4x^2y\,dy = 0$$

5. Show how to solve an equation having the form

$$\frac{dy}{dx} = F\left(\frac{a_1x + b_1y + c_1}{a_2x + b_2y + c_2}\right)$$

where F is a given function and a_1, b_1, c_1, a_2, b_2, c_2 are constants.

6. Solve $\dfrac{dy}{dx} = \left(\dfrac{x - 3y - 5}{x + y - 1}\right)^2$.

7. Show how to solve $y' = F(ax + by)$, where F is a given function and a and b are constants. Hence, solve

$$\sqrt{x + y + 1}\,y' = \sqrt{x + y - 1}$$

8. Solve $\dfrac{dy}{dx} = \dfrac{y(1 + xy)}{x(1 - xy)}$.

9. Show that $x\,dy - y\,dx = \arctan(y/x)dx$ can be solved by the substitution $y = vx$ even though the equation is not homogeneous. Explain.

2. The method of inspection. In Section III, Article 2, it was mentioned that an integrating factor of a differential equation could sometimes be found by inspection, a process based on ingenuity and experience. In that section we avoided the method of inspection for cases where the integrating factor involved only one variable. However in some instances integrating factors depend on both variables and "inspection" may be helpful. The inspection method usually applies when one notices certain special facts about the equation. It is definitely not a generally applicable method.

ILLUSTRATIVE EXAMPLE 1

Solve

$$(x^2 + y^2 + y)dx - x\,dy = 0$$

Solution. All standard methods discussed so far fail for this equation. However if we write the equation as

$$(x^2 + y^2)dx + y\,dx - x\,dy = 0$$

and "happen to notice" that this can be written

$$dx + \frac{y\,dx - x\,dy}{x^2 + y^2} = 0 \quad \text{or} \quad dx - d\left[\arctan\frac{y}{x}\right] = 0$$

we immediately obtain by integration the solution

$$x - \arctan\frac{y}{x} = c$$

The student will observe that an integrating factor for this equation is $1/(x^2 + y^2)$.

ILLUSTRATIVE EXAMPLE 2

Solve

$$x\,dx + (y - \sqrt{x^2 + y^2})dy = 0$$

Solution. Writing this in the form

$$\frac{x\,dx + y\,dy}{\sqrt{x^2 + y^2}} = dy$$

it may be noticed that the left side can be written $d(\sqrt{x^2 + y^2})$, and so the equation may be written $d(\sqrt{x^2 + y^2}) = dy$. Integration leads to

$$\sqrt{x^2 + y^2} = y + c \quad \text{or} \quad x^2 = 2cy + c^2$$

The student might also have solved this problem by writing

$$\frac{dy}{dx} = \frac{x}{\sqrt{x^2 + y^2} - y}$$

and then using the transformation $y = vx$.

The following easily established results may help in the solution of differential equations by "inspection." One must realize that these are but a few of many possible combinations which can occur.

$$\frac{x\,dy - y\,dx}{x^2} = d\left(\frac{y}{x}\right)$$

$$\frac{x\,dy - y\,dx}{y^2} = -d\left(\frac{x}{y}\right)$$

$$\frac{x\,dy - y\,dx}{x^2 + y^2} = d\left[\arctan\left(\frac{y}{x}\right)\right]$$

$$\frac{x\,dx + y\,dy}{x^2 + y^2} = d\left[\frac{1}{2}\ln(x^2 + y^2)\right]$$

$$\frac{x\,dx + y\,dy}{\sqrt{x^2 + y^2}} = d(\sqrt{x^2 + y^2})$$

$$\frac{x\,dx - y\,dy}{\sqrt{x^2 - y^2}} = d(\sqrt{x^2 - y^2})$$

A EXERCISES

Solve each equation by the method of inspection or any other method.

1. $y\,dx + (2x^2y - x)dy = 0.$ **2.** $y\,dx + (y^3 - x)dy = 0.$

3. $(x^3 + xy^2 + y)dx - x\,dy = 0.$

4. $(x - \sqrt{x^2 + y^2})dx + (y - \sqrt{x^2 + y^2})dy = 0.$

5. $(x^3 + y)dx + (x^2y - x)dy = 0.$

6. $(x^2 + y^2 + y)dx + (x^2 + y^2 - x)dy = 0.$

7. $(x - x^2 - y^2)dx + (y + x^2 + y^2)dy = 0.$

8. $(x^2y + y^3 - x)dx + (x^3 + xy^2 - y)dy = 0.$

B EXERCISES

1. Show that $\sqrt{x^2 + y^2}\,(x\,dx + y\,dy) = \frac{1}{3}d[(x^2 + y^2)^{3/2}]$. Hence, solve

$$(y - x\sqrt{x^2 + y^2})dx + (x - y\sqrt{x^2 + y^2})dy = 0$$

2. Show that $\dfrac{x\,dy + y\,dx}{(xy)^4} = -\dfrac{1}{3}d[(xy)^{-3}]$. Hence, solve

$$(y - x^5y^4)dx + (x - x^4y^5)dy = 0$$

3. Show that $\dfrac{y\,dx - x\,dy}{x^2 - y^2} = \dfrac{1}{2}\,d\left[\ln\left|\dfrac{x-y}{x+y}\right|\right]$. Hence, solve

$$(x^3 - xy^2 + y)dx + (y^3 - x^2y - x)dy = 0$$

C EXERCISES

Solve:

1. $(x^3 + 2xy^2 - x)dx + (x^2y + 2y^3 - 2y)dy = 0$.

2. $\dfrac{dy}{dx} = \dfrac{x^3 + 2y}{x^3 + x}$.

3. $(xy^2 + x\sin^2 x - \sin 2x)dx - 2y\,dy = 0$.

V. Equations of Order Higher than the First Which Are Easily Solved

Some differential equations of order higher than the first may be solved so easily that we shall take them up now. The methods discussed in this section are very useful and turn up often in applications.

1. Equations immediately integrable. Consider the following:

ILLUSTRATIVE EXAMPLE

Solve $y^{(IV)} = x$, given that $y = 0$, $y' = 1$, $y'' = y''' = 0$ where $x = 0$.
Solution. By one integration of the given equation we have

$$y''' = \frac{x^2}{2} + c_1$$

Since $y''' = 0$ where $x = 0$, this leads to $c_1 = 0$. Thus,

$$y''' = \frac{x^2}{2}$$

Integrating again,

$$y'' = \frac{x^3}{6} + c_2$$

Using $y'' = 0$ where $x = 0$, we have $c_2 = 0$. Hence,

$$y'' = \frac{x^3}{6}$$

Integrating again,

$$y' = \frac{x^4}{24} + c_3$$

Using $y' = 1$ where $x = 0$, we have $c_3 = 1$. Thus,

$$y' = \frac{x^4}{24} + 1$$

Integrating again,

$$y = \frac{x^5}{120} + x + c_4$$

Since $y = 0$ where $x = 0$, $c_4 = 0$. Thus,

$$y = \frac{x^5}{120} + x$$

Note that we actually had four constants involved. This agrees with the fact that we started with a fourth-order equation.

2. Equations having one variable missing. A method next to be discussed is available when one of the variables is missing in the equation. The method is often useful in applications.

ILLUSTRATIVE EXAMPLE 1

Solve

$$xy'' + y' = 4x$$

Solution. Here one of the variables, y, is absent from the equation. The method in such case is to let $y' = v$. Then $y'' = v'$, and the equation may be written

$$xv' + v = 4x$$

We may write this as

$$\frac{d}{dx}(xv) = 4x$$

Hence, upon integration, $xv = 2x^2 + c_1$, $v = 2x + (c_1/x)$. Replacing v by y', we have

$$y' = 2x + \frac{c_1}{x}$$

Integration leads to

$$y = x^2 + c_1 \ln x + c_2$$

which involves two arbitrary constants as expected.

ILLUSTRATIVE EXAMPLE 2

Solve

$$2yy'' = 1 + (y')^2$$

Solution. In this case x is missing. Letting $y' = v$ as before, we find

$$2yv' = 1 + v^2 \quad \text{or} \quad 2y\frac{dv}{dx} = 1 + v^2 \tag{1}$$

Unfortunately we now have three variables x, v, and y. However, we may write

$$\frac{dv}{dx} = \frac{dv}{dy} \cdot \frac{dy}{dx} = \frac{dv}{dy} \cdot v$$

FROM PREV PAGE

so that (1) becomes

$$2yv \frac{dv}{dy} = 1 + v^2$$

Separating the variables and integrating, we have

$$\int \frac{2v\, dv}{1 + v^2} = \int \frac{dy}{y}, \qquad \ln(1 + v^2) = \ln y + c$$

Thus, $\qquad \dfrac{1 + v^2}{y} = c_1 \quad$ or $\quad v = \pm\sqrt{c_1 y - 1}$

i.e., $\qquad \dfrac{dy}{dx} = \pm\sqrt{c_1 y - 1} \quad$ or $\quad \displaystyle\int \frac{dy}{\sqrt{c_1 y - 1}} = \pm \int dx$

Integration yields $2\sqrt{c_1 y - 1} = \pm c_1 x + c_2$, from which y can be obtained.

ILLUSTRATIVE EXAMPLE 3

Solve

$$y'' + y = 0$$

Solution. Letting $y' = v$, the given equation can be written

$$\frac{dv}{dx} + y = 0, \qquad \frac{dv}{dy} \cdot \frac{dy}{dx} + y = 0$$

or $\qquad\qquad\qquad v \dfrac{dv}{dy} + y = 0$

Separating the variables and integrating, we find

$$\int v\, dv + \int y\, dy = c \quad \text{or} \quad \tfrac{1}{2}v^2 + \tfrac{1}{2}y^2 = c$$

Then choosing $2c = c_1^2$ we have

$$v = \pm\sqrt{c_1^2 - y^2}$$

i.e., $\qquad \dfrac{dy}{dx} = \pm\sqrt{c_1^2 - y^2} \quad$ or $\quad \displaystyle\int \frac{dy}{\sqrt{c_1^2 - y^2}} = \pm \int dx$

Integration yields

$$\arcsin(y/c_1) = \pm x + c_2$$

or $\qquad y = c_1 \sin(\pm x + c_2) = c_1 \sin c_2 \cos x \pm c_1 \cos c_2 \sin x$

which can be written

$$y = A \sin x + B \cos x$$

A EXERCISES

Solve each of the following subject to conditions where indicated.

1. $y'' = 2x$; $y(0) = 0$, $y'(0) = 10$.   **2.** $y^{(IV)} = \dfrac{x}{3}$.

3. $y''' = 3 \sin x$; $y(0) = 1$, $y'(0) = 0$, $y''(0) = -2$.

4. $2y^{(IV)} = e^x - e^{-x}$; $y(0) = y'(0) = y''(0) = y'''(0) = 0$.

5. $I''(t) = t^2 + 1$; $I(0) = 2$, $I'(0) = 3$.   **6.** $x^2 y'' = x^2 + 1$; $y(1) = 1$, $y'(1) = 0$.

7. $x^3 y''' = 1 + \sqrt{x}$.   **8.** $y''y' = 1$; $y(0) = 5$, $y'(0) = 1$.

9. $y'' + 4y = 0$; $y(0) = 3$, $y'(0) = 2$.   **10.** $xy'' + 2y' = 0$.

11. $y'' - y = 0$.   **12.** $yy'' = y'$.   **13.** $y'' + (y')^2 = 1$.

14. $y'' = y'(1 + y)$.   **15.** $y'' + xy' = x$.

B EXERCISES

Solve each of the following subject to conditions where indicated.

1. $y^{(IV)} = \ln x$; $y(1) = y'(1) = y''(1) = y'''(1) = 0$.

2. $y^{(V)} + 2y^{(IV)} = x$; $y(0) = y'(0) = y''(0) = y'''(0) = y^{(IV)}(0) = 0$.

3. $xy''' + y'' = 1$.   **4.** $(y''')^2 = (y'')^3$.   **5.** $y''' - y' = 0$.

6. $1 + (y')^2 + yy'' = 0$.   **7.** $x^2 y''' + 2xy'' = 1$.

C EXERCISES

1. If $y'' = -4/y^3$ and $y(2) = 4$, $y'(2) = 0$, find $y(4)$.

2. Solve $1 + (y')^2 + 2yy'' = 0$.

3. Solve $y'' = [1 + (y')^2]^{3/2}$ and interpret geometrically.

4. Solve $\dfrac{d^2 y}{dx^2} \cdot \dfrac{d^2 x}{dy^2} = 1$.

Miscellaneous Exercises on Chapter 2

A EXERCISES

Solve each of the following differential equations.

1. $(x^2 + 1)(y^3 - 1)dx = x^2 y^2 \, dy$.   **2.** $(y^2 + 2xy)dx + (x^2 + 2xy)dy = 0$.

3. $(x^2 + 2xy)dx + (y^2 + 2xy)dy = 0.$ **4.** $\dfrac{dy}{dx} + \dfrac{2y}{x} = x^2.$

5. $(3 - y)dx + 2x\,dy = 0;\; y(1) = 1.$ **6.** $\dfrac{dy}{dx} + 2x = 2.$

7. $s^2t\,ds + (t^2 + 4)dt = 0.$ **8.** $2xyy' + x^2 + y^2 = 0.$

9. $\dfrac{dy}{dx} = \dfrac{2x^2 - ye^x}{e^x}.$ **10.** $x^2y' + xy = x + 1.$

11. $\dfrac{dy}{dx} = \dfrac{y}{x} + \arctan \dfrac{y}{x}.$ **12.** $\dfrac{dy}{dx} = x + y.$

13. $y' + xy = x^3.$ **14.** $(3 - x^2y)y' = xy^2 + 4.$

15. $r^2 \sin \theta\, d\theta = (2r \cos \theta + 10)dr.$ **16.** $y' = x^2 + 2y.$

17. $y' = \dfrac{2xy - y^4}{3x^2}.$ **18.** $(x^2 + y^2)dx + 2y\,dy = 0;\; y(0) = 2.$

19. $(x^2 + y^2)dx + (2xy - 3)dy = 0.$ **20.** $y'(2x + y^2) = y.$

21. $u^2v\,du - (u^3 + v^3)dv = 0.$

22. $(\tan y - \tan^2 y \cos x)dx - x \sec^2 y\,dy = 0.$

23. $\dfrac{dy}{dx} = \dfrac{x + 2y}{y - 2x}.$ **24.** $y' \sin x = y \cos x + \sin^2 x.$

25. $(x^2 - y^2)dx + 2xy\,dy = 0.$ **26.** $(2x^2 - ye^x)dx - e^x\,dy = 0.$

27. $(x + y)y' = 1.$ **28.** $(x + 2y)dx + x\,dy = 0.$

29. $\sin y\,dx + (x \cos y - y)dy = 0.$ **30.** $y' = e^{y/x} + \dfrac{y}{x}.$

31. $\sin x \cos y\,dx + \cos x \sin y\,dy = 0.$ **32.** $xy' = x^3 + 2y.$

33. $(3xy^2 + 2)dx + 2x^2y\,dy = 0.$ **34.** $(2y^2 - x)dy + y\,dx = 0.$

35. $y'' = y' + 2x.$ **36.** $(1 + y)y' = x\sqrt{y}.$

37. $\tan x \sin y\,dx + 3\,dy = 0.$ **38.** $x\,dy - y\,dx = x \cos \left(\dfrac{y}{x}\right)dx.$

39. $\dfrac{ds}{dt} = \sqrt{\dfrac{1 - t}{1 - s}};\; s = 0$ where $t = 1.$ **40.** $(2y + 3x)dx + x\,dy = 0.$

41. $x^2y\,dx + (1 + x^3)dy = 0.$ **42.** $(\sin y - x)y' = 2x + y;\; y(1) = \dfrac{\pi}{2}.$

43. $\dfrac{dN}{dt} = -\alpha N$; $N = N_0$ at $t = 0$.

44. $\dfrac{dy}{dx} = \dfrac{y(x + y)}{x(x - y)}$.

45. $\dfrac{dI}{dt} + I = e^t$.

46. $xy' + y = x^2$; $y(1) = 2$.

47. $x\,dy - y\,dx = x^2 y\,dy$.

48. $\dfrac{dq}{dp} = \dfrac{p}{q}\,e^{p^2 - q^2}$.

49. $(3y \cos x + 2)y' = y^2 \sin x$; $y(0) = -4$.

50. $(x + x \cos y)dy - (y + \sin y)dx = 0$.

51. $y' = 3x + 2y$.

52. $y^2\,dx = (2xy + x^2)dy$.

53. $\dfrac{dr}{d\theta} = \dfrac{r(1 + \ln \theta)}{\theta(1 + \ln r)}$; $\theta = e^2$ where $r = e$.

54. $\dfrac{dU}{dt} = -a(U - 100t)$; $U(0) = 0$.

55. $(uv - 2v)du + (u - u^2)dv = 0$.

56. $\dfrac{dI}{dt} + 3I = 10 \sin t$; $I(0) = 0$.

57. $\dfrac{ds}{dt} = \dfrac{1}{s + t + 1}$.

58. $yy'' = (y')^2$.

59. $x\sqrt{1 - y^2} + yy'\sqrt{1 - x^2} = 0$.

60. $y' + (\cot x)y = \cos x$.

61. $y' = \left(\dfrac{y + 3}{2x}\right)^2$.

62. $xy' - 3y = x^4 e^{-x}$.

63. $y' = \sin x \tan y$.

64. $y' = \dfrac{x}{y} + \dfrac{y}{x}$.

65. $x\,dy - y\,dx = 2x^2 y^2\,dy$.

66. $xy' + y \ln x = y \ln y + y$.

67. $y' = 2 - \dfrac{y}{x}$.

68. $xy'' + y' = 1$.

69. $\dfrac{dI}{dt} = \dfrac{It^2}{t^3 - I^3}$.

70. $(e^y + x + 3)y' = 1$.

71. $\dfrac{dr}{d\theta} = e^\theta - 3r$; $r = 1$ at $\theta = 0$.

72. $yy'' = (y')^2$.

73. $x^4 y''' + 1 = 0$.

74. $\dfrac{dy}{dx} = \dfrac{x + 3y}{x - 3y}$.

75. $y' \cos x = y - \sin 2x$.

76. $e^{2x-y}\,dx + e^{y-2x}\,dy = 0$.

77. $r^3 \dfrac{dr}{d\theta} = \sqrt{a^8 - r^8}$.

78. $(2x^2 - ye^x)dx - e^x\,dy = 0$.

79. $x\,dy + 2y\,dx - x \cos x\,dx = 0$.

80. $\sqrt{1 + x^3}\,\dfrac{dy}{dx} = x^2 y + x^2$.

81. $(3y^2 + 4xy)dx + (2xy + x^2)dy = 0$.

B EXERCISES

1. Solve $xyy' + y^2 = \sin x$ by letting $y^2 = u$.

2. Show that $\arcsin x + \arcsin y = c_1$ and $x\sqrt{1 - y^2} + y\sqrt{1 - x^2} = c_2$ are general solutions of

$$\sqrt{1 - y^2}\, dx + \sqrt{1 - x^2}\, dy = 0$$

Can one of these solutions be obtained from the other?

3. (a) Solve $(1 + x^2)dy + (1 + y^2)dx = 0$, given that $y(0) = 1$. (b) Show that $y = (1 - x)/(1 + x)$ is a solution. Reconcile this with the solution obtained in (a).

4. Solve $y' = 2/(x + 2y - 3)$ by letting $x + 2y - 3 = v$.

5. Solve $y' = \sqrt{y + \sin x} - \cos x$. (*Hint:* Let $\sqrt{y + \sin x} = v$.)

6. Solve $y' = \tan (x + y)$.

7. Solve $y' = e^{x+3y} + 1$.

8. Solve $y^{(IV)} = 2y''' + 24x$ subject to

$$y(0) = 1, \qquad y'(0) = y''(0) = y'''(0) = 0$$

9. Find solutions to the equation $y = xy' + (y')^2$ by differentiating both sides with respect to x. Do you think that the same method will work on the equation $y = xy' + F(y')$? Illustrate by considering $y = xy' + \tan y'$. The equation $y = xy' + F(y')$ is called *Clairaut's equation* (see C Exercise 4, page 13 and C Exercise 9 (b), page 25).

10. If a differential equation can be easily solved for y in terms of x and $v = y'$, i.e., $y = F(x,v)$, then by differentiating with respect to x we obtain $v = \phi(x,v,v')$. If this last equation can be solved for v in terms of x, say $v = \psi(x,c)$ the solution to the original equation can be obtained as $y = F(x,\psi)$. Illustrate this method by obtaining solutions to (a) $y = xy' + (y')^2$; (b) $y = 2xy' + \ln y'$.

11. Discuss how Exercise 10 can be modified in case the differential equation can be solved easily for x in terms of y and y'.

12. Solve (a) $y = x^2 + (y')^2$; (b) $y = 2xy' + x(y')^2$; (c) $x = y - \ln y'$.

13. Show that the equation $yF(xy)dx + xG(xy)dy = 0$ can be solved by the transformation $xy = u$. Thus, solve

$$(x^2y^3 + 2xy^2 + y)dx + (x^3y^2 - 2x^2y + x)dy = 0$$

14. Solve $(y')^2 + (3y - 2x)y' - 6xy = 0$.

C EXERCISES

1. Solve $\dfrac{dy}{dx} = \sqrt{\dfrac{5x - 6y}{5x + 6y}}$.

2. Show that if y_1 and y_2 are two different solutions of

$$y' + P(x)y = Q(x)$$

then they must be related by

$$y_2 = y_1(1 + ce^{-\int Q\,dx/y_1})$$

Hence, by observing that $y = x$ is a solution of $y' + xy = x^2 + 1$, find the general solution.

3. Show that

$$x^p y^q(\alpha y\, dx + \beta x\, dy) + x^r y^s(\gamma y\, dx + \delta x\, dy) = 0$$

where $p, q, r, s, \alpha, \beta, \gamma, \delta$ are given constants, has an integrating factor of the form $x^a y^b$, where a and b are suitable constants.

4. Solve $(x^2 y + 2y^4)dx + (x^3 + 3xy^3)dy = 0$, using the method of Exercise 3.

5. Show that $\dfrac{dy}{dx} = \dfrac{y(y^2 - x^2 - 1)}{x(y^2 - x^2 + 1)}$ can be solved by transforming to polar co-ordinates r, θ, where $x = r\cos\theta$, $y = r\sin\theta$. Hence, determine its solution.

6. Show that, if μ is an integrating factor of $M\, dx + N\, dy = 0$ so that $\mu M\, dx + \mu N\, dy = dU(x,y)$, then $\mu\psi(U)$, where ψ is an arbitrary function, is also an integrating factor. Illustrate this by some examples.

7. Show that the differential equation $y' = P(x)F(y) + Q(x)G(y)$ can be reduced to a linear equation by the transformations

$$u = \frac{F(y)}{G(y)} \quad \text{or} \quad u = \frac{G(y)}{F(y)}$$

according as

$$\frac{FG' - GF'}{G} \quad \text{or} \quad \frac{FG' - GF'}{F}$$

is a constant.

8. Using the results of Exercise 7, obtain the general solutions of:
(a) $y' = \sec y + x \tan y$.
(b) $y' = P(x)y + Q(x)y^n$ (Bernoulli's equation).

9. Show that if the equation $M\, dx + N\, dy = 0$ is such that

$$\frac{x^2}{xM + yN}\left(\frac{\partial N}{\partial x} - \frac{\partial M}{\partial y}\right) = F\left(\frac{y}{x}\right)$$

then an integrating factor is given by $e^{\int F(u)du}$, where $u = y/x$.

10. Prove that if a differential equation $M\,dx + N\,dy = 0$ is both exact and homogeneous, then its solution is $Mx + Ny = c$. Illustrate by using the differential equation $(x^2 + y^2)dx + 2xy\,dy = 0$.

11. (a) Prove that if μ and ν are two different integrating factors of the equation $M\,dx + N\,dy = 0$ then its general solution is $\mu = c\nu$. (b) Illustrate part (a) by finding two different integrating factors of $x\,dy - y\,dx = 0$.

12. The *Riccati equation* is given by $y' = P(x)y^2 + Q(x)y + R(x)$.
(a) Show that if one solution of this equation, say $y_1(x)$, is known, then the general solution can be found by using the transformation $y = y_1 + 1/u$ where u is a new dependent variable.
(b) Show that if two solutions are known, say $y_1(x)$ and $y_2(x)$, the general solution is

$$\frac{y - y_1}{y - y_2} = ce^{\int P(y_1 - y_2)dx}$$

(c) Show that if three solutions are known, say $y_1(x)$, $y_2(x)$, and $y_3(x)$, then the general solution is

$$\frac{(y - y_1)(y_2 - y_3)}{(y - y_2)(y_1 - y_3)} = c$$

13. Solve the equation $y' = xy^2 - 2y + 4 - 4x$ by noting that $y = 2$ is a particular solution.

14. (a) Show that by means of the substitution

$$y = -\frac{1}{Pu}\frac{du}{dx}$$

the Riccati equation of Exercise 12 is transformed into the second-order linear differential equation

$$\frac{d^2u}{dx^2} - \left(\frac{P'}{P} + Q\right)\frac{du}{dx} + PRu = 0$$

(b) Use the method of (a) to solve $y' = xy^2 + 2y + 1$.

15. Solve $\dfrac{dy}{dx} + y^2 = 1 + x^2$.

Chapter Three

APPLICATIONS OF FIRST-ORDER AND SIMPLE HIGHER-ORDER DIFFERENTIAL EQUATIONS

In this chapter we discuss applications of first-order and simple higher-order differential equations to problems of mechanics, electric circuits, geometry, rockets, chemistry, bending of beams, and others. The sections are arranged so that a student may emphasize those topics which are particularly adapted to his interest or needs.

I. Applications to Mechanics

1. Introduction. The subject of physics deals with the investigation of the laws which govern the behavior of the physical universe. By physical universe is meant the totality of objects about us, not only things which we observe, but the things which we do not observe, such as atoms and molecules. The study of the motion of objects in our universe is a branch of mechanics called *dynamics*. Newton's three laws of motion, known to students of elementary physics, form the fundamental basis for its study. It turns out, however, that for objects moving very fast (for example, near the speed of light, 186,000 miles per second) we cannot use Newton's laws. Instead we must use a revision of these laws, evolved by Einstein and known as *relativistic mechanics*, or the mechanics of relativity. For objects of atomic dimensions, Newton's laws are not valid either. In fact, to obtain accurate pictures of the motion of objects of atomic dimensions, we need a set of laws studied in an advanced subject called *quantum mechanics*. Both relativistic and quantum mechanics are far too complicated to investigate in this book, since the student would need more extensive background in mathematics and ·physics to begin a study of these subjects.

Fortunately, to study motion of objects encountered in our everyday lives, neither objects which attain speeds near that of light nor objects which are of atomic dimensions, we do not need relativity or quantum mechanics. Newton's laws are accurate enough in these cases and we shall therefore embark on a discussion of these laws and their applications.

2. Newton's laws of motion. The three laws of motion first developed by Newton are:

1. *A body at rest tends to remain at rest, while a body in motion tends to persist in motion in a straight line with constant velocity unless acted upon by external forces.*

2. *The time rate of change in momentum of a body is proportional to the net force acting on the body and has the same direction as the force.*

3. *To every action there is an equal and opposite reaction.*

The second law provides us with an important relation known to students of elementary physics.

The momentum of an object is defined to be its mass m multiplied by its velocity v. The time rate of change in momentum is thus $\dfrac{d}{dt}(mv)$. Denoting by F the net force which is acting on the body the second law states that

$$\frac{d}{dt}(mv) \propto F \tag{1}$$

where the symbol $\propto$ denotes proportionality. Introducing the constant of proportionality k, we obtain

$$\frac{d}{dt}(mv) = kF$$

If m is a constant, this may be written

$$m\frac{dv}{dt} = kF \quad \text{or} \quad ma = kF$$

where $a = dv/dt$ is the acceleration. Thus we see that

$$F = \frac{ma}{k} \tag{2}$$

The value of k depends on the units which we wish to use. At present two main systems are in use.

(a) The cgs system or centimeter, gram, second system. In this system length is measured in centimeters (cm), mass in grams (g), and time in seconds (sec). The simplest value for k is $k = 1$, so that the law (2) is

$$F = ma \tag{3}$$

If a certain force produces an acceleration of one centimeter per second per second (1 cm/sec²) in a mass of 1 g, then from (3)

$$F = 1 \text{ g} \cdot 1 \text{ cm/sec}^2 = 1 \text{ g cm/sec}^2$$

We call such a force a *dyne*. The cgs system is also called the *metric system*.

(b) The fps system, or foot, pound, second system. In this system we may also use $k = 1$, so that the law is $F = ma$. If a certain force produces an acceleration of one foot per second per second (1 ft/sec²) in a mass of one pound (lb), we call this force a *poundal*. Thus, from $F = ma$ we have 1 poundal = 1 lb ft/sec².

Another way of expressing Newton's law involves use of weight rather than the mass of an object. Whereas the mass of an object is the same everywhere on the earth (or actually anywhere in the universe)* the weight changes from place to place.† It will be observed that for a body acted on only by its weight W, the corresponding acceleration is that due to gravity g. The force is W, and Newton's law is

$$W = mg \qquad (4)$$

Dividing equation (3) by equation (4), we have

$$\frac{F}{W} = \frac{a}{g} \quad \text{or} \quad F = \frac{Wa}{g} \qquad (5)$$

We may use equation (5) with either cgs or fps units. In such case it is clear that F and W have the same units if a and g have.

With cgs units: If W is in grams weight, a and g in cm/sec², then F is in grams weight. If W is in dynes, a and g in cm/sec², then F is in dynes. On the earth's surface $g = 980$ cm/sec², approximately.

With fps units: If W is in pounds weight, a and g in ft/sec², then F is in pounds weight. On the earth's surface $g = 32$ ft/sec², approximately.

In certain fields it is customary to use the cgs system in conjunction with the law $F = ma$, and to use the fps system in conjunction with the law $F = Wa/g$. Sometimes use is made of mass in terms of *slugs*.‡

Note: It will be the custom in this book to use
1. $F = ma$, where F is in dynes, m in grams, a in cm/sec².
2. $F = Wa/g$, where F and W are in pounds, a and g in ft/sec².§

When other units are desired, appropriate changes can be made. If in a problem units are not specified, any system can be used so long as consistency prevails.‖

---

* Actually, we are talking here about "rest mass," because in relativity theory when an object is in motion its mass changes.

† On the earth's surface this change does not exceed 2 per cent.

‡ The number of pounds weight divided by g ($= 32$) is known as the *number of slugs*. Thus, the mass of a 64 lb weight is 2 slugs.

§ Whenever we use the abbreviation lb we refer to pounds weight.

‖ For some purposes a variation of the cgs system known as the *meter, kilogram, second* system or *mks system* is sometimes used. Here length is in meters (100 cm), mass in kilograms (1000 gm) and time in seconds. The force required to move a 1 kilogram mass at an acceleration of 1 meter/sec² is called a *newton*. The abbreviations for meter, kilogram and newton are m, kg, and n respectively.

In the notation of the calculus we may write Newton's law in different forms by realizing that the acceleration can be expressed as a first derivative of a velocity v (i.e., dv/dt) or as a second derivative of a displacement s (i.e., d^2s/dt^2). Thus we may write

$$F = m\frac{dv}{dt} = m\frac{d^2s}{dt^2} \qquad \text{(cgs)}$$

$$F = \frac{W}{g}\frac{dv}{dt} = \frac{W}{g}\frac{d^2s}{dt^2} \qquad \text{(fps)}$$

We now consider mathematical formulations of various mechanics problems involving the concepts just introduced, and the solution and interpretation of such problems.

ILLUSTRATIVE EXAMPLE 1

A mass of m grams falls vertically downward under the influence of gravity starting from rest. Set up a differential equation and associated conditions describing the motion and solve.

Mathematical Formulation. In the mathematical formulation of physical problems (or for that matter, any problems) it is useful to draw diagrams wherever possible. They help to fix ideas and consequently help us to translate physical ideas into mathematical equations. Let A (Fig. 6) be the position

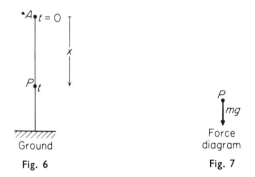

Ground
Fig. 6

Force diagram
Fig. 7

of mass m at time $t = 0$, and let P be the position of m at any subsequent time t. In any physical problem involving vector quantities, such as force, displacement, velocity, and acceleration which necessarily require a knowledge of direction, it is convenient to set up a coordinate system, together with the assignment of positive and negative directions. In the present problem let A be the origin of our coordinate system and choose the x axis as vertical with "down" as the positive direction (and consequently "up" as the negative direction). The instantaneous velocity at P is $v = dx/dt$. The instantaneous acceleration at P is $a = dv/dt$ or $a = d^2x/dt^2$. The net force acts vertically downward (considered positive as shown in the force diagram of Fig. 7).

Its magnitude is *mg*. By Newton's law we have

[handwritten: THIS IS THE ACCELERATION OF A FALLING OBJECT (a)]

$$m\frac{dv}{dt} = mg \quad \text{or} \quad \frac{dv}{dt} = g$$

Since we are told that the mass falls from rest we see that $v = 0$ when $t = 0$, or in other words $v(0) = 0$. Our mathematical formulation or boundary-value problem is

$$\frac{dv}{dt} = g, \qquad v(0) = 0 \tag{6}$$

Here we have a first-order, first-degree equation and the required one condition necessary for solution.

Another way of formulating the problem is to write

$$m\frac{d^2x}{dt^2} = mg \quad \text{or} \quad \frac{d^2x}{dt^2} = g$$

In such case we have a second-order equation in the variables x and t, and we require two conditions for the determination of x. One of them is $v = 0$ or $dx/dt = 0$ at $t = 0$. The second may be arrived at by noting that $x = 0$ at $t = 0$ (since we chose the origin of our coordinate system at A). The mathematical formulation is

$$\frac{d^2x}{dt^2} = g, \qquad x = 0 \quad \text{and} \quad \frac{dx}{dt} = 0 \quad \text{at} \quad t = 0 \tag{7}$$

The procedure will be typical in the mathematical formulations of problems. When we set up differential equations to describe some phenomena or law, we shall always accompany them by enough conditions necessary to determine the arbitrary constants in the general solution.

Solution. Starting with $dv/dt = g$, we obtain by integration

$$v = gt + c_1$$

[handwritten: IMPORTANT CONCEPT FOR SOLUTION OF PROBS.]

Since $v = 0$ when $t = 0$, $c_1 = 0$, or $v = gt$, i.e.,

[handwritten: V = dx/dt FROM BOTTOM OF PREV PAGE.]

$$\frac{dx}{dt} = gt$$

Another integration yields

$$x = \tfrac{1}{2}gt^2 + c_2$$

Since $x = 0$ at $t = 0$, $c_2 = 0$. Hence,

$$x = \tfrac{1}{2}gt^2$$

We could have arrived at the same result by starting with (7).

As an application, suppose we wish to know where the object is after 2 sec. Then, by the cgs system,

$$x = \tfrac{1}{2} \times 980 \text{ cm/sec}^2 \times (2 \text{ sec})^2 = 1960 \text{ cm}$$

By the fps system,

$$x = \tfrac{1}{2} \times 32 \text{ ft/sec}^2 \times (2 \text{ sec})^2 = 64 \text{ ft}$$

To find the velocity after 2 sec we write (in the fps system)

$$dx/dt = gt = 32 \text{ ft/sec}^2 \times 2 \text{ sec} = +64 \text{ ft/sec}$$

The plus sign indicates that the object is moving in the positive direction, i.e., downward. It should be noted that if we had taken the positive direction as upward the differential equation would have been $m(dv/dt) = -mg$, i.e.,

$$\frac{dv}{dt} = -g \quad \text{or} \quad \frac{d^2x}{dt^2} = -g$$

This would, of course, lead to results equivalent to those obtained.

ILLUSTRATIVE EXAMPLE 2

A ball is thrown vertically upward with an initial velocity of 128 ft/sec. What is its velocity after 2, 4, and 6 sec? When will it return to its starting position? What is the maximum height to which it will rise before returning?

Mathematical Formulation. Here we shall take the x axis as vertical, with the origin on the ground at A so that $x = 0$ when $t = 0$ (Fig. 8). We shall

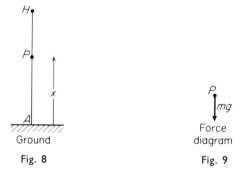

Fig. 8

Fig. 9

consider "up" as positive. The force acting on the ball (Fig. 9) is its weight and we must therefore consider it to be $-mg$ (the minus signifying down). The differential equation for the motion is

$$m\frac{d^2x}{dt^2} = -mg \quad \text{or} \quad \frac{d^2x}{dt^2} = -g$$

Two conditions are needed to determine x. One is supplied by the fact that $x = 0$ at $t \doteq 0$. The other is supplied by the fact that the initial velocity is 128 ft/sec. This velocity is in the upward direction and we therefore consider it as positive. Thus, the condition is

$$v = \frac{dx}{dt} = +128 \quad \text{at} \quad t = 0$$

The complete mathematical formulation is

$$\frac{d^2x}{dt^2} = -g, \qquad x = 0 \ \text{ and } \ \frac{dx}{dt} = 128 \ \text{ at } \ t = 0 \tag{8}$$

Solution. Integration of the differential equation in (8) yields

$$\frac{dx}{dt} = -gt + c_1$$

and since $dx/dt = 128$ where $t = 0$, $c_1 = 128$, so that

$$\frac{dx}{dt} = -gt + 128$$

Another integration yields

$$x = -\tfrac{1}{2}gt^2 + 128t + c_2$$

and since $x = 0$ where $t = 0$, $c_2 = 0$. Hence,

$$x = -\tfrac{1}{2}gt^2 + 128t \quad \text{or} \quad x = 128t - 16t^2$$

Velocity after 2, 4, 6 seconds. We have for the velocity at time t

$$v = \frac{dx}{dt} = 128 - 32t$$

Letting $t = 2$, we find $v = 64$, which means that the ball is rising at the rate of 64 ft/sec. Letting $t = 4$, we find $v = 0$, which means that the ball has stopped. Letting $t = 6$, we find $v = -64$, which means that the ball has turned and is coming down at the rate of 64 ft/sec.

Time for return. The ball is at position A, the starting position, when $x = 0$. This happens when

$$-16t^2 + 128t = 0 \quad \text{or} \quad -16t(t - 8) = 0$$

i.e., $t = 0$ or $t = 8$. The value $t = 0$ is trivial, since we already know that $x = 0$ at $t = 0$. The other value $t = 8$ shows that the ball returns after 8 sec.

Maximum height of rise. The maximum value of x may be found by setting $dx/dt = 0$, which is equivalent to finding when $v = 0$. We have

$$v = \frac{dx}{dt} = 128 - 32t = 0 \quad \text{where} \quad t = 4$$

Since d^2x/dt^2 is negative, x is actually a maximum for $t = 4$. The value of x for $t = 4$ is 256. Hence, the maximum height to which the ball rises is 256 ft.

ILLUSTRATIVE EXAMPLE 3

A paratrooper (and of course his parachute) falls from rest. The combined weight of paratrooper and parachute is W pounds. The parachute has a force acting on it (due to air resistance) which is proportional to the speed at any instant during the fall. Assuming the paratrooper falls vertically downward and that the parachute is already open when the jump takes place, describe the ensuing motion.

Mathematical Formulation. We draw, as usual, a physical and force diagram (Figs. 10 and 11). Assume A to be the origin and AB the direction of the positive x axis. The forces acting are: (a) the combined weight W acting downward; (b) the air resistance force R acting upward. The net force in the positive (downward) direction is $W - R$. Since the resistance is proportional to the speed we have

$$R \propto |v| \quad \text{or} \quad R = \beta|v|$$

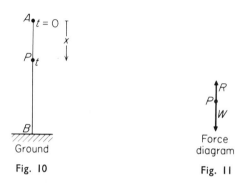

Fig. 10

Fig. 11

where β is the constant of proportionality. Since v is always positive, we do not need absolute value signs, and may write simply $R = \beta v$. Hence the net force is $W - \beta v$, and we obtain by Newton's law

$$\frac{W}{g} \cdot \frac{dv}{dt} = W - \beta v$$

Since the paratrooper starts from rest, $v = 0$ at $t = 0$. Thus the complete mathematical formulation is

$$\frac{W}{g} \cdot \frac{dv}{dt} = W - \beta v, \qquad v = 0 \quad \text{at} \quad t = 0$$

Solution. The differential equation has its variables separable. Thus,

$$\int \frac{W \, dv}{W - \beta v} = \int g \, dt \quad \text{or} \quad -\frac{W}{\beta} \ln (W - \beta v) = gt + c_1$$

Since $v = 0$ at $t = 0$, $c_1 = -\dfrac{W \ln W}{\beta}$ and, thus,

$$-\frac{W}{\beta} \ln (W - \beta v) = gt - \frac{W}{\beta} \ln W, \qquad \ln \left(\frac{W}{W - \beta v} \right) = \frac{\beta g t}{W}$$

Hence,
$$v = \frac{W}{\beta} (1 - e^{-\beta g t / W})$$

It will be noted that as $t \to \infty$, v approaches W/β, a constant limiting velocity. This accounts for the fact that we notice parachutes traveling at very nearly uniform speeds after a certain length of time has elapsed. We may also determine the distance traveled by the paratrooper as a function of time.

From
$$\frac{dx}{dt} = \frac{W}{\beta}(1 - e^{-\beta gt/W})$$

we have
$$x = \frac{W}{\beta}\left(t + \frac{W}{\beta g}e^{-\beta gt/W}\right) + c_2$$

Using the fact that $x = 0$ at $t = 0$, we find $c_2 = -W^2/\beta^2 g$. Hence,
$$x = \frac{W}{\beta}\left(t + \frac{W}{\beta g}e^{-\beta gt/W} - \frac{W}{\beta g}\right)$$

The graphs of v and x as functions of t are shown in Figs. 12 and 13.

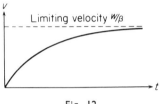

Fig. 12

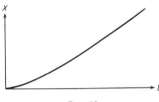

Fig. 13

ILLUSTRATIVE EXAMPLE 4

A particle starts from rest, a distance 10 cm from a fixed point O. It moves along a horizontal straight line toward O under the influence of an attractive force at O. This force at any time varies as the distance of the particle from O. If the acceleration of the particle is 9 cm/sec^2 directed toward O when the particle is 1 cm from O, describe the motion.

Mathematical Formulation. Assume the particle starts at A (Fig. 14) at $t = 0$. Take the fixed point O as the origin of a coordinate system and choose OA as positive direction. Let P be the position of the particle at any time t. Since the magnitude of the force of attraction F toward point O is proportional to the distance from point O, we have

$$|F| \propto |x| \quad \text{or} \quad |F| = k\,|x| \qquad (9)$$

Force diagram

Fig. 14

where k is a positive constant. Let us assume $x \geq 0$. From (9) it follows that the magnitude of F is kx. Since the force F is directed toward O (the negative direction) we must have $F = -kx$, $x \geq 0$. If $x \leq 0$, we see from (9) that the magnitude of the force is $-kx$ and is directed toward the right (the positive direction) so that $F = -kx$, $x \leq 0$. Thus, the force is given by $-kx$, regardless of whether $x > 0$,

$x = 0$, or $x < 0$. Hence, from Newton's law,

$$m\frac{d^2x}{dt^2} = -kx \quad \text{or} \quad \frac{d^2x}{dt^2} = -\frac{k}{m}x \tag{10}$$

Since the acceleration is 9 cm/sec^2 directed toward O when the particle is 1 cm from O, we have $x = 1$, $a = d^2x/dt^2 = -9$. Hence, from (10), $-9 = -k/m$, or $k/m = 9$. Thus,

$$\frac{d^2x}{dt^2} = -9x$$

Two conditions are required, because we have a second-order equation.

Since the particle starts from rest 10 cm from O, we have $x = 10$, $v = 0$ at $t = 0$. The complete mathematical formulation is

$$\frac{d^2x}{dt^2} = -9x, \quad x = 10 \quad \text{and} \quad \frac{dx}{dt} = 0 \quad \text{at} \quad t = 0 \tag{11}$$

Solution. To solve the differential equation of (11) note that one variable, namely t, is missing. Hence let $dx/dt = v$ so that

$$\frac{d^2x}{dt^2} = \frac{dv}{dt} = \frac{dv}{dx}\cdot\frac{dx}{dt} = \frac{dv}{dx}\cdot v$$

The equation can therefore be written

$$v\frac{dv}{dx} = -9x \quad \text{or} \quad v\,dv = -9x\,dx$$

Integrating, we get,

$$v^2 = -9x^2 + c_1$$

Since $v = 0$ when $x = 10$, $c_1 = 900$. Thus, $v^2 = 9(100 - x^2)$, and

$$v = \frac{dx}{dt} = \pm 3\sqrt{100 - x^2} \quad \text{or} \quad \frac{dx}{\sqrt{100 - x^2}} = \pm 3\,dt$$

Integrating, we have

$$\text{arc sin }\frac{x}{10} = \pm 3t + c_2$$

Since $x = 10$ when $t = 0$, we have $c_2 = \pi/2$. Thus,

$$\text{arc sin }\frac{x}{10} = \frac{\pi}{2} \pm 3t \quad \text{or} \quad x = 10\cos 3t \tag{12}$$

The graph for x vs. t is shown in Fig. 15. It will be seen from the graph that the particle starts at $x = 10$ where $t = 0$, then proceeds through O to the place $x = -10$, whence it returns to O again, passes through, and goes to $x = 10$. This cycle then repeats over and over again. The behavior is similar to that of the bob of a pendulum swinging back and forth. The type of motion described in this problem is called *simple harmonic motion*.

We call the maximum displacement of the particle from the mean position

O the *amplitude*. In our case the amplitude is 10 cm. The time for one complete cycle is called the *period*. From the graph it is seen that the period is $2\pi/3$ seconds. Another way to see that the period is $2\pi/3$ without the graph is to determine when the particle is at an extremity of its path, for example, when $x = 10$. From (12) it is seen that this will occur when

$$\cos 3t = 1, \quad \text{i.e.,} \quad 3t = 0, 2\pi, 4\pi, \ldots$$

Hence the first time that $x = 10$ is $t = 0$, the next time $t = 2\pi/3$; the next time $t = 4\pi/3$, and so on. The difference between successive times is $2\pi/3$, which is the period.

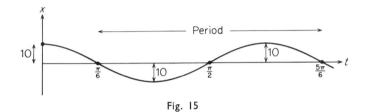

Fig. 15

The number of cycles per second is called the *frequency*. In our case
Number of seconds per cycle is $2\pi/3$;

Number of cycles per second is $\dfrac{1}{2\pi/3} = \dfrac{3}{2\pi}$.

In general, if T is the period, the frequency is given by $f = 1/T$.

As another application, let us calculate the times when the particle is 5 cm to the left of O. In this case $x = -5$, and so from $x = 10 \cos 3t$ we have

$$10 \cos 3t = -5, \quad \cos 3t = -\frac{1}{2}, \quad 3t = \frac{2\pi}{3}, \frac{4\pi}{3}, \frac{8\pi}{3}, \ldots$$

Thus $t = 2\pi/9, 4\pi/9, 8\pi/9, \ldots$, which are the successive times. Note that the difference between the successive times is not equal to the period in this case.

A EXERCISES

1. A mass of 25 g falls from rest under the influence of gravity. (a) Set up a differential equation and conditions for the motion. (b) Find the distance traveled and velocity attained 3 sec after the motion has begun. (c) How far does the mass travel between the 3rd and 4th seconds? between the 4th and 5th seconds?

2. A 200 g mass is thrown upward with initial velocity 2450 cm/sec. (a) Find the distances from the starting point and the velocities attained 2 and 4 sec after the motion has begun. (b) Find the highest point reached and the time required. (c) What are the total distances traveled after 2 sec? after 4 sec?

3. A 6 lb weight is dropped from a cliff $\frac{1}{4}$ mile high. Assuming no air resistance, at what time and with what velocity does it reach the ground?

4. An oil droplet, mass 0.2 g, falls from rest in air. For a velocity of 40 cm/sec, the force due to air resistance is 160 dynes. Assuming air resistance force proportional to instantaneous velocity: (a) Find the velocity and distance traveled as a function of time. (b) Find the limiting velocity.

5. The force of water resistance acting on a boat is proportional to its instantaneous velocity, and is such that at 20 ft/sec the water resistance is 40 lb. If the boat weighs 320 lb and the only passenger weighs 160 lb, and if the motor can exert a steady force of 50 lb in the direction of motion: (a) Find the maximum velocity at which the boat will travel. (b) Find the distance traveled and velocity at any time, assuming the boat starts from rest.

6. A paratrooper and parachute weigh 200 lb. At the instant the parachute opens, he is traveling vertically downward at 40 ft/sec. If the air resistance varies directly as the instantaneous velocity and the air resistance is 80 lb when the velocity is 20 ft/sec: (a) Find the limiting velocity. (b) Determine the position and velocity at any time.

7. A 192 lb weight has limiting velocity 16 ft/sec when falling in air, which provides a resisting force proportional to the weight's instantaneous velocity. If the weight starts from rest: (a) Find the velocity of the weight after 1 sec. (b) How long is it before the velocity is 15 ft/sec?

8. Solve the previous problem if the force of air resistance varies as the square of the instantaneous velocity.

9. A particle starts from rest 1 ft from a fixed point O. It moves along a horizontal line toward O subject to an attractive force at O which varies directly as its distance from O. The acceleration of the particle is 8 ft/sec^2 toward O when it is $\frac{1}{2}$ ft from O. (a) Find the velocity when the particle is $\frac{1}{2}$ ft from O. (b) Find the amplitude, period, and frequency of the motion. (c) Determine the position, velocity, and acceleration after $\pi/16$ sec.

10. A particle starts from rest 20 cm from a fixed point O. It moves along a horizontal line toward O under an attractive force at O which varies directly as its distance from O. At O its velocity is 40 cm/sec. (a) Find its velocity and acceleration 10 cm from O. (b) Determine the amplitude, period, and frequency of the motion. (c) Find its position, velocity, and acceleration after $\pi/3$ sec. (d) Find the times when the particle passes through O.

11. A particle moves along the x axis acted upon only by an opposing force proportional to its instantaneous velocity. It starts at the origin with a velocity of 10 ft/sec, which is reduced to 5 ft/sec after moving 2.5 ft. Find its velocity when it is 4 ft from the origin.

12. A particle of mass 2 g moves on a straight line attracted toward a fixed point O on the line by a force which is directly proportional to its distance from O. At $t = 0$ the particle passes through O with velocity 20 cm/sec. The force on the particle is 100 dynes 2 cm from O. (a) Find the position, velocity, and acceleration as a function of time. (b) Find the amplitude, period, and frequency of the vibration. (c) Find the force on the particle at $t = \pi/4$.

B EXERCISES

1. Show that a ball thrown vertically upward with initial velocity v_0 takes twice as much time to return as to reach the highest point. Find the velocity upon return. Air resistance is assumed negligible.

2. A body moves on a straight line with constant acceleration a. If v_0 is the initial velocity, v is the velocity, and s is the distance traveled after time t, show that:

(a) $v = v_0 + at$.   (b) $s = v_0 t + \frac{1}{2}at^2$.   (c) $v^2 = v_0^2 + 2as$.

3. A mass m is thrown upward with initial velocity v_0. Air resistance is proportional to its instantaneous velocity, the constant of proportionality being k. Show that the maximum height attained is

$$\frac{mv_0}{k} - \frac{m^2 g}{k^2} \ln\left(1 + \frac{kv_0}{mg}\right)$$

What happens as $k \to 0$?

4. A paratrooper and his parachute weigh W pounds. When the parachute opens he is traveling vertically downward at v_0 feet per second. If the force of air resistance varies directly as the square of the instantaneous velocity and if air resistance is F pounds, where velocity is V feet per second: (a) Write differential equations for the velocity as a function of time and also of distance. (b) Find the velocity t sec after the parachute opens and the limiting velocity. What simplifications result if $v_0 = 0$? (c) Find the velocity as a function of distance traveled.

5. An object weighing 1000 lb sinks in water starting from rest. Two forces act on it, a buoyant force of 200 lb, and a force of water resistance which in pounds is numerically equal to $100v$, where v is in ft/sec. Find the distance traveled after 5 sec and the limiting velocity.

6. A 10 lb object is dropped vertically downward from a very high cliff. The law of resistance in the fps system is given by $0.001v^2$, where v is the instantaneous velocity. Determine (a) the velocity as a function of distance, (b) the velocity as a function of time, (c) the velocity of the object after having fallen 500 ft, (d) the limiting velocity, (e) the distance traveled after 10 sec.

7. A particle moves along a straight line toward a fixed point O under the influence of a force of attraction at O which varies directly as distance of the particle from O. At $t = 0$ the particle is 4 cm from O and is moving toward O with velocity 6 cm/sec and acceleration 16 cm/sec^2. (a) Find the velocity and position as a function of time. (b) Find the amplitude, period, and frequency of the motion. (c) Find the maximum velocity and acceleration.

8. A particle moves in a straight line toward a fixed point O on the line with an instantaneous speed which is proportional to the nth power of its instantaneous distance from O. (a) Show that if $n \geq 1$ the particle will never reach O. (b) Discuss the cases $n \leq 1$.

9. When a ball is thrown upward it reaches a particular height after time T_1 on the way up and time T_2 on the way down. (a) Assuming air resistance to be negligible, show that the height is given by $\frac{1}{2}gT_1T_2$. (b) How can the result be used to find the height of a tree without climbing it?

10. Show that the ball in Exercise 9 was thrown upward with initial speed $\frac{1}{2}g(T_1 + T_2)$.

11. If a hole were bored through the center of the earth, one would discover that an object placed in it would be acted upon by a force of attraction varying directly as the distance between the object and the center of the earth. Assuming the earth a perfect sphere of 4000 mile radius: (a) Find the time for an object dropped in the hole to return. (b) Find its velocity on passing through the earth's center.

12. A projectile of mass 50,000 kilograms (kg) is shot vertically upward from the earth's surface with initial velocity 200 miles per hour (mph). According to Newton's universal law of gravitation, the force of attraction between any two objects varies directly as the product of their masses and inversely as the square of the distance between their centers. Neglecting air resistance and assuming only the earth's influence: (a) Determine the maximum height reached by the projectile. (b) Find the time to reach the maximum height.

C EXERCISES

1. A 100 lb weight slides from rest down an inclined plane (Fig. 16) which makes an angle of 30° with the horizontal. Assuming no friction: (a) Set up a differential equation and conditions describing the motion. (b) What distance will the weight travel 5 sec after starting and what will be its velocity and acceleration at that instant? (*Hint:* Resolve the force due to the weight into two components, one parallel and one perpendicular to the plane. The component P parallel to the plane is the net force producing motion.)

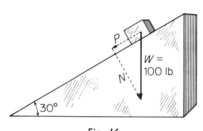

$$W = 100 \text{ lb}$$

Fig. 16

2. Show that a weight W given an initial velocity v_0 slides a distance s down a frictionless inclined plane of inclination α in the time

$$\frac{\sqrt{v_0^2 + 2gs \sin \alpha} - v_0}{g \sin \alpha}$$

3. An object of mass m is thrown up an inclined plane of inclination α. Assuming no friction, show that the maximum distance reached is $v_0^2/(2g \sin \alpha)$.

4. If air resistance proportional to the instantaneous velocity (constant of proportionality k) is taken into account, show that the object in Exercise 3 reaches a maximum distance up the incline given by

$$\frac{mv_0}{k} - \frac{m^2g}{k^2} \sin \alpha \ln \left(1 + \frac{kv_0}{mg \sin \alpha}\right)$$

Verify that this distance reduces to that of Exercise 3 as $k \to 0$.

5. A 100 lb weight starts from rest down a 30° incline. If the coefficient of friction between weight and incline is 0.2, what distance will the weight travel after 5 sec? Find its velocity and acceleration at that instant (assume the weight does get started). (*Hint:* Referring to Fig. 16, the frictional force acting is given by the normal component N multiplied by the coefficient of friction.)

6. · A weight W is given initial velocity v_0 down an incline of angle α. If the coefficient of friction between weight and plane is μ, show that after time T the weight travels a distance

$$v_0 T + \tfrac{1}{2}(g \sin \alpha - \mu g \cos \alpha) T^2$$

provided $\tan \alpha > \mu$.

7. According to Einstein's special theory of relativity, the mass of a particle varies with its velocity v according to the formula

$$m = \frac{m_0}{\sqrt{1 - v^2/c^2}}$$

where m_0 is the rest mass and c is the velocity of light (186,000 miles/sec). The differential equation of motion is

$$F = m_0 \frac{d}{dt}\left(\frac{v}{\sqrt{1 - v^2/c^2}}\right)$$

If a particle starts from rest at $t = 0$ and moves in a straight line acted upon only by a constant force F, what distance will it cover and what will be its velocity in time t. Show that as time goes by, the velocity of the particle approaches the velocity of light.

8. An object having rest mass m_0 of 10,000 g moves on the x axis under a constant force of 50,000 dynes. If it starts from rest at $x = 0$ at time $t = 0$, determine where it will be at any time assuming: (a) The mass of the object is constant and equal to m_0. (b) The mass varies according to the law of special relativity.

9. Work B Exercise 11 for the case where the hole connects two points on the earth's surface but does not pass through the center of the earth.

II. Applications to Electric Circuits

1. Introduction. Just as mechanics has as fundamental basis the laws of Newton, so the subject of electricity has laws describing the behavior of electric circuits, known as Kirchhoff's laws, which we shall describe and use in this section. Actually, electrical theory is governed by a certain set of equations known in electromagnetic theory as Maxwell's equations. Just as we cannot enter into a discussion of relativity or quantum mechanics because of the student's insufficient background, so we cannot enter into discussion of Maxwell's equations. However, just as Newton's laws proved sufficient for motion of "everyday objects," so Kirchhoff's laws are amply suited for study of the simple properties of electric circuits. For thorough study of electric circuits the student must, of course, take laboratory practice and watch demonstrations in lectures. In a mathematical book we can hope to present only a brief discussion.

The simplest electric circuit is a series circuit in which we have an emf (*electromotive force*), which acts as a source of energy such as a battery or generator, and a *resistor*, which uses energy, such as an electric light bulb, toaster, or other appliance.

In elementary physics we find that the emf is related to the current flow in the circuit. Simply stated, the law says that the instantaneous current I (in a circuit containing only an emf E and a resistor) is directly proportional to the emf. In symbols,

$$I \propto E \quad \text{or} \quad E \propto I$$

Hence,

$$E = IR \tag{1}$$

where R is a constant of proportionality called the coefficient of resistance or, simply, resistance. The units, generally known as "practical units" are such that E is in *volts*, I is in *amperes* and R is in *ohms*. Equation (1) is familiar to the student of elementary physics under the name *Ohm's law*.

More complicated, but for many cases more practical, are circuits consisting of elements other than resistors. Two important elements are *inductors* and *capacitors*. An inductor opposes a change in current. It has an inertia effect in electricity in much the same way as mass has an inertia effect in mechanics. In fact the analogy is strong, and much could be said about it. A capacitor is an element which stores energy.

In physics we speak of a *voltage drop* across an element. In practice we can determine this voltage drop, or as it is sometimes called, *potential drop* or *potential difference*, by use of an instrument called a voltmeter. Experimentally the following laws are found to hold.

1. *The voltage drop across a resistor is proportional to the current passing through the resistor.*

If E_R is the voltage drop across the resistor and I is the current, then

$$E_R \propto I \quad \text{or} \quad E_R = RI$$

where R is the constant of proportionality called coefficient of resistance or simply resistance.

    2. *The voltage drop across an inductor is proportional to the instantaneous time rate of change of the current.*

If E_L is the voltage drop across the inductor, then

$$E_L \propto \frac{dI}{dt} \quad \text{or} \quad E_L = L\frac{dI}{dt}$$

where L is the constant of proportionality called the coefficient of inductance or simply the inductance.

    3. *The voltage drop across a capacitor is proportional to the instantaneous electric charge on the capacitor.*

If E_C is the voltage drop across the capacitor and Q is the instantaneous charge, then

$$E_C \propto Q \quad \text{or} \quad E_C = \frac{Q}{C}$$

where we have taken $1/C$ as the constant of proportionality, C being known as the coefficient of capacitance or simply capacitance.

    2. Units. In electricity, as in mechanics, there exist more than one system of units. We consider and use only one such system in this book. The following summarizes the important electrical quantities and their units, symbols, and abbreviations. As in mechanics, time is in seconds.

Quantity	Symbol	Unit	Abbreviation
Voltage, emf, or potential	E or V	volt	v
Resistance	R	ohm	ω or Ω
Inductance	L	henry	h
Capacitance	C	farad	f
Current	I	ampere	amp
Charge.................	Q	coulomb	none

    The unit of current, the ampere, corresponds to a coulomb of charge passing a given point in the circuit per second.

    3. Kirchhoff's law:

    The algebraic sum of all the voltage drops around an electric loop or circuit is zero. [Another way of stating this is to say that the voltage supplied (emf) is equal to the sum of the voltage drops.]

It is customary to indicate the various circuit elements as shown:

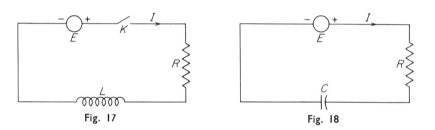

As an example, consider an electric circuit consisting of a voltage supply E (battery or generator), a resistor R, and inductor L connected in series as shown in Fig. 17.* We adopt the following

R

Fig. 17   Fig. 18

Convention: The current flows from the positive $(+)$ side of the battery or generator through the circuit to the negative $(-)$ side, as shown in Fig. 17.

Since, by Kirchhoff's law, the emf supplied (E) is equal to the voltage drop across the inductor $(L\, dI/dt)$ added to the voltage drop across the resistor (RI), we have

$$L\frac{dI}{dt} + RI = E$$

as the required differential equation for the circuit.

As another example, suppose we are given an electric circuit consisting of a battery or generator of E volts in series with a resistor of R ohms and a capacitor of C farads as in Fig. 18. Here the voltage drop across the resistor is RI and the voltage drop across the capacitor is Q/C, so that by Kirchhoff's law

$$RI + \frac{Q}{C} = E \tag{2}$$

As it stands this is not a differential equation. However by noting that the current is the time rate of change in charge, i.e., $I = dQ/dt$, (2) becomes

$$R\frac{dQ}{dt} + \frac{Q}{C} = E$$

---

* Sometimes, for brevity, we shall speak of a battery E, resistor R, capacitor C, etc., instead of a battery having an emf of E volts, a resistor having a resistance of R ohms, a capacitor having a capacitance of C farads, etc.

which is the differential equation for the instantaneous charge. Accompanying the differential equations obtained are conditions which are derived, of course, from the specific problem considered.

ILLUSTRATIVE EXAMPLE 1

A generator having emf 100 volts is connected in series with a 10 ohm resistor and an inductor of 2 henries. If the switch K is closed at time $t = 0$, set up a differential equation for the current and determine the current at time t.

Mathematical Formulation. As usual we draw the physical diagram (Fig. 19). Calling I the current in amperes flowing as shown, we have:

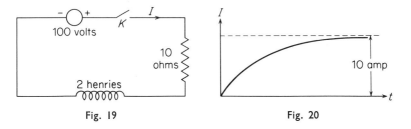

Fig. 19   Fig. 20

(1) voltage supplied = 100 volts, (2) voltage drop across resistance $(RI) = 10I$, (3) voltage drop across inductor $(L \, dI/dt) = 2 \, dI/dt$. Hence, by Kirchhoff's law,

$$100 = 10I + 2\frac{dI}{dt} \quad \text{or} \quad \frac{dI}{dt} + 5I = 50 \tag{3}$$

Since the switch is closed at $t = 0$, we must have $I = 0$ at $t = 0$.

Solution. The differential equation (3) is a first-order linear equation with integrating factor e^{5t}. Multiplying by this factor gives   *SEE PAGE 44 FOR MAXImum of SoLUTION*

$$\frac{d}{dt}(e^{5t}I) = 50e^{5t} \quad \text{or} \quad e^{5t}I = 10e^{5t} + c$$

i.e., $$I = 10 + ce^{-5t}$$

Since $I = 0$ at $t = 0$, $c = -10$. Thus,

$$I = 10(1 - e^{-5t})$$

Another Method. Equation (3) may be also solved by separation of variables.

The graph of I vs. t is shown in Fig. 20. Note that the current is zero at $t = 0$ and builds toward the maximum of 10 amp although theoretically it never reaches it. The student should note the similarity between this problem and the problem of the falling paratrooper in Illustrative Example 3 of the last section.

ILLUSTRATIVE EXAMPLE 2

Set up and solve a differential equation for the circuit of Illustrative Example 1 if the 100 volt generator is replaced by one having an emf of 20 cos 5t volts.

Mathematical Formulation. The only difference is that 20 cos 5t replaces 100 in equation (3). Hence, the required equation is

$$10I + 2\frac{dI}{dt} = 20\cos 5t \quad \text{or} \quad \frac{dI}{dt} + 5I = 10\cos 5t \qquad (4)$$

Solution. Multiplying the second equation in (4) by the integrating factor e^{5t}, we have

$$\frac{d}{dt}(e^{5t}I) = 10e^{5t}\cos 5t$$

$$e^{5t}I = 10\int e^{5t}\cos 5t\, dt = e^{5t}(\cos 5t + \sin 5t) + c$$

or
$$I = \cos 5t + \sin 5t + ce^{-5t}$$

Since $I = 0$ at $t = 0$, we have $c = -1$. Thus,

$$I = \cos 5t + \sin 5t - e^{-5t}$$

ILLUSTRATIVE EXAMPLE 3

A decaying emf $E = 200e^{-5t}$ is connected in series with a 20 ohm resistor and 0.01 farad capacitor. Assuming $Q = 0$ at $t = 0$, find the charge and current at any time. Show that the charge reaches a maximum, calculate it, and find when it is reached.

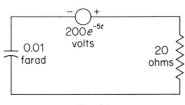

Fig. 21

Mathematical Formulation. Referring to Fig. 21 we have: (1) voltage supplied $(E) = 200e^{-5t}$, (2) voltage drop in resistor $(RI) = 20I$, (3) voltage drop across capacitor $(Q/C) = Q/0.01 = 100Q$. Hence, by Kirchhoff's law, $20I + 100Q = 200e^{-5t}$ and, using $I = dQ/dt$,

$$20\frac{dQ}{dt} + 100Q = 200e^{-5t} \quad \text{or} \quad \frac{dQ}{dt} + 5Q = 10e^{-5t}$$

Solution. An integrating factor is e^{5t}. Hence,

$$\frac{d}{dt}(Qe^{5t}) = 10, \qquad Qe^{5t} = 10t + c$$

Since $Q = 0$ at $t = 0$, $c = 0$. Hence, $Q = 10te^{-5t}$.
Current at any time. Since $I = dQ/dt$,

$$I = \frac{d}{dt}(10te^{-5t}) = 10e^{-5t} - 50te^{-5t}$$

Maximum charge. To find when Q is a maximum, set $dQ/dt = 0$, i.e., $I = 0$.

$$10e^{-5t} - 50te^{-5t} = 0, \quad \text{i.e.,} \quad t = \tfrac{1}{5} \text{ sec}$$

The student should show that this value of t actually gives a maximum. The value of the maximum charge is the value of Q when $t = \tfrac{1}{5}$, i.e.,

$$Q = 10 \times \frac{1}{5} e^{-1} = \frac{2}{e} \sim 0.74 \text{ coulomb}$$

A EXERCISES

1. At $t = 0$ an emf of 20 volts is applied to a circuit consisting of an inductor of 2 henries in series with a 40 ohm resistor. If the current is zero at $t = 0$, what is it at any time $t \geq 0$?

2. Work the previous problem if the emf is $100 \sin 10t$.

3. A 20 ohm resistor and 5 henry inductor are in series in an electric circuit in which there is a current flow of 20 amp at time $t = 0$. Find the current for $t \geq 0$ if the emf is zero for $t > 0$.

4. A capacitor of 5×10^{-3} farads is in series with a 25 ohm resistor and an emf of 50 volts. The switch is closed at $t = 0$. Assuming that the charge on the capacitor is zero at $t = 0$, determine the charge and current at any time.

5. Work the previous exercise if the emf is $50 \cos 6t$, $t \geq 0$.

6. A circuit consists of a 10 ohm resistor and a 0.01 farad capacitor in series. The charge on the capacitor is 0.05 coulomb. Find the charge and the current flow at time t after the switch is closed.

7. A 4 ohm resistor and an inductor of 1 henry are connected in series with a voltage $100e^{-4t} \cos 50t$, $t \geq 0$. Find $I(t)$ if $I = 0$ at $t = 0$.

8. A 20 ohm resistor is connected in series with a capacitor of 0.01 farad and an emf in volts given by $40e^{-3t} + 20e^{-6t}$. If $Q = 0$ at $t = 0$, show that the maximum charge on the capacitor is 0.25 coulomb.

B EXERCISES

1. A circuit consists of a constant resistance R ohms in series with a constant emf E volts and a constant inductance L henries. If the initial current is zero, show that the current builds up to half its theoretical maximum in $(L \ln 2)/R$ sec.

2. An emf of $E_0 \cos \omega t$ volts, where E_0, ω are constants, is applied at $t = 0$ to a series circuit consisting of R ohms and C farads, where R and C are constants. If $Q = 0$ at $t = 0$, show that the charge at $t > 0$ is

$$Q = \frac{CE_0}{R^2C^2\omega^2 + 1} \left(\cos \omega t + \omega RC \sin \omega t - e^{-t/RC} \right)$$

Discuss the case where $\omega = 0$.

3. A resistance of R ohms varies with time t (seconds) according to $R = 1 + 0.01t$, $0 \leq t \leq 1000$. It is connected in series with a 0.1 farad capacitor and 100 volt emf. The initial charge on the capacitor is 5 coulombs. Find (a) the charge and current as a function of time, (b) the theoretically maximum charge.

4. An inductor of L henries varies with time t (seconds) according to $L = 0.05 + 0.001t$, $0 \leq t \leq 1000$. It is connected in series with a 40 volt emf and a 10 ohm resistor. If $I = 0$ at $t = 0$, find (a) $I(t)$, $t > 0$; (b) the theoretically maximum current.

5. A circuit has R ohms, C farads, and E volts in series with a switch, the quantities R, C, E being constants. The initial charge on the capacitor is zero. If the switch is closed until the charge is 99% of its theoretical maximum and E is then suddenly reduced to zero, find Q thereafter.

C EXERCISES

1. An inductor of 0.1 henry, a resistor of 10 ohms, and an emf $E(t)$ volts, where

$$E(t) = \begin{cases} 10, & 0 < t \leq 5 \\ 0, & t > 5 \end{cases}$$

are connected in series. Find the current $I(t)$, assuming $I(0) = 0$.

2. A periodic emf $E(t)$ shown graphically in Fig. 22 is applied at $t = 0$ to a circuit consisting of R ohms and C farads in series, where R and C are constants. Find the charge when $t = 4T$, assuming that at $t = 0$ the charge is zero.

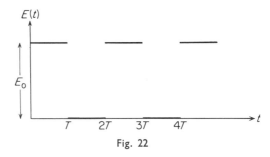

Fig. 22

3. An emf $E_0 \cos \omega t$, $t \geq 0$ is applied to a circuit consisting of L henries and R ohms in series. The quantities E_0, ω, L, R are given constants. If the current is zero

at $t = 0$; (a) Show that the current is composed of *transient terms* which become negligible after some time and *steady-state terms* which have the same period as the applied emf. (b) Show that the root-mean-square current (rms) defined by

$$\sqrt{\frac{\displaystyle\int_a^b I^2 \, dt}{b - a}}$$

where $b - a$ is the period $2\pi/\omega$ of the emf, approaches

$$\frac{\sqrt{2}}{2} \cdot \frac{E_0}{\sqrt{R^2 + L^2 \omega^2}}$$

III. Differential Equations of Families of Curves and Orthogonal Trajectories

Suppose we are given a family of curves as in Fig. 23 (heavy part). We may think of another family of curves (shown dashed) such that each member of this family cuts each member of the first family at right angles. For example, curve AB meets several members of the dashed family at right angles at the points L, M, N, O, and P. We say that the families are *mutually orthogonal*, or that either family forms a set of *orthogonal trajectories* of the other family. As an illustration, consider the family of all circles having center at the origin; a few such circles appear in Fig. 24. The orthogonal trajectories for this family of circles would be members of the family of straight lines (shown dashed). Similarly the orthogonal trajectories of the family of straight lines passing through the origin are the circles having center at the origin.

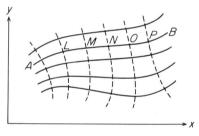

Fig. 23

As a more complicated situation, consider the family of ellipses (Fig. 25) and the family of curves orthogonal to them. The curves of one family are the orthogonal trajectories of the other family. Applications of orthogonal trajectories in physics and engineering are numerous. As a very elementary application, consider Fig. 26. Here NS represents a bar magnet, N being its north pole, and S its south pole. If iron filings are sprinkled around the magnet we find that they arrange themselves like the dashed curves of Fig. 26. These curves are called *lines of force*. The curves perpendicular to these (shown heavy) are called *equipotential lines*, or *curves of equal potential*. Here, too, the members of one family constitute the orthogonal trajectories of the other family.

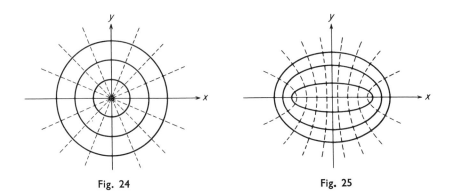

Fig. 24   Fig. 25

As another physical example consider Fig. 27, which represents a weather map so familiar in many of our daily newspapers. The curves represent *isobars*, which are curves connecting all cities which report the same barometric pressure to the weather bureau. The orthogonal trajectories of the family of isobars would indicate the general direction of the wind from high to low pressure areas. Instead of isobars, Fig. 27 could represent *isothermal curves* which are curves connecting points having the same temperature. In such case the orthogonal trajectories represent the general direction of heat flow.

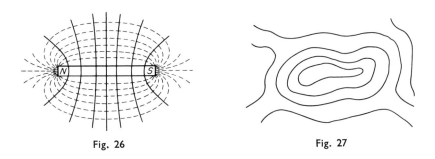

Fig. 26   Fig. 27

Consider the example of isobars. Given any point (x,y), we may theoretically find the pressure at that point. Hence we may say that $P = f(x,y)$, i.e., pressure is a function of position. Letting P be a definite value, say P_1, we see that $f(x,y) = P_1$ represents a curve, all points of which have pressure P_1, and thus is an isobar. By giving other values to P, other isobars are obtained. It is clear that these isobars could not intersect, for if they did, then the point of intersection would have two different pressures, and this would be impossible. If we use c instead of P we see that

$$f(x,y) = c \qquad (1)$$

where c may take on values within a certain prescribed set, represents a family of isobars. In the first chapter we learned how to find the differential equation for a family of curves by differentiating so as to eliminate the arbitrary constants (c in our case). The problem which we face now is how to obtain the family of orthogonal trajectories. Actually this is simple because the differential equation of the family (1) is given by

$$df = \frac{\partial f}{\partial x} dx + \frac{\partial f}{\partial y} dy = 0 \quad \text{or} \quad \frac{dy}{dx} = -\frac{\partial f / \partial x}{\partial f / \partial y} \tag{2}$$

Now the slope of the orthogonal trajectories should be the negative reciprocal of the slope in (2), namely,

$$\frac{\partial f / \partial y}{\partial f / \partial x}$$

Thus the differential equation for the family of orthogonal trajectories is

$$\frac{dy}{dx} = \frac{\partial f / \partial y}{\partial f / \partial x} \tag{3}$$

Upon solving this equation, the orthogonal trajectories are obtained. Illustrations of the procedure will now be given. A common mistake of students is to forget to eliminate the arbitrary constant in finding the differential equation of a family.

ILLUSTRATIVE EXAMPLE 1

Find the orthogonal trajectories of $x^2 + y^2 = cx$.

Mathematical Formulation. There are two ways for determining the differential equation of the family.
First way. Solve for c to obtain $c = (x^2 + y^2)/x$.
Differentiating with respect to x, we have

$$\frac{x(2x + 2yy') - (x^2 + y^2)(1)}{x^2} = 0$$

and we find

$$y' = \frac{dy}{dx} = \frac{y^2 - x^2}{2xy}$$

Second way. Differentiating $x^2 + y^2 = cx$ with respect to x, we find

$$2x + 2yy' = c$$

Eliminating c between this last equation and the given one, we find the same equation as before.
The family of orthogonal trajectories thus has the differential equation

$$\frac{dy}{dx} = \frac{2xy}{x^2 - y^2} \tag{4}$$

Solution. To solve (4), note that it is a homogeneous equation. Letting $y = vx$, the student may show that the solution is

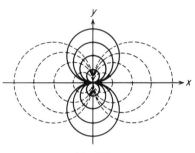

$$x^2 + y^2 = c_1 y$$

The solution is also obtained by noting that (4), cleared of fractions, has an integrating factor depending on one variable $(1/y^2)$.

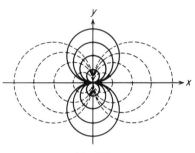

Fig. 28

The two orthogonal families are shown in Fig. 28. The originally given family is shown dashed.

ILLUSTRATIVE EXAMPLE 2

Find the orthogonal trajectories of the family $y = x + ce^{-x}$ and determine that particular member of each family which passes through (0,3).

Mathematical Formulation. By differentiation of the given relation we have

$$y' = 1 - ce^{-x}$$

Elimination of c yields

$$y' = 1 + x - y$$

Thus, the differential equation for the family of orthogonal trajectories is

$$\frac{dy}{dx} = \frac{-1}{1 + x - y} \tag{5}$$

Solution. Write (5) in the form

$$dx + (1 + x - y)dy = 0$$

Here

$$M = 1, \qquad N = 1 + x - y$$

$$\frac{\partial M}{\partial y} = 0, \qquad \frac{\partial N}{\partial x} = 1$$

so the equation is not exact. Now $\dfrac{0 - 1}{1 + x - y}$ is not a function of x alone. But $\dfrac{1 - 0}{1} = 1$ is a function of y. Hence, $e^{\int 1 dy} = e^y$ is an integrating factor.

Multiplying by this factor and proceeding as usual for exact equations, we obtain

$$xe^y - e^y(y - 2) = c_1$$

The required curves passing through $(0,3)$ are found to be

$$y = x + 3e^{-x}, \qquad x - y + 2 + e^{3-y} = 0 \tag{6}$$

The student may find it instructive to obtain the graphs of equations (6). He may also find it instructive to solve (5) by writing it as

$$\frac{dx}{dy} + x = y - 1$$

a linear equation with x as dependent variable.

A EXERCISES

1. The equation $y^2 = cx$ defines a family of parabolas.
   (a) Find a differential equation for the family.
   (b) Find a differential equation for the orthogonal trajectories and solve.
   (c) Graph several members of both families on the same set of axes.

2. Find the orthogonal trajectories of the family $y^3 = cx^2$ and draw a graph showing the two families.

3. Determine the orthogonal trajectories of each family and find particular members of each passing through the indicated points.

   (a) $x^2 + cy^2 = 1$; $(2,1)$.

   (b) $x^2 = cy + y^2$; $(3,-1)$.

   (c) $y = c \tan 2x + 1$; $\left(\dfrac{\pi}{8}, 0\right)$

   (d) $y = ce^{-2x} + 3x$; $(0,3)$.

   (e) $y^2 = c(1 + x^2)$; $(-2,5)$.

4. Show that the families $x^2 + 4y^2 = c_1$ and $y = c_2 x^4$ are orthogonal.

B EXERCISES

1. Find the value of the constant a so that the families $y^3 = c_1 x$ and $x^2 + ay^2 = c_2$ are orthogonal.

2. Show that the family of parabolas $y^2 = 4cx + 4c^2$ is "self-orthogonal."

3. Show that the family

$$\frac{x^2}{a^2 + c} + \frac{y^2}{b^2 + c} = 1$$

where a and b are given constants, is "self-orthogonal." This is called a family of "confocal conics."

4. Determine the orthogonal trajectories of

(a) $x^p + cy^p = 1; p = $ given constant.
(b) $x^2 + cxy + y^2 = 1.$

C EXERCISES

1. Determine the family of curves each member of which cuts each member of the family of straight lines $y = mx$ at an angle of 45°.

2. Determine the curve passing through $(\frac{1}{2}, \sqrt{3}/2)$ which cuts each member of the family $x^2 + y^2 = c^2$ at an angle of 60°.

3. Find all curves cutting the family $y = ce^x$ at constant angle α.

4. Show that if a differential equation of a family of curves in polar coordinates (r,θ) is given by

$$\frac{dr}{d\theta} = F(r,\theta)$$

then a differential equation for the family of orthogonal trajectories is

$$\frac{dr}{d\theta} = -\frac{r^2}{F(r,\theta)}$$

(*Hint:* Use the fact from elementary calculus that in polar coordinates the tangent of the angle formed by the radius vector and the tangent line to a curve is $r\, d\theta/dr$.)

5. Find the orthogonal trajectories of $r = c \cos \theta$ and graph.

6. Determine the orthogonal trajectories of the spirals $r = e^{\alpha\theta}$.

7. Find the orthogonal trajectories of the cardioids $r = c(1 - \cos \theta)$.

8. Let $F(z) = u(x,y) + iv(x,y)$ where $z = x + iy$ and the functions $u(x,y)$, $v(x,y)$ are real. (a) Find $u(x,y)$ and $v(x,y)$ corresponding to $F(z) = z^2$ and show that the families $u(x,y) = c_1$ and $v(x,y) = c_2$ are orthogonal. (b) Work part (a) for the functions $F(z) = z^3$ and $F(z) = 2z^2 - iz - 3$. (c) Do you think the results indicated by these special cases hold in general? Explain (compare C Exercise 4, page 35).

IV. Applications to Chemistry and Chemical Mixtures

There are many applications of differential equations to chemical processes. Some of these will be indicated in the following illustrative examples. Others are presented in the exercises.

ILLUSTRATIVE EXAMPLE 1

A tank is filled with 10 gallons (abbreviation *gal*) of brine in which is dissolved 5 lb of salt. Brine containing 3 lb of salt per gallon enters the tank at 2 gal per minute, and the well-stirred mixture leaves at the same rate.

(a) Find the amount of salt in the tank at any time.
(b) How much salt is present after 10 min?
(c) How much salt is present after a long time?

Mathematical Formulation. Let A be the number of pounds of salt in the tank after t minutes. Then dA/dt is the time rate of change of this amount of salt. This is given by

$$\frac{dA}{dt} = \text{rate of amount gained} - \text{rate of amount lost} \qquad (1)$$

Since 2 gal/min enter and there are 3 lb/gal salt we have as the amount of salt entering per minute

$$\frac{2 \text{ gal}}{\min} \cdot \frac{3 \text{ lb}}{\text{gal}} = \frac{6 \text{ lb}}{\min} \qquad (2)$$

which is the rate at which salt is gained. Since there are always 10 gal in the tank and since there are A pounds of salt at any time t, the concentration of salt at time t is A pounds per 10 gal. The amount of salt leaving per minute is, therefore,

$$\frac{A \text{ lb}}{10 \text{ gal}} \cdot \frac{2 \text{ gal}}{\min} = \frac{2A \text{ lb}}{10 \min} = \frac{A \text{ lb}}{5 \min} \qquad (3)$$

From (1), (2), and (3) we have

$$\frac{dA}{dt} = 6 - \frac{A}{5}$$

Since initially there are 5 lb of salt, we have $A = 5$ at $t = 0$. Thus, the complete mathematical formulation is

$$\frac{dA}{dt} = 6 - \frac{A}{5}, \qquad A = 5 \quad \text{at} \quad t = 0$$

Solution. Using the method of separation of variables, we have

$$\int \frac{dA}{30 - A} = \int \frac{dt}{5} \quad \text{or} \quad -\ln(30 - A) = \frac{t}{5} + c$$

Since $A = 5$ at $t = 0$, $c = -\ln 25$. Thus,

$$-\ln(30 - A) = \frac{t}{5} - \ln 25, \qquad \ln \frac{30 - A}{25} = -\frac{t}{5}$$

$$A = 30 - 25e^{-t/5}$$

which is the amount of salt in the tank at any time t.
At the end of 10 minutes the amount of salt is

$$A = 30 - 25e^{-2} = 26.6 \text{ lb}$$

After a long time, i.e., as $t \to \infty$, we see that $A \to 30$ lb. This could also be seen from the differential equation by letting $dA/dt = 0$, since A is constant when equilibrium is reached.

Illustrative Example 2

Two chemicals, A and B, react to form another chemical C. It is found that the rate at which C is formed varies as the product of the instantaneous amounts of chemicals A and B present. The formation requires 2 lb of A for each pound of B. If 10 lb of A and 20 lb of B are present initially, and if 6 lb of C are formed in 20 min, find the amount of chemical C at any time.

Mathematical Formulation. Let x pounds be the amount of C formed in time t hours. Then dx/dt is the rate of its formation. To form x pounds of C, we need $2x/3$ lb of A and $x/3$ lb of B, since twice as much of chemical A as B is needed. Thus, the amount of A present at time t when x pounds of C is formed is $10 - 2x/3$, and the amount of B at this time is $20 - x/3$. Hence,

$$\frac{dx}{dt} \propto \left(10 - \frac{2x}{3}\right)\left(20 - \frac{x}{3}\right) \quad \text{or} \quad \frac{dx}{dt} = K\left(10 - \frac{2x}{3}\right)\left(20 - \frac{x}{3}\right)$$

where K is the constant of proportionality. This equation may be written

$$\frac{dx}{dt} = k(15 - x)(60 - x)$$

where k is another constant. There are two conditions. Since no chemical C is present initially, we have $x = 0$ at $t = 0$. Also $x = 6$ at $t = \frac{1}{3}$. We need two conditions, one to determine k, the other to determine the arbitrary constant from the solution of the differential equation. The complete formulation is

$$\frac{dx}{dt} = k(15 - x)(60 - x), \qquad x = 0 \quad \text{at} \quad t = 0, \qquad x = 6 \quad \text{at} \quad t = \frac{1}{3}$$

Solution. Separation of variables yields

$$\int \frac{dx}{(15 - x)(60 - x)} = \int k \, dt = kt + c_1$$

Now

$$\int \frac{dx}{(15 - x)(60 - x)} = \int \frac{1}{45}\left(\frac{1}{15 - x} - \frac{1}{60 - x}\right) dx = \frac{1}{45} \ln\left(\frac{60 - x}{15 - x}\right)$$

Thus, we may show that

$$\frac{60 - x}{15 - x} = ce^{45kt}$$

Since $x = 0$ at $t = 0$, we find $c = 4$. Thus,

$$\frac{60 - x}{15 - x} = 4e^{45kt}$$

Since $x = 6$ at $t = \frac{1}{3}$, we have $e^{15k} = \frac{3}{2}$. Thus,

$$\frac{60 - x}{15 - x} = 4(e^{15k})^{3t} = 4\left(\frac{3}{2}\right)^{3t}$$

from which

$$x = \frac{15[1 - (\frac{2}{3})^{3t}]}{1 - \frac{1}{4}(\frac{2}{3})^{3t}}$$

As $t \to \infty$, $x \to 15$ lb.

The preceding problem is a special case of the *law of mass action*, which is fundamental in the theory of rates of chemical reactions. For problems involving description and application of this law see the C exercises.

A EXERCISES

1. A tank is filled with 8 gal of brine in which 2 lb of salt is dissolved. Brine having 3 lb of salt per gallon enters the tank at 4 gal per minute, and the well-stirred mixture leaves at the same rate. (a) Set up a differential equation for the amount of salt at time t. (b) Find the amount of salt as a function of time. (c) Find the concentration of salt after 8 min. (d) How much salt is there after a long time?

2. A tank has 40 gal of pure water. A salt water solution with 1 lb of salt per gallon enters at 2 gal per minute, and the well-stirred mixture leaves at the same rate. (a) How much salt is in the tank at any time? (b) When will the water leaving have $\frac{1}{2}$ lb of salt per gallon?

3. A tank has 60 gal of salt water with 2 lb of salt per gallon. A solution with 3 lb of salt per gallon enters at 2 gal per minute, and the mixture leaves at the same rate. When will 150 lb of salt be in the tank?

4. A tank has 100 gal brine with 40 lb of dissolved salt. Pure water enters at 2 gal per minute and leaves at the same rate. When will the salt concentration be 0.2 lb/gal? When will the concentration be less than 0.01 lb/gal?

5. Chemical A is transformed into chemical B. The rate at which B is formed varies directly as the amount of A present at any instant. If 10 lb of A is present initially and if 3 lb is transformed into B in 1 hr: (a) How much of A is transformed after 2, 3, and 4 hr? (b) In what time is 75 % of chemical A transformed? (This type of reaction is called a *first-order reaction*.)

6. Chemical C is produced from a reaction involving chemicals A and B. The rate of production of C varies as the product of the instantaneous amounts of A and B present. The formation requires 3 lb of A for every 2 lb of B. If 60 lb each of A and B are present initially and 15 lb of C are formed in 1 hr find: (a) the amount of C at any time; (b) the amount of C after 2 hr; (c) the maximum quantity of C which can be formed.

B EXERCISES

1. A tank has 10 gal brine having 2 lb of dissolved salt. Brine with 1.5 lb of salt per gallon enters at 3 gal/min, and the well-stirred mixture leaves at 4 gal/min. (a) Find the amount of salt in the tank at any time. (b) Find the concentration of

salt after 10 min. (c) Draw graphs of amount and concentration of salt vs. time and give maxima in each case.

2. A tank has 60 gal of pure water. A salt solution with 3 lb of salt per gallon enters at 2 gal/min and leaves at 2.5 gal/min. (a) Find the concentration of salt in the tank at any time. (b) Find the salt concentration when the tank has 30 gal of salt water. (c) Find the amount of water in the tank when the concentration is greatest. (d) Determine the maximum amount of salt present at any time.

3. A chemical C is to be dissolved in water. Experimentally, the rate at which C enters into solution varies as the product of (i) the instantaneous amount of C which remains undissolved, (ii) the difference between the instantaneous concentration of the dissolved chemical and the maximum concentration possible at the given conditions of temperature and pressure (this maximum occurs when the solution is *saturated* and further increase of the chemical dissolved is not possible).

If 5 lb of C are placed in 2 gal of water, it is found that 1 lb dissolves in 1 hr. Assuming a saturated solution to have a concentration of 4 lb/gal: (a) how much of chemical C remains undissolved after 4 hr? (b) What is the concentration of the solution after 3 hr? (c) When will the concentration be 2 lb/gal?

4. When a pounds of a chemical are placed in b gallons of water, A pounds of the chemical dissolve in time T. If a saturated solution contains S pounds of the chemical per gallon (S is constant), show that the amount of the chemical undissolved at time t is

$$\frac{aR(bS - a)}{bS - aR} \quad \text{where} \quad R = \left[\frac{AbS}{a(A + bS - a)}\right]^{t/T}$$

Show that if $S \to \infty$ the amount of the chemical which is undissolved approaches $a[A/a]^{t/T}$.

5. Two tanks (Fig. 29) each contain v gallons of water. Starting at time $t = 0$, a solution containing a lb/gal of a chemical solvent flows into tank I at the rate of b gal/min. The mixture then enters and leaves tank II at the same rate. Assuming

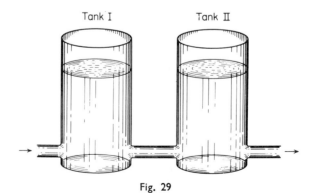

Fig. 29

thorough stirring in both tanks, show that the amount of the chemical in tank II after time $t > 0$ is

$$av(1 - e^{-bt/v}) - abte^{-bt/v}$$

C EXERCISES

Velocity of Chemical Reactions and the Law of Mass Action

A chemical equation describes how molecules of various substances combine to give other substances. For example,

$$2\,H_2 + O_2 \to 2\,H_2O$$

states that 2 molecules of hydrogen combine with 1 molecule oxygen to yield 2 molecules water. In general, a chemical equation reads

$$aA + bB + cC + \cdots \to mM + nN + pP + \cdots$$

where A, B, C, ... represent molecules of the reacting substances, M, N, P, ... represent molecules of the substances formed by the reaction, and $a, b, c, \ldots, m,$ n, p are positive integers signifying the number of molecules taking part in the reaction. The rate at which a substance is formed is called the *velocity of the reaction*. Although no general rule applies in all cases, the law of mass action may apply in the determination of this rate.

LAW OF MASS ACTION. *If the temperature is kept constant, the velocity of a chemical reaction is proportional to the product of the concentrations of the substances which are reacting.*

If we let [A], [B], [C], ... denote the concentrations of A, B, C, ... at time t, these concentrations being expressed in moles per liter,* and if x is the number of moles per liter which have reacted after time t, the rate dx/dt of the reaction is given by

$$\frac{dx}{dt} = k[A]^a[B]^b[C]^c \cdots$$

where the constant of proportionality k is called the *velocity constant*. The *order* of the reaction is the sum of the exponents. The reactions are called unimolecular, bimolecular, trimolecular, etc., according as the order is one, two, three, etc.

1. In the bimolecular reaction A + B → M, α moles per liter of A and β moles per liter of B are combined. If x denotes the number of moles per liter which have reacted after time t, the rate of reaction is given by

$$\frac{dx}{dt} = k(\alpha - x)(\beta - x)$$

---

* A mole is the molecular weight of a substance in grams, taking the atomic weight of oxygen as 16 g; hydrogen, H, as 1.008 g; carbon, C, as 12.01 g, etc. Thus, 1 mole $O_2 =$ $2(16) = 32$ g; 1 mole $H_2O = 16 + 2(1.008) = 18.016$ g; 1 mole $C_2H_6 = 2(12.01) +$ $6(1.008) = 30.068$ g.

(a) Show that if $\alpha \neq \beta$,

$$x = \frac{\alpha\beta[1 - e^{(\beta - \alpha)kt}]}{\alpha - \beta e^{(\beta - \alpha)kt}}$$

and find $\lim_{t \to \infty} x$, considering the two cases $\alpha > \beta$, $\beta > \alpha$.

(b) If $\alpha = \beta$, show that $x = \alpha^2 kt/(1 + \alpha kt)$ and find $\lim_{t \to \infty} x$.

2. In the third-order or trimolecular reaction $A + B + C \to M + N$, α, β, and γ moles per liter of A, B, and C are combined. If x denotes the number of moles per liter of A, B, or C which have reacted after time t (or the number of moles per liter of M or N which have been formed), then the rate of reaction is given by

$$\frac{dx}{dt} = k(\alpha - x)(\beta - x)(\gamma - x)$$

Solve the equation, considering that $x = 0$ at $t = 0$ and treating the cases: (a) α, β, γ are equal; (b) α, β, γ are not equal; (c) only two of α, β, γ are equal.

3. Substances A and B react chemically to yield P and Q according to the second-order reaction $A + B \to P + Q$. At time $t = 0$, M_A grams of A and M_B grams of B are combined. If x grams react in time t and if the law of mass action applies: (a) show that

$$\frac{dx}{dt} = K\left(M_A - \frac{m_A}{m_A + m_B}x\right)\left(M_B - \frac{m_B}{m_A + m_B}x\right)$$

where m_A and m_B are the molecular weights of A and B, respectively. (b) Show that the number of grams of P and Q formed after time t are $m_P s$ and $m_Q s$, where

$$s = \frac{1 - e^{rt}}{M_A m_B - M_B m_A e^{rt}}, \qquad r = \frac{KM_A M_B(M_B m_A - M_A m_B)(m_A + m_B)}{(M_A + m_B)^2 m_A m_B}$$

and where we assume that $M_B/m_B \neq M_A/m_A$. Note that $m_A + m_B = m_P + m_Q$. Derive a similar result for the case $M_B/m_B = M_A/m_A$.

4. The amount 260 g of $CH_3COOC_2H_5$ (ethyl acetate) is combined with 175 g of NaOH (sodium hydroxide) in a water solution to yield CH_3COONa (sodium acetate) and C_2H_5OH (ethyl alcohol), according to the equation

$$CH_3COOC_2H_5 + NaOH \to CH_3COONa + C_2H_5OH$$

At the end of 10 min, 60 g of sodium acetate have been formed. If the reaction is known to obey the law of mass action, (a) calculate the velocity constant; (b) find the number of grams of sodium acetate and ethyl alcohol present after $\frac{1}{2}$ hr. (*Hint:* use the atomic weights $C = 12.01$, $H = 1.008$, $O = 16$, $Na = 22.997$.)

V. Applications to Steady-State Heat Flow

Consider a slab of material of indefinite length bounded by two parallel planes A and B, as in Fig. 30. We assume the material uniform in all properties, e.g., specific heat, density, etc. Suppose planes A and B are kept at 50°C and 100°C, respectively. Every point in the region between A and B reaches some temperature and does not change thereafter. Thus, all points on plane C midway between A and B will be at 75°C; plane E at 90°C. When the temperature at each point of a body does not vary with time, we say that *steady-state conditions* prevail or that we have *steady-state heat flow*.

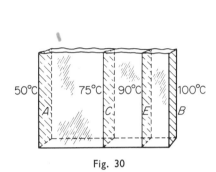

Fig. 30

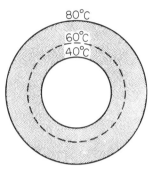

Fig. 31

As another example consider a pipe of uniform material, the cross section of which is shown in Fig. 31. Suppose the outer surface kept at 80°C and the inner at 40°C. There will be a surface (shown dashed) each point of which will be at 60°C. This will not be midway between the inner and outer surfaces, however. Lines parallel to A and in a plane perpendicular to A (Fig. 30) are called *isothermal lines*. The dashed curve of Fig. 31 is an *isothermal curve*. The corresponding planes of Fig. 30 and cylinders of Fig. 31 are called *isothermal surfaces*. In the general case, isothermal curves will not be lines or circles, as in Figs. 30 or 31, but may be a family of curves as shown in Fig. 32 (dashed curves). The orthogonal trajectories of the family are called *flow lines* (see Section III on orthogonal trajectories).

Consider small portions of two neighboring isothermal surfaces (Fig. 33) separated by a distance Δn. Assume that the temperature corresponding to surface S_1 is U_1, and that corresponding to S_2 is U_2. Call the temperature difference $U_2 - U_1 = \Delta U$. It is found experimentally that the amount of heat flowing from S_1 to S_2 per unit area per unit time is approximately proportional to $\Delta U/\Delta n$. The approximation becomes more accurate as Δn (and hence ΔU) gets smaller. In the limiting case as $\Delta n \to 0$, $\Delta U/\Delta n \to dU/dn$* which is called the *gradient* of U (rate of change of U in the direction normal to the isothermal surface or curve). If H is the amount of heat flow per unit area per unit time, we take as our physical law:

$$H \propto \frac{dU}{dn} \quad \text{or} \quad H = K\frac{dU}{dn} \tag{1}$$

* In case U depends on other factors besides n, then dU/dn is to be replaced by $\partial U/\partial n$.

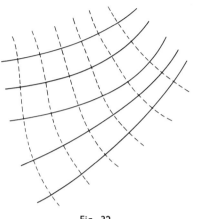

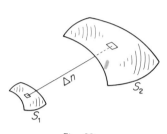

Fig. 32   Fig. 33

If we wish to consider H a vector quantity (having direction as well as magnitude), we reason as follows. Consider as positive the direction from S_1 to S_2. If dU/dn is positive, then U is increasing and, hence, we must have $U_2 > U_1$. Thus, heat actually flows from S_2 to S_1 (higher to lower temperature); i.e., heat flow is in the negative direction. Similarly, if dU/dn is negative, U is decreasing, $U_2 < U_1$, and the flow is from S_1 to S_2; i.e., heat flow is in the positive direction. The direction of heat flow can be taken into account by a minus sign in (1), i.e.,

$$H(\text{vector quantity}) = -K \frac{dU}{dn} \qquad (2)$$

The amount of heat per unit time flowing across an area A is given by

$$q = -KA \frac{dU}{dn} \qquad (3)$$

The constant of proportionality K, used above, depends on the material used and is called the *thermal conductivity*. The quantity of heat is expressed in *calories* in the cgs system, and in *British thermal units, Btu.*, in the fps system. Consider now an illustration using the above principles.

ILLUSTRATIVE EXAMPLE

A long steel pipe, of thermal conductivity $K = 0.15$ cgs units, has an inner radius of 10 cm and an outer radius of 20 cm. The inner surface is kept at 200°C and the outer surface is kept at 50 C. (a) Find the temperature as a function of distance r from the common axis of the concentric cylinders. (b) Find the temperature when $r = 15$ cm. (c) How much heat is lost per minute in a portion of the pipe which is 20 m long?

Mathematical Formulation. It is clear that the isothermal surfaces are cylinders concentric with the given ones. The area of such a surface having radius r and length l is $2\pi r l$. The distance dn is dr in this case. Thus, equation (3) can be written

$$q = -K(2\pi r l)\frac{dU}{dr} \tag{4}$$

Since $K = 0.15$, $l = 20$ m $= 2000$ cm, we have

$$q = -600\pi r\frac{dU}{dr} \tag{5}$$

In this equation, q is of course a constant. The conditions are

$$U = 200°\text{C} \quad \text{at} \quad r = 10, \qquad U = 50°\text{C} \quad \text{at} \quad r = 20 \tag{6}$$

Solution. Separating the variables in (5) and integrating yields

$$-600\pi U = q \ln r + c \tag{7}$$

Using the conditions (6), we have

$$-600\pi(200) = q \ln 10 + c, \qquad -600\pi(50) = q \ln 20 + c$$

from which we obtain $q = 408,000$, $c = -1,317,000$. Hence, from (7) we find

$$U = 699 - 216 \ln r \tag{8}$$

If $r = 15$, we find by substitution that $U = 114°\text{C}$. From the value of q above, which is in calories per second, it is clear that the answer to part (c) is

$$q = 408,000 \times 60 \text{ cal/min} = 24,480,000 \text{ cal/min}$$

since the length 20 m has already been taken into account.

A EXERCISES

1. A long steel pipe, of thermal conductivity $K = 0.15$ cgs units, has an inner radius of 20 cm and outer radius of 30 cm. The outer surface is kept at 400°C, and the inner surface is kept at 100°C. (a) Find the temperature as a function of distance r from the common axis of the concentric cylinders. (b) Find the temperature where $r = 25$ cm. (c) How much heat is lost per minute in a portion of the pipe 10 m long?

2. A long hollow pipe has an inner diameter of 10 cm and outer diameter of 20 cm. The inner surface is kept at 200°C, and the outer surface is kept at 50°C. The thermal conductivity is 0.12 cgs units. (a) Find the temperature as a function of distance r from the common axis of the concentric cylinders. (b) Find the temperature where $r = 7.5$ cm. (c) How much heat is lost per minute in a portion of the pipe 20 m long?

3. A slab of metal 500 cm thick and with its other two dimensions very much larger has one face kept at 25°C and the opposite face at 65°C. If the thermal conductivity is 0.005 cgs units: (a) find the temperature in the slab as a function of

distance x from the face having the lower temperature. (b) How much heat is transmitted per hour through a cross section parallel to the faces and having an area of 100 cm².

B EXERCISES

1. Show that the differential equation for steady-state temperature in a region bounded by two long coaxial cylinders is

$$\frac{d}{dr}\left(r\frac{dU}{dr}\right) = 0 \quad \text{or} \quad \frac{d^2U}{dr^2} + \frac{1}{r}\cdot\frac{dU}{dr} = 0$$

where U is the temperature at distance r from the common axis.

2. Show that the temperature U at distance r from the common axis of two coaxial cylinders of radii a and b $(a < b)$ kept at constant temperatures T_1 and T_2, respectively, is

$$U = \frac{T_1 \ln b/r + T_2 \ln r/a}{\ln b/a}$$

3. Show that the differential equation for steady-state temperature in a region bounded by two concentric spheres is

$$\frac{d}{dr}\left(r^2\frac{dU}{dr}\right) = 0 \quad \text{or} \quad \frac{d^2U}{dr^2} + \frac{2}{r}\cdot\frac{dU}{dr} = 0$$

where U is the temperature at distance r from the common center.

4. Show that the temperature U at distance r from the common center of two concentric spheres of radii a and b $(a < b)$ kept at constant temperatures T_1 and T_2, respectively, is

$$U = \frac{bT_2 - aT_1}{b - a} + \frac{ab(T_1 - T_2)}{(b - a)r}$$

VI. Applications to Miscellaneous Problems of Growth and Decay

The differential equation

$$\frac{dy}{dt} = ay \tag{1}$$

states that the time rate of change of a quantity y is proportional to y. If the constant of proportionality a is positive and y is positive, then dy/dt is positive and y is increasing. In this case we speak of y growing, and the problem is one of growth. On the other hand, if a is negative and y is positive, then dy/dt is negative and y is decreasing. Here the problem is one involving decay. In the following illustrative examples, and in the exercises, equations very similar to (1) arise from many fields seemingly unrelated.

In the two illustrative examples which follow we consider two such problems, one involving temperature, the other the phenomenon of radioactive disintegration.

Illustrative Example 1

Water is heated to the boiling point temperature 100°C. The water is then removed from the heat and kept in a room which is at a constant temperature of 60°C. After 3 min the water temperature is 90°C. (a) Find the water temperature after 6 min. (b) When will the water temperature be 75°C? 61°C?

Mathematical Formulation. Denote by U the temperature of the water t min after removal from the heat source. The temperature difference between water and room is $U - 60$. The time rate of change in U is dU/dt. On the basis of experience, one expects that temperature will change most rapidly when $(U - 60)$ is greatest and most slowly when $(U - 60)$ is small. Let us perform an experiment in which we take temperatures at various intervals of time, ΔU being the change in temperature and Δt the time to produce this change. By taking small Δt we expect that $\Delta U/\Delta t$ will be very close to dU/dt. If we plot $-\Delta U/\Delta t$ against $(U - 60)$, we could produce a graph similar to that in Fig. 34. The crosses are points determined by experiment. Since the graph is a straight line, approximately, we assume that dU/dt is proportional to $(U - 60)$, i.e.,

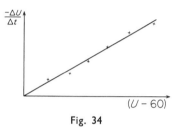

Fig. 34

$$\frac{dU}{dt} = a(U - 60)$$

where a is a constant of proportionality. Now dU/dt is negative when $(U - 60)$ is positive, and so we shall write $a = -k$ where $k > 0$. The equation is

$$\frac{dU}{dt} = -k(U - 60)$$

This equation is known in physics as *Newton's law of cooling* and is of importance in many temperature problems. Actually, it is but an approximation of the true physical situation. The conditions which accompany this equation are provided from the facts that

$$U = 100°C \quad \text{where } t = 0, \qquad U = 90°C \quad \text{where } t = 3 \text{ (minutes)}$$

Solution. Solving the equation by separation of variables we have

$$\int \frac{dU}{U - 60} = \int -k \, dt, \qquad \ln (U - 60) = -kt + c_1$$

or

$$U - 60 = ce^{-kt}$$

Where $t = 0$, $U = 100$, so that $c = 40$. Hence, $U - 60 = 40e^{-kt}$. Where $t = 3$, $U = 90$, so that $e^{-3k} = \frac{3}{4}$ or $e^{-k} = (\frac{3}{4})^{1/3}$. Hence,

$$U - 60 = 40(e^{-k})^t = 40(\tfrac{3}{4})^{t/3}$$

i.e., $$U = 60 + 40(\tfrac{3}{4})^{t/3} \qquad (2)$$

Temperature after 6 minutes. Let $t = 6$ in (2), and obtain $U = 82.5°C$.

Times where temperature is 75°C, 61°C. If $U = 75°C$, then we find that $75 = 60 + 40(\frac{3}{4})^{t/3}$, $(\frac{3}{4})^{t/3} = \frac{3}{8}$, and $t = 10.2$.

If $U = 61°C$, then $(\frac{3}{4})^{t/3} = \frac{1}{40}$ and $t = 38.5$.

Thus, it takes 10.2 min for the water at 100°C to drop in temperature to 75°C, and 38.5 min to drop in temperature from 100°C to 61°C.

By experimental methods similar to those indicated in the temperature problem we may arrive at the following:

LAW OF RADIOACTIVE DISINTEGRATION. *The rate of disintegration of a radio-active substance is proportional, at any instant, to the amount of the substance which is present.*

Before we formulate this law mathematically, let us consider the phenom-enon of radioactivity in a little detail. When a radioactive element like radium or uranium disintegrates, it emits particles in a random fashion. Each of these particles has a definite mass, which is very small. If we start with a mass of 1 g of the radioactive material and consider what happens when particles are emitted, we find a situation similar to that shown in the graph of Fig. 35. Here, x is the amount of substance left after time t, assuming we start with 1 g at $t = 0$. Each time there is a drop in the value of x it means that particles have been emitted; the greater the drop, the larger the number of particles emitted. Thus, the quantity of radioactive substance is, in reality, a discontinuous function of t. What, then, is meant by dx/dt? To surmount this mathematical difficulty we approximate the

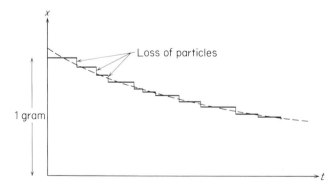

Fig. 35

actual graph by a smooth curve (dashed in Fig. 35). Thus, we are not much in error physically, and at the same time insure that we have a graph for which dx/dt will exist everywhere. Here we are forming a mathematical abstraction of a physical situation. The ideas presented here occur often in physics because of the finite size of even the smallest particle, in other words because of the atomic theory. Even in problems of electric circuits, the mathematical abstraction occurs (the student should try to see how). As a consequence one must always be alert in cases where these ideas are of importance. We now consider an example.

ILLUSTRATIVE EXAMPLE 2

It is found that 0.5% of radium disappears in 12 years.
(a) What percentage will disappear in 1000 years?
(b) What is the half-life of radium?

Mathematical Formulation. Let A be the quantity of radium, in grams, present after t years. Then dA/dt (which exists by virtue of our mathematical abstraction) represents the rate of disintegration of radium. According to the law on p. 100, we have

$$\frac{dA}{dt} \propto A \quad \text{or} \quad \frac{dA}{dt} = \alpha A$$

where α is a constant of proportionality. Since $A > 0$ and is decreasing, then $dA/dt < 0$ and we see that α must be negative. Writing $\alpha = -k$,

$$\frac{dA}{dt} = -kA$$

Let A_0 be the amount, in grams, of radium present initially. Then $0.005A_0$ gram disappears in 12 years, so that $0.995A_0$ gram remains. We thus have

$$A = A_0 \quad \text{at} \quad t = 0, \qquad A = 0.995A_0 \quad \text{at} \quad t = 12 \text{ (years)}$$

Solution. Separating the variables, we have on integrating:

$$\ln A = -kt + c_1 \quad \text{or} \quad A = ce^{-kt}$$

Since $A = A_0$ at $t = 0$, $c = A_0$. Hence,

$$A = A_0 e^{-kt}$$

Since $A = 0.995A_0$ at $t = 12$,

$$0.995A_0 = A_0 e^{-12k}, \qquad e^{-12k} = 0.995, \qquad e^{-k} = (0.995)^{1/12} \tag{3}$$

Hence,

$$A = A_0 e^{-kt} = A_0(e^{-k})^t = A_0(0.995)^{t/12} \tag{4}$$

or, if we solve for k in (3), we find $k = 0.000418$, so that

$$A = A_0 e^{-0.000418t} \tag{5}$$

Per cent disappearing in 1000 years. Where $t = 1000$ we have, from (4) or (5), $A = 0.658A_0$, so that 34.2% disappears in 1000 years.

Half-life of radium. The half-life of a radioactive substance is defined as the time it takes for 50% of the substance to disappear. Thus, for our problem, we wish to find the time when $A = \frac{1}{2}A_0$. Using (5) we find $e^{-0.000418t} = \frac{1}{2}$ or $t = 1660$ years, approximately.

A EXERCISES

1. Water at temperature 100°C cools in 10 min to 80°C in a room of temperature 25°C. (a) Find the temperature of the water after 20 min. (b) When is the temperature 40°C? 26°C?

2. Water at temperature 10°C takes 5 min to warm up to 20°C in a room at temperature 40°C. (a) Find the temperature after 20 min; after $\frac{1}{2}$ hr. (b) When will the temperature be 25°C?

3. If the half-life of radium is 1700 years, what percentage radium may be expected to remain after 50, 100, and 200 years?

4. Find the half-life of a radioactive substance if 25% of it disappears in 10 years.

5. If 30% of a radioactive substance disappears in 10 days, how long will it take for 90% to disappear?

6. The electric charge, in coulombs, on a spherical surface leaks off at a rate proportional to the instantaneous charge. Initially, 5 coulombs are present, and one-third leaks off in 20 min. When will there be 1 coulomb remaining?

7. Bacteria in a certain culture increase at a rate proportional to the number present. If the original number increases by 50% in $\frac{1}{2}$ hr, in how many hours can one expect three times the original number? Five times the original number?

B EXERCISES

1. Neutrons in an atomic pile increase at a rate proportional to the number of neutrons present at any instant (due to nuclear fission). If N_0 neutrons are initially present, and N_1 and N_2 neutrons are present at times T_1 and T_2, respectively, show that

$$\left(\frac{N_2}{N_0}\right)^{T_1} = \left(\frac{N_1}{N_0}\right)^{T_2}$$

2. Uranium disintegrates at a rate proportional to the amount present at any instant. If M_1 and M_2 grams of uranium are present at times T_1 and T_2, respectively, show that the half-life of uranium is

$$\frac{(T_2 - T_1)\ln 2}{\ln (M_1/M_2)}$$

3. A man borrows $1000 subject to the condition that interest be compounded continuously. If the interest rate is 4% per annum, how much will he have to pay back in 10 years? What is the equivalent simple interest rate?

4. Show that the time required, in years, for a sum of money to double itself if interest is compounded continuously at r per cent per annum is $(100 \ln 2)/r$.

C EXERCISES

1. When light passes through a window glass some of it is absorbed. Experimentally, the amount of light absorbed by a small thickness of glass is proportional to the thickness of the glass and to the amount of incident light. Show that if r per cent of the light is absorbed by a thickness w, then the percentage of the light absorbed by a thickness nw is

$$100 \left[1 - \left(1 - \frac{r}{100} \right)^n \right] \qquad 0 \leq r \leq 100$$

2. The amount of radioactive isotope C^{14} (carbon 14) present in all living organic matter bears a constant ratio to the amount of the stable isotope C^{12}. An analysis of fossil remains of a dinosaur shows that the ratio is only 6.24% of that for living matter. Assuming that the half-life of C^{14} is approximately 5600 years, determine how long ago the dinosaur was alive.

VII. The Hanging Cable

Let a cable or rope be hung from two points, A and B (Fig. 36), not necessarily at the same level. Assume that the cable is flexible so that due to loading (which may be due to the weight of the cable, to external forces acting, or to a combination of these) it takes a shape as in the figure. Let C be the lowest position on the cable, and choose x and y axes as in the figure, so that the y axis passes through C.

Consider that part of the cable between the minimum point C and any point P on the cable having coordinates (x,y). This part will be in equilibrium due to the tension T at P (Fig. 37), the horizontal force H at C, and the total

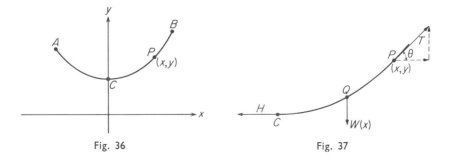

Fig. 36   Fig. 37

vertical loading on the portion CP of the cable which we denote by $W(x)$ and which we assume acts at some point Q, not necessarily the center of arc CP. For equilibrium, the algebraic sum of the forces in the x (or horizontal) direction must equal zero, and the algebraic sum of the forces in the y (or vertical) direction must equal zero. Another way to say this is that the sum of forces to the right equals the sum of forces to the left, and the sum of forces in the upward direction equals the sum of forces in the downward direction.

Let us resolve the tension T into two components (dashed in Fig. 37), the horizontal component having magnitude $T\cos\theta$, and the vertical component having magnitude $T\sin\theta$.

The forces in the x direction are H to the left and $T\cos\theta$ to the right, while the forces in the y direction are W down and $T\sin\theta$ up. Hence,

$$T\sin\theta = W, \qquad T\cos\theta = H \tag{1}$$

Dividing these, using the fact that $\tan\theta = dy/dx$ = slope of tangent at P,

$$\frac{dy}{dx} = \frac{W}{H} \tag{2}$$

In this equation, H is a constant, since it is the tension at the lowest point, but W may depend on x. By differentiation of (2) with respect to x,

$$\frac{d^2y}{dx^2} = \frac{1}{H} \cdot \frac{dW}{dx} \tag{3}$$

Now dW/dx represents the increase in W per unit increase in x; i.e., it is the load per unit distance in the horizontal direction.

Equation (3) is fundamental. In the following illustrative examples and in the exercises we shall see that for different loads per unit horizontal distance we obtain various differential equations which yield various shapes of the cable.

ILLUSTRATIVE EXAMPLE 1

A flexible cable of small (negligible) weight supports a uniform bridge (Fig. 38). Determine the shape of the cable. (This is the problem of determining the shape of the cable in a *suspension bridge*, which is of great use in modern bridge construction.)

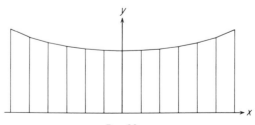

Fig. 38

Mathematical Formulation. Equation (3) holds here and it remains only for us to determine dW/dx, the load per unit increase in the horizontal direction. In this case dW/dx is a constant, namely, the weight per unit length of the bridge. Calling this constant w, we have

$$\frac{d^2y}{dx^2} = \frac{w}{H} \qquad (4)$$

Denoting by b the distance of the lowest point of the cable from the bridge, we have the conditions

$$y = b \quad \text{where} \quad x = 0, \qquad \frac{dy}{dx} = 0 \quad \text{where} \quad x = 0$$

the second due to the fact that the point where $x = 0$ is a minimum point.

Solution. Integrating (4) twice, making use of the given conditions, we find that

$$y = \frac{wx^2}{2H} + b$$

The cable thus assumes the shape of a parabola.

ILLUSTRATIVE EXAMPLE 2

A flexible rope having constant density hangs between two fixed points. Determine the shape of the rope.

Mathematical Formulation. Here, too, differential equation (3) holds and we have only to determine dW/dx. To do this, consider a portion of the rope (Fig. 39). This portion, supposedly infinitesimal, is magnified in the figure. The weight is distributed uniformly over the arc PQ in the figure. It is easy to see that if the density of the rope is w (a constant) then $dW/ds = w$. However, we want dW/dx. This is accomplished by writing

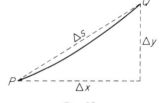

Fig. 39

$$\frac{dW}{ds} = \frac{dW}{dx} \cdot \frac{dx}{ds} = w \quad \text{or} \quad \frac{dW}{dx} = w\frac{ds}{dx}$$

Since
$$\frac{ds}{dx} = \sqrt{1 + \left(\frac{dy}{dx}\right)^2}, \qquad \frac{dW}{dx} = w\sqrt{1 + \left(\frac{dy}{dx}\right)^2}$$

and the equation becomes

$$\frac{d^2y}{dx^2} = \frac{w}{H}\sqrt{1 + \left(\frac{dy}{dx}\right)^2} \qquad (5)$$

The same conditions prevail here as for Illustrative Example 1, namely, $y = b$ where $x = 0$, $dy/dx = 0$ where $x = 0$.

Solution. Equation (5) has both x and y missing. Letting $dy/dx = p$, we have

$$\frac{dp}{dx} = \frac{w}{H}\sqrt{1 + p^2}$$

Separating the variables and integrating yields

$$\int \frac{dp}{\sqrt{p^2 + 1}} = \int \frac{w}{H} dx \quad \text{or} \quad \ln(p + \sqrt{p^2 + 1}) = \frac{wx}{H} + c_1$$

i.e.,

$$p + \sqrt{p^2 + 1} = c_2 e^{wx/H}$$

Since $p = dy/dx = 0$ where $x = 0$, we have $c_2 = 1$, so that

$$p + \sqrt{p^2 + 1} = e^{wx/H} \tag{6}$$

We could now solve this equation by isolating the radical and squaring. However, we shall proceed as follows. Note that

$$(\sqrt{p^2 + 1})^2 - p^2 = 1, \quad \text{i.e.,} \quad (\sqrt{p^2 + 1} + p)(\sqrt{p^2 + 1} - p) = 1$$

Using (6) we find

$$e^{wx/H}(\sqrt{p^2 + 1} - p) = 1 \quad \text{or} \quad \sqrt{p^2 + 1} - p = e^{-wx/H} \tag{7}$$

Subtracting (7) from (6), we have

$$p = \frac{dy}{dx} = \frac{1}{2}(e^{wx/H} - e^{-wx/H})$$

Hence, by integration,

$$y = \frac{H}{2w}(e^{wx/H} + e^{-wx/H}) + c_3$$

By using $y = b$ where $x = 0$, we find $c_3 = b - H/w$. If we make the choice $b = H/w$, by suitably shifting the x axis, then $c_3 = 0$ and we have

$$y = \frac{H}{2w}(e^{wx/H} + e^{-wx/H}) \tag{8}$$

If we use the notation of hyperbolic functions we have

$$\tfrac{1}{2}(e^{wx/H} + e^{-wx/H}) = \cosh wx/H$$

and (8) may be written

$$y = \frac{H}{w} \cosh \frac{wx}{H} \tag{9}$$

The graph of (8) or (9) is called a *catenary* (from the Latin, meaning "chain").

A EXERCISES

1. A flexible cable of negligible weight supports a uniform bridge, as shown in Fig. 40. The dimensions are as indicated: P is the minimum point of curve APB. Using an appropriate set of axes, determine an equation for the curve APB.

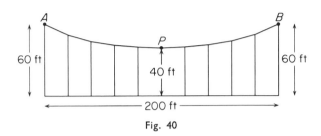

Fig. 40

2. A cable of a suspension bridge has its supports at the same level, at a distance 500 ft apart. If the supports are 100 ft higher than the minimum point of the cable, use an appropriate set of axes to determine an equation for the curve in which the cable hangs, assuming the bridge is of uniform weight and that the weight of the cable is negligible. Find the slope of the cable at the supports.

3. The bridge of Fig. 40 has a variable weight of $400 + 0.001x^2$ pounds per foot of length, where x is the distance in feet measured from the center of the bridge. Find an equation for the curve APB of the cable.

B EXERCISES

1. A cable weighs 0.5 lb/ft. It is hung from two supports which are at the same level, 100 ft apart. If the slope of the cable at one support is $\frac{12}{5}$: (a) find the tension in the cable at its lowest point; (b) determine an equation for the curve in which the cable hangs.

2. A cable of a suspension bridge has its supports at the same level, at a distance L feet apart. The supports are a feet higher than the minimum point of the cable. If the weight of the cable is negligible but the bridge has a uniform weight of w pounds per foot show that: (a) the tension in the cable at its lowest point is $wL^2/8a$ pounds; (b) the tension at the supports is $\dfrac{wL}{8a} \sqrt{L^2 + 16a^2}$ pounds.

3. A cable has constant density w pounds per foot and is hung from two supports which are at the same level L feet apart. If the tension at the lowest point of the cable is H pounds, show that the tension in the cable at the supports is given, in pounds, by $H \cosh(wL/2H)$.

4. Show that the total weight of the cable in Exercise 3 is $2H \sinh(wL/2H)$.

C EXERCISES

1. A cable P feet long has a constant density w pounds per foot. It is hung from supports which are at the same level a distance L feet apart. The supports are a feet higher than the lowest point of the cable. Show that the tension H at the lowest point of the cable is given, in pounds, by

$$H = \frac{wL}{2 \ln \left[(P + 2a)/(P - 2a) \right]}$$

2. A cable of density 0.4 lb/ft is 250 ft long. It is hung from two supports which are at the same level 200 ft apart. Calculate (a) the distance of the supports above the lowest point of the cable, (b) the tension at that point.

3. A cable of density 0.5 lb/ft is hung from two supports which are at the same level 50 ft apart. The supports are 10 ft higher than the lowest point of the cable. Find (a) the length of the cable, (b) the tension at the lowest point of the cable, (c) the tension at the supports of the cable.

VIII. A Trip to the Moon

From time immemorial, mankind has gazed at the moon, wondering about many things, one of them being whether a day might come when men could travel there. Jules Verne wrote a fantastic novel about the possibilities. With the advent of modern technology this dream is not entirely out of reach, particularly because of the invention of rockets, which we discuss in the next section.

It was about the time of Newton's enunciation of his famous law of gravitation that speculations about possibilities of space travel were first made on a mathematical basis.

NEWTON'S LAW OF UNIVERSAL GRAVITATION. *Any two objects in the universe are attracted to each other with a force which varies directly as the product of their masses and inversely as the square of the distance between them.* In symbols

$$F = \frac{GM_1 M_2}{d^2} \tag{1}$$

where M_1, M_2 are the masses of the objects; d is the distance between them; F is the force of attraction; and G is the constant of proportionality.

In this section we use this law to investigate the possibility of firing a projectile out of a huge cannon, for example, vertically upward toward the moon. While this means of transportation is practically useless, unless for some reason we have no desire to return, the problem is interesting for a variety of reasons, one of which is in estimating the muzzle velocity which this cannon ought to have. In attempting to solve this problem we make the following assumptions:

1. The earth and moon are perfect spheres having respective radii R_e and R_m, with masses M_e and M_m.
2. The projectile (or spaceship) of mass m is fired vertically upward toward the center of the moon with initial velocity v_0.
3. Rotations of the earth and moon are not taken into account.
4. Influence of the sun and other planets is not considered.
5. Air resistance is not taken into account.

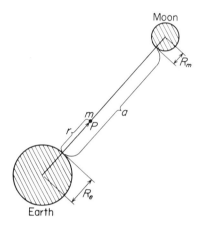

Fig. 41

Referring to Fig. 41, taking the direction from earth to moon as positive, we have by Newton's law and (1),

$$m\frac{d^2r}{dt^2} = -\frac{GM_e m}{(r + R_e)^2} + \frac{GM_m m}{(a + R_m - r)^2}$$

or

$$\frac{d^2r}{dt^2} = -\frac{GM_e}{(r + R_e)^2} + \frac{GM_m}{(a + R_m - r)^2} \tag{2}$$

showing that the results are independent of the projectile's mass. It is possible to replace GM_e by more familiar quantities. To see this, note that the attraction of a mass m to the earth is its weight mg. Hence, from (1),

$$\frac{GM_e m}{R_e^2} = mg \quad \text{or} \quad GM_e = gR_e^2 \tag{3}$$

In a similar manner, denoting by g_m the acceleration due to gravity on the moon, we have

$$GM_m = g_m R_m^2 \tag{4}$$

Using (3) and (4) in (2), then

$$\frac{d^2r}{dt^2} = -\frac{gR_e^2}{(r + R_e)^2} + \frac{g_m R_m^2}{(a + R_m - r)^2} \tag{5}$$

The initial conditions are $r = 0$ and $dr/dt = v_0$, where $t = 0$. Since equation (5) does not involve t, let $dr/dt = v$. Then

$$v\frac{dv}{dr} = -\frac{gR_e^2}{(r + R_e)^2} + \frac{g_m R_m^2}{(a + R_m - r)^2}$$

Integrating and using the conditions at $t = 0$, we find

$$v^2 = \frac{2gR_e^2}{r + R_e} + \frac{2g_m R_m^2}{a + R_m - r} + v_0^2 - 2gR_e - \frac{2g_m R_m^2}{a + R_m} \tag{6}$$

which enables us to determine the instantaneous velocity v. Upon replacing v by dr/dt, we may determine r as a function of t. From this we may theoretically calculate the time taken to reach the moon. Actually the integrations which arise cannot be performed in closed form, and approximate techniques must be employed.*

Let us determine the muzzle velocity of our cannon needed to reach the *neutral point* (the place between earth and moon where there is zero gravitation) with velocity zero. The neutral position denoted by $r = r_n$ is determined from the equation

$$\frac{M_e}{(r_n + R_e)^2} = \frac{M_m}{(a + R_m - r_n)^2} \tag{7}$$

obtained by setting the right-hand side of (2) equal to zero. Since we want $v = 0$ when $r = r_n$, we have from (6),

$$v_0^2 = 2gR_e - \frac{2g_m R_m^2}{a + R_m - r_n} + \frac{2g_m R_m^2}{a + R_m} - \frac{2gR_e^2}{r_n + R_e} \tag{8}$$

To get some idea as to the magnitude of v_0, we employ the following approximate figures from astronomy:

$$a = 240{,}000 \text{ miles}, \quad R_e = 4000 \text{ miles}, \quad g = 32 \text{ ft/sec}^2$$
$$g_m = 5.3 \text{ ft/sec}^2 \text{ (about } \tfrac{1}{6}g\text{)}, \quad M_e = 81M_m$$

Since $M_e = 81M_m$, approximately, equation (7) can be written

$$\frac{81M_m}{(r_n + R_e)^2} = \frac{M_m}{(a + R_m - r_n)^2} \quad \text{or} \quad \frac{81}{(r_n + R_e)^2} = \frac{1}{(a + R_m - r_n)^2}$$

Solving for r_n, we find

$$r_n = \frac{9a + 9R_m - R_e}{10}$$

---

* However, the integrals can be evaluated in terms of elliptic integrals.

Using this in (8), we have

$$v_0^2 = 2gR_e - \frac{20g_mR_m^2}{a + R_m + R_e} + \frac{2g_mR_m^2}{a + R_m} - \frac{20gR_e^2}{9(a + R_m + R_e)} \tag{9}$$

From (3) and (4) and the fact that $M_e = 81M_m$, we have

$$gR_e^2 = 81g_mR_m^2 \tag{10}$$

and since $g_m = g/6$, approximately, it follows from (10) that

$$R_m = \frac{\sqrt{6R_e}}{9} \tag{11}$$

approximately. Using (10) in (9), we have

$$v_0^2 = 2gR_e - \frac{200gR_e^2}{81(a + R_m + R_e)} + \frac{2gR_e^2}{81(a + R_m)} \tag{12}$$

Now a is approximately $60R_e$, and, from (11), R_m is approximately $\frac{1}{4}R_e$. Hence, (12) may be written

$$v_0^2 = 2gR_e - \frac{200gR_e}{81 \times 61.25} + \frac{2gR_e}{81 \times 60.25}$$

so that $v_0^2 = 2gR_e(1 - 0.02 + 0.0002)$, approximately, or

$$v_0 = \sqrt{2gR_e}(1 - 0.01)$$

by the binomial theorem. It follows that the velocity needed to reach the neutral point with zero velocity is given, approximately, by

$$v_0 = 0.99\sqrt{2gR_e}$$

Using the values of g and R_e, we find that $v_0 = 6.9$ miles/sec, approximately. At present this speed is well out of attainment. The "Big Bertha" cannon of World War I had a muzzle velocity of 1 mile per second, so perhaps there may still be a chance.

From equation (9) we can determine the so-called *escape velocity*, which is the velocity that a projectile should have in order to leave the earth never to return, assuming no other planets, suns, or anything else are taken into account. To find this velocity we have only to put $g_m = 0$ and let $a \to \infty$ in (9). The result is $v_0 = \sqrt{2gR_e}$, which is approximately 1% greater than the velocity required to reach the neutral point. Actually, the escape velocity could have been found more easily by starting with (2) and removing the second term on the right.

A EXERCISES

1. A projectile is fired vertically upward from the earth's surface with an initial velocity v_0 equal to the escape velocity. Neglecting the influence of the moon and other planets: (a) Show that the velocity of the projectile at distance r from the starting point is

$$v = \sqrt{\frac{2gR_e^2}{r + R_e}}$$

   where R_e is the radius of the earth. (b) Calculate the velocity of the projectile after traveling 120,000 miles.

2. Show that the time for the projectile of Exercise 1 to travel the distance r is

$$\frac{2}{3R_e\sqrt{2g}} [(r + R_e)^{3/2} - R_e^{3/2}]$$

3. Assuming the moon and planets other than the earth to have no influence, how long would it take the projectile of Exercise 1 to cover the distances 120,000 miles and 240,000 miles?

B EXERCISES

1. An object is projected vertically upward from the earth's surface with an initial velocity v_0 of magnitude less than the escape velocity. If only the earth's influence is taken into account, show that the maximum height reached is $v_0^2 R_e/(2gR_e - v_0^2)$.

2. Assuming constant gravitational acceleration everywhere, show that an object projected from the earth's surface with velocity v_0 reaches a maximum height $v_0^2/2g$. Obtain this also by letting $R_e \to \infty$ in Exercise 1.

3. Compare the maximum heights reached according to Exercises 1 and 2 for an object projected upward with velocity 50 ft/sec, 6 miles/sec.

4. What is the velocity beyond which the heights in Exercises 1 and 2 differ by more than 5%?, 50%?

C EXERCISES

1. Show that the time for the projectile in Exercise 1 of the B exercises to reach the maximum height is

$$\frac{2gR_e^2}{(2gR_e - v_0^2)^{3/2}} \left(\text{arc sin} \frac{v_0}{\sqrt{2gR_e}} + \frac{v_0\sqrt{2gR_e - v_0^2}}{2gR_e} \right)$$

2. Show, by series or otherwise, that if $v_0^2 \ll 2gR_e$ (i.e., initial velocity much smaller than escape velocity), then the time to reach the maximum height is approximately v_0/g. This is the result obtained if the acceleration due to gravity is assumed constant everywhere.

3. An object falls a distance a from the center of the earth (radius R_e). Show that it (a) hits the earth's surface with a speed equal to $\sqrt{2gR_e(1 - R_e/a)}$; (b) reaches the earth's surface in a time given by

$$\sqrt{\frac{a}{2gR_e^2}} \left\{ \sqrt{R_e(a - R_e)} + \tfrac{1}{2}a \text{ arc cos}\left(\frac{2R_e - a}{a}\right) \right\}$$

assuming that air resistance is negligible.

4. Show that the velocity of escape from the surface of the moon is approximately 1.5 miles/sec.

IX. Applications to Rockets

A rocket moves by the backward expulsion of a mass of gas formed by the burning of a fuel. This rejection of mass has the effect of increasing the forward velocity of the rocket, thus enabling it to continue onward. To consider the motion of rockets, we must treat the motion of an object whose mass is changing. In Section I of this chapter we pointed out that the net force acting on an object is equal to the time rate of change in momentum (Newton's second law). We will use this in finding the law of motion of a rocket.

Suppose that the total mass of the rocket at time t is M and that at the later time $t + \Delta t$ the mass is $M + \Delta M$, i.e., a mass $-\Delta M$ of gas has been expelled from the back of the rocket (note that the mass of gas expelled in the time Δt is $-\Delta M$, since ΔM is a negative quantity). Suppose that the velocity of the rocket relative to the earth at time t is V and at time $t + \Delta t$ is $V + \Delta V$, and let us take the upward direction of the rocket as positive. The expelled gas will have velocity $V + v$ relative to the earth, where v is a negative quantity, so that $-v$ represents the actual magnitude of the velocity of the gas relative to the rocket, which for our purposes will be considered constant. The total momentum of the rocket before the loss of gas is MV. After the loss of gas, the rocket has momentum $(M + \Delta M)(V + \Delta V)$, and the gas has momentum $-\Delta M(V + v)$, so that the total momentum after the loss is $(M + \Delta M)(V + \Delta V) - \Delta M(V + v)$. The change in momentum, i.e., the total momentum after the loss of gas minus the total momentum before the loss, is

$$(M + \Delta M)(V + \Delta V) - \Delta M(V + v) - MV$$
$$= M \Delta V - v \Delta M + \Delta M \Delta V$$

The instantaneous time rate of change in momentum is the limit of the change in momentum divided by Δt as $\Delta t \to 0$, i.e.,

$$\lim_{\Delta t \to 0} M \frac{\Delta V}{\Delta t} - v \frac{\Delta M}{\Delta t} + \frac{\Delta M}{\Delta t} \Delta V \tag{1}$$

Since $\Delta M \to 0$, $\Delta V \to 0$, $\dfrac{\Delta M}{\Delta t} \to \dfrac{dM}{dt}$, and $\dfrac{\Delta V}{\Delta t} \to \dfrac{dV}{dt}$ as $\Delta t \to 0$, (1) becomes

$$M \frac{dV}{dt} - v \frac{dM}{dt}$$

Now the time rate of change in momentum is the force F. Hence

$$F = M \frac{dV}{dt} - v \frac{dM}{dt} \tag{2}$$

is our basic equation for rocket motion.

ILLUSTRATIVE EXAMPLE

A rocket having initial mass M_0 grams starts radially from the earth's surface. It expels gas at the constant rate a grams per second, at a constant velocity b centimeters per second relative to the rocket, where $a > 0$ and $b > 0$. Assuming no external forces act on the rocket, find its velocity and distance traveled at any time.

Mathematical Formulation. Referring to the fundamental equation, we have $F = 0$, since there are no external forces. Since the rocket loses a grams per second, it will lose at grams in t seconds, and hence its mass after t seconds is given by $M = M_0 - at$. Also, the velocity of the gas relative to the rocket is given by $v = -b$. Thus, (2) becomes

$$(M_0 - at) \frac{dV}{dt} - ab = 0 \quad \text{or} \quad \frac{dV}{dt} = \frac{ab}{M_0 - at} \tag{3}$$

with the assumed initial condition $V = 0$ at $t = 0$.

Solution. Integrating (3), we find

$$V = -b \ln (M_0 - at) + c_1$$

Since $V = 0$ at $t = 0$, $c_1 - b \ln M_0$, and

$$V = b \ln M_0 - b \ln (M_0 - at) \tag{4}$$

which is the required velocity of the rocket. Letting x be the distance which the rocket moves in time t measured from the earth's surface, we have $V = dx/dt$, and (4) becomes

$$\frac{dx}{dt} = b \ln M_0 - b \ln (M_0 - at) = -b \ln \left(\frac{M_0 - at}{M_0} \right)$$

from which we obtain, upon integration, taking $x = 0$ at $t = 0$,

$$x = bt + \frac{b}{a} (M_0 - at) \ln \left(\frac{M_0 - at}{M_0} \right) \tag{5}$$

which is the required distance traveled. Note that equations (4) and (5) are valid only for $t < M_0/a$, which is the theoretical limit for the time of flight. The practical limit is much smaller than this.

A EXERCISES

1. If a constant gravitational field acts on the rocket in the illustrative example of the text, show that the equation of motion is

$$(M_0 - at)\frac{dV}{dt} - ab = -g(M_0 - at)$$

Find the velocity of the rocket at any time $t < M_0/a$ after leaving the earth, assuming that its initial velocity is zero.

2. Determine the height of the rocket of Exercise 1, at time t.

B EXERCISES

1. A rocket has a mass of 25,000 kilograms (kg), which includes 20,000 kg of a fuel mixture. During the burning process the combustion products are discharged at a velocity relative to the rocket of 400 meters per second, involving a loss per second of 1000 kg of the fuel mixture. The rocket starts on the ground with zero velocity and travels vertically upward. If the only external force acting is that of gravitation (variation with distance neglected): (a) Find the velocity of the rocket after 15, 20, and 30 seconds. (b) Find the height reached when half the fuel mixture is burned.

2. A rocket has mass M, which includes a mass m of a fuel mixture. During the burning process the combustion products are discharged at a velocity $q > 0$ relative to the rocket. This burning involves a loss per second of a mass p of the fuel mixture. Neglecting all external forces except a constant gravitational force, show that the maximum theoretical height attained by the rocket is

$$\frac{qm}{p} + \frac{qM}{p}\ln\left(\frac{M - m}{M}\right) + \frac{q^2}{2g}\ln^2\left(\frac{M - m}{M}\right)$$

if the rocket starts radially from the earth's surface with velocity zero.

3. In addition to the gravitational force acting on the rocket of Exercise 2, there is a force due to air resistance which is proportional to the instantaneous velocity of the rocket. (a) Find the velocity of the rocket at any time assuming that its initial velocity is zero. (b) Determine the height of the rocket at any time. (c) Find the maximum theoretical height attained.

4. An object of mass M_0, which is not acted upon by any external forces, moves in a straight line through space with velocity v_0. At $t = 0$ it begins to increase its mass at the constant rate of r grams per second. Show that the velocity at any time t is $V = M_0v_0/(M_0 + rt)$, and find the distance traveled.

C EXERCISES

1. A spherical mass grows at a rate proportional to its instantaneous surface area. Assuming that the sphere has an initial radius a and that it falls from rest under the influence of gravity (no variation with distance), show that its instantaneous acceleration is

$$\frac{g}{4}\left(1 + \frac{3a^4}{r^4}\right)$$

where r is its instantaneous radius. Thus show that a necessary and sufficient condition that the acceleration be constant is that the sphere have zero initial radius.

2. According to Einstein's special theory of relativity, the mass m of a particle varies with velocity v according to the formula

$$m = \frac{m_0}{\sqrt{1 - v^2/c^2}}$$

where c is the velocity of light and m_0 is the "rest mass." Assuming a particle to fall from rest under a constant gravitational field, show that the velocity of the particle at any time t is

$$v = c \tanh \frac{gt}{c}$$

and determine the distance fallen in time t.

X. Physical Problems Involving Geometry

Many types of physical problems are dependent in some way upon geometry. For example, imagine a right circular cylinder, half full of water, rotating with constant angular velocity about its axis. The shape of the water's surface will be determined by the angular velocity of the cylinder. Here physics determines the geometrical shape of the water surface.

As another example, consider water emptying through a hole at the base of a conical tank. Here the geometrical shape of the container determines the physical behavior of the water.

In the illustrative examples which follow we consider three physical problems involving geometry; namely, the flow of water from a tank, the shape of a water surface in a rotating cylinder, and the shape of a reflector.

ILLUSTRATIVE EXAMPLE 1

A container having constant cross section A is filled with water to height H. The water flows out through an orifice, of cross section B, at the base of the container. Find the height of water at any time and find the time to empty the tank.

Mathematical Formulation. Let the container appear as in Fig. 42, where A is the constant cross-sectional area of the container, and B is the cross-sectional area of the orifice. Let h be the height of water in the tank at time t (level 1) and $h + \Delta h$ the height at time $t + \Delta t$ (level 2).

The basic principle which we use is the obvious one that the amount of water lost when the level drops from 1 to 2 is equal to the amount of water which escapes through the orifice. When the water level drops from 1 to 2,

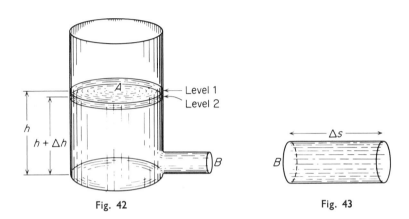

Fig. 42   Fig. 43

the volume lost is numerically equal to $A \, \Delta h$. However, we must be careful of signs. Since Δh is actually a negative quantity, we have, for the actual volume lost in time Δt, the amount $-A \, \Delta h$. The volume of water which escapes through the orifice is that volume which would be contained in a cylinder of cross section B and length Δs (Fig. 43), where Δs is the distance which the water would travel in time Δt if it were to keep traveling horizontally. We then have

$$-A \, \Delta h = B \, \Delta s$$

Dividing by Δt and taking the limit as $\Delta t \to 0$, we find

$$-A \frac{dh}{dt} = B \frac{ds}{dt} = Bv \quad \text{or} \quad -A \, dh = Bv \, dt \tag{1}$$

where $v = ds/dt$ is the instantaneous velocity of efflux through the orifice.

We now need to have an expression for the velocity v of efflux of the water. It is clear that the greater the height of water, the greater is v. In fact, it is not hard to show that for ideal conditions* $v = \sqrt{2gh}$. Thus, (1) becomes

$$-A \, dh = B\sqrt{2gh} \, dt \tag{2}$$

Since the height is H initially, we have $h = H$ at $t = 0$.

---

* This follows from the fact that the potential energy mgh of a mass m of water equals the kinetic energy $\frac{1}{2}mv^2$, assuming no losses.

Solution. Separation of variables in (2) yields

$$\int \frac{dh}{\sqrt{h}} = -\frac{B}{A}\sqrt{2g}\int dt, \qquad 2\sqrt{h} = -\frac{B}{A}\sqrt{2g}\,t + c$$

Using $h = H$ at $t = 0$, we find $c = 2\sqrt{H}$, so that

$$2\sqrt{h} = -\frac{B}{A}\sqrt{2g}\,t + 2\sqrt{H} \tag{3}$$

which expresses the height as a function of t.

The time for the tank to empty is found by finding t where $h = 0$. We obtain, from (3),

$$t = \frac{A}{B}\sqrt{\frac{2H}{g}}$$

If, for example, $A = 4$ ft^2, $B = 1$ in.^{2}, $H = 16$ ft, $g = 32$ ft/sec^2, then $t = 576$ sec, or 9.6 min.

ILLUSTRATIVE EXAMPLE 2

A right circular cylinder having vertical axis is filled with water and is rotated about its axis with constant angular velocity ω. What shape does the water surface take?

Mathematical Formulation. When the cylinder rotates, the water surface assumes a shape as indicated in Fig. 44. Consider a particle of water P, of

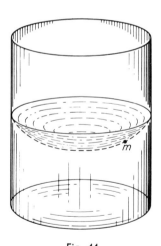

mass m, on the surface of the water. When steady-state conditions prevail, this particle will be moving in a circular path, the circle having center on the axis of rotation. For convenience we choose an xy coordinate system as shown in Fig. 45, where the y axis is the axis of rotation and where the x axis is perpendicular to the y axis and passes through the lowest point O of the surface. It will be clear that the surface is symmetric with respect to the y axis. Let us investigate the forces on particle P when steady-state conditions are attained. First, there is the force due to the weight of the particle given by mg (Fig. 45). There is also a force on P due to the reaction of the other particles in the liquid. This reaction force is denoted by R and must be normal to the surface of the liquid.* The resultant of R and mg points to the center of the circle in which P rotates. This resultant force is the centripetal force acting on P and has magnitude $m\omega^2 x$, where x is the distance from P to the axis of rotation.

Fig. 44

* If R were not normal to the surface, there would be a component of R tangential to the surface and the particle would move either toward or away from the axis of rotation.

From the figure it is clear that

$$R \cos \alpha = mg, \qquad R \sin \alpha = m\omega^2 x$$

Dividing these equations and noting that the slope of the tangent APB is the same as the slope of the curve $DOPC$ at P and is therefore equal to $\tan \alpha$, or dy/dx, we have

$$\frac{dy}{dx} = \frac{\omega^2 x}{g} \qquad (4)$$

which we must solve subject to $y = 0$ where $x = 0$.

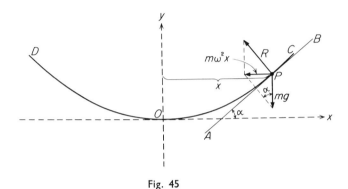

Fig. 45

Solution. Integration of (4) yields

$$y = \frac{\omega^2 x^2}{2g} + c$$

Since $x = 0$ where $y = 0$, $c = 0$, so that

$$y = \frac{\omega^2 x^2}{2g} \qquad (5)$$

Thus, in any plane through the y axis the water level assumes the shape of a parabola. In three dimensions it is a paraboloid of revolution.

ILLUSTRATIVE EXAMPLE 3

Find the shape of a reflector in order that light rays emitted by a point source be reflected parallel to a fixed line.

Mathematical Formulation. Let point O (origin of an xy coordinate system), Fig. 46, represent the point source of light. Light rays such as OA emerge from O, hit the reflector at A, and "bounce off" or are reflected, from then on traveling in a straight line. We wish to find the shape of the reflector so that all the rays emanating from O "bounce off" from the reflector parallel to the line Ox.

Let CD (Fig. 47) be a portion of the reflector and consider any point $P(x,y)$ on it. If θ_1 is the angle of incidence and θ_2 is the angle of reflection, then by an elementary principle of optics $\theta_1 = \theta_2$.* We wish to find a relation between the slope dy/dx of the curve (reflector) at P and the coordinates (x,y) of P. This may be obtained by use of elementary geometry.

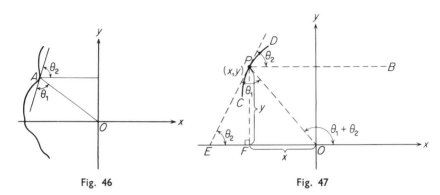

Fig. 46   Fig. 47

Since BP (Fig. 47) is parallel to Ox, we have $\angle OEP = \theta_2$. Hence $\angle xOP = \theta_1 + \theta_2 = 2\theta_1$ since $\theta_2 = \theta_1$. The slope of OP is $\tan 2\theta_1$ but by use of triangle OPF it is seen to be y/x. Hence $\tan 2\theta_1 = y/x$. But by an elementary trigonometric formula,

$$\tan 2\theta_1 = \frac{2 \tan \theta_1}{1 - \tan^2 \theta_1}$$

Since $\tan \theta_1 = \tan \theta_2 = dy/dx = y'$, we have therefore

$$\frac{2y'}{1 - (y')^2} = \frac{y}{x} \tag{6}$$

Solving for $y' = dy/dx$, we obtain

$$\frac{dy}{dx} = \frac{-x \pm \sqrt{x^2 + y^2}}{y} \tag{7}$$

Solution. Equation (7) is homogeneous; hence, letting $y = vx$ we find

$$x \frac{dv}{dx} = \frac{-1 - v^2 \pm \sqrt{v^2 + 1}}{v}$$

Separating the variables and integrating,

$$\int \frac{dx}{x} = - \int \frac{v \, dv}{v^2 + 1 \pm \sqrt{v^2 + 1}}$$

* Actually $90 - \theta_1$, the angle which ray OP makes with the normal to arc CD at P, is the angle of incidence. Similarly $90 - \theta_2$, the angle between the reflected ray and the normal, is the angle of reflection. Clearly if $90 - \theta_1 = 90 - \theta_2$, then $\theta_1 = \theta_2$.

Letting $v^2 + 1 = u^2$ in the second integral so that $v\,dv = u\,du$, we find

$$\ln x + c_1 = -\int \frac{du}{u \pm 1} = -\ln(u \pm 1) = -\ln(\sqrt{v^2 + 1} \pm 1)$$

It follows that

$$x(\sqrt{v^2 + 1} \pm 1) = c \quad \text{or} \quad \sqrt{x^2 + y^2} = c \pm x$$

Squaring and simplifying, this becomes

$$y^2 = \pm 2cx + c^2 \tag{8}$$

For a given value of c ($c \neq 0$) equation (8) represents two parabolas symmetric with respect to the x axis as shown in Fig. 48. The heavy curve has equation $y^2 = 2cx + c^2$, $c > 0$. The dashed curve has equation

$$y^2 = -2cx + c^2, \quad c > 0 \quad \text{or} \quad y^2 = 2cx + c^2, \quad c < 0$$

The focus for the family of parabolas is at the origin. In Fig. 48 we have also shown several light rays emanating from the focus and "bouncing off" the reflector parallel to the x axis.

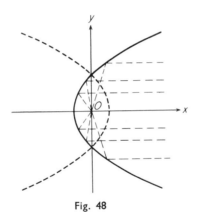

Fig. 48

If we revolve the parabola about the x axis, we obtain a paraboloid of revolution. An electric light bulb placed at the origin sends rays of light "bouncing off" the reflector to produce a direct beam of light rays which is, of course, the most efficient way of lighting. This important property accounts for the paraboloid shape of automobile headlights.

It might be mentioned that the differential equation (7) could have been solved by writing it in the form

$$\frac{x\,dx + y\,dy}{\sqrt{x^2 + y^2}} = \pm dx$$

and noting that the left-hand side can be written $d(\sqrt{x^2 + y^2})$. Hence

$$d(\sqrt{x^2 + y^2}) = \pm dx \quad \text{or} \quad \sqrt{x^2 + y^2} = \pm x + c$$

which leads to the same result as before.

A EXERCISES

1. A right circular cylinder of radius 10 ft and height 20 ft is filled with water. A small circular hole at the bottom is 1 in. in diameter. When will all the water flow out if (a) $v = \sqrt{2gh}$; (b) $v = 0.6\sqrt{2gh}$?

2. A tank is in the form of a 12 ft cube. A leak at the bottom develops due to a small hole 2 in.^{2} in area. If the tank is initially three-quarters full, when will it be (a) half full; (b) empty? Assume $v = \sqrt{2gh}$.

3. A tank in the form of a right circular cone of height H, radius R, with its vertex below the base is filled with water. A hole, having cross section a at the vertex, causes the water to leak out. Assuming $v = c\sqrt{2gh}$, where c is the discharge coefficient, show that the time for the cone to empty is

$$T = \frac{2\pi R^2}{5ac}\sqrt{\frac{H}{2g}} = \frac{2A}{5ac}\sqrt{\frac{H}{2g}}$$

where $A = \pi R^2$ is the area of the base of the cone. If $H = 16$ ft, $a = 1$ in.^{2}, $R = 5$ ft, find T for the cases $c = 1$, $c = 0.6$.

4. The conical tank of Exercise 3 is inverted so that the vertex is above the base and a hole of area a is in the base. Find the time required to empty the tank. Compare with Exercise 3.

B EXERCISES

1. A cylindrical can is filled with a liquid of density ρ and is rotated about its axis with constant angular velocity ω. Show that the pressure at a distance r from the axis exceeds the pressure on the axis by $\frac{1}{2}\rho\omega^2 r^2$.

2. If the liquid in Exercise 1 is replaced by an ideal gas obeying Boyle's law (the pressure in a gas varies inversely as the volume if the temperature is constant), find the pressure as a function of distance from the axis.

3. If Boyle's law in Exercise 2 is replaced by the law $\rho = kP^\alpha$ where P and ρ are, respectively, the pressure and density of the gas, and α and k are constants, show that the pressure at distance r from the axis is

$$P = \left[\frac{k(1-\alpha)\omega^2 r^2}{2} + P_0^{1-\alpha}\right]^{1/(1-\alpha)}, \qquad \alpha \neq 1$$

Obtain the result of Exercise 2 by letting $\alpha \to 1$.

4. Find the shape which a reflector should have so that sound waves (or light rays) emitted by a point source A will be reflected toward another point B.

5. The pressure p and density ρ of the atmosphere above the earth's surface are related by the formula $p = k\rho^\gamma$ where k and γ are positive constants. Assuming that at sea level the pressure and density are given by p_0 and ρ_0 respectively, show that (a) the pressure variation with height h is given by

$$p^{1-1/\gamma} = p_0^{1-1/\gamma} - (1 - 1/\gamma)\rho_0 p_0^{-1/\gamma} h$$

(b) the height of the atmosphere can be considered as $\gamma p_0/(\gamma - 1)\rho_0$. (c) Discuss the cases $\gamma = 1$ and $\gamma > 1$.

C EXERCISES

1. A famous problem considered in an advanced phase of mathematics called the *calculus of variations* is that of determining the shape of a wire in order that a bead placed on it will, under influence of gravity, travel from a given point to a given lower point in the shortest time, friction being neglected. Taking a rectangular coordinate system with y axis positive downward and x axis positive to the right and letting the bead start at $(0,0)$ and travel to (a,b) it can be shown that the shape of the wire is given by the differential equation

$$1 + (y')^2 + 2yy'' = 0$$

Show that the curve is a portion of a cycloid. This problem is called the *brachistochrone* (shortest time) problem and was proposed by John Bernoulli in 1696.

2. Another problem of the calculus of variations is the determination of a curve joining points (a,b) and (c,d), having the property that the surface generated by revolving the curve about the x axis is a minimum. The required curve may be obtained from the differential equation

$$1 + (y')^2 = yy''$$

Show that the curve is a portion of a *catenary*.

The minimum surface property has an interesting physical significance. If two thin circular rings initially in contact are placed in a soap solution and then pulled carefully apart so that a soap film surface is formed, the surface has the property that its area is a minimum.

3. A man initially at O (see Fig. 49) walks along the straight shore Ox of a lake towing a rowboat, initially at A, by means of a rope of length a, which is always

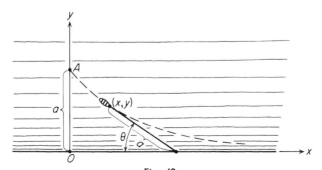

Fig. 49

held taut. Show that the boat moves in a path (called a *tractrix*) with parametric
equations

$$x = a \ln [\cot (\theta/2) - \cos \theta], \qquad y = a \sin \theta$$

4. Towns A and B (Fig. 50) are directly opposite each other on the banks of a river
of width D which flows east with constant speed U. A boat leaving town A

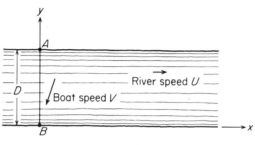

Fig. 50

travels with constant speed V always aimed toward town B. Show that (a) its
path is given by

$$x = \tfrac{1}{2}D[t^{1-U/V} - t^{1+U/V}], \qquad y = Dt$$

(b) it will not arrive at town B unless $V > U$.

5. Two electric light bulbs having strengths
I_1 and I_2 are situated at the points $(-a,0)$
and $(a,0)$ of a rectangular coordinate
system (see Fig. 51). Show that the locus
of all points in the plane at which the intensities of illumination from both lights
are equal is given by

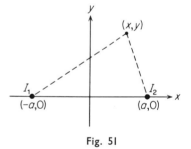

Fig. 51

$$\frac{I_1(x + a)}{\sqrt{(x + a)^2 + y^2}} + \frac{I_2(x - a)}{\sqrt{(x - a)^2 + y^2}} = I_1 - I_2$$

(*Hint:* The intensity of illumination varies
inversely as the square of the distance from the light source.)

XI. Miscellaneous Problems in Geometry

Geometrical problems provide a fertile source of differential equations.
We have already seen how differential equations arise in connection with
orthogonal trajectories. In this section we consider various other geometrical
problems.

ILLUSTRATIVE EXAMPLE 1

The slope at any point of a curve is $2x + 3y$. If the curve passes through the origin, determine its equation.

Mathematical Formulation. The slope at (x,y) is dy/dx. Hence

$$\frac{dy}{dx} = 2x + 3y \tag{1}$$

is the required differential equation, which we solve subject to $y(0) = 0$.

Solution. Equation (1) written as a first-order linear equation

$$\frac{dy}{dx} - 3y = 2x$$

has integrating factor e^{-3x}. Hence,

$$\frac{d}{dx}(ye^{-3x}) = 2xe^{-3x} \quad \text{or} \quad ye^{-3x} = \frac{-2xe^{-3x}}{3} - \frac{2e^{-3x}}{9} + c$$

Thus, since $y(0) = 0$, $c = \frac{2}{9}$ and we find

$$y = \frac{2}{9}e^{3x} - \frac{2x}{3} - \frac{2}{9}$$

ILLUSTRATIVE EXAMPLE 2

The tangent line to a curve at any point (x,y) on it has its intercept on the x axis always equal to $\frac{1}{2}x$. If the curve passes through $(1,2)$ find its equation.

Mathematical Formulation. To solve this problem we must find an expression for the x intercept OA of the tangent line AP to the curve QPR (Fig. 52). To accomplish this, let (X, Y) be any point on AP. Since y' is the slope of the line, its equation is

$$Y - y = y'(X - x)$$

The required intercept is the value of X, where $Y = 0$. This is found to be

$$X = x - \frac{y}{y'}$$

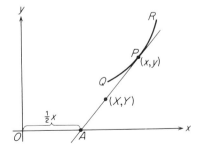

Fig. 52

The required differential equation is

$$x - \frac{y}{y'} = \frac{1}{2}x \qquad (2)$$

which must be solved subject to the condition $y = 2$ where $x = 1$.

Solution. Equation (2) may be written

$$\frac{y}{y'} = \frac{1}{2}x \quad \text{or} \quad \frac{dy}{dx} = \frac{2y}{x}$$

Separating the variables, integrating, and using the condition $y(1) = 2$, we find

$$y = 2x^2$$

In Illustrative Example 2 we were required to determine the x intercept of the tangent line to a curve. We could just as well have been required to determine the y intercept of the tangent line or the length of the tangent line included between point P and the x or y axes. Since many geometrical problems are based on such considerations, we discuss them briefly. Referring to Fig. 53, P is any point (x,y) on curve QPR. It is customary to call the tangent line from P to point A on the x axis briefly the "tangent." Similarly PB is called the "normal." The projections of AP and PB on the x axis are called the "subtangent" and "subnormal," respectively. By procedures analogous to that used in Illustrative Example 2 the student may verify the entries in the following table.

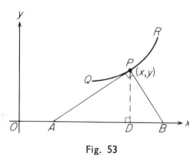

Fig. 53

Intercept of tangent line:

On x axis: $x - \dfrac{y}{y'}$

On y axis: $y - xy'$

Intercept of normal line:

On x axis: $x + yy'$

On y axis: $y + \dfrac{x}{y'}$

Length of tangent line from P:

To x axis: $\left| \dfrac{y\sqrt{1 + (y')^2}}{y'} \right|$

To y axis: $\left| x\sqrt{1 + (y')^2} \right|$

Length of normal line from P:

To x axis: $|y\sqrt{1 + (y')^2}|$

To y axis: $\left| \dfrac{x\sqrt{1 + (y')^2}}{y'} \right|$

Length of subtangent: $\left| \dfrac{y}{y'} \right|$

Length of subnormal: $|yy'|$

It should be observed that since length is a positive quantity we have used absolute value signs in the table. Also we have used rectangular coordinates. Similar considerations involving polar coordinates may be formulated. These are given in the C exercises.

A EXERCISES

1. The slope at any point (x,y) of a curve is $1 + y/x$. If the curve passes through $(1,1)$ find its equation.

2. Find an equation for the family of curves such that the slope at any point is the sum of half the ordinate and twice the abscissa of the point.

3. The y intercept of the normal line to a curve at any point is 2. If the curve passes through $(3,4)$ find its equation.

4. The y intercept of the tangent line to a curve at any point is always equal to the slope at that point. If the curve passes through $(2,1)$ find its equation.

5. The length of the normal line from any point of a curve to the x axis is always equal to a constant $a > 0$. Show that the curve is a circle of radius a.

6. Find the equation of a curve passing through $(1,1)$ having the property that the x intercept of its tangent line equals the y intercept of its normal line.

B EXERCISES

1. Find the equation of the curve through $(3,4)$ such that the length of its subtangent at any point is equal to the distance of the point from the origin.

2. Show that the lengths of the tangent and normal lines from P (Fig. 53) to the x and y axes are given by the entries in the table on pages 126 and 127.

3. The difference between the lengths of the "subtangent" and "subnormal" of a family of curves is 2. Find the equation of the family.

4. A curve in the first quadrant passes through $(0,1)$. If the length of arc from $(0,1)$ to any point (x,y) is numerically equal to the area bounded by the curve, x axis, y axis, and ordinate at (x,y) show that the curve is a portion of a catenary.

5. A point moves in the first quadrant of the xy plane in such a way that the tangent to its path makes with the coordinate axes a triangle whose area is equal to the constant a^2. Find the path.

6. Find the path of the point in Exercise 5 if the tangent cut off by the coordinate axes is of length a.

C EXERCISES

1. Let (r,θ) be polar coordinates of any point on curve APB (Fig. 54). Point O is the pole of the coordinate system, Ox is the initial line, and OP is the radius vector. Let COD be a line perpendicular to OP at O. We define CP as the *polar*

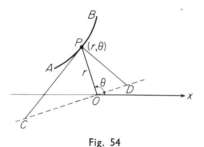

Fig. 54

tangent, PD as the *polar normal,* CO as the *polar subtangent,* and OD as the *polar subnormal.* Demonstrate the validity of each of the following, where $r' = dr/d\theta$.

$$\text{Length of } subtangent = \left| \frac{r^2}{r'} \right|$$

$$\text{Length of } tangent = \left| \frac{r}{r'} \sqrt{r^2 + (r')^2} \right|$$

$$\text{Length of } subnormal = |r'|$$

$$\text{Length of } normal = |\sqrt{r^2 + (r')^2}|$$

2. Find the family of curves whose polar subtangents are of constant length.

3. Find the family of curves whose polar normals are of constant length.

4. Find the family of curves whose polar subtangents and normals are equal in length.

5. Find the curve passing through the point with polar coordinates $(1,\pi/3)$ and such that the length of its polar subtangent at any point is equal to the distance of the point from the initial line.

6. (a) Show that the length of the perpendicular from the pole to the tangent line of any curve is

$$\frac{r^2}{\sqrt{r^2 + (r')^2}}$$

(b) Find all curves such that the length of the perpendicular from the pole to their tangent lines is constant and equal to $a > 0$.

XII. The Deflection of Beams

Consider a horizontal beam AB of Fig. 55(a). We make the assumption that the beam is uniform in cross section and of homogeneous material. The axis of symmetry is indicated by the dashed line. When acted upon by forces which we assume are in a vertical plane containing the axis of symmetry, the beam, due to its elasticity, may become distorted in shape as shown in Fig. 55(b). These forces may be due to the weight of the beam, to externally applied loads, or a combination of both. The resulting distorted axis of symmetry dashed in Fig. 55(b) is called the *elastic curve*. The determination of this

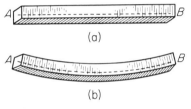

(a)

(b)

Fig. 55

curve is of importance in the theory of elasticity and it will be part of the purpose of this section to show how this is done.

There are many ways in which beams can be supported. For example, Fig. 56(a) shows a beam in which the end A is rigidly fixed, while end B is free to move. This is called a *cantilever beam*. In Fig. 56(b) the beam is supported at ends A and B. This is called a *simply supported beam*. Figure 56(c) shows still another way of supporting beams.

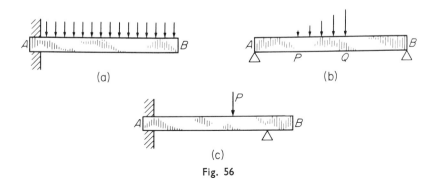

(a)

(b)

(c)

Fig. 56

Just as there are different ways of supporting beams, there are different ways in which external loading forces may be applied. For example, in Fig. 56(a) there is a *uniformly distributed load* over the whole beam. There may be a *variable loading* over the whole beam or just part of it as in Fig. 56(b). On the other hand there may be a *concentrated load* as indicated in Fig. 56(c).

Consider the horizontal beam OB of Fig. 57(a). Let the axis of symmetry (shown dashed) lie on the x axis taken as positive to the right and having origin at O. Choose the y axis as positive downward. Due to the action of the external forces F_1, F_2, ... (and the weight of the beam if appreciable) the axis of symmetry is distorted into the elastic curve shown dashed in

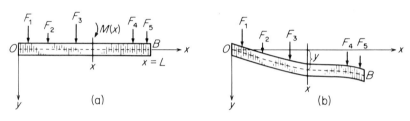

Fig. 57

Fig. 57(b), where we have taken the beam as fixed at O. The displacement y of the elastic curve from the x axis is called the *deflection* of the beam at position x. Thus if we determine the equation of the elastic curve, the deflection of the beam will be known. We now show how this can be accomplished.

Let $M(x)$ denote the *bending moment* in a vertical cross section of the beam through x. This bending moment is defined as the algebraic sum of the moments of those forces which act *on one side of x*, the moments being taken about a horizontal line in the cross section at x. In computing moments we shall adopt the convention that *upward* forces produce *negative* moments and *downward* forces produce *positive* moments, assuming of course that the positive y axis is taken downward as stated above. As will be shown in Illustrative Example 1, it makes no difference which side of x we take since the bending moments computed from either side are equal.*

In the theory of beams, it is shown† that the bending moment at x is related simply to the radius of curvature of the elastic curve at x, the relation being

$$EI\,\frac{y''}{[1 + (y')^2]^{3/2}} = M(x) \qquad (1)$$

* This is true because the beam is in equilibrium.
† See, for example, [21].

where E is Young's modulus of elasticity and depends on the material used in designing the beam, and I is the moment of inertia of the cross section of the beam at x with respect to a horizontal line passing through the center of gravity of this cross section. The product EI is called the *flexural rigidity*, and we shall take it as constant.

If we assume that the beam bends only slightly, which is the case for many practical purposes, the slope y' of the elastic curve is so small that its square is negligible compared with unity, and equation (1) may be replaced by the good approximation

$$EIy'' = M(x) \tag{2}$$

Let us see how this equation can be used.

ILLUSTRATIVE EXAMPLE 1

A horizontal, simply supported, uniform beam of length L bends under its own weight, which is w pounds per foot. Find the equation of its elastic curve.

Mathematical Formulation. In Fig. 58 the elastic curve of the beam (dashed) is shown relative to a rectangular set of axes having origin at

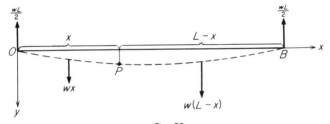

Fig. 58

O and indicated positive directions. Since the beam is simply supported at O and B, each of these supports carries half the weight of the beam, or $wL/2$. The bending moment $M(x)$ is the algebraic sum of the moments of these forces acting at one side of point P. Let us first choose the side to the *left* of P. In this case two forces act:

1. Upward force $wL/2$, distance x from P, producing a negative moment.
2. Downward force wx, distance $x/2$ (center of gravity of OP) from P, producing a positive moment.

The total bending moment at P is thus

$$M(x) = -\frac{wL}{2}x + wx\left(\frac{x}{2}\right) = \frac{wx^2}{2} - \frac{wLx}{2} \tag{3}$$

If we had chosen the side to the *right* of P, two forces would act:

1. Downward force $w(L - x)$, distance $(L - x)/2$ from P, producing a positive moment.

2. Upward force $wL/2$, distance $L - x$ from P, producing a negative moment.

In this case the bending moment is

$$M(x) = w(L - x)\left(\frac{L - x}{2}\right) - \frac{wL}{2}(L - x) = \frac{wx^2}{2} - \frac{wLx}{2} \qquad (4)$$

which agrees with (3) and shows that in computing bending moments it makes no difference which side of P is used.

Using the value of $M(x)$ obtained, the fundamental equation (2) is

$$EIy'' = \frac{wx^2}{2} - \frac{wLx}{2} \qquad (5)$$

Two conditions are necessary for determination of y. These are

$$y = 0 \text{ where } x = 0 \quad \text{and} \quad \text{where } x = L$$

since the beam is not deflected at the ends.

Solution. Integrating (5) twice:

$$EIy = \frac{wx^4}{24} - \frac{wLx^3}{12} + c_1 x + c_2$$

Since $y = 0$ when $x = 0$, we have $c_2 = 0$. Hence,

$$EIy = \frac{wx^4}{24} - \frac{wLx^3}{12} + c_1 x$$

Since $y = 0$ when $x = L$, $c_1 = wL^3/24$ and we have, finally,

$$y = \frac{w}{24EI}(x^4 - 2Lx^3 + L^3 x) \qquad (6)$$

as the required equation of the elastic curve. It is of practical interest to use (6) to find the maximum deflection. From symmetry or by calculus, the maximum is found to occur at $x = L/2$. Hence,

$$\text{maximum deflection} = \frac{5wL^4}{384EI}$$

ILLUSTRATIVE EXAMPLE 2

Find the elastic curve of a uniform cantilever beam of length L having a constant weight w pounds per foot and determine the deflection of the free end.

Mathematical Formulation. The dashed curve in Fig. 59 is the elastic curve of the cantilever beam. The origin O of the coordinate system is taken at the fixed end, and the positive x and y axes are as shown. In computing $M(x)$ it is simpler to consider the portion of the beam to the right of P, since only one force acts here, namely, the downward force $w(L - x)$, producing a positive moment given by

$$M(x) = w(L - x)\left(\frac{L - x}{2}\right) = \frac{w(L - x)^2}{2}$$

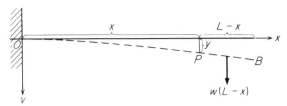

Fig. 59

Thus, equation (2) becomes

$$EIy'' = \frac{w(L - x)^2}{2}$$

which we must solve subject to the conditions $y = y' = 0$ where $x = 0$, since there is no deflection at $x = 0$, and since the slope of the tangent to the elastic curve at $x = 0$ is zero.

Solution. Upon integrating twice and making use of the conditions it is easy to show that

$$y = \frac{w}{24EI}(x^4 - 4Lx^3 + 6L^2x^2)$$

is the equation of the elastic curve. By placing $x = L$ we find

$$\text{deflection of free end} = \frac{wL^4}{8EI}$$

ILLUSTRATIVE EXAMPLE 3

A horizontal, simply supported, uniform beam of length L and negligible weight bends under the influence of a concentrated load of S pounds, distance $L/3$ from one end. Find the equation of the elastic curve.

Mathematical Formulation. The elastic curve is shown dashed in Fig. 60. The supports at O and B are at distances having a ratio $1:2$ from the load S. Hence, they support loads having ratio $2:1$, so that at O the amount $2S/3$ is supported, while at B the amount $S/3$ is supported. In determining the bending moment at P, three cases must be considered:

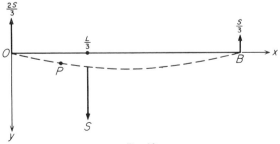

Fig. 60

Case 1. P is to the left of S, i.e., $0 \leq x < L/3$.

The portion OP has only one (upward) force acting at a distance x from P. The bending moment is $-2Sx/3$. Hence,

$$EIy'' = -\frac{2Sx}{3}, \qquad 0 \leq x < \frac{L}{3} \tag{7}$$

Case 2. P is to the right of S, i.e., $L/3 < x \leq L$.

The portion OP has two forces, an upward force $2S/3$, distance x from P, and a downward force S, distance $x - L/3$ from P. The bending moment is $-2Sx/3 + S(x - L/3)$. Hence,

$$EIy'' = -\frac{2Sx}{3} + S\left(x - \frac{L}{3}\right), \qquad \frac{L}{3} < x \leq L \tag{8}$$

Case 3. P is at S. In this case the portion OP has two forces, an upward force $2S/3$, distance $L/3$ from P, and a downward force S, distance zero from P. The bending moment is

$$-\frac{2S}{3}\left(\frac{L}{3}\right) + S(0) = -\frac{2SL}{9}$$

Since this agrees with the bending moments in equations (7) and (8) we may combine Case 3 with those cases, merely by rewriting the equations as

$$EIy'' = -\frac{2Sx}{3}, \qquad 0 \leq x \leq \frac{L}{3}$$

$$EIy'' = -\frac{2Sx}{3} + S\left(x - \frac{L}{3}\right), \qquad \frac{L}{3} \leq x \leq L \tag{9}$$

Since each equation is of second order, we expect to need four conditions. Two of these are clearly

$$y = 0 \text{ at } x = 0, \qquad y = 0 \text{ at } x = L \tag{10}$$

A third condition is obtained by realizing that the two values of y obtained from equations (9) must be equal at $x = L/3$. This is the *condition of continuity*. A fourth condition is obtained by realizing that there must be a tangent at $x = L/3$. This is the *condition for continuity in the derivative.*

Solution. Integrating equations (9) each once, we have

$$EIy' = -\frac{Sx^2}{3} + c_1, \qquad 0 \leq x \leq \frac{L}{3}$$

$$EIy' = -\frac{Sx^2}{3} + \frac{S}{2}\left(x - \frac{L}{3}\right)^2 + c_2, \qquad \frac{L}{3} \leq x \leq L \tag{11}$$

Since these two values of y' must be equal at $x = L/3$, we have $c_1 = c_2$. Thus,

$$EIy' = -\frac{Sx^2}{3} + c_1, \qquad 0 \le x \le \frac{L}{3}$$

$$EIy' = -\frac{Sx^2}{3} + \frac{S}{2}\left(x - \frac{L}{3}\right)^2 + c_1, \qquad \frac{L}{3} \le x \le L \tag{12}$$

Integrating these each once, we have

$$EIy = -\frac{Sx^3}{9} + c_1 x + c_3, \qquad 0 \le x \le \frac{L}{3}$$

$$EIy = -\frac{Sx^3}{9} + \frac{S}{6}\left(x - \frac{L}{3}\right)^3 + c_1 x + c_4, \qquad \frac{L}{3} \le x \le L \tag{13}$$

Using the first and second conditions of (10) in the first and second equations of (13), respectively, and also using the condition for continuity, we find

$$c_3 = 0, \qquad c_4 = 0, \qquad c_1 = \frac{5SL^2}{81}$$

and it follows that

$$y = \begin{cases} \dfrac{S}{81EI}(5L^2 x - 9x^3), & 0 \le x \le \dfrac{L}{3} \\[3mm] \dfrac{S}{81EI}\left[5L^2 x - 9x^3 + \dfrac{27}{2}\left(x - \dfrac{L}{3}\right)^3\right], & \dfrac{L}{3} \le x \le L \end{cases} \tag{14}$$

A EXERCISES

1. A uniform cantilever beam of length L and of negligible weight has a concentrated load of S pounds at the free end. Find (a) the equation of the elastic curve, (b) the maximum deflection.

2. A beam of length L and negligible weight is simply supported at both ends. A concentrated load of S pounds acts at its center. Find (a) the equation of the elastic curve, (b) the maximum deflection, (c) the numerical value of the slope at the ends.

3. Assume that, in addition to the concentrated load, the beam of Exercise 1 weighs w pounds per foot, where w is constant. (a) Find the equation of the elastic curve. (b) Find the maximum deflection. (c) Show that by letting $S = 0$, the results of Illustrative Example 2 are obtained.

4. Assume that, in addition to the concentrated load, the beam of Exercise 2 weighs w pounds per foot, where w is constant. (a) Find the equation of the elastic curve. (b) Find the maximum deflection. (c) Letting $S = 0$, obtain the results of Illustrative Example 1. (d) By letting $w = 0$, show that the results of Exercise 2 are obtained.

5. A beam of length L and negligible weight is simply supported at both ends and at the center. It carries a uniform load of w pounds per foot. Determine the equation of the elastic curve.

6. A uniform cantilever beam of length L and of negligible weight has a concentrated load of S pounds at its center. Find the equation of the elastic curve, and determine the maximum deflection.

7. Determine the elastic curve for the beam of Exercise 6 if it is assumed that the beam has, in addition, a uniform weight w pounds per foot.

B EXERCISES

1. A beam of length L and uniform weight w pounds per foot has both ends horizontally fixed in masonry. Determine the equation of the elastic curve and find the maximum deflection. (*Hint:* Assume that the unknown moment at either of the ends is A, and determine A from the boundary conditions.)

2. Solve the previous problem if a concentrated load of S pounds acts at the center of the beam, in addition to the uniform weight.

3. One end of a beam of length L and uniform weight w pounds per foot is simply supported, while the other end is horizontally fixed. (a) Find the equation of the elastic curve. (b) Show that the maximum deflection occurs at a distance $(15 - \sqrt{33})L/16 = 0.578L$, approximately, from the fixed end and has an approximate magnitude given by $0.00542wL^4/EI$.

C EXERCISES

1. If $y_1(x)$ is the deflection at point x of a beam, due to a concentrated load of S_1 pounds at point P_1 of the beam, and $y_2(x)$ is the deflection at point x, due to a concentrated load of S_2 pounds at point P_2 of the beam, show that the deflection at point x, due to both concentrated loads, is given by $y_1(x) + y_2(x)$. This is the "principle of superposition" for beams.

2. Generalize Exercise 1 to n concentrated loads $S_1, \ldots, S_n$ at points $P_1, \ldots, P_n$.

3. Using the results of Exercises 1 and 2 and Illustrative Example 3, find the elastic curve formed by a beam of length L, which is simply supported at both ends and which has concentrated loads of S pounds at distances $L/3$ from each end.

4. A beam of length L feet is simply supported at both ends. It carries a variable load given by $w(x)$ pounds per foot, where x is the distance measured from one end of the beam. (a) Show that the differential equation for the determination of the elastic curve is

$$EIy'' = -\int_0^L \frac{u}{L} w(u)(L - x)du + \int_x^L w(u)(u - x)du \tag{15}$$

(*Hint:* Assume the interval $0 \leq x \leq L$, subdivided into n equal parts by the points

$$\frac{L}{n}, \quad \frac{2L}{n}, \quad \ldots, \quad \frac{(n-1)L}{n}$$

at which concentrated loads

$$\frac{L}{n} w\left(\frac{L}{n}\right), \quad \frac{L}{n} w\left(\frac{2L}{n}\right), \quad \ldots, \quad \frac{L}{n} w\left(\frac{(n-1)L}{n}\right) \qquad \text{act, respectively.}$$

Consider the limit as $n \to \infty$, applying the fundamental theorem of integral calculus. Note that the subdivisions need not be taken equal.) (b) **By differentiations of (15) with respect to x, obtain**

$$\text{(A)} \quad EIy''' = -\left[\int_x^L w(u)du - \int_0^L \frac{u}{L} w(u)du\right], \qquad \text{(B)} \quad EIy^{(\text{IV})} = w(x) \quad (16)$$

assuming EI constant. Equations (16) are of great importance in beam theory. The quantity on the right of (16)A is the negative of the total loading to the right of x and is called the *vertical shear at x*. Equations (16) are valid for beams other than simply supported ones (see Exercise 8).

5. Using equation (16)B of Exercise 4(b) with $w(x)$ constant, arrive at the result of Illustrative Example 1.

6. Using equation (16)B of Exercise 4(b), determine the elastic curve of a beam of length L, which is simply supported at both ends and which has a loading proportional to (a) the distance from one end, (b) the square of the distance from one end.

7. A beam of length L and negligible weight is simply supported at both ends. A concentrated load of S pounds acts at distance p from one end. Show that the maximum deflection of the beam never exceeds the deflection of the center by more than 3%.

8. Consider a portion of a beam between sections at x and $x + \Delta x$ (Fig. 61). Let M and $M + \Delta M$ denote the respective bending moments at these sections. Let $w(x)$ represent the loading per unit length at x, so that $w(x)\Delta x$ represents the loading on the portion between x and $x + \Delta x$, apart from infinitesimals of order higher than Δx. Let V be the vertical shear at x (i.e., the algebraic sum of the

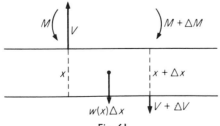

Fig. 61

vertical forces to one side of x, say to the right) and $V + \Delta V$ the corresponding vertical shear at $x + \Delta x$. (a) From equilibrium considerations of this portion of the beam show that

$$\Delta V + w(x)\Delta x + \alpha(\Delta x)^2 = 0 \quad \text{(sum of forces} = 0)$$
$$\Delta M + (V + \Delta V)\Delta x + w(x)\Delta x\theta\,\Delta x = 0, \quad 0 \leq \theta \leq 1$$
$$\text{(sum of moments} = 0)$$

and thus dividing by Δx and letting $\Delta x \to 0$, show that

$$\frac{dV}{dx} = -w(x), \qquad \frac{dM}{dx} = -V$$

(b) Using the results in (a), show that the equation $EIy'' = M(x)$ becomes

$$EIy^{(IV)} = w(x)$$

assuming EI is constant. Compare with Exercise 4.

Chapter Four

LINEAR DIFFERENTIAL EQUATIONS

I. The General nth-Order Linear Differential Equation

In Chapter 2 we called the differential equation

$$\frac{dy}{dx} + Py = Q \tag{1}$$

where P and Q were functions of x, a linear first-order equation. We extend this in the following

DEFINITION. A linear differential equation of order n has the form

$$a_0(x)\frac{d^n y}{dx^n} + a_1(x)\frac{d^{n-1}y}{dx^{n-1}} + a_2(x)\frac{d^{n-2}y}{dx^{n-2}} + \cdots + a_{n-1}(x)\frac{dy}{dx} + a_n(x)y = F(x) \tag{2}$$

where $a_0(x), a_1(x), \ldots, a_n(x)$, and $F(x)$ depend only on x and not on y.*

If $n = 1$, equations (1) and (2) are equivalent. If $n = 2$, then (2) becomes

$$a_0(x)\frac{d^2 y}{dx^2} + a_1(x)\frac{dy}{dx} + a_2(x)y = F(x) \tag{3}$$

a second-order linear differential equation. Whereas (1) can always be solved in terms of P and Q, (3) or (2) with $n \geq 2$ cannot always be solved exactly. In many important cases the coefficients $a_0, a_1, \ldots, a_n$ are constants, and we call the equation a linear differential equation with constant coefficients.

In discussing equation (2) it is convenient to use the symbols D, D^2, D^3, $\ldots$ to indicate the *operations* of taking the first, second, third, $\ldots$ derivatives of whatever follows. Thus Dy is the same as dy/dx, $D^2 y$ is the same as d^2y/dx^2, $\ldots$. We call the symbols D, D^2, $\ldots$ *operators* because they define an operation to be performed. Similarly xD^2 is an operator denoting the operation of taking a second derivative and then multiplying by x.

---

* An nth-order differential equation which is not of this form is called *non-linear*.

With this symbolic notation (2) may be written

$$a_0 D^n y + a_1 D^{n-1} y + a_2 D^{n-2} y + \cdots + a_{n-1} D y + a_n y = F \qquad (4)$$

or $\qquad (a_0 D^n + a_1 D^{n-1} + a_2 D^{n-2} + \cdots + a_{n-1} D + a_n) y = F \qquad (5)$

in which it is understood that each term in the parentheses is operating on y and the results are added. If we write for brevity

$$\phi(D) \equiv a_0 D^n + a_1 D^{n-1} + a_2 D^{n-2} + \cdots + a_{n-1} D + a_n \qquad (6)$$

equation (5) may be written conveniently as $\phi(D)y = F$. For example, the differential equation $\phi(D)y = F$, where $F = x^2 + e^x$, and $\phi(D) \equiv D^3 + 5D^2 + 6D - 8$ actually is a short-cut way of writing

$$\frac{d^3 y}{dx} + 5\frac{d^2 y}{dx^2} + 6\frac{dy}{dx} - 8y = x^2 + e^x$$

On considering what the symbols mean, it should be clear to the student that

$$D^n(u + v) = D^n u + D^n v, \qquad D^n(au) = a D^n u \qquad (7)$$

where u and v are differentiable functions, a is any constant, and n is any positive integer. Any operator such as D^n which has the properties shown in (7) is called a *linear operator*.* It is not difficult to show that the operator $\phi(D)$ given by (6) is a linear operator, i.e., that

$$\phi(D)(u + v) = \phi(D)u + \phi(D)v, \qquad \phi(D)(au) = a\phi(D)u \qquad (8)$$

The results follow directly by interpreting both sides and showing that they are equal.

Let us consider the general nth-order linear equation (2). We are particularly interested in knowing how we may obtain its general solution. In order to do this we associate with the general equation

$$\phi(D)y = F(x) \qquad (9)$$

another equation

$$\phi(D)y = 0 \qquad (10)$$

obtained by replacing $F(x)$ by zero. Of course, if $F(x)$ is already zero, then equations (9) and (10) are really the same. We assume $F(x) \not\equiv 0$.

Terminology. We refer to equation (9) with $F(x)$ not identically zero as the given equation, or the equation with right-hand member not zero, and shall refer to the associated equation (10) as the complementary equation, the reduced equation, or the equation with right-hand member zero.†

* It is possible to extend these ideas to cases where n is a negative integer (see p. 172) or a fraction. For example, we may define a "half derivative" operator $D^{1/2} \equiv d^{1/2}/dx^{1/2}$ as one which, when operating twice on a function, yields the first derivative of the function. For an interesting account of such operators see [6].

† The term *homogeneous* is used in many texts. However, this word is used in too many different and unrelated connections in mathematics. In this text we give the word a much needed rest.

FUNDAMENTAL THEOREM I. If $y = u(x)$ is any solution of the given equation (9), and $y = v(x)$ is any solution of the complementary equation (10), then $y = u(x) + v(x)$ is a solution of (9).
Proof. Since u is a solution of (9), we have

$$\phi(D)u = F(x) \tag{11}$$

Since v is a solution of (10),

$$\phi(D)v = 0 \tag{12}$$

Adding (11) and (12), we have, using (8),

$$\phi(D)(u + v) = F(x)$$

which is another way of saying that $y = u(x) + v(x)$ is a solution.

In Chapter 1 we defined a general solution of an nth-order differential equation as one having n arbitrary constants. From Fundamental Theorem I above it follows that $y = u(x) + v(x)$ will be a general solution if $u(x)$ has no arbitrary constants, while $v(x)$ has n arbitrary constants. If $v(x)$ has n arbitrary constants, then it is the general solution of the complementary equation (10). If $u(x)$ has no arbitrary constants it is the simplest particular solution of the given equation (9).

Terminology. We shall call the general solution of the complementary or reduced equation (10) the *complementary solution** and will sometimes denote it by y_c. We shall refer to a selected solution of the given equation (no arbitrary constant) as a *particular solution*† of the given equation and will sometimes denote it by y_p. The above remarks are of such importance for the later work of this chapter that we summarize them in the following

FUNDAMENTAL THEOREM II. The general solution of $\phi(D)y = F(x)$ may be obtained by finding a particular solution y_p of this equation and adding it to the complementary solution y_c, which is the general solution of $\phi(D)y = 0$.

ILLUSTRATIVE EXAMPLE

Find the general solution of

$$\frac{d^2y}{dx^2} - 5\frac{dy}{dx} + 6y = 3x$$

Solution. In operator notation this may be written

$$(D^2 - 5D + 6)y = 3x \tag{13}$$

The complementary or reduced differential equation is

$$(D^2 - 5D + 6)y = 0 \tag{14}$$

---

* The term *complementary function* or *complementary integral* is also used.
† The term *particular integral* is also used.

It can be verified that

You really to study pages 145-149 / have the pages 145-149 / undertand this. See 146 to understand this.

$$y_c = c_1 e^{3x} + c_2 e^{2x}$$

is the complementary solution of (13) since it has two arbitrary constants and is thus the general solution of (14).

It can also be verified that

$$y_p = \tfrac{1}{2}x + \tfrac{5}{12}$$

satisfies (13) and is thus a particular solution since it has no arbitrary constant.

From the Fundamental Theorem II it follows that the required general solution is

$$y = y_c + y_p = c_1 e^{3x} + c_2 e^{2x} + \tfrac{1}{2}x + \tfrac{5}{12}$$

From this illustrative example it is clear that to obtain the general solution of $\phi(D)y = F(x)$, the following questions must be answered.

Questions

1. How do we find the complementary solution?
2. How do we find the particular solution?

We shall answer these questions in Sections III and IV for the very important case where the differential equations have constant coefficients. It must however be emphasized that the fundamental theorems hold for variable coefficients as well. Such equations will be considered in the remainder of the book.

II. Existence and Uniqueness of Solutions of Linear Equations

In Section V of Chapter 1, an existence and uniqueness theorem for first-order differential equations was stated. We now state without proof a corresponding theorem for the general nth-order linear equation

$$[a_0(x)D^n + a_1(x)D^{n-1} + \cdots + a_n(x)]y = F(x) \tag{1}$$

THEOREM. Let $a_0(x), a_1(x), \ldots, a_n(x)$, and $F(x)$ be functions which are continuous in the interval $a \leq x \leq b$ and suppose that $a_0(x) \neq 0$ for any value of x in the interval. Then there *exists* a solution $y(x)$ satisfying the differential equation (1) and also the conditions

$$y(c) = p_0, \quad y'(c) = p_1, \quad y''(c) = p_2, \quad \ldots, \quad y^{(n-1)}(c) = p_{n-1}$$

where $a \leq c \leq b$ and $p_0, p_1, \ldots, p_{n-1}$ are given constants. Furthermore, this solution is *unique*.

As in the existence and uniqueness theorem on first-order equations, this theorem provides only sufficient conditions. That is, even if the conditions stated are not all satisfied, unique solutions may still exist.

A EXERCISES

1. Write each of the following in "operator notation."

(a) $\dfrac{d^2y}{dx^2} + 3\dfrac{dy}{dx} + 2y = x^3$.

(b) $3y^{(IV)} - 5y''' + y = e^{-x} + \sin x$.

(c) $\dfrac{d^2s}{dt^2} = -\beta\dfrac{ds}{dt} - \omega^2 s$.

(d) $x^2y'' - 2xy' = y + 1$.

2. If $y = x^3 - 3x^2 + 2e^{-x}$ and $z = \sin 2x + 3\cos 2x$ evaluate:

(a) $(D^2 + 3D + 1)y$.

(b) $(2D^3 - D^2 - 4)z$.

(c) $(D^2 + 2D)(y + z)$.

(d) $(x^2D^2 + 3xD - 2)(2y - 3z)$.

3. Complete the entries in the table. Verify that the general solutions in the fourth column satisfy the differential equations in the first column.

Differential Equation	Complementary Solution	Particular Solution	General Solution
$y'' - 3y' + 2y = x$	$y_c = c_1e^x + c_2e^{2x}$	$y_p = \dfrac{x}{2} + \dfrac{3}{4}$	*(handwritten)* $y = c_1 e^x + c_2 e^{2x} + \dfrac{x}{2} + \dfrac{3}{4}$
$(D^2 - 1)y = e^{-x}$	*(handwritten)* $y_c = c_1 e^x + c_2 e^{-x}$	$y_p = -\dfrac{x}{2}e^{-x}$	$y = c_1e^x + c_2e^{-x} - \dfrac{x}{2}e^{-x}$
$(D^3 + D)y = \sin 2x$	*(handwritten)* $y_c = A\sin x + B\cos x$	*(handwritten)* $c + \tfrac{1}{6}\cos 2x$	$y = A\sin x + B\cos x$ $+ C + \tfrac{1}{6}\cos 2x$
(handwritten) $(D^2 - 5D + 5)y = e^x$	*(handwritten)* $y_c = c_1 e^{3x} + c_2 e^{2x}$	*(handwritten)* $y_p = e^x$	$y = c_1e^{3x} + c_2e^{2x} + e^x$
$(x^2D^2 + xD - 4)y = x^3$	$y_c = Ax^2 + \dfrac{B}{x^2}$	$y_p = \dfrac{x^3}{5}$	*(handwritten)* $y = Ax^2 + \dfrac{B}{x^2} + \dfrac{x^3}{5}$

B EXERCISES

1. Evaluate $F(x) \equiv (D - 1)(x^3 + 2x)$, where $D \equiv d/dx$. Then evaluate $(D - 2)F(x)$. The result may be written $(D - 2)(D - 1)(x^3 + 2x)$. Is this the same as $(D^2 - 3D + 2)(x^3 + 2x)$? Is the operator $(D - 2)(D - 1)$ the same as the operator $D^2 - 3D + 2$ when the operations are performed on any differentiable function? Prove your answer.

2. (a) Does $(D - a)(D - b) = D^2 - (a + b)D + ab$, where a and b are constants? (b) Two operators $\phi_1(D)$ and $\phi_2(D)$ are called *commutative* with respect to multiplication if $\phi_1(D)\phi_2(D)u = \phi_2(D)\phi_1(D)u$. Are the operators $(D - a)$ and

$(D - b)$ commutative? (c) Operators $\phi_1(D), \phi_2(D)$, and $\phi_3(D)$ are called *associative* with respect to multiplication if

$$\phi_1(D)[\phi_2(D)\phi_3(D)]u = [\phi_1(D)\phi_2(D)]\phi_3(D)u$$

Are the operators $(D - a)$, $(D - b)$, and $(D - c)$, where a, b, c are constants, associative?

C EXERCISES

1. Evaluate $F(x) \equiv (D - x)(2x^3 - 3x^2)$. Then evaluate $(D + x)F(x)$. The result may be written $(D + x)(D - x)(2x^3 - 3x^2)$. Is this result the same as $(D^2 - x^2)(2x^3 - 3x^2)$? Is $(D - x)(D + x)$ the same as $(D + x)(D - x)$?

2. Answer Questions 2 of the B exercises when a, b, c are not all constants.

3. Represent $D^3 - 6D^2 + 11D - 6$ as a "product" of three factors if possible. Does the order make any difference? Prove your statements.

4. Discuss the existence and uniqueness of solutions of
   (a) $y'' - 3y' + 2y = x^2$; $y(0) = y'(0) = 0$.
   (b) $xy'' + y' + xy = 0$; $y(c) = p_1$, $y'(c) = p_2$.

5. Write the differential equation $(D^2 - 3D + 2)y = x$ as $(D - 1)(D - 2)y = x$. Letting $(D - 2)y = v$, write the equation as $(D - 1)v = x$ and thus find v. From this find y. Do you have the general solution? If so, write the complementary and particular solutions. This is called the method of *reduction of order*.

6. Use the method of Exercise 5 to obtain general solutions of each of the following and verify your answer in each case.
   (a) $(D^2 + D - 2)y = e^{-x}$.
   (b) $(D - 3)(D + 2)(D - 1)y = 3e^x - 2$.
   (c) $(D - 1)^2y = 1$.   (d) $(D - x)(D + 1)y = x$.

III. How Do We Obtain the Complementary Solution?

1. The auxiliary equation. In this section we concentrate our attention on methods of finding the general solution of the equation $\phi(D)y = 0$. Consider the following

Problem for Discussion. What is the general solution of the differential equation

$$y'' - 3y' + 2y = 0?$$

In operator notation this equation can be written $(D^2 - 3D + 2)y = 0$. Before we consider this further, let us return to a first-order linear differential equation with constant coefficients, for example, $(D - 2)y = 0$. We may write this equation

$$\frac{dy}{dx} - 2y = 0 \tag{1}$$

Solving this by one of many possible methods we find that $y = ce^{2x}$ is a general solution and in particular $y = e^{2x}$. This solution could be found by assuming a solution of the form $y = e^{mx}$, where m is an as yet undetermined constant. In order for this to be a solution, we have by substitution in (1) $(m - 2)e^{mx} = 0$, i.e., $m = 2$, since e^{mx} is never zero. From this it is a simple step to deduce that ce^{2x} is also a solution which gives the general solution. We now wonder whether the same technique will work as well on the equation $(D^2 - 3D + 2)y = 0$. Letting $y = e^{mx}$, the equation becomes

$$m^2 e^{mx} - 3m e^{mx} + 2 e^{mx} = 0 \quad \text{or} \quad (m^2 - 3m + 2)e^{mx} = 0$$

and it is clear that this will be satisfied if $m^2 - 3m + 2 = 0$ or $m = 1, 2$. Thus, it follows that $y = e^x$ and $y = e^{2x}$ are solutions. We now ask the question: What is the general solution? We know that the general solution has two arbitrary constants and the student may suspect that a good guess for this general solution would be $y = c_1 e^x + c_2 e^{2x}$. This suspicion is confirmed by simply substituting into the equation and showing that it is satisfied. If the student likes he can strengthen his suspicions by the following

Illustrative Example

Solve

$$y''' - 6y'' + 11y' - 6y = 0$$

Solution. Letting $y = e^{mx}$, where m is constant, it will be verified that m must be such that

$$m^3 - 6m^2 + 11m - 6 = 0$$

By trial or otherwise, the student may verify that this equation has three roots $m = 1, 2, 3$. Hence, solutions are e^x, e^{2x}, and e^{3x}, and going along with our suspicions we guess that

$$y = c_1 e^x + c_2 e^{2x} + c_3 e^{3x}$$

is the required general solution. Our suspicions are once more confirmed by actual substitution.

We may confirm permanently our suspicions by the following

THEOREM. If y_1 and y_2 are two solutions of $\phi(D)y = 0$, then $c_1 y_1 + c_2 y_2$, where c_1 and c_2 are arbitrary constants, is also a solution.

Proof. Since y_1 and y_2 are solutions, $\phi(D)y_1 = 0$, $\phi(D)y_2 = 0$. Multiplying these equations by c_1 and c_2 respectively, and remembering that $\phi(D)$ is a linear operator, we have $\phi(D)(c_1 y_1 + c_2 y_2) = 0$, which shows that $c_1 y_1 + c_2 y_2$ is a solution and proves the theorem.

The student should be able to extend this to the following

THEOREM. If $y_1, y_2, \ldots, y_p$ are p solutions of $\phi(D)y = 0$, then $c_1 y_1 + c_2 y_2 + \cdots + c_p y_p$ is also a solution.

In case the number of arbitrary constants in the solution is equal to the order of the differential equation, we have the general solution.* This theorem confirms the suspicions which we had above.

The student has probably noticed that the equation for determination of m has the same form as the differential equation written in terms of operators. Thus, for $(D^2 - 3D + 2)y = 0$, the "m equation" is $m^2 - 3m + 2 = 0$. In general for *constant coefficients* the differential equation $\phi(D)y = 0$ has the "m equation" $\phi(m) = 0$. This "m equation" is called the *auxiliary equation* and we shall refer to it by this name. For variable coefficients it is rare that solutions of the form $y = e^{mx}$ exist, and consequently the auxiliary equation is to be used only in the constant coefficient case.

A EXERCISES

1. Find general solutions of each of the following:

(a) $y'' + 4y' - 5y = 0$.   (b) $(4D^2 - 25)y = 0$.

(c) $\dfrac{d^2 y}{dx^2} = 4y$.   *DON'T REALLY SHOW THIS? UNDERSTAND LIKE*   (d) $2y''' - 5y'' + 2y' = 0$.

(e) $I''(t) - 4I'(t) + 2I(t) = 0$.   (f) $(D^3 + 2D^2 - 5D - 6)y = 0$.

2. Find solutions satisfying the given conditions:

(a) $y'' - y = 0$, $y(0) = 2$, $y'(0) = -3$.
(b) $(D^2 - 3D + 2)y = 0$, $y(0) = -1$, $y'(0) = 0$.
(c) $(D^3 - 16D)y = 0$, $y(0) = 0$, $y'(0) = 0$, $y''(0) = 16$.

(handwritten annotations)
$m^2 - 3m + 2 = 0$
$(m-2)(m-1) = 0$
$m = 2, 1$
$y = c_1 e^{2x} + c_2 e^x$
$y' = 2c_1 e^{2x} + c_2 e^x$
$-1 = c_1 + c_2$
$0 = 2c_1 + c_2$
$-1 = -c_1$
$c_1 = 1$
$c_2 = -2$

ANS: $y = e^{2x} - 2e^x$

B EXERCISES

1. Solve $(D^3 + 5D^2 + 2D - 12)y = 0$.

2. Can the substitution $y = e^{mx}$, where m is a constant, be used in solving a differential equation such as $y'' - xy' + y = 0$? Explain.

3. (a) Find the general solution of $[D^2 - (m_1 + m_2)D + m_1 m_2]y = 0$, m_1, m_2 constant, subject to the conditions $y(0) = 0$, $y'(0) = 1$ if $m_1 \neq m_2$. (b) What does the solution to (a) become if we assume that $m_2 \to m_1$? (c) Does the limiting solution of (b) satisfy the differential equation of (a) if $m_1 = m_2$? Can you devise a rule for repeated roots?

---

* The student should recall that when we speak of arbitrary constants we mean to imply *essential* arbitrary constants as indicated on page 15. This concept is intimately connected with that of linear independence of functions which is considered on page 153.

C EXERCISES

1. Solve $(D^4 - 20D^2 + 4)y = 0$.

2. $(D^4 - 2D^3 - 16D^2 + 12D + 12)y = 0$.

2. The case of repeated roots. Consider the following
Problem for Discussion. Solve

$$(D^2 - 6D + 9)y = 0$$

Writing the auxiliary equation as usual, we have $m^2 - 6m + 9 = 0$. Solving this, we have $m = 3, 3$, i.e., two equal roots. Without thinking, we might write $y = c_1 e^{3x} + c_2 e^{3x}$ as the general solution. However, although this seems to have two arbitrary constants, in reality it does not since it can be written $y = (c_1 + c_2)e^{3x}$ or $y = ce^{3x}$, which has but one arbitrary constant. Hence we ask ourselves: What do we do in the case where the roots of the auxiliary equation are repeated?

The following method, which is of great generality and which is useful in later work, can come to our aid now. We state it as a

> THEOREM. If we know one solution, say $y = y_1$ of the nth-order equation $\phi(D)y = 0$, then the substitution $y = y_1 v$ will transform the given equation into an equation of the $(n-1)$st order in v', i.e., dv/dx.

> *Remark:* This theorem is valid for constant or variable coefficients and is also valid for the equation $\phi(D)y = F(x)$.

Let us illustrate the theorem by application to $(D^2 - 6D + 9)y = 0$. We have seen that a solution is e^{3x}. According to the theorem we thus let $y = ve^{3x}$. Since

$$Dy = v'e^{3x} + 3ve^{3x}, \qquad D^2y = v''e^{3x} + 6v'e^{3x} + 9ve^{3x}$$

we have on substituting into the equation and simplifying,

$$v''e^{3x} = 0$$

It follows that $v'' = 0$, or $v = c_1 + c_2 x$. Hence, we have $y = (c_1 + c_2 x)e^{3x}$. Thus, the general solution is $y = c_1 e^{3x} + c_2 x e^{3x}$. The dilemma raised in our problem for discussion is thus solved. It appears that to get another solution besides e^{3x} we simply multiply e^{3x} by x. We raise the rather obvious question now as to what happens when we have 3 roots which are the same. For example, suppose the roots are 2, 2, 2. This will occur when the auxiliary equation is $(m - 2)^3 = 0$, i.e., $m^3 - 6m^2 + 12m - 8 = 0$. The differential equation in such case would be

$$(D^3 - 6D^2 + 12D - 8)y = 0$$

Since e^{2x} is one solution, we substitute $y = ve^{2x}$ in accordance with the theorem and find that the given equation becomes, after simplification,

$$v''' e^{3x} = 0 \quad \text{or} \quad v''' = 0$$

so that $v = c_1 + c_2x + c_3x^2$ upon integration and the solution is given by

$$y = (c_1 + c_2x + c_3x^2)e^{2x}$$

The idea should now be apparent to the student. If we had 5 roots all equal to -1, the solution would be

$$(c_1 + c_2x + c_3x^2 + c_4x^3 + c_5x^4)e^{-x}$$

ILLUSTRATIVE EXAMPLE

Solve

$$(D^6 - 6D^5 + 12D^4 - 6D^3 - 9D^2 + 12D - 4)y = 0$$

Solution. The auxiliary equation

$$m^6 - 6m^5 + 12m^4 - 6m^3 - 9m^2 + 12m - 4 = 0$$

has roots $m = 1, 1, 1, 2, 2, -1$. Thus, there are (a) three roots equal to 1, (b) two roots equal to 2, (c) one root equal to -1, and the general solution (with the required six arbitrary constants) is

$$y = (c_1 + c_2x + c_3x^2)e^x + (c_4 + c_5x)e^{2x} + c_6e^{-x}$$

A EXERCISES

1. Find general solutions of each of the following:

(a) $(D^2 - 4D + 4)y = 0$.   (b) $16y'' - 8y' + y = 0$.
(c) $4I''(t) - 12I'(t) + 9I(t) = 0$.   (d) $(D^6 - 4D^4)y = 0$.
(e) $(D^4 - 2D^3 + D^2)y = 0$.   (f) $4y^{(IV)} - 20y'' + 25y = 0$.

2. Find solutions satisfying the given conditions:

(a) $(D^2 - 2D + 1)y = 0$; $y(0) = 1$, $y'(0) = -2$.
(b) $(D^3 - D^2)y = 0$; $y(0) = 1$, $y'(0) = y''(0) = 0$.
(c) $\dfrac{d^2s}{dt^2} = -16\dfrac{ds}{dt} - 64s$; $s = 0$, $\dfrac{ds}{dt} = -4$ where $t = 0$.

B EXERCISES

1. If a is constant and u is differentiable, prove the following.

$$(D - a)(e^{ax}u) = e^{ax}Du, \qquad (D - a)^2(e^{ax}u) = e^{ax}D^2u,$$
$$(D - a)^3(e^{ax}u) = e^{ax}D^3u$$

Can you prove by mathematical induction that

$$(D - a)^n(e^{ax}u) = e^{ax}D^nu$$

where n is any positive integer? This is sometimes called the *exponential shift theorem*.

2. Use the results of Exercise 1 to show that the equation $(D - a)^n y = 0$ has general solution

$$y = (c_1 + c_2x + c_3x^2 + \cdots + c_nx^{n-1})e^{ax}$$

and thus establish the result of this section.

C EXERCISES

1. Find the general solution of $y'' - xy' + y = 0$, given that $y = x$ is a solution.

2. For what value of the constant p will $y = x^p$ be a solution of $x^2y'' + 3xy' + y = 0$. Write the general solution.

3. Given that $y = x$ is a solution of $(1 - x^2)y'' - 2xy' + 2y = 0$, find its general solution and also the general solution of

$$(1 - x^2)y'' - 2xy' + 2y = x$$

4. Given that $y = Y_1(x)$ is a solution of $[a_0(x)D^2 + a_1(x)D + a_2(x)]y = 0$, find its general solution and also the general solution of

$$[a_0(x)D^2 + a_1(x)D + a_2(x)]y = R(x)$$

3. The case of imaginary roots. Consider the following

Problem for Discussion. Solve the equation

$$y'' + y = 0 \tag{2}$$

If we let $y = e^{mx}$ as customary, we find $m^2 + 1 = 0$, and the roots are $m = \pm i$, i.e., the roots are *imaginary*. Formally the general solution is

$$y = c_1e^{ix} + c_2e^{-ix} \tag{3}$$

but the question naturally arises: What do we mean by e^{ix} and e^{-ix}? A clue as to the possible meaning may be obtained by noticing that equation (2) has one of the variables missing. This equation has in fact been solved before (see page 54) and the general solution is easily seen to be

$$y = A \sin x + B \cos x \tag{4}$$

where A and B are arbitrary constants. Now it can be shown that the differential equation cannot have more than one general solution, so that we have to admit that although (3) and (4) look different they are actually the same. Let us therefore see what we can deduce from this. We have

$$c_1e^{ix} + c_2e^{-ix} \equiv A \sin x + B \cos x \tag{5}$$

Putting $x = 0$ in this identity and supposing that $e^{\pm i \cdot 0} = 1$, we find

$$c_1 + c_2 = B \tag{6}$$

Differentiating both sides of the identity (5), assuming that the usual rules hold when imaginaries are present, we have

$$c_1 i e^{ix} - c_2 i e^{-ix} \equiv A \cos x - B \sin x \tag{7}$$

Placing $x = 0$ in this identity, we have

$$(c_1 - c_2)i = A \tag{8}$$

Using the values of A and B from (6) and (8), equation (5) becomes

$$c_1 e^{ix} + c_2 e^{-ix} \equiv c_1(\cos x + i \sin x) + c_2(\cos x - i \sin x) \tag{9}$$

Since c_1 and c_2 are arbitrary, we may put $c_2 = 0$ and $c_1 = 1$. Then, from (9),

$$e^{ix} \equiv \cos x + i \sin x \tag{10}$$

Similarly, putting $c_1 = 0$ and $c_2 = 1$, (9) becomes

$$e^{-ix} \equiv \cos x - i \sin x \tag{11}$$

which also could have been obtained from (10) by replacing x by $-x$. We shall use (10) and (11), called *Euler's formulas*, as definitions of e^{ix} and e^{-ix}, since what we have done above makes plausible, but does not prove, these results.*

Problem for Discussion. Solve

$$(D^2 + 2D + 5)y = 0$$

The auxiliary equation is $m^2 + 2m + 5 = 0$, and $m = -1 \pm 2i$. Our formal solution is

$$y = c_1 e^{(-1+2i)x} + c_2 e^{(-1-2i)x} \tag{12}$$

Let us write this as

$$y = c_1 e^{-x} e^{2ix} + c_2 e^{-x} e^{-2ix} \quad \text{or} \quad y = e^{-x}(c_1 e^{2ix} + c_2 e^{-2ix})$$

By analogy with the above results,

$$c_1 e^{2ix} + c_2 e^{-2ix} \equiv A \sin 2x + B \cos 2x$$

so that (12) becomes

$$y = e^{-x}(A \sin 2x + B \cos 2x)$$

---

* For those who are acquainted with series we may obtain these results by using the series:

$$e^u = 1 + u + \frac{u^2}{2!} + \frac{u^3}{3!} + \frac{u^4}{4!} + \cdots$$

replacing u by ix and noting that

$$e^{ix} = 1 - \frac{x^2}{2!} + \frac{x^4}{4!} - \cdots + i\left(x - \frac{x^3}{3!} + \frac{x^5}{5!} - \cdots\right) = \cos x + i \sin x$$

However, the method needs justification.

This may, in fact, be verified as the required general solution. In general, if $a \pm bi$ are roots of the auxiliary equation, a corresponding solution is

$$e^{ax}(A \sin bx + B \cos bx)$$

ILLUSTRATIVE EXAMPLE

Solve

$$(D^4 - 5D^2 + 12D + 28)y = 0$$

Solution. The auxiliary equation $m^4 - 5m^2 + 12m + 28 = 0$ has the roots $m = -2, -2, 2 \pm \sqrt{3}\,i$.

Since $m = -2$ is a double root, $(c_1 + c_2x)e^{-2x}$ is a solution.

Since $2 \pm \sqrt{3}\,i$ are roots, $e^{2x}(c_3 \sin \sqrt{3}\,x + c_4 \cos \sqrt{3}\,x)$ is a solution.

Hence, the general solution is

$$y = (c_1 + c_2x)e^{-2x} + e^{2x}(c_3 \sin \sqrt{3}\,x + c_4 \cos \sqrt{3}\,x)$$

Problem for Discussion. What is the general solution of a differential equation whose auxiliary equation has as roots

$$2, -1, 0, 0, 3 \pm 5i, 2, 0, 3 \pm 5i?$$

We have ten roots. These are:

(1) the triple root 0	(2) the root -1
(3) the double root 2	(4) the double roots $3 \pm 5i$

From (1) a solution is

$$(c_1 + c_2x + c_3x^2)e^{0x} = c_1 + c_2x + c_3x^2$$

From (2) a solution is c_4e^{-x}.

From (3) a solution is $(c_5 + c_6x)e^{2x}$.

To obtain a solution corresponding to (4), note that a solution corresponding to the single pair $3 \pm 5i$ would be

$$e^{3x}(c_7 \sin 5x + c_8 \cos 5x)$$

It turns out that, since the pair is repeated, another solution is

$$xe^{3x}(c_9 \sin 5x + c_{10} \cos 5x)$$

This is by analogy with our results on repeated roots. [If $3 \pm 5i$ were a triple root, another solution would be $x^2e^{3x}(c_{11} \sin 5x + c_{12} \cos 5x)$.] From the above it follows that the general solution would be

$$y = c_1 + c_2x + c_3x^2 + c_4e^{-x} + (c_5 + c_6x)e^{2x}$$
$$+ e^{3x}(c_7 \sin 5x + c_8 \cos 5x) + xe^{3x}(c_9 \sin 5x + c_{10} \cos 5x)$$

and involves the necessary ten arbitrary constants.

We have now answered adequately the question: How do we obtain the complementary solution?

A EXERCISES

1. Find the general solution of each of the following:

(a) $y'' + 4y = 0$.

(b) $(D^2 + 4D + 5)y = 0$.

(c) $4\dfrac{d^2s}{dt^2} = -9s$.

(d) $4y'' - 8y' + 7y = 0$.

(e) $y^{IV} = -16y''$.

(f) $(D^3 + D^2 - 2)y = 0$.

2. Find solutions satisfying the given conditions.

(a) $(D^2 + 1)y = 0$; $y(0) = 4$, $y'(0) = 0$.

(b) $U''(t) = -16U(t)$; $U(0) = 0$, $U'(0) = 4$.

(c) $I''(t) + 2I'(t) + 5I(t) = 0$; $I(0) = 2$, $I'(0) = 0$.

B EXERCISES

1. Find the general solution of $(D^6 - 64)y = 0$; $D \equiv d/dx$.

2. (a) Find the solution of $(D^2 + a^2)(D^2 + b^2)y = 0$, subject to $y(0) = 1$, $y'(0) = y''(0) = y'''(0) = 0$, if $a \neq b$. (b) What does the solution in (a) become if $b \to a$? Is this a solution of the given equation when $b = a$? Does your result agree with the general results concerning repeated roots of the auxiliary equation?

3. Find the general solution of $(D^4 + 4D^2 + 4)y = 0$.

C EXERCISES

1. Solve $(D^4 + 4)y = 0$; $D \equiv d/dx$.

2. Solve $(D^4 + 6D^2 + 25)y = 0$; $D \equiv d/dx$.

Miscellaneous Review Exercises on Complementary Solutions

A EXERCISES

1. Write the general solution of the differential equations whose auxiliary equations have the following roots:

(a) $3, -1$.

(b) $4, 0, -2$.

(c) $2, 2, 2, 0, 0$.

(d) $-1, -i, i, -2$.

(e) $2 \pm 3i, -1 \pm 2i, 5, -1$.

(f) $1 \pm \sqrt{3}\,i, -2, -2, 0, -1$.

(g) $-1, 1, 0, -2, -1, 1, -1 \pm 2i$.

(h) $1 \pm i, 1 \pm i$.

(i) $\pm\sqrt{3}, \pm 4, \tfrac{1}{2} \pm 2i, -1 \pm 3i$.

(j) $1, 1, 1, 0, 0, \pm i, \pm i$.

2. Find the general solution of each of the following:

(a) $(D^2 + D + 1)y = 0$.   (b) $(D^4 - 1)y = 0$.
(c) $(D^6 + 2D^4 + D^2)y = 0$.   (d) $(D^3 - 4D^2 + 4D)y = 0$.
(e) $y''' = y''$.   (f) $S^{(\text{IV})}(t) + 2S''(t) - 8S(t) = 0$.

B EXERCISES

1. The equation $(D^3 + aD^2 + bD + c)y = 0$ where a, b, c are constants has
solution

$$y = c_1 e^{-x} + e^{-2x}(c_2 \sin 4x + c_3 \cos 4x)$$

Determine a, b, and c.

2. Find a differential equation whose auxiliary equation has roots -1, -1, $1 \pm 2i$,
$1 \pm 2i$. Write the general solution.

C EXERCISES

1. Show that the general solution of $D^n y = y$, where n is a positive integer, is

$$y = \sum_{k=1}^{n} c_k e^{m_k x}$$

where $m_k = e^{2k\pi i/n}$, $k = 1, \ldots, n$. Can the solution be expressed in real form?

2. Find real solutions of (a) $D^3 y = y$; (b) $D^5 y = y$.

3. Solve $D^3 y = 4y$.

4. Let X_1 and X_2 be any two solutions of the differential equation $\ddot{X} + k^2 X = 0$
such that $X_1^2 + X_2^2 = 1$. Prove that $\dot{X}_1^2 + \dot{X}_2^2 = k^2$ and $\ddot{X}_1^2 + \ddot{X}_2^2 = k^4$. Generalize to higher-ordered derivatives.

4. Linear independence and Wronskians. In the Illustrative Example on
page 145 we were required to solve the differential equation

$$(D^3 - 6D^2 + 11D - 6)y = 0$$

By direct substitution we found that e^x, e^{2x}, e^{3x} are solutions from which we
obtained the general solution

$$y = c_1 e^x + c_2 e^{2x} + c_3 e^{3x}$$

Suppose, however, we somehow arrive at the three functions

$$e^{2x} + 2e^x, \qquad 5e^{2x} + 4e^x, \qquad e^x - e^{2x} \tag{13}$$

all of which are easily shown to be solutions. Could we then say that

$$y = A(e^{2x} + 2e^x) + B(5e^{2x} + 4e^x) + C(e^x - e^{2x}) \tag{14}$$

with the three constants A, B, C, is the general solution? The observant student on noting that (14) can be written

$$y = (2A + 4B + C)e^x + (A + 5B - C)e^{2x}$$

or

$$y = c_1 e^x + c_2 e^{2x}$$

would say that the solution does not really have three arbitrary constants and so cannot be the general solution. We now ask the question, "What is there about the functions (13) from which we could have foreseen this situation?" A clue is supplied by noting that there are constants α_1, α_2, α_3, not all zero, such that

$$\alpha_1(e^{2x} + 2e^x) + \alpha_2(5e^{2x} + 4e^x) + \alpha_3(e^x - e^{2x}) \equiv 0$$

i.e., identically zero; for example $\alpha_1 = 3$, $\alpha_2 = -1$, $\alpha_3 = -2$. Thus we are led to the idea that although we have three solutions they are in a way dependent. This has led mathematicians to the following

> DEFINITION. A set of functions $y_1(x), y_2(x), \ldots, y_n(x)$ denoted briefly by $y_1, y_2, \ldots, y_n$, is said to be *linearly dependent* in an interval if there exists a set of n constants, not all zero, such that in the interval
>
> $$\alpha_1 y_1 + \alpha_2 y_2 + \cdots + \alpha_n y_n \equiv 0$$
>
> otherwise the set is said to be *linearly independent*.

From the above ideas we feel, at least intuitively, that linearly independent solutions must play an important role in solving linear differential equations and this does in fact happen.

In solving linear differential equations up to now we have essentially *used* this concept of linear independence without actually stating it. For example, in dealing with the equation

$$(D^2 - 3D + 2)y = 0$$

we found the solutions e^x and e^{2x} and from this the general solution $y = c_1 e^x + c_2 e^{2x}$. Implicit in this is the assumption of the linear independence of these functions. To show this, let us assume that there are constants α_1 and α_2, not both zero, such that

$$\alpha_1 e^x + \alpha_2 e^{2x} \equiv 0$$

i.e., let us assume that the functions are linearly dependent. Then, on dividing both sides by e^x, we arrive at the result

$$\alpha_2 e^x \equiv -\alpha_1$$

which is clearly impossible unless both α_1 and α_2 are zero. Thus the functions are linearly independent.

We would like to have a condition for linear dependence or independence which does not involve the constants $\alpha_1, \ldots, \alpha_n$ required in the definition since this can become tedious. Let us first examine the case for two functions y_1 and y_2. By definition, if y_1 and y_2 are linearly dependent, then we can find constants α_1 and α_2, not both zero, such that

$$\alpha_1 y_1 + \alpha_2 y_2 \equiv 0 \tag{15}$$

By differentiating both sides of this identity,* we find

$$\alpha_1 y_1' + \alpha_2 y_2' \equiv 0 \tag{16}$$

Multiplying (15) by y_2', (16) by y_2 and subtracting we find

$$\alpha_1(y_1 y_2' - y_2 y_1') \equiv 0 \tag{17}$$

Similarly, multiplying (15) by y_1', (16) by y_1 and subtracting, we find

$$\alpha_2(y_1 y_2' - y_2 y_1') \equiv 0 \tag{18}$$

From (17) and (18) we see that if α_1 and α_2 are not both zero then

$$W(y_1, y_2) = y_1 y_2' - y_2 y_1' = \begin{vmatrix} y_1 & y_2 \\ y_1' & y_2' \end{vmatrix} \equiv 0 \tag{19}$$

We call the determinant $W(y_1, y_2)$ in (19) the *Wronskian* of y_1 and y_2.

Conversely, we can show that if the Wronskian is identically zero,† then the functions are linearly dependent. To show this we note that if the Wronskian is identically zero then we have

$$y_1 y_2' - y_2 y_1' = 0$$

Dividing by y_1^2 assumed to be different from zero, we can write the result as

$$d(y_2/y_1) = 0 \quad \text{or} \quad y_2/y_1 = k$$

on integrating. Thus $y_2 = ky_1$ and the functions are linearly dependent. We can summarize the above conclusions in the following

> THEOREM 1. The set of functions y_1 and y_2 is linearly dependent if and only if the Wronskian
>
> $$W(y_1, y_2) = \begin{vmatrix} y_1 & y_2 \\ y_1' & y_2' \end{vmatrix} \equiv 0$$

* We assume, unless otherwise stated, that the derivatives exist at each point in the interval.

† Some writers use the terminology "vanishing identically" instead of "identically zero." We use the latter terminology so as not to risk giving the Wronskian any undeserved "ghostly qualities."

The result in this theorem can be generalized to the case of n functions $y_1, y_2, \ldots, y_n$ where the corresponding Wronskian is

$$W(y_1, y_2, \ldots, y_n) = \begin{vmatrix} y_1 & y_2 & \cdots & y_n \\ y_1' & y_2' & \cdots & y_n' \\ \cdot & \cdot & & \cdot \\ \cdot & \cdot & & \cdot \\ \cdot & \cdot & & \cdot \\ y_1^{(n-1)} & y_2^{(n-1)} & \cdots & y_n^{(n-1)} \end{vmatrix}$$

Example 1. The functions $2 \sin 3x$ and $-5 \sin 3x$ have the Wronskian

$$\begin{vmatrix} 3 \sin 2x & -4 \sin 2x \\ 6 \cos 2x & -8 \cos 2x \end{vmatrix} = (3 \sin 2x)(-8 \cos 2x) - (-4 \sin 2x)(6 \cos 2x) = 0$$

identically and the functions are linearly dependent in any interval.

Example 2. The functions $e^{2x} + 2e^x$, $5e^{2x} + 4e^x$, $e^x - e^{2x}$, which we have already considered, have Wronskian

$$\begin{vmatrix} e^{2x} + 2e^x & 5e^{2x} + 4e^x & e^x - e^{2x} \\ 2e^{2x} + 2e^x & 10e^{2x} + 4e^x & e^x - 2e^{2x} \\ 4e^{2x} + 2e^x & 20e^{2x} + 4e^x & e^x - 4e^{2x} \end{vmatrix} = 0$$

identically* and the functions are linearly dependent.

We can also prove a corresponding theorem for linear independence.

THEOREM 2. The functions y_1 and y_2 are linearly independent in an interval if and only if the Wronskian is not identically zero in the interval. An analogous theorem holds for $y_1, y_2, \ldots, y_n$.

Example 1. The functions e^x and e^{2x} have the Wronskian

$$W = \begin{vmatrix} e^x & e^{2x} \\ e^x & 2e^{2x} \end{vmatrix} = (e^x)(2e^{2x}) - (e^{2x})(e^x) = e^{3x}$$

Since e^{3x} is not zero in any interval, the functions are linearly independent in any interval.

* The student is reminded that

$$\begin{vmatrix} a_1 & a_2 & a_3 \\ b_1 & b_2 & b_3 \\ c_1 & c_2 & c_3 \end{vmatrix} = a_1 b_2 c_3 + a_2 b_3 c_1 + a_3 b_1 c_2 - (a_3 b_2 c_1 + a_2 b_1 c_3 + a_1 b_3 c_2)$$

Example 2. The functions x^2 and x^3 have the Wronskian

$$W = \begin{vmatrix} x^2 & x^3 \\ 2x & 3x^2 \end{vmatrix} = (x^2)(3x^2) - (x^3)(2x) = x^4$$

In spite of the fact that the Wronskian is zero at $x = 0$, the functions are linearly independent in any interval regardless of whether $x = 0$ is included in the interval or not.

The connection between linear differential equations and their linearly independent solutions is provided in the following fundamental

THEOREM 3. *If $y_1, y_2, \ldots, y_n$ are n linearly independent solutions of the nth order linear differential equation*

$$\phi(D)y = (a_0 D^n + a_1 D^{n-1} + \cdots + a_n)y = 0$$

where $a_0, a_1, \ldots, a_n$ may be constants or continuous functions of x, then all solutions have the form

$$y = c_1 y_1 + c_2 y_2 + \cdots + c_n y_n$$

which is the general solution.

There are very interesting and important relationships between the Wronskian for a linear differential equation and the coefficients in the equation. Let us consider for example the second-order equation,

$$a_0(x)y'' + a_1(x)y' + a_2(x)y = 0 \tag{20}$$

If we denote the coefficients briefly by a_0, a_1, a_2 and two solutions by y_1 and y_2, then, since these solutions satisfy the equation, we have

$$a_0 y_1'' + a_1 y_1' + a_2 y_1 = 0 \qquad a_0 y_2'' + a_1 y_2' + a_2 y_2 = 0 \tag{21}$$

Multiplying the first equation of (21) by y_2, the second by y_1, and subtracting we find

$$a_0(y_1 y_2'' - y_2 y_1'') + a_1(y_1 y_2' - y_2 y_1') = 0 \tag{22}$$

Since the Wronskian is given by $W = y_1 y_2' - y_2 y_1'$ and since

$$\frac{dW}{dx} = \frac{d}{dx}(y_1 y_2' - y_2 y_1') = y_1 y_2'' - y_2 y_1''$$

(22) becomes $\qquad\qquad a_0 \dfrac{dW}{dx} + a_1 W = 0$

Solving, we obtain an important relation known as *Abel's identity*, given by

$$W = ce^{-\int (a_1/a_0)\, dx} \tag{23}$$

Further results on Wronskians and linear independence are in the Exercises.

A EXERCISES

1. Determine which of the following sets of functions are linearly dependent and which are linearly independent. In each case use both the direct definition and the theorems involving the Wronskian.

(a) e^{-4x}, e^{4x}.

(b) $2x^3$, $-3x^3$.

(c) 1, $\cos x$.

(d) $x + 2$, $2x - 3$.

(e) x^2, $x^2 + 1$, $x^2 - 1$.

(f) $(x + 1)(x - 2)$, $(2x - 1)(x + 3)$, $(x + 2)(x - 1)$.

(g) $\sin^2 x$, $\cos^2 x$, 2.

(h) $\sin x + \cos x$, $3 \sin x - 2 \cos x$, $4 \cos x$.

2. (a) Show that two linearly independent solutions of the equation $(D^2 - 6D + 9)y = 0$ are given by e^{3x} and xe^{3x}. (b) How can you write the general solution of the equation in (a)? Justify your answer.

3. Write the general solutions of each of the following equations and justify your results.

(a) $(D^2 + 2D - 3)y = 0$.

(b) $(D^2 - 2D + 5)y = 0$.

(c) $(D^3 - 3D^2)y = 0$.

(d) $(D^4 - 8D^2 + 16)y = 0$.

B EXERCISES

1. (a) Prove that any three polynomials of the first degree must be linearly dependent. (b) What is the greatest number of polynomials of the second degree which will be linearly independent? Could some of these be of lower degree? Explain. (c) Can you generalize the results in (a) and (b)?

2. Prove that if zero is added to any linearly independent set of functions, the resulting set is linearly dependent.

3. Let $P_n(x)$ be polynomials of degree n where $n = 1, 2, 3, \ldots$. Prove that any finite set of these polynomials is linearly independent.

4. Investigate the linear dependence of the set of functions

$$\text{arc tan } x, \quad \text{arc tan } (2x), \quad \text{arc tan } \left(\frac{3x}{1 - 2x^2} \right)$$

5. (a) Prove without using Wronskians that the functions x^2 and x^3 are linearly independent in the interval $1 \leq x \leq 2$, and also in the interval $-1 \leq x \leq 1$.
(b) Find the Wronskian of x^2 and x^3. In view of the fact that this Wronskian is zero at some point in the interval $-1 \leq x \leq 1$, does this conflict with the result in (a)? Explain.

6. Show that the functions x^2 and $x |x|$ are either linear dependent or linear independent according as to which interval is considered.

7. Find n linearly independent solutions of the equation $D^n y = 0$ and write the general solution. Justify your results.

C EXERCISES

1. Suppose that in the differential equation (20), $a_0(x)$, $a_1(x)$, and $a_2(x)$ are continuous in an interval and $a_0(x) \neq 0$ at any point of the interval. (a) Prove that if the Wronskian corresponding to two solutions y_1 and y_2 is zero at some point of the interval then it is identically zero in the interval and the solutions y_1 and y_2 are linearly dependent. (b) Show that the functions x^2 and x^3 of B Exercise 5 are linearly independent solutions of the equation

$$x^2y'' - 4xy' + 6y = 0$$

Is there any conflict with (a)? Explain.

2. Write Abel's identity for the equations (a) $y'' - 3y' + 2y = 0$; (b) $x^2y'' + xy' + (x^2 - n^2)y = 0$; (c) $(1 - x^2)y'' - 2xy' + 2y = 0$.

3. Given one solution of a linear second-order differential equation, how could you get a linearly independent solution from Abel's identity? How could you then find the general solution? Illustrate by finding the general solution of the equations   (a) $(D^2 - 2D + 1)y = 0$,   and   (b) $(1 - x^2)y'' - 2xy' + 2y = 0$. (*Hint:* In (b) note that x is a solution.)

4. (a) Show that the function $3x^2 - 1$ satisfies the differential equation $(1 - x^2)y'' - 2xy' + 6y = 0$ and has a minimum at $x = 0$. (b) Show that any linearly independent solution of the equation in (a) cannot have a minimum or maximum at $x = 0$.

5. Generalize the result of Exercise 4.

6. Obtain a generalization of *Abel's identity* for third- and higher-order linear differential equations.

7. Show that if y_1 and y_2 are linearly independent solutions of the equation $a_0y'' + a_1y' + a_2y = 0$ where a_0, a_1, and a_2 are polynomials having no common factor other than a constant then the Wronskian is zero at only those points of the interval where $a_0 = 0$, and conversely.

8. Generalize the result of Exercise 7.

9. Prove Theorem 2, page 156.

IV. How Do We Obtain a Particular Solution?

To find the general solution of $\phi(D)y = F(x)$ we must find a particular solution of this equation and add it to the general solution of the complementary or reduced equation $\phi(D)y = 0$. In the last section we discovered how to obtain the general solution of $\phi(D)y = 0$. In this section we shall discover how to obtain particular solutions of $\phi(D)y = F(x)$.

There are many methods whereby particular solutions can be obtained. A method of general use in physics and engineering is the method of undetermined coefficients. This method is simple to understand, where it applies, but unfortunately it cannot be used in certain cases. However, such cases are rare in practice, and when they do arise, other methods must be used. Because of its simplicity and widespread use, we discuss this method first.

1. Method of undetermined coefficients. The method of undetermined coefficients is applicable for the differential equation $\phi(D)y = F(x)$, where $F(x)$ contains a polynomial, terms of the form $\sin px$, $\cos px$, e^{px} where p is constant, or combinations of sums and products of these. To gain some insight, consider the

Problem for Discussion. Solve

$$y'' + 4y = 4e^{2x}$$

We are looking for a function whose second derivative added to four times the function yields $4e^{2x}$. Since the various derivatives of e^{2x} involve e^{2x}, we are led to consider $y = ae^{2x}$ where a is an undetermined constant, as a possible solution. Substituting in the given equation we have

$$4ae^{2x} + 4ae^{2x} = 4e^{2x}, \qquad 8ae^{2x} = 4e^{2x}, \qquad a = \tfrac{1}{2}$$

Thus, a particular solution is $y_p = \tfrac{1}{2}e^{2x}$. By methods of the last section, the general solution of $y'' + 4y = 0$ is

$$y = y_c = c_1 \cos 2x + c_2 \sin 2x$$

The general solution of the given equation is, therefore,

$$y = y_c + y_p = c_1 \cos 2x + c_2 \sin 2x + \tfrac{1}{2}e^{2x}$$

ILLUSTRATIVE EXAMPLE 1

Solve

$$(D^2 + 4D + 4)y = 6 \sin 3x$$

Solution. The complementary solution is

$$y_c = (c_1 + c_2 x)e^{-2x}$$

To find a particular solution we ask ourselves: What functions differentiated once or twice yield $\sin 3x$ or constant multiples thereof? The answer is that terms like $\sin 3x$ or $\cos 3x$ will do. We therefore attempt as particular solution

$$y = a \sin 3x + b \cos 3x$$

where a and b are our undetermined coefficients. Substituting in the given equation, we find after simplifying

$$(D^2 + 4D + 4)y = (-5a - 12b) \sin 3x + (12a - 5b) \cos 3x = 6 \sin 3x$$

This will be an identity if and only if

$$-5a - 12b = 6, \qquad 12a - 5b = 0$$

Solving, $a = -\tfrac{30}{169}, b = -\tfrac{72}{169}.$

The particular solution is, therefore,

$$-\tfrac{30}{169}\sin 3x - \tfrac{72}{169}\cos 3x$$

Hence, the general solution is

$$y = (c_1 + c_2 x)e^{-2x} - \tfrac{30}{169}\sin 3x - \tfrac{72}{169}\cos 3x$$

ILLUSTRATIVE EXAMPLE 2

Solve

$$(D^2 + 4D + 9)y = x^2 + 3x$$

Solution. The complementary solution is

$$y_c = e^{-2x}(c_1 \cos \sqrt{5}\, x + c_2 \sin \sqrt{5}\, x)$$

To find a particular solution we ask ourselves: What function when differentiated will yield a polynomial? Clearly polynomials when differentiated yield polynomials. Let us therefore assume as particular solution $y = y_p = ax^3 + bx^2 + cx + d$, i.e., a polynomial of the third degree. Substituting this assumed solution in the given equation and simplifying, we find

$$9ax^3 + (12a + 9b)x^2 + (6a + 8b + 9c)x + 2b + 4c + 9d = x^2 + 3x$$

Hence,

$$9a = 0, \qquad 12a + 9b = 1, \qquad 6a + 8b + 9c = 3, \qquad 2b + 4c + 9d = 0$$

Solving, we have $a = 0$, $b = \tfrac{1}{9}$, $c = \tfrac{19}{81}$, $d = -\tfrac{94}{729}$. Hence,

$$y_p = \tfrac{1}{9}x^2 + \tfrac{19}{81}x - \tfrac{94}{729}$$

The general solution is, thus,

$$y = e^{-2x}(c_1 \cos \sqrt{5}\, x + c_2 \sin \sqrt{5}\, x) + \frac{x^2}{9} + \frac{19x}{81} - \frac{94}{729}$$

The fact that $a = 0$ means that we did not have to use a third-degree polynomial in our assumed solution; a second-degree polynomial would have done as well. In general, when a polynomial of nth degree occurs on the right of $\phi(D)y = F(x)$ we assume as particular solution a polynomial of nth degree.*

ILLUSTRATIVE EXAMPLE 3

Solve

$$(D^2 + 2D + 1)y = 2 \cos 2x + 3x + 2 + 3e^x$$

The complementary solution is

$$y_c = (c_1 + c_2 x)e^{-x}$$

We have to decide what to assume as particular solution.
For the term $2 \cos 2x$, we assume

$$a \sin 2x + b \cos 2x$$

---

* In the next section we shall see that there are some exceptions to this rule. The reasoning in those cases are, however, based on assumptions used here.

For the terms $3x + 2$ (first-degree polynomial) assume $cx + d$.
For the term $3e^x$, assume fe^x.
Hence, assume as particular solution

$$y_p = a \sin 2x + b \cos 2x + cx + d + fe^x$$

Substituting this particular solution in the given differential equation and simplifying, we have

$$(-3a - 4b) \sin 2x + (4a - 3b) \cos 2x + cx + d + 2c + 4fe^x$$
$$= 2 \cos 2x + 3x + 2 + 3e^x$$

It follows that

$$-3a - 4b = 0, \qquad 4a - 3b = 2, \qquad c = 3, \qquad 2c + d = 2, \qquad 4f = 3$$

Solving these, we find

$$a = \tfrac{8}{25}, \qquad b = -\tfrac{6}{25}, \qquad c = 3, \qquad d = -4, \qquad f = \tfrac{3}{4}$$

Thus, the particular solution is

$$y_p = \tfrac{8}{25} \sin 2x - \tfrac{6}{25} \cos 2x + 3x - 4 + \tfrac{3}{4}e^x$$

and the general solution of the given equation is

$$y = (c_1 + c_2 x)e^{-x} + \tfrac{8}{25} \sin 2x - \tfrac{6}{25} \cos 2x + 3x - 4 + \tfrac{3}{4}e^x$$

A EXERCISES

1. Find the general solution of each of the following:

(a) $y'' + y = 2e^{3x}$.
(b) $(D^2 + 2D + 1)y = 4 \sin 2x$.
(c) $(D^2 - 4)y = 8x^2$.
(d) $(D^2 + 4D + 5)y = e^{-x} + 15x$.
(e) $4I''(t) + I(t) = t^2 + 2 \cos 3t$.
(f) $(D^3 + 4D)y = e^x + \sin x$.

2. Find solutions satisfying the given conditions:

(a) $y'' + 16y = 5 \sin x$; $y(0) = y'(0) = 0$.
(b) $s''(t) - 3s'(t) + 2s(t) = 8t^2 + 12e^{-t}$; $s(0) = 0, s'(0) = 2$.

B EXERCISES

1. Solve $y'' + y = 6 \cos^2 x$, given that $y(0) = 0, y(\pi/2) = 0$.

2. Solve the differential equation arising in an electric circuit problem:

$$\left(LD^2 + RD + \frac{1}{C} \right) Q = E_0 \sin \omega t$$

where $D \equiv d/dt$; L, R, C, E_0, and ω are given constants and $Q(0) = Q'(0) = 0$.

C EXERCISES

1. Find the general solution of $y'' - 3y' + 2y = 4\sin^3 3x$.

2. Solve $y'' + y = F(x)$, where

$$F(x) = \begin{cases} x & 0 \leq x \leq \pi \\ 0 & x > \pi \end{cases}$$

assuming that $y(0) = y'(0) = 0$ and that y and y' are continuous at $x = \pi$.

2. Exceptions in the method of undetermined coefficients. Let us consider the following

Problem for Discussion. Solve

$$(D^2 + 3D + 2)y = 4e^{-2x}$$

The complementary solution is

$$y_c = c_1 e^{-2x} + c_2 e^{-x}$$

From the fact that $4e^{-2x}$ is on the right-hand side of the given equation, we would be led by the usual (and reasonable) assumption to the particular solution $y = ae^{-2x}$. Substituting, we find

$$4ae^{-2x} - 6ae^{-2x} + 2ae^{-2x} = 4e^{-2x}, \quad \text{or} \quad 0 = 4e^{-2x},$$

an *impossible* situation! If we think a little about what we have done, we should be able to see that this "catastrophe" could have been foreseen. We assumed the solution ae^{-2x}, which is no different essentially from the term $c_1 e^{-2x}$ of the complementary solution. It is therefore expected that ae^{-2x} would satisfy $(D^2 + 3D + 2)y = 0$.

A little experimentation shows that if we assume as particular solution axe^{-2x} instead of ae^{-2x} we get results. For if $y = axe^{-2x}$,

$$(D^2 + 3D + 2)(axe^{-2x}) = -ae^{-2x} = 4e^{-2x}, \quad \text{i.e.,} \quad a = -4$$

Hence, a particular solution is $-4xe^{-2x}$ and the general solution is

$$y = c_1 e^{-2x} + c_2 e^{-x} - 4xe^{-2x}$$

Before jumping to any conclusions concerning rules, let us look at a few more examples.

ILLUSTRATIVE EXAMPLE 1

Solve

$$(D^2 + 4)y = 6\sin 2x + 3x^2$$

Solution. The complementary solution is

$$c_1 \sin 2x + c_2 \cos 2x$$

We would normally assume as particular solution $a \sin 2x + b \cos 2x$ corresponding to the term $6 \sin 2x$, and $cx^2 + dx + f$ corresponding to the term $3x^2$. We will not, however, fall into the same trap as before because we see that the assumed particular solution has both terms contained in the complementary solution. We are thus inclined, by virtue of previous experience, to write as our assumed particular solution $x(a \sin 2x + b \cos 2x)$, i.e., the result assumed previously, multiplied by x. Since $cx^2 + dx + f$ has no term appearing in the complementary solution, we use it as it is. Our assumed particular solution is therefore

$$y_p = x(a \sin 2x + b \cos 2x) + cx^2 + dx + f$$

Substitution into the differential equation yields

$$4a \cos 2x - 4b \sin 2x + 4cx^2 + 4\,dx + (4f + 2c) = 6 \sin 2x + 3x^2$$

Thus,

$$4a = 0, \qquad -4b = 6, \qquad 4c = 3, \qquad 4d = 0, \qquad 4f + 2c = 0,$$

and, hence,

$$a = 0, \qquad b = -\tfrac{3}{2}, \qquad c = \tfrac{3}{4}, \qquad d = 0, \qquad f = -\tfrac{3}{8}$$

The particular solution is, therefore,

$$y_p = -\tfrac{3}{2}x \cos 2x + \tfrac{3}{4}x^2 - \tfrac{3}{8}$$

and so the general solution is

$$y = c_1 \sin 2x + c_2 \cos 2x - \tfrac{3}{2}x \cos 2x + \tfrac{3}{4}x^2 - \tfrac{3}{8}$$

ILLUSTRATIVE EXAMPLE 2

Solve

$$(D^3 - 3D^2 + 3D - 1)y = 2e^x \tag{1}$$

Solution. From the auxiliary equation $m^3 - 3m^2 + 3m - 1 = (m - 1)^3 = 0$ we have $m = 1, 1, 1$. The complementary solution is, thus,

$$(c_1 + c_2 x + c_3 x^2)e^x$$

Because of the term $2e^x$ on the right of (1) we would normally take as particular solution ae^x. This, however, is present in the complementary solution. Hence we are led from experience to assume as particular solution axe^x. Since this is also present, we are led to $ax^2 e^x$. However, this too is present and we are led to $ax^3 e^x$. At last, this is not in the complementary solution. Substituting $ax^3 e^x$ in the given equation, we have

$$(D^3 - 3D^2 + 3D - 1)y = 6ae^x = 2e^x$$

Hence, $6a = 2$, $a = \tfrac{1}{3}$, and a particular solution is $\tfrac{1}{3}x^3 e^x$. The general solution is, thus,

$$y = (c_1 + c_2 x + c_3 x^2)e^x + \tfrac{1}{3}x^3 e^x$$

From these two examples, a general rule is apparent. This rule may be proved in the general case but we omit the proof here.

To solve a linear differential equation with constant coefficients:

1. Write the complementary solution y_c.
2. Assume a particular solution corresponding to the terms on the right-hand side of the equation:
   (a) For a polynomial of degree n, assume a polynomial of degree n.
   (b) For terms $\sin px$, $\cos px$, or sums and differences of such terms, assume $a \sin px + b \cos px$.
   (c) For terms like e^{px} assume ae^{px}.
3. If any of the assumed terms in 2(a), (b), or (c) occur in the complementary solution, we must multiply these assumed terms by a power of x which is sufficiently high (but not higher) so that none of these assumed terms will occur in the complementary solution.
4. Write the assumed form for the particular solution and evaluate the coefficients, thus obtaining y_p.
5. Add y_p to y_c to obtain the required general solution.

A EXERCISES

1. Find the general solution of each of the following:

   (a) $(D^2 + 2D - 3)y = 2e^x$. (b) $(D^2 + 1)y = x^2 + \sin x$.
   (c) $(D^2 + D)y = x^2 + 3x + e^{3x}$. (d) $(D^2 - 2D + 1)y = e^x$.
   (e) $y'' + 4y = 8 \cos 2x - 4x$. (f) $(D^3 + D)y = x + \sin x + \cos x$.

2. Find solutions satisfying the given conditions:

   (a) $\dfrac{d^2I}{dt^2} + 9I = 12 \cos 3t$; $I(0) = 4$, $I'(0) = 0$.

   (b) $\dfrac{d^2s}{dt^2} + \dfrac{ds}{dt} = t + e^{-t}$; $s = 0$, $\dfrac{ds}{dt} = 0$ at $t = 0$.

B EXERCISES

1. Find the general solution of $(D^4 - 1)y = \cosh x$.

2. Solve: $(D^2 + 1)y = x \sin x$.

C EXERCISES

1. (a) Solve $(D^2 + \omega^2)y = A \cos \lambda x$; ω, $\lambda > 0$, $\omega \neq \lambda$, where A, ω, λ are constants, subject to $y(0) = \alpha$, $y'(0) = \beta$. (b) What is the limit of the solution in (a) as $\lambda \to \omega$? (c) Is the limiting solution of (b) a solution of the given differential equation when $\lambda = \omega$?

2. Solve $y'' + 4y = \sin^4 x$.

3. How can the results of Exercise 4 of the C exercises, page 149, be used in solving the problems of this section. Give illustrations.

3. Cases where more complicated functions appear on the right-hand side.

In case the right-hand side contains products of terms like e^{px}, $\sin px$, $\cos px$, and polynomials, the method of undetermined coefficients can still be used, although the method may become unwieldy and lose its appeal. In such cases other methods to be discussed in sections which follow may yield results easier and faster. For the sake of completeness we shall now demonstrate a general procedure for determining what to use as assumed particular solution. To motivate this procedure consider the

Problem for Discussion. Solve

$$(D^2 + D + 1)y = x^3 e^x$$

The complementary solution is

$$e^{-x/2}\left(c_1 \cos \frac{\sqrt{3}}{2} x + c_2 \sin \frac{\sqrt{3}}{2} x\right)$$

To see what a particular solution might be we ask: What function when differentiated might yield $x^3 e^x$? If we assume the particular solution $ax^3 e^x$, as we very well might on first thought, we obtain upon substitution in the given differential equation the result

$$6axe^x + 9ax^2 e^x + 3ax^3 e^x = x^3 e^x \tag{2}$$

and it is clear that we cannot determine a, and so $ax^3 e^x$ cannot be a solution. To get rid of the terms of (2) involving $x^2 e^x$, xe^x, and e^x, we might be led to try as particular solution $ax^3 e^x + bx^2 e^x + cxe^x + de^x$. Actually when this is substituted in the given equation, we find

$$(D^2 + D + 1)y = 3ax^3 e^x + (9a + 3b)x^2 e^x + (6a + 6b + 3c)xe^x$$
$$+ (2b + 3c + 3d)e^x = x^3 e^x$$

so that

$$3a = 1, \quad 9a + 3b = 0, \quad 6a + 6b + 3c = 0, \quad 2b + 3c + 3d = 0$$

and

$$a = \tfrac{1}{3}, \quad b = -1, \quad c = \tfrac{4}{3}, \quad d = -\tfrac{2}{3}$$

Hence, the particular solution is

$$y_p = \tfrac{1}{3}x^3 e^x - x^2 e^x + \tfrac{4}{3}xe^x - \tfrac{2}{3}e^x$$

and the general solution is

$$y = e^{-x/2}\left(c_1 \cos \frac{\sqrt{3}}{2} x + c_2 \sin \frac{\sqrt{3}}{2} x\right) + \frac{1}{3}x^3 e^x - x^2 e^x + \frac{4}{3}xe^x - \frac{2e^x}{3}$$

On the basis of observations of examples such as the one shown, mathematicians have been able to formulate and prove a general rule for arriving at the assumed particular solution. The method consists of differentiating the right-hand side of the equation indefinitely and keeping track of all essentially different terms which arise. If there are a finite number of these terms the method of undetermined coefficients is applicable and the assumed particular solution can be formed by taking each of these terms, multiplying it by an undetermined constant and then adding the results. We illustrate this in the following

ILLUSTRATIVE EXAMPLE

Solve

$$(D^2 + 1)y = x^2 \cos 5x$$

Solution. The complementary solution is $y_c = c_1 \cos x + c_2 \sin x$. To find a particular solution consider the right-hand side $x^2 \cos 5x$. A single differentiation would give rise to terms (disregarding numerical coefficients) like

$$x^2 \sin 5x, \qquad x \cos 5x$$

Differentiation of each of these would produce terms like

$$x^2 \cos 5x, \qquad x \sin 5x, \qquad \cos 5x$$

Continuing in this manner, we find that no terms other than those in the following group arise:

$$x^2 \cos 5x, \qquad x^2 \sin 5x, \qquad x \cos 5x, \qquad x \sin 5x, \qquad \cos 5x, \qquad \sin 5x$$

Thus, we assume as particular solution,

$$y_p = ax^2 \cos 5x + bx^2 \sin 5x + cx \cos 5x + dx \sin 5x + f \cos 5x + g \sin 5x$$

If the right-hand side were $\ln x$, for example, successive differentiations would yield the infinite set of functions $1/x, 1/x^2, \ldots$, and in this case the method is inapplicable. For such cases, other methods to be described in the following two articles may be employed.

A EXERCISES

1. For each of the following, write the complementary solution and the expression in terms of undetermined coefficients which you would use in attempting to find a particular solution. You need not evaluate these coefficients.

(a) $(D^2 + 1)y = xe^{-x} + 3 \sin x$.
(b) $(D^2 - 2D - 3)y = x \sin 2x + x^3 e^{3x}$.
(c) $(D^4 + D^2)y = 3x^2 - 4e^x$.   (d) $(D^2 - 2D + 1)y = x^2 e^x$.
(e) $(D^2 + 1)y = e^{-x} \cos x + 2x$.
(f) $(D^2 - 4D + 3)y = 3e^x + 2e^{-x} + x^3 e^{-x}$.

2. Find the general solution of each of the following:

(a) $(D^2 - 1)y = xe^x$.

(b) $(D^2 + 4)y = x^2 + 3x \cos 2x$.

(c) $(D^2 + 2D + 1)y = \sin 3x + xe^{-x}$.

(d) $Q''(t) + Q(t) = t \sin t + \cos t$.

B EXERCISES

1. Find the general solution of $(D^3 - 5D^2 - 2D + 24)y = x^2 e^{3x}$.

2. Solve $(D^2 + \omega^2)y = t(\sin \omega t + \cos \omega t)$; $D \equiv d/dt$ subject to $y(0) = y'(0) = 0$.

3. Solve $y'' - 3y' + 2y = e^{-x}(1 + \cos 2x)$.

C EXERCISES

1. Solve $y'' + 4y = \cos x \cos 2x \cos 3x$.

2. Solve $y''' + 4y'' - 6y' - 12y = (\sinh x)^4$.

3. Solve $(D^2 + 1)y = x^2 \cos 5x$ by using the results of Exercise 4 of the C exercises, p. 149.

4. The method of variation of parameters. It has been mentioned that the method of undetermined coefficients is effective only when the right-hand side of the equation is of special type. It is natural for us, being true scientists, to worry about what can be done in case the method of undetermined coefficients is inapplicable. Fortunately we have been saved from too much worry by the efforts of a famous mathematician named Lagrange, who discovered a very ingenious and powerful method which applies in cases where the method of undetermined coefficients does not work as well as to where it does. In fact by knowing this method alone one can do very well without the method of undetermined coefficients. The only disadvantage which Lagrange's method appears to have is that to use it one might have to know how to integrate, and this is perhaps the strongest reason for avoiding it.

To show how the method of Lagrange works, we shall try to obtain the general solution of the innocent-looking differential equation

$$y'' + y = \tan x \tag{3}$$

The only disturbing thing about this is the presence of the term $\tan x$. The complementary solution is

$$A \cos x + B \sin x \tag{4}$$

where A and B are arbitrary constants.

The ingenuity of Lagrange lay in his assumption, which at first sight (like many nonobvious assumptions) looks ridiculous. He said:

> Assume that A and B in (4) are not constants but instead are functions of x. The question is: What functions must they be so that $A(x) \cos x + B(x) \sin x$ will be a solution of (3)?

Since the method assumes that the quantities A and B vary, the method is generally called the *method of variation of parameters* or *variation of constants*. It is clear that since two functions $A(x)$ and $B(x)$ are to be determined, we expect that two conditions ought to be imposed. One of these arises from the fact that the assumed solution satisfies the differential equation. We are therefore at liberty to impose *one other condition*. With this in mind let us proceed. By differentiation of

$$y = A(x) \cos x + B(x) \sin x \qquad (5)$$

we have

$$y' = -A(x) \sin x + B(x) \cos x + A'(x) \cos x + B'(x) \sin x \qquad (6)$$

Upon realizing that a further differentiation would introduce a few more terms, we take advantage of our liberty to choose one condition on $A(x)$ and $B(x)$. We choose a condition which simplifies (6), i.e.,

$$A'(x) \cos x + B'(x) \sin x = 0 \qquad (7)$$

identically. Thus, (6) becomes

$$y' = -A(x) \sin x + B(x) \cos x$$

One further differentiation yields

$$y'' = -A(x) \cos x - B(x) \sin x - A'(x) \sin x + B'(x) \cos x \qquad (8$$

Substituting (5) and (8) in the given differential equation, we find

$$-A'(x) \sin x + B'(x) \cos x = \tan x \qquad (9)$$

From the two equations (7) and (9), it is a simple exercise to obtain

$$A'(x) = -\frac{\sin^2 x}{\cos x}, \qquad B'(x) = \sin x$$

Hence, by integration,

$$A(x) = \int \frac{\cos^2 x - 1}{\cos x} dx$$

$$= \int (\cos x - \sec x)dx = \sin x - \ln (\sec x + \tan x) + c_1$$

$$B(x) = -\cos x + c_2$$

It follows that the required solution (5) is

$$y = A(x) \cos x + B(x) \sin x$$

$$= c_1 \cos x + c_2 \sin x - \cos x \ln (\sec x + \tan x)$$

BY PLUGGING $A(x)$
$A(x)$ & $B(x)$ INTO THE
ORIGINAL EQ,

This may be verified by substitution as the general solution. It is not difficult to show that if $y = Au_1(x) + Bu_2(x)$ is the complementary solution of the equation $y'' + Py' + Qy = F(x)$, where P and Q may depend on x, the two principal equations (7) and (9) are

$$A'u_1(x) + B'u_2(x) = 0, \qquad A'u_1'(x) + B'u_2'(x) = F(x)$$

from which A and B may be obtained.

Lagrange's method may be extended to higher-order linear equations. Such extension is considered in the exercises.

A EXERCISES

Solve each of the following by variation of parameters:

1. $y'' + y = \cot x.$

2. $y'' + y = \sec x.$

3. $y'' + 4y = \csc 2x.$

4. $y'' - y = e^x.$

5. $y'' + 3y' + 2y = 3e^{-2x} + x.$

6. $y'' + y' - 2y = \ln x.$

7. $2y'' + 3y' + y = e^{-3x}.$

8. $(D^2 - 1)y = x^2 e^x.$

B EXERCISES

1. Use the method of variation of parameters to solve $y' + P(x)y = Q(x)$.

2. Show that the solution of $y'' + a^2y = F(x)$ (a = constant) subject to the conditions $y(0) = y'(0) = 0$ is

$$y = \frac{1}{a} \int_0^x F(u) \sin a(x - u)du$$

3. Solve $y''' - 2y'' - y' + 2y = e^x$ by variation of parameters. [*Hint:* In the complementary solution $Au_1(x) + Bu_2(x) + Cu_3(x)$ impose two conditions on A, B, C considered as functions of x.]

4. Show that the general solution of $x^2y'' - 2xy' + 2y = 0$ is $y = Ax^2 + Bx$. Hence, find the general solution of $x^2y'' - 2xy' + 2y = xe^{-x}$.

C EXERCISES

1. If the complementary solution of $y'' + P(x)y' + Q(x)y = R(x)$ is $Au_1(x) + Bu_2(x)$, show that its general solution is

$$y = c_1u_1(x) + c_2u_2(x) + u_2(x)\int \frac{R(x)u_1(x)dx}{W(u_1, u_2)} - u_1(x)\int \frac{R(x)u_2(x)dx}{W(u_1, u_2)}$$

where

$$W(u_1,u_2) = \begin{vmatrix} u_1(x) & u_2(x) \\ u_1'(x) & u_2'(x) \end{vmatrix} = u_1(x)u_2'(x) - u_2(x)u_1'(x)$$

is the *Wronskian* if $u_1(x)$ and $u_2(x)$ and is not identically zero. Discuss the case where $W \equiv 0$.

2. Use *Abel's identity* and Exercise 1 to show that the general solution of $y'' + P(x)y' + Q(x)y = R(x)$ is

$$y = c_1 u_1(x) + c_2 u_2(x) + \frac{u_2(x)}{c} \int R(x)u_1(x)e^{\int P(x)dx} \, dx$$

$$- \frac{u_1(x)}{c} \int R(x)u_2(x)e^{\int P(x)dx} \, dx$$

3. Apply the results of Exercises 1 and 2 to Exercise 4 of the B exercises.

5. Short-cut methods involving operators. For most practical purposes the method of undetermined coefficients supplemented by the method of variation of parameters in cases where the former is inapplicable are enough to solve any linear equation with constant coefficients. In view of this, the so-called *operator* or *operational methods* to be described in this section may appear superfluous and in some sense they are. However, before the student turns quickly to the next section, several reasons for including them should be pointed out. First, such methods often supply solutions to problems in a shorter, less tedious manner than other methods. Second, they illustrate the power of "symbolic methods" in general. Third, they serve as a fore-runner of Laplace transform methods to be discussed in Chapter 7,* although they are of interest in themselves. With these comments we now present a brief discussion of operator methods.

Consider the differential equation

$$\phi(D)y = F(x) \tag{10}$$

where $\phi(D)$ is the linear polynomial operator in $D \equiv d/dx$, i.e.,

$$\phi(D) \equiv a_0 D^n + a_1 D^{n-1} + \cdots + a_{n-1} D + a_n$$

where we shall here take $a_0, a_1, \ldots, a_n$ as given constants. If we "solve" formally for y in (10), treating the equation algebraically,

$$y = \frac{1}{\phi(D)} F(x) \tag{11}$$

Here $1/\phi(D)$ represents an operation to be performed on $F(x)$. A question

---

* Historically, the electrical engineer *Heaviside* used such operational methods formally with great success. Laplace transform methods were developed to a large extent in an effort to place his methods on a sound mathematical basis.

which needs answering is: What is the nature of the operation? To gain insight, consider the simple equation $Dy = x$. Here we have symbolically

$$y = \frac{1}{D} x$$

What shall we mean by this? A clue appears if we solve the equation $Dy = x$. We obtain, of course,

$$y = \int x \, dx = \frac{x^2}{2} + c$$

and hence it is natural to make the definition

$$\frac{1}{D} x \equiv \int x \, dx \tag{12}$$

the interpretation being that the operation of "multiplying" a function by $1/D$ corresponds to an integration of the function. It is natural to ask whether $1/D^2$ operating on a function corresponds to a double integration of the function, and in general whether $1/D^n$, n an integer, corresponds to an n-fold integration. The student can easily convince himself of this interpretation. Operators such as $1/D$, $1/D^2$, etc. are called inverse operators. Let us investigate other such operators. Consider

$$(D - p)y = f(x) \tag{13}$$

where p is a constant. Formally, we have

$$y = \frac{1}{D - p} f(x) \tag{14}$$

Since equation (13) can be solved exactly to give

$$y = e^{px} \int e^{-px} f(x) dx \tag{15}$$

it is natural to make the interpretation

$$\frac{1}{D - p} f(x) \equiv e^{px} \int e^{-px} f(x) dx \tag{16}$$

Note that this reduces to (12) if $p = 0$ and $f(x) = x$.

It is of interest to ask what one might mean by

$$(D - p_1)(D - p_2)y = f(x) \tag{17}$$

where p_1 and p_2 are constants. We know that

$$(D - p_2)y \equiv \frac{dy}{dx} - p_2 y$$

It thus seems plausible that

$$(D - p_1)(D - p_2)y \equiv \left(\frac{d}{dx} - p_1\right)\left(\frac{dy}{dx} - p_2 y\right)$$

$$\equiv \frac{d}{dx}\left(\frac{dy}{dx} - p_2 y\right) - p_1\left(\frac{dy}{dx} - p_2 y\right)$$

$$\equiv \frac{d^2 y}{dx^2} - (p_1 + p_2)\frac{dy}{dx} + p_1 p_2 y$$

$$\equiv [D^2 - (p_1 + p_2)D + p_1 p_2]y$$

Thus, the operator $(D - p_1)(D - p_2)$ is equivalent to $D^2 - (p_1 + p_2)D + p_1 p_2$. The converse may similarly be established. It follows that operators may be multiplied or factored like algebraic quantities. This is not, however, always possible if p_1 and p_2 are not constants. One may show that the operational factorization

$$a_0 D^n + a_1 D^{n-1} + \cdots + a_n \equiv a_0(D - p_1)(D - p_2)\cdots(D - p_n)$$

is always possible (and unique) when $a_0, \ldots, a_n$, and consequently $p_1, \ldots, p_n$ are constants. Furthermore the order of the factors is immaterial, i.e., the operators obey the commutative, associative, and distributive laws just as do algebraic quantities.* This important fact enables us to treat equation (17) in the same way that we treated the other equations; i.e., we may write (17) formally as

$$y = \frac{1}{(D - p_1)(D - p_2)}f(x)$$

By a double application of (16) we have

$$\frac{1}{(D - p_1)(D - p_2)}f(x) \equiv \frac{1}{D - p_1}\left[e^{p_2 x}\int e^{-p_2 x}f(x)dx\right]$$

$$\equiv e^{p_1 x}\int e^{-p_1 x}\left[e^{p_2 x}\int e^{-p_2 x}f(x)dx\right]dx$$

In a similar manner we may write

$$\frac{1}{(D - p_1)(D - p_2)\cdots(D - p_n)}f(x)$$

$$\equiv e^{p_1 x}\int e^{-p_1 x}e^{p_2 x}\int e^{-p_2 x}e^{p_3 x}\int \cdots e^{p_n x}\int e^{-p_n x}f(x)\,dx^n \quad (18)$$

The method works even when some or all of the constants $p_1, \ldots, p_n$ are equal. Since the left side of (18) looks so much like an algebraic fraction, it is natural to ask whether one can, as in algebra, resolve it into partial fractions; i.e., can we write for example, in the case where $p_1, \ldots, p_n$ are

* See the B and C exercises on pages 143 and 144.

distinct constants, the identity

$$\frac{1}{(D - p_1)(D - p_2) \cdots (D - p_n)}$$
$$\equiv \frac{A_1}{D - p_1} + \frac{A_2}{D - p_2} + \cdots + \frac{A_n}{D - p_n} \quad (19)$$

for suitably determined constants $A_1, A_2, \ldots, A_n$. If (19) is true, then

$$\frac{1}{(D - p_1)(D - p_2) \cdots (D - p_n)} f(x)$$
$$\equiv \frac{A_1}{D - p_1} f(x) + \frac{A_2}{D - p_2} f(x) + \cdots + \frac{A_n}{D - p_n} f(x)$$

and the right-hand side may be interpreted, by using (16) as

$$A_1 e^{p_1 x} \int e^{-p_1 x} f(x) dx + A_2 e^{p_2 x} \int e^{-p_2 x} f(x) dx + \cdots + A_n e^{p_n x} \int e^{-p_n x} f(x) dx$$

This turns out to be correct and is easier than the interpretation (18), since it involves only single integrations.

As illustrations of the foregoing ideas we consider some examples.

ILLUSTRATIVE EXAMPLE 1

Find the general solution of $(D^2 - 1)y = e^{-x}$.

Solution. We may write the equation as $(D - 1)(D + 1)y = e^{-x}$. Hence,

$$y = \frac{1}{(D - 1)(D + 1)} e^{-x} = \left(\frac{\frac{1}{2}}{D - 1} - \frac{\frac{1}{2}}{D + 1} \right) e^{-x}$$
$$= \tfrac{1}{2} e^x \int e^{-x}(e^{-x}) dx - \tfrac{1}{2} e^{-x} \int e^x(e^{-x}) dx$$
$$= c_1 e^x + c_2 e^{-x} - \tfrac{1}{4} e^{-x} - \tfrac{1}{2} x e^{-x}$$
$$= A e^x + B e^{-x} - \tfrac{1}{2} x e^{-x}$$

It should be remarked that by omitting the constants of integration our methods can be used to obtain particular solutions.

ILLUSTRATIVE EXAMPLE 2

Find a particular solution of $(D^2 + 4D + 4)y = x^3 e^{-2x}$.

Solution. We write $(D + 2)^2 y = x^3 e^{-2x}$. Thus,

$$y = \frac{1}{(D + 2)^2} (x^3 e^{-2x}) = \frac{1}{D + 2} \cdot \frac{1}{D + 2} (x^3 e^{-2x})$$
$$= \frac{1}{D + 2} \left[e^{-2x} \int e^{2x}(x^3 e^{-2x}) dx \right] = \frac{1}{D + 2} \left(e^{-2x} \int x^3 \, dx \right)$$
$$= \frac{1}{D + 2} \left[e^{-2x} \left(\frac{x^4}{4} \right) \right] = e^{-2x} \int e^{2x} \cdot e^{-2x} \left(\frac{x^4}{4} \right) dx$$
$$= \frac{x^5}{20} e^{-2x}$$

In this example the work is much shorter than it would have been had we used the method of undetermined coefficients.

Operator methods are of great use in finding particular solutions. The methods employed may not always be easily justifiable, as is shown in the following

ILLUSTRATIVE EXAMPLE 3

Find a particular solution of

$$(D^2 - D + 1)y = x^3 - 3x^2 + 1$$

Solution. Let us write

$$y = \frac{1}{1 - D + D^2} (x^3 - 3x^2 + 1)$$

By ordinary long division in ascending powers of D we find

$$\frac{1}{1 - D + D^2} = 1 + D - D^3 - D^4 + \cdots$$

Hence, formally,

$$\begin{aligned}
y &= (1 + D - D^3 - D^4 + \cdots)(x^3 - 3x^2 + 1) \\
&= 1(x^3 - 3x^2 + 1) + D(x^3 - 3x^2 + 1) - D^3(x^3 - 3x^2 + 1) \\
&\qquad\qquad\qquad\qquad\qquad\qquad - D^4(x^3 - 3x^2 + 1) + \cdots \\
&= x^3 - 6x - 5
\end{aligned}$$

The *remarkable* thing about this is that $y = x^3 - 6x - 5$ is actually a particular solution.

Because of the example just completed, the student must not get the impression that any manipulation of operators will lead to profitable results. While there are many ways in which they can be manipulated, there are also many ways in which they cannot. In the B and C exercises we have presented a few of the more common short operator techniques and have indicated their proofs. The student may find them useful in getting results quickly in many cases.

A EXERCISES

Using operator methods, find the general solution of each equation.

1. $(D^2 - D)y = 1$.   2. $(D^2 - 2D + 1)y = e^x$.
3. $(D^2 + 3D + 2)y = e^x - e^{-x}$.   4. $(D^2 - 1)y = 2x^4 - 3x + 1$.
5. $(D^2 + D)y = 4x^3 - 2e^{2x}$.   6. $(D^2 + 2D + 1)y = x^2e^{-x} + 1$.
7. $(D^2 - 4D + 4)y = e^{2x} \sin 3x$.   8. $(D^3 - D)y = 1 + x^5$.

B EXERCISES

1. If $\phi(D)$ is a polynomial operator in D with constant coefficients, and m is any constant, show that $\phi(D)e^{mx} = \phi(m)e^{mx}$. Hence, show that a solution of $\phi(D)y = 0$ is $y = e^{mx}$, where m may take on values which satisfy $\phi(m) = 0$. Note that $\phi(m) = 0$ is the auxiliary equation.

2. Show that

$$\frac{1}{\phi(D)}(ay_1 + by_2) = a\,\frac{1}{\phi(D)}\,y_1 + b\,\frac{1}{\phi(D)}\,y_2$$

where a and b are constants and y_1, y_2 are suitable functions of x. This shows that $1/\phi(D)$ is a linear operator.

3. Show that

$$\frac{1}{\phi(D)}(e^{mx}) = \frac{1}{\phi(m)}(e^{mx}), \qquad \phi(m) \neq 0$$

if arbitrary constants are omitted. Hence, evaluate $\dfrac{1}{D^2 - 2D - 3}\,e^{4x}$ and obtain the general solution of $(D^2 - 2D - 3)y = e^{4x}$.

4. Obtain a particular solution of $(D^3 + 3D^2 - 4D - 12)y = 2e^{3x} - 4e^{-5x}$. Also find the general solution.

5. (a) Prove that if m is a constant and F is differentiable,

$$D(e^{mx}F) = e^{mx}(D + m)F, \qquad D^2(e^{mx}F) = e^{mx}(D + m)^2F$$

(b) By mathematical induction, extend the results of (a) to

$$D^n(e^{mx}F) = e^{mx}(D + m)^nF$$

6. Use Exercise 5 to show that

$$\phi(D)(e^{mx}F) = e^{mx}\phi(D + m)F$$

where $\phi(D)$ is a polynomial in D with constant coefficients. The result is called the *operator-shift theorem*.

7. Use the operator-shift theorem of Exercise 6 to show that the equation $(D - m)^p y = 0$ has general solution

$$y = e^{mx}(c_1 + c_2x + \cdots + c_px^{p-1})$$

8. Use the operator-shift theorem to show that

$$\frac{1}{\phi(D)}(e^{mx}G) = e^{mx}\,\frac{1}{\phi(D + m)}\,G$$

[*Hint:* Let $\phi(D + m)F = G$ in the operator-shift theorem of Exercise 6.] The result is the *inverse operator-shift theorem*. Note that by this theorem, $1/\phi(D)$ has the same property as $\phi(D)$ in Exercise 6.

9. Using Exercise 8, evaluate

(a) $\dfrac{1}{D^2 - 4D + 3}(x^3 e^{2x})$ and obtain a particular solution of

$$(D^2 - 4D + 3)y = x^3 e^{2x}$$

(b) $\dfrac{1}{D^2 + 2D + 1}(2x^2 e^{-2x} + 3e^{2x})$ and obtain a particular solution of

$$(D^2 + 2D + 1)y = 2x^2 e^{-2x} + 3e^{2x}$$

10. Show that if ϕ is a polynomial with constant coefficients,

$$\phi(D^2)(\sin ax) = \phi(-a^2)(\sin ax)$$
$$\phi(D^2)(\cos ax) = \phi(-a^2)(\cos ax)$$

Hence, derive the results,

$$\frac{1}{\phi(D^2)}(\sin ax) = \frac{1}{\phi(-a^2)}(\sin ax), \qquad \phi(-a^2) \neq 0$$

$$\frac{1}{\phi(D^2)}(\cos ax) = \frac{1}{\phi(-a^2)}(\cos ax), \qquad \phi(-a^2) \neq 0$$

11. Using Exercise 10 evaluate:

(a) $\dfrac{1}{D^2 + 1}(\sin 3x).$ (b) $\dfrac{1}{D^4 - 3D^2 + 2}(2 \cos 2x - 4 \sin 2x).$

12. The results of Exercise 10 can be used to find particular solutions of $\phi(D^2)y = \sin ax$ or $\phi(D^2)y = \cos ax$, but they fail for the equations

$$\phi(D)y = \sin ax \quad \text{or} \quad \phi(D)y = \cos ax$$

(a) Show that $\phi(D)$ can always be written as $F_1(D^2) + DF_2(D^2)$. Consider

$$[F_1(D^2) + DF_2(D^2)]y = \sin ax$$

Operate on both sides by $F_1(D^2) - DF_2(D^2)$ to obtain

$$\{[F_1(D^2)]^2 - D^2[F_2(D^2)]^2\}y = F_1(-a^2)\sin ax - aF_2(-a^2)\cos ax$$

and hence show that a particular solution is

$$\frac{F_1(-a^2)\sin ax - aF_2(-a^2)\cos ax}{[F_1(-a^2)]^2 + a^2[F_2(-a^2)]^2}$$

(b) Obtain the result in (a) formally by writing

$$\frac{1}{\phi(D)}\sin ax = \frac{1}{F_1(D^2) + DF_2(D^2)}\sin ax$$

$$= \frac{F_1(D^2) - DF_2(D^2)}{[F_1(D^2) + DF_2(D^2)][F_1(D^2) - DF_2(D^2)]}\sin ax$$

$$= \frac{F_1(-a^2) - DF_2(-a^2)}{[F_1(-a^2)]^2 + a^2[F_2(-a^2)]^2}\sin ax$$

$$= \frac{F_1(-a^2)\sin ax - aF_2(-a^2)\cos ax}{[F_1(-a^2)]^2 + a^2[F_2(-a^2)]^2}$$

Arrive at a similar result for $\dfrac{1}{\phi(D)}\cos ax.$

13. Use the results of Exercise 12 to find particular solutions of:

(a) $(D^2 - 3D + 2)y = \sin 3x$.

(b) $(2D^3 + D^2 - 2D - 1)y = 3 \sin 2x + 4 \cos 2x$.

14. By combining the operator-shift theorem of Exercise 8 and the results of Exercise 12, evaluate

(a) $\dfrac{1}{D^2 + D - 2} (e^{2x} \sin 3x)$.

(b) $\dfrac{1}{D^3 + 2D^2 - 1} (e^{-x} \cos 2x)$.

15. Show how the identities

$$\sin \theta = \frac{e^{i\theta} - e^{-i\theta}}{2i}, \qquad \cos \theta = \frac{e^{i\theta} + e^{-i\theta}}{2}$$

may be employed to obtain the results of Exercises 10–14.

16. Using the methods of Exercises 1–15 evaluate:

(a) $\dfrac{1}{D^2 + 2D - 5} (e^{3x})$.

(b) $\dfrac{1}{D^3 - 1} (x^5 + 3x^4 - 2x^3)$.

(c) $\dfrac{1}{D^2 + 1} (x^2 e^{2x})$.

(d) $\dfrac{1}{D^2 + D} (8 \sin 4x)$.

(e) $\dfrac{1}{D^3 + 1} (\sin x + \cos x)$.

(f) $\dfrac{1}{(D - 3)^3} (e^{3x} \cos 4x)$.

(g) $\dfrac{1}{D^2 - 4D + 3} [e^x(2 \sin x - 3 \cos x)]$.

(h) $\dfrac{1}{(D + 2)^2(D + 1)^3} (x^3 e^{-x} + e^{-x} \sin x)$.

(i) $\dfrac{1}{D^3 + D^2 - D - 1} (x^2 + 3 \sin x)$.

(j) $\dfrac{1}{D^3 - D^2 + D} (x^2 e^x - 4x^4)$.

C EXERCISES

1. (a) Use partial fractions to obtain

$$\frac{1}{(D - 2)^2(D + 3)} (x^2 e^{2x})$$

and verify your result by other methods. (b) Justify the manipulations in (a) by proving that

$$\left(\frac{a}{\phi_1(D)} + \frac{b}{\phi_2(D)} \right) F = a \frac{1}{\phi_1(D)} F + b \frac{1}{\phi_2(D)} F$$

where a and b are constants.

2. (a) Show how to modify the result of B Exercise 3 in case $\phi(m) = 0$ but $\phi'(m) \neq 0$ (i.e., m is a root but not a double root of $\phi(m) = 0$), obtaining

$$\frac{1}{\phi(D)} e^{mx} = \frac{1}{\phi'(m)} x e^{mx}$$

(b) In case $\phi(m) = 0$, $\phi'(m) = 0$, $\phi''(m) = 0$, ..., $\phi^{(p-1)}(m) = 0$, $\phi^{(p)}(m) \neq 0$, (i.e., m is a p-fold root of $\phi(r) = 0$), show that

$$\frac{1}{\phi(D)} e^{mx} = \frac{1}{\phi^{(p)}(m)} x^p e^{mx}$$

[*Hint:* If m is a p-fold root of $\phi(r) = 0$, then $(r - m)^p$ is a factor of $\phi(r)$; similarly $(D - m)^p$ is a factor of $\phi(D)$.]

3. Use the results of Exercise 2 to investigate the case of B Exercise 10 in case $\phi(-a^2) = 0$.

4. Evaluate:

(a) $\dfrac{1}{(D - 1)^2} (e^x)$.

(b) $\dfrac{1}{D^2 - 3D + 2} (2e^x - e^{2x})$.

(c) $\dfrac{1}{(D + 2)^4} (e^{-2x})$.

(d) $\dfrac{1}{D^2 + 9} (\sin 3x)$.

(e) $\dfrac{1}{D^3 + D} (\cos x + \sin x)$.

(f) $\dfrac{1}{D^4 + 2D^2 + 1} (\sin x)$.

5. Solve $(D^2 + 1)y = x^2 \cos x$ by writing $\cos x$ as the real part of e^{ix} and factoring $D^2 + 1$ into $(D - i)(D + i)$.

6. By use of operators solve $(aD^2 + bD + c)y = F(x)$ where a, b, c are constants. Treat all cases.

6. Remarks concerning equations which can be transformed into linear equations with constant coefficients. The student has had occasion to see how some differential equations could be solved by the use of suitable and often ingenious transformations. It should come as no surprise that some differential equations can be solved by transforming them into linear differential equations with constant coefficients. The particular transformation used may not always be obvious, and the student should not develop a sense of inferiority if he does not see it immediately. Consider the following

Problem for Discussion. Solve

$$x^2 y'' + xy' + 4y = 1$$

It is far from obvious how to proceed to solve this linear equation with variable coefficients. Mathematicians have found, however, that this equation belongs to a special type which can be solved by the transformation

$x = e^z$. To see this, note that

$$y' = \frac{dy}{dx} = \frac{dy}{dz} \cdot \frac{dz}{dx} = \frac{dy}{dz} \bigg/ \frac{dx}{dz} = e^{-z} \frac{dy}{dz}$$

so that

$$xy' = x\frac{dy}{dx} = \frac{dy}{dz} \tag{20}$$

Similarly,

$$y'' = \frac{d^2y}{dx^2} = \frac{d}{dx}\left(e^{-z}\frac{dy}{dz}\right)$$

$$= \frac{d}{dz}\left(e^{-z}\frac{dy}{dz}\right)\bigg/\frac{dx}{dz} = e^{-2z}\left(\frac{d^2y}{dz^2} - \frac{dy}{dz}\right)$$

so that

$$x^2y'' = x^2\frac{d^2y}{dx^2} = \frac{d^2y}{dz^2} - \frac{dy}{dz} \tag{21}$$

Using (20) and (21), the differential equation becomes

$$\frac{d^2y}{dz^2} + 4y = 1$$

which has the general solution

$$y = A\cos 2z + B\sin 2z + \tfrac{1}{4}$$

Since $z = \ln x$, the solution of the required equation is*

$$y = A\cos(2\ln x) + B\sin(2\ln x) + \tfrac{1}{4}$$

The transformation $x = e^z$ will transform

$$(a_0x^nD^n + a_1x^{n-1}D^{n-1} + \cdots + a_{n-1}xD + a_n)y = F(x)$$

where $a_0, a_1, \ldots, a_n$ are constants into a linear equation with constant coefficients. This was first discovered by Euler, and is known as *Euler's differential equation*, although it is sometimes attributed to Cauchy.

Other problems related to linear differential equations are considered in the advanced exercises.

A EXERCISES

1. Use the transformation $x = e^z$ to solve each equation:

(a) $x^2y'' - 2y = x$.   (b) $(x^2D^2 - xD + 2)y = \ln x$.
(c) $x^2y'' + 5xy' + 4y = x^2 + 16(\ln x)^2$.

---

* We have tacitly assumed here that $x > 0$. For $x < 0$ we can let $x = -e^z$ and obtain the solution

$$y = C\cos[2\ln(-x)] + D\sin[2\ln(-x)]$$

2. If $x = e^z$, show that

$$xy' = Dy, \qquad x^2y'' = D(D-1)y, \qquad x^3y''' = D(D-1)(D-2)y$$

where $D \equiv d/dz$. Hence, solve $x^3y''' + 3x^2y'' = 1 + x$.

B EXERCISES

1. If $x = e^z$, show that

$$x^n y^{(n)} = D(D-1)(D-2)\cdots(D-n+1)y, \qquad \text{where} \quad D \equiv d/dz$$

(*Hint:* Use mathematical induction.)

2. Determine the constant m so that $y = x^m$ is a solution of $x^2y'' + 3xy' - 3y = 0$. Hence, obtain the general solution. How can this be used to find the general solution of

$$x^2y'' + 3xy' - 3y = x^2 - 4x + 2$$

3. Can the method of Exercise 2 be used to determine general solutions of the equations (a) $x^2y'' - xy' + y = 0$, and (b) $x^2y'' - xy' + 4y = 0$? Use the method of the text to obtain the solutions. Discuss the advantages and the disadvantages to the method of Exercise 2.

4. Use the transformation $2x + 3 = e^z$ to solve

$$(2x+3)^2 y'' + (2x+3)y' - 2y = 24x^2$$

5. Solve $(x+2)^2 y'' - y = 4$.

C EXERCISES

1. Use the transformation $z = \sin x$ to solve

$$y'' + (\tan x)y' + (\cos^2 x)y = 0$$

2. Use the transformation $x = z^m$ and choose the constant m appropriately to solve $xy'' - y' - 4x^3y = 0$.

3. (a) Show that when the transformation $x = F(z)$ is made in the equation

$$y'' + P(x)y' + Q(x)y = R(x)$$

the resulting equation is

$$\frac{d^2y}{dz^2} + p(z)\frac{dy}{dz} + q(z)y = r(z)$$

where

$$p(z) \equiv \frac{z'' + Pz'}{(z')^2}, \qquad q(z) \equiv \frac{Q}{(z')^2}, \qquad r(z) \equiv \frac{R}{(z')^2}$$

the primes denoting derivatives with respect to x. (b) Use the result of (a) to show that if z is chosen so that $q(z)$ is a constant (say unity), i.e., $z' = \sqrt{Q}$, $z = \int \sqrt{Q}\, dx$, and if this choice makes $p(z)$ also constant, the first equation of (a) can be solved. (c) Use the result of (a) to show that if z is chosen so that $z'' + Pz' = 0$ and if by this choice $q(z)$ is a constant, then the first equation of (a) can be solved.

4. Using Exercise 3, solve the equations of Exercises 1 and 2.

5. Use Exercise 3 to solve the Euler equation $x^2 y'' - 2xy' + 2y = 3x - 2$.

6. Solve
   (a) $(\sin x)y'' + (3 \sin^2 x - \cos x)y' + 2(\sin^3 x)y = 0$.
   (b) $x^4 y'' + 2x^3 y' + y = x^{-2}$.

7. Show that the equation

$$y'' + P(x)y' + Q(x)y = 0$$

can be transformed into $u'' + f(x)u = 0$ by letting $y = u(x)v(x)$ and choosing $v(x)$ appropriately. Hence, solve $y'' + 4xy' + (3 + 4x^2)y = 0$.

8. Solve $xy'' + 2y' + xy = 0$.

9. Show that the equation $y'' + \lambda y = 0$, subject to the conditions $y(0) = y(\pi) = 0$, has nonzero solutions only for a certain set of values of the parameter λ. These values are called *eigenvalues*, or *characteristic values*, and the corresponding solutions are called *eigenfunctions*, or *characteristic functions*. Differential equations giving rise to eigenvalues, and eigenfunctions are of importance in advanced work.

10. Let $Y_1(x)$ and $Y_2(x)$ be linearly independent solutions of the equation

$$y'' + P(x)y' + Q(x)y = 0$$

If $Y_1(x) = 0$ for $x = a$ and $x = b$, show that $Y_2(x) = 0$ for some value $x = c$ where $a < c < b$. Is there only one such value? Explain. Illustrate by considering the equations $y'' + 4y = 0$ and $y'' - 2y' + 5y = 0$. Does the result hold for the equation $y'' - 4y = 0$?

11. The equation $a_0(x)y'' + a_1(x)y' + a_2(x)y = 0$ is said to be *exact* if there exist functions $p(x)$ and $q(x)$ such that

$$a_0(x)y'' + a_1(x)y' + a_2(x)y \equiv \frac{d}{dx}\{p(x)y' + q(x)y\}$$

(a) Prove that a necessary and sufficient condition for an equation to be exact is that

$$a_0''(x) - a_1'(x) + a_2(x) \equiv 0$$

(b) Show that the equation $xy'' + xy' + y = 0$ is exact and obtain its solution.

12. If the equation $a_0(x)y'' + a_1(x)y + a_2(x)y = 0$ of Exercise 11 is not exact but there exists a function $\mu(x)$ such that $\mu a_0 y'' + \mu a_1 y' + \mu a_2 y = 0$ is exact then we call μ an *integrating factor*. (a) Show that the differential equation satisfied by μ is

$$a_0\mu'' + (2a_0' - a_1)\mu' + (a_0'' - a_1' + a_2)\mu = 0$$

called the *adjoint* of the given equation. (b) Solve the equation $x(1 - x)y'' + (2 - 5x)y' + (2x - 7)y = 0$ by finding an integrating factor.

13. Show that a differential equation having the form

$$\frac{d}{dx}\left\{P(x)\frac{dy}{dx}\right\} + Q(x)y = 0$$

is *self-adjoint*, i.e., the equation is equivalent to its adjoint. Can any second-order linear differential equation be put into self-adjoint form? Explain.

14. Generalize the results of Exercises 11–13 to nth-order linear differential equations.

15. (a) Show that the solution of $y'' = F(x)$, $y(0) = y(1) = 0$ is

$$y = \int_0^1 G(x,t)F(t)dt$$

where
$$G(x,t) = \begin{cases} t(x-1) & 0 \le t \le x \\ x(t-1) & x \le t \le 1 \end{cases}$$

The function $G(x,t)$ is often called a *Green's function*.

(b) Discuss how you might obtain $G(x,t)$ if it were not given. (*Hint:* One possibility is to write

$$y = \int_0^x G(x,t)F(t)dt + \int_x^1 G(x,t)F(t)dt$$

substitute into the given equation and conditions to find suitable conditions on G in the two regions $0 \le t \le x$, $x \le t \le 1$.)

(c) Apply your method in (b) to solve $y'' + y = F(x)$, $y(0) = y(1) = 0$.

Chapter Five

APPLICATIONS OF LINEAR DIFFERENTIAL

EQUATIONS

In the preceding chapter, methods were given for the solution of

$$a \frac{d^2x}{dt^2} + b \frac{dx}{dt} + cx = F(t) \qquad (1)$$

where a, b, c are given constants or functions of t and $F(t)$ is a given function of t. This equation occurs very frequently in applications of physics and engineering, so that it is worthy of special study. In this chapter we shall study applications of such differential equations to:

    I Vibratory or oscillatory motion of mechanical systems.
    II Electric circuit problems.
    III Miscellaneous problems.

I. Vibratory Motion of Mechanical Systems

1. The vibrating spring. Perhaps the simplest system available for study of vibratory motion consists of an ordinary spring of negligible weight [Fig. 62(a)] suspended vertically from a fixed support. Suppose that a

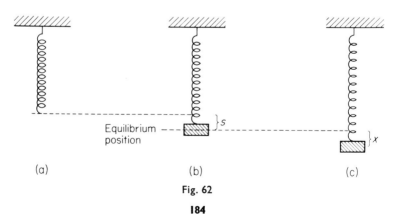

(a)   (b)   (c)

Fig. 62

184

weight W is hung on the spring [Fig. 62(b)]. When the weight is at rest we describe its position as the *equilibrium position*. If the weight is pulled down a certain distance and then released, it will undergo a vibratory motion about the equilibrium position [Fig. 62(c)]. It is our purpose in this section to discuss the motion of the weight in this and similar cases. In order to accomplish this purpose, we shall have to know the forces acting on the weight during its motion. It is clear from experience that there is some force tending to return or restore a displaced weight to its equilibrium position. This force is called the *restoring force*. The first to enunciate a law governing this restoring force was Robert Hooke, and we now state

HOOKE'S LAW. *The force exerted by a spring, tending to restore the weight W to the equilibrium position, is proportional to the distance of W from the equilibrium position.* (Sometimes this is worded briefly as "force is proportional to stretch.")

Denote the magnitude of the restoring force by $|f|$, and let x denote the position of W measured from the equilibrium position. Assume the positive direction downward, so that x is positive when W is below the equilibrium position and negative when W is above this position. According to Hooke's law,

$$|f| \propto |x| \quad \text{or} \quad |f| = k |x|$$

where $k > 0$ is a constant of proportionality depending on the stiffness of the spring and called the *spring constant*. To determine the direction of the force, note that when $x > 0$ the force is directed upward and should therefore be negative. When $x < 0$ the force is directed downward and should therefore be positive. This can be satisfied only if the force is given both in magnitude and direction by $-kx$, so that Hooke's law reads

$$f = -kx \tag{2}$$

When weight W is put on the spring, it stretches a distance s as in Fig. 62(b). According to Hooke's law, the tension T_1 in the spring is proportional to the stretch, and so $T_1 = ks$. Since the spring and weight are in equilibrium it follows that

$$T_1 = ks = W \tag{3}$$

When the weight is pulled further and released, its position at any time is shown in Fig. 62(c). The tension T_2 in the spring at this time is, according to Hooke's law,

$$T_2 = k(s + x) \tag{4}$$

It follows that the net force in the positive direction is given by

$$W - T_2 = W - ks - kx = -kx$$

upon making use of (3). Thus by Newton's law the equation of motion is

$$\frac{W}{g} \cdot \frac{d^2x}{dt^2} = -kx$$

It thus follows that the net force is simply the restoring force and does not depend on the weight W.

ILLUSTRATIVE EXAMPLE 1

It is found experimentally that a 6 lb weight stretches a certain spring 6 in. If the weight is pulled 4 in. below the equilibrium position and released: (a) set up a differential equation and associated conditions describing the motion; (b) find the position of the weight as a function of time; (c) find the amplitude, period, and frequency of the motion; (d) determine the position, velocity, and acceleration of the weight $\frac{1}{2}$ sec after it has been released.

Mathematical Formulation. By Hooke's law (since 6 in. $= \frac{1}{2}$ ft), $|f| = k |x|$, or $6 = k \cdot \frac{1}{2}$; i.e., $k = 12$. The differential equation describing the motion is therefore

$$\frac{6}{32} \cdot \frac{d^2x}{dt^2} = -12x \quad \text{or} \quad \frac{d^2x}{dt^2} + 64x = 0 \tag{5}$$

Since initially ($t = 0$) the weight is 4 in. below the equilibrium position, we have the condition

$$x = \tfrac{1}{3} \text{ (ft)} \qquad \text{at} \quad t = 0 \tag{6}$$

Also, since the weight is released (i.e., it has zero velocity) at $t = 0$,

$$\frac{dx}{dt} = 0 \qquad \text{at} \quad t = 0 \tag{7}$$

Solution. The auxiliary equation for (5) is $m^2 + 64 = 0$ and has roots $m = \pm 8i$. Hence the differential equation has solution

$$x = A \cos 8t + B \sin 8t \tag{8}$$

From condition (6) we find $A = \frac{1}{3}$, so that

$$x = \tfrac{1}{3} \cos 8t + B \sin 8t$$

Differentiation yields

$$\frac{dx}{dt} = -\frac{8}{3} \sin 8t + 8B \cos 8t$$

Using condition (7), we now find $B = 0$. Hence, the required solution is

$$x = \tfrac{1}{3} \cos 8t \tag{9}$$

Note that in equation (9), x is in feet. If it were desired to measure x in inches, the equation would be $x = 4 \cos 8t$.

From (9) it is clear that the amplitude is $\frac{1}{3}$ ft, the frequency f is given by $8/2\pi = 4/\pi$ cycles per second, and the period T is given by

$$T = \frac{1}{f} = \frac{2\pi}{8} = \frac{\pi}{4} \sec$$

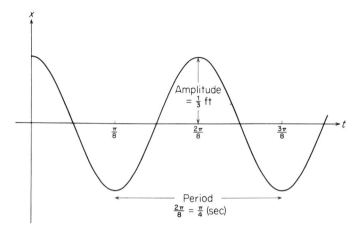

Fig. 63

These facts are clear from the graph of (9) shown in Fig. 63. The motion is simple harmonic motion, which has already been discussed in Chapter 3, Section I, Illustrative Example 4. The student should compare the method of solving the differential equation obtained there with that used here.

By differentiation with respect to t of $x = \frac{1}{3} \cos 8t$, we have

$$v = \frac{dx}{dt} = -\frac{8}{3} \sin 8t, \qquad a = \frac{d^2x}{dt^2} = -\frac{64}{3} \cos 8t$$

Placing $t = \frac{1}{2}$ and using the fact that 4 radians $= 4 \times (180/\pi)$ degrees $= 229$ degrees, approximately, we find

$$x = \tfrac{1}{3}(-0.656) = -0.219$$
$$v = -\tfrac{8}{3}(-0.755) = +2.01$$
$$a = -\tfrac{64}{3}(-0.656) = +14.0$$

It is thus seen that $\frac{1}{2}$ sec after the weight has been released it is 0.219 ft *above* the equilibrium position, is traveling *downward* with velocity 2.01 ft/sec, and has an acceleration *downward* of 14.0 ft/sec².

ILLUSTRATIVE EXAMPLE 2

In Illustrative Example 1, suppose the weight is pulled 4 in. below the equilibrium position and is then given a downward velocity of 2 ft/sec instead of being released. Determine the amplitude, period, and frequency of the motion.

Mathematical Formulation. The differential equation is

$$\frac{d^2x}{dt^2} + 64x = 0 \tag{10}$$

as in Illustrative Example 1. The initial conditions are

$$x = \frac{1}{3}, \qquad \frac{dx}{dt} = 2 \quad \text{at} \quad t = 0 \tag{11}$$

Solution. The general solution of (10) is $x = A \cos 8t + B \sin 8t$. From the first of conditions (11), $A = \frac{1}{3}$. Hence, $x = \frac{1}{3} \cos 8t + B \sin 8t$. Differentiation with respect to t yields

$$\frac{dx}{dt} = -\frac{8}{3} \sin 8t + 8B \cos 8t$$

and using the second of conditions (11), we find $B = \frac{1}{4}$. The required solution is

$$x = \frac{1}{3} \cos 8t + \frac{1}{4} \sin 8t \tag{12}$$

If x is measured in inches, the equation is

$$x = 4 \cos 8t + 3 \sin 8t \tag{13}$$

It is often useful to write (12) in an equivalent form, making use of the identity*

$$a \cos \omega t + b \sin \omega t = \sqrt{a^2 + b^2} \sin (\omega t + \phi)$$

where $\qquad \sin \phi = \dfrac{a}{\sqrt{a^2 + b^2}}$ and $\cos \phi = \dfrac{b}{\sqrt{a^2 + b^2}}$ $\qquad$ (14)

(ϕ is sometimes called the phase angle). With the aid of this identity, (12) becomes

$$x = \sqrt{(\tfrac{1}{3})^2 + (\tfrac{1}{4})^2} \sin (8t + \phi) = \tfrac{5}{12} \sin (8t + \phi) \tag{15}$$

where $\sin \phi = \frac{4}{5}$, $\cos \phi = \frac{3}{5}$. From tables we easily find that $\phi = 53°8'$ or 0.9274 radian. Hence (15) becomes

$$x = \tfrac{5}{12} \sin (8t + 0.9274) \tag{16}$$

if x is in feet, and

$$x = 5 \sin (8t + 0.9274) \tag{17}$$

if x is in inches. The graph of (16) is shown in Fig. 64. The amplitude is 5 in., or $\frac{5}{12}$ ft, the period is $2\pi/8 = \pi/4$ seconds and the frequency is the reciprocal of the period, or $4/\pi$ cycles per second. In general if a motion can be described by an equation of the form $x = A \sin (\omega t + \phi)$, then

$$\text{amplitude} = A, \qquad \text{period} = T = \frac{2\pi}{\omega}$$
$$\text{frequency} = f = \frac{1}{T} = \frac{\omega}{2\pi} \tag{18}$$

From the third statement, we have the relation $\omega = 2\pi f$, which is often useful.

---

* This is easy to prove, since

$$\sqrt{a^2 + b^2} \sin (\omega t + \phi) = \sqrt{a^2 + b^2} (\sin \omega t \cos \phi + \cos \omega t \sin \phi)$$
$$= \sqrt{a^2 + b^2} \left[(\sin \omega t) \left(\frac{b}{\sqrt{a^2 + b^2}} \right) + (\cos \omega t) \left(\frac{a}{\sqrt{a^2 + b^2}} \right) \right]$$
$$= a \cos \omega t + b \sin \omega t$$

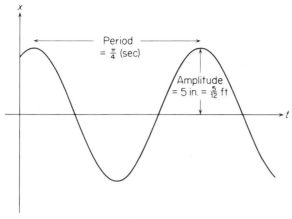

Fig. 64

A EXERCISES

1. A 2 lb weight suspended from a spring stretches it 1.5 in. If the weight is pulled 3 in. below the equilibrium position and released: (a) Set up a differential equation and conditions describing the motion. (b) Find the velocity and position of the weight as a function of time. (c) Find the amplitude, period, and frequency of the motion. (d) Determine the position, velocity, and acceleration $\pi/64$ sec after the weight is released.

2. A 3 lb weight on a spring stretches it 6 in. When equilibrium is reached the weight is struck so as to give it a downward velocity of 2 ft/sec. Find: (a) the velocity and position of the weight at time t sec after the impact; (b) the amplitude, period, and frequency of the motion; (c) the velocity and acceleration when the weight is 1 in. above the equilibrium position and moving upward.

3. A spring suspended from the ceiling has a constant of 12 lb/ft. An 8 lb weight is placed on the spring, and when equilibrium is reached, the weight is raised 5 in. above the equilibrium position and dropped. Describe the motion giving amplitude, period, and frequency.

4. Solve Exercise 3 if the weight is raised 5 in. and then thrust upward with velocity 5 ft/sec.

5. A spring is stretched 2 cm by a force of 40 dynes. A particle of mass 1 g is placed on the spring, and when equilibrium is reached, the mass is raised 5 cm above the equilibrium and then released. (a) Find the amplitude, period, and frequency of the vibration. (b) At what times is the particle 2.5 cm above the equilibrium position?

6. A 256 lb weight is suspended from a vertical spring having spring constant of 200 lb/ft. If the weight is raised 3 in. above its equilibrium position and released: (a) Find the position of the weight at a time $\pi/3$ sec afterward and determine

which way and how fast the weight is moving at this time. (b) Find the amplitude, period, and frequency of the vibration. (c) At what times is the weight 1.5 in. below the equilibrium position and moving downward?

B EXERCISES

1. A weight W is suspended from a vertical spring and produces a stretch of magnitude a. When the weight is in equilibrium it is acted upon by a force which imparts to it a velocity v_0 downward. Show that the weight travels a distance $v_0 \sqrt{a/g}$ for a time $(\pi/2) \sqrt{a/g}$ before it starts to return.

2. A weight W on a vertical spring having constant k is oscillating with simple harmonic motion. When the weight reaches its lowest position it receives a blow which imparts to it a velocity v_0 downward. Assuming that this does not affect the properties of the spring, show that the weight oscillates with the same period as before but has a new amplitude given by $\sqrt{A_0^2 + (Wv_0^2/gk)}$, where A_0 is the original amplitude.

3. When a certain weight at the end of a vertical spring is set into vibration, the period is 1.5 sec. When 8 lb is added, the period becomes 2.5 sec. How much weight was originally on the spring?

4. A spring oscillates vertically. The numerical values of the maximum velocity and acceleration are given, respectively, by v_m and a_m. Show that the period of oscillation is $2\pi v_m/a_m$, and the amplitude is v_m^2/a_m.

5. A spring oscillates with amplitude A and period T. Show that the maximum velocity occurs at the center of the path and has magnitude $2\pi A/T$, while the maximum acceleration occurs at the ends of the path and has magnitude $4\pi^2 A/T^2$.

C EXERCISES

1. A spring rests taut but unstretched on a horizontal table. One end is attached to a point O on the table and the other to a weight W. The weight is displaced so that the spring is stretched a distance a and it is then released. If the coefficient of friction between weight and table is μ, and if the spring constant is k, show that when the spring returns to its unstretched position the magnitude of its velocity is

$$\sqrt{\frac{g}{W}(ka^2 - 2\mu Wa)}$$

and that this takes a time given by

$$\sqrt{\frac{W}{gk}} \left[\pi - \arccos\left(\frac{\mu W}{ka - \mu W}\right) \right]$$

Show that if $\mu > ka/2W$, the spring will not return to the unstretched position.

2. When the spring of the previous exercise is in its unstretched position, the weight W is given a velocity v_0 away from O. Show that it travels a distance

$$\sqrt{\frac{\mu^2 W^2}{k^2} + \frac{W v_0^2}{gk} - \frac{\mu W}{k}}$$

before it starts to return, and that this takes a time given by

$$\sqrt{\frac{W}{gk}} \left(\operatorname{arc\,cot} \frac{\mu}{v_0} \sqrt{\frac{gW}{k}} \right)$$

3. Compare Exercises 1 and 2 with B Exercises 1 and 2.

4. A particle moves with simple harmonic motion along the x axis described by the equation $x = a \sin \omega t$. (a) Show that the probability of finding the particle between positions x_1 and x_2, where $-a \leq x_1 < x_2 \leq a$, is given by

$$\frac{1}{\pi} \left(\operatorname{arc\,sin} \frac{x_2}{a} - \operatorname{arc\,sin} \frac{x_1}{a} \right)$$

(b) Where do you expect would be the greatest chance of finding the particle? Explain.

5. (a) Referring to Exercise 4, show that if $F(x)$ is the probability of finding the particle to the left of x then

$$F(x) = \int_{-\infty}^{x} P(v)\,dv$$

where

$$P(x) = \begin{cases} \dfrac{1}{\pi \sqrt{a^2 - x^2}} & |x| \leq a \\[2mm] 0 & |x| > a \end{cases}$$

We often call $F(x)$ the *distribution function* and $P(x)$ the *density function*.
(b) Show that the root mean square displacement of the particle from its equilibrium position is $a/\sqrt{2}$.

2. The vibrating spring with damping. The vibrating springs just considered were not very realistic, since the oscillations did not decrease, as one would expect from experience, but were instead forever maintained. In practice, frictional and other forces (such as air resistance) act to decrease the amplitude of the oscillations and ultimately to bring the system to rest. One way to get a better approximation to reality is to assume a *damping force*. The exact law for this force is not known, since it depends on so many variable factors, but it has been found from experiment that for small speeds, the magnitude of the damping force is approximately proportional to the instantaneous speed of the weight on the spring. The magnitude is therefore given by

$$\beta \left| \frac{dx}{dt} \right|$$

where β is the constant of proportionality called the *damping constant*.

The damping force opposes the motion, so that when the weight is coming down the damping force acts up, while it acts downward when the weight is going up. Assuming downward as the positive direction, as we did before, it is clear that the damping force must be negative when dx/dt is positive, and must be positive when dx/dt is negative. Thus, taking $\beta > 0$, it is clear that the damping force must be given both in magnitude and direction by $-\beta\, dx/dt$. Taking into account the restoring force already considered, it follows by Newton's law that

$$\frac{W}{g}\cdot\frac{d^2x}{dt^2} = -\beta\frac{dx}{dt} - kx \quad \text{or} \quad \frac{W}{g}\cdot\frac{d^2x}{dt^2} + \beta\frac{dx}{dt} + kx = 0$$

is the differential equation of motion.

ILLUSTRATIVE EXAMPLE 3

Assume that a damping force given in pounds numerically by 1.5 times the instantaneous velocity in feet per second, acts on the weight in Illustrative Example 1, page 188. (a) Set up the differential equation and associated conditions. (b) Find the position x of the weight as a function of time t.

Mathematical Formulation. Taking into account the damping force $-1.5\, dx/dt$ in Illustrative Example 1, we find for the equation of motion

$$\frac{6}{32}\cdot\frac{d^2x}{dt^2} = -12x - 1.5\frac{dx}{dt} \quad \text{or} \quad \frac{d^2x}{dt^2} + 8\frac{dx}{dt} + 64x = 0 \qquad (19)$$

The initial conditions are as in Illustrative Example 1:

$$x = \frac{1}{3} \quad \text{at} \quad t = 0 \quad \text{and} \quad \frac{dx}{dt} = 0 \quad \text{at} \quad t = 0 \qquad (20)$$

Solution. The auxiliary equation corresponding to (19) has roots $m = -4 \pm 4\sqrt{3}\, i$, and so the general solution is

$$x = e^{-4t}(A \cos 4\sqrt{3}\, t + B \sin 4\sqrt{3}\, t)$$

Determining the constants A and B subject to conditions (20), we find

$$x = \tfrac{1}{9}e^{-4t}(3 \cos 4\sqrt{3}\, t + \sqrt{3} \sin 4\sqrt{3}\, t) \qquad (21)$$

If we make use of the identity given in (14), page 188, (21) may be written

$$x = \frac{2\sqrt{3}}{9}\, e^{-4t} \sin\left(4\sqrt{3}\, t + \frac{\pi}{3}\right) \qquad (22)$$

The graph of (22), shown in Fig. 65 lies between the graphs of

$$x = \frac{2\sqrt{3}}{9}\, e^{-4t} \quad \text{and} \quad x = -\frac{2\sqrt{3}}{9}\, e^{-4t}$$

(shown dashed in Fig. 65), since the sine varies between -1 and $+1$.

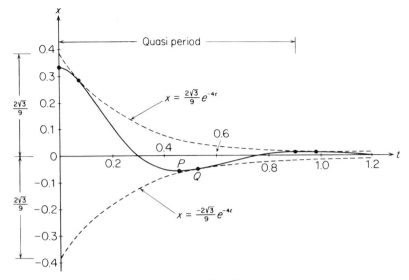

Fig. 65

The difference between the times of the successive maxima (or minima) of this graph can be shown to be constant and equal to $2\pi/4\sqrt{3}$ (see Exercise 2 of the B exercises). It should be noted that the maxima (or minima) of the graph *do not* lie on the dashed curves as might be imagined (see Exercises 2 and 4 of the B exercises). Thus, as shown in Fig. 65, point P represents a relative minimum, while point Q lies on the dashed curve. The constant difference in times between successive maxima (or minima) is called the *quasi period*, although we sometimes refer to it as the period. The adjective quasi is used, since the functional values do not repeat as they would if there were actual periodicity. The quasi period is also equal to twice the time taken between successive zeros, i.e., twice the time between successive passages of the weight through the equilibrium position (see Exercise 4 of the B exercises).

The motion described in this example is called *damped oscillatory* or *damped vibratory* motion. It should be noted that (22) has the form

$$x = A(t) \sin(\omega t + \phi) \tag{23}$$

where

$$A(t) = \frac{2\sqrt{3}}{9} e^{-4t}, \qquad \omega = 4\sqrt{3}, \qquad \phi = \frac{\pi}{3}$$

The quasi period is given by $2\pi/\omega = 2\pi/4\sqrt{3}$.

By analogy with the undamped case, $A(t)$ is called the *amplitude*, or more exactly the *time-varying amplitude*. It is seen that the amplitude decreases with time, thus agreeing with our experience. One fact that should be noted is that the frequency with damping is less than that without damping. This is plausible since one would expect opposition to motion to increase the time for a complete cycle. The undamped frequency, i.e., with $\beta = 0$, is often called the *natural frequency*. It is of great importance in connection with the phenomenon of resonance to be discussed later.

A EXERCISES

1. A 4 lb weight suspended from a spring stretches it 3 in. The weight is pulled 6 in. below the equilibrium position and released. Assume that the weight is acted upon by a damping force which in pounds is numerically equal to $2v$, where v is the instantaneous velocity in feet per second. (a) Set up a differential equation and conditions describing the motion. (b) Determine the position of the spring at any time after the weight is released. (c) Write the result of (b) in the form $\mathcal{A}(t) \sin (\omega t + \phi)$. Thus, determine the time-varying amplitude, quasi period, and phase angle.

2. A 2 lb weight suspended from a spring stretches it 6 in. A velocity of 5 ft/sec upward is imparted to the weight at its equilibrium position. Assume a damping force in pounds numerically equal to $0.6v$, where v is the instantaneous velocity in feet per second. (a) Find the position and velocity of the spring at any time. (b) Write the result of (a) in the form $\mathcal{A}(t) \sin (\omega t + \phi)$.

3. A 64 lb weight is suspended from a spring having a constant of 50 lb/ft. The weight is acted upon by a resisting force in pounds which is numerically equal to 12 times the instantaneous velocity in feet per second. If the weight is pulled 6 in. below the equilibrium position and then released, describe the motion, giving the time-varying amplitude and quasi period of the motion.

B EXERCISES

1. The differential equation for the motion of a mass m suspended from a vertical spring of constant k, if damping proportional to the instantaneous velocity is taken into account, is $m\ddot{x} + \beta\dot{x} + kx = 0$, where the dots denote differentiation with respect to time t. Show that damped oscillations will take place provided that the damping constant is small enough so that $\beta < 2\sqrt{km}$ and that x is given by

$$x = Ce^{-\beta t/2m} \sin (\omega t + \phi)$$

where $\omega = \sqrt{k/m - \beta^2/4m^2}$ and C and ϕ represent two arbitrary constants.

2. (a) Show that the times at which $x = Ce^{-\alpha t} \sin (\omega t + \phi)$ is a maximum (in absolute value) are given by $t_1, t_2, \ldots$, where

$$t_n = \frac{1}{\omega} \left[\arctan \frac{\omega}{\alpha} + (n-1)\pi - \phi \right]$$

Hence show that the quasi period is $2\pi/\omega$. (b) Show that the quasi period for the motion described in Exercise 1 is greater than the natural period (reciprocal of natural frequency).

3. By using the result of Exercise 2(a) show that the successive maximum distances from the equilibrium position are given by

$$x_n = Ce^{-\beta t_n/2m}\sqrt{1 - \beta^2/4mk}$$

where t_n is given in Exercise 2(a). Hence, show that

$$\frac{x_{n+1}}{x_n} = e^{-\beta\pi/2m\omega}$$

i.e., the successive swings decrease in geometric progression. In engineering, the quantity $\beta\pi/2m\omega$ is called the *logarithmic decrement*.

4. (a) Show that the times at which

$$x = Ce^{-\alpha t}\sin(\omega t + \phi)$$

intersects the curves $x = Ce^{-\alpha t}$ and $x = -Ce^{-\alpha t}$ are given by

$$\tau_n = \frac{1}{\omega}\left[(2n - 1)\frac{\pi}{2} - \phi\right] \qquad n = 1, 2, 3, \ldots$$

Hence, show that the quasi period may also be obtained by considering the difference of the successive times where $\sin(\omega t + \phi) = 1$ (or -1). Compare with Exercise 2(a) above. (b) Let $X_1, X_2, \ldots$ denote the absolute values of the successive values of x corresponding to the times $\tau_1, \tau_2, \ldots$. Show that

$$\frac{X_{n+1}}{X_n} = e^{-\beta\pi/2m\omega}$$

and compare with the result of Exercise 3.

5. Compare the times t_n and τ_n of Exercises 2 and 4, respectively, and show that

$$\omega(\tau_n - t_n) = \frac{\pi}{2} - \text{arc tan}\,\frac{\omega}{\alpha} = \text{arc tan}\,\frac{\alpha}{\omega}$$

Also show that $\tau_n > t_n$ and that $\tau_n - t_n$ becomes smaller as the damping decreases.

3. Overdamped and critically damped vibrations of a spring.
The damping force may be too great compared with the restoring force to permit oscillatory motion. We consider this situation in the

ILLUSTRATIVE EXAMPLE 4

In Illustrative Example 1, page 186, assume that a damping force in pounds numerically equal to 3.75 times the instantaneous velocity is taken into account. Find x as a function of t.

Mathematical Formulation. Taking into account the damping force $-3.75\,dx/dt$ in the differential equation of Illustrative Example 1, we find

$$\frac{6}{32}\cdot\frac{d^2x}{dt^2} = -12x - 3.75\frac{dx}{dt} \quad \text{or} \quad \frac{d^2x}{dt^2} + 20\frac{dx}{dt} + 64x = 0 \qquad (24)$$

The initial conditions are as before

$$x = \frac{1}{3} \quad \text{at} \quad t = 0 \quad \text{and} \quad \frac{dx}{dt} = 0 \quad \text{at} \quad t = 0 \tag{25}$$

Solution. The auxiliary equation corresponding to (24) has roots $m = -4, -16$. Hence,

$$x = Ae^{-4t} + Be^{-16t}$$

Using conditions (25), we find

$$x = \tfrac{4}{9}e^{-4t} - \tfrac{1}{9}e^{-16t}$$

The graph appears in Fig. 66. It is seen that no oscillations occur; the weight has so much damping that it just gradually returns to the equilibrium position without passing through it. This type of motion is called *overdamped motion.*

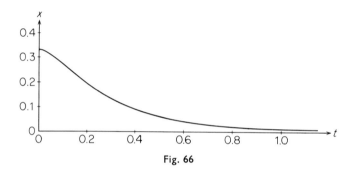

Fig. 66

An interesting case occurs when damping is such that any decrease in it produces oscillations. The motion is then *critically damped.*

ILLUSTRATIVE EXAMPLE 5

Instead of 3.75 in Illustrative Example 4, use 3, and find x as a function of t.

Mathematical Formulation. The equation becomes

$$\frac{6}{32} \cdot \frac{d^2x}{dt^2} = -12x - 3\frac{dx}{dt} \quad \text{or} \quad \frac{d^2x}{dt^2} + 16\frac{dx}{dt} + 64x = 0 \tag{26}$$

and the conditions are still $x = \tfrac{1}{3}$ at $t = 0$ and $dx/dt = 0$ at $t = 0$.

Solution. The roots of the auxiliary equation are $-8, -8$. Hence

$$x = Ae^{-8t} + Bte^{-8t}$$

and using the conditions at $t = 0$ we have

$$x = \tfrac{1}{3}e^{-8t} + \tfrac{8}{3}te^{-8t}$$

The graph appears in Fig. 67 (heavy curve) and is to be compared with the curve of Fig. 66 (shown dashed in Fig. 67). A slight decrease in damping would produce oscillations such as is shown in Fig. 65.

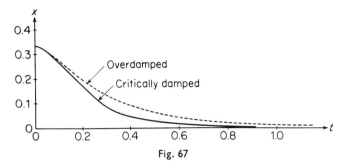

Fig. 67

It is interesting to inquire what would happen if the initial conditions in preceding illustrative examples were changed. It will be clear with but little thought that such a modification could not possibly change overdamped or critically damped motion into oscillatory motion. However some characteristics of the motion may be changed.

ILLUSTRATIVE EXAMPLE 6

Assume the differential equation of Illustrative Example 5 but change the initial conditions to $x = 0$, $dx/dt = 5$ at $t = 0$.

Solution. The solution to the differential equation is, as in Illustrative Example 5, $x = Ae^{-8t} + Bte^{-8t}$. Using the given conditions, we find

$$x = 5te^{-8t}$$

The graph appears in Fig. 68. To interpret this motion, observe that initially the weight is at the equilibrium position and is given a velocity downward

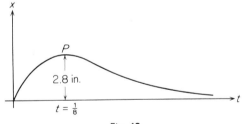

Fig. 68

(positive direction) of 5 ft/sec. It travels until it reaches a maximum displacement (point P in figure) and then slowly returns to the equilibrium position, never passing it. The maximum displacement, occurring after $\frac{1}{8}$ sec, is found by elementary calculus to be approximately 2.8 in.

A EXERCISES

1. A 2 lb weight on a spring stretches it 1.5 in. The weight is pulled 6 in. below its equilibrium position and released. Assume a damping force in pounds numerically equal to $2v$, where v is the instantaneous velocity in feet per second. (a) Find

the position of the weight at any time. (b) Determine whether the motion is overdamped or critically damped.

2. In the previous exercise assume the initial conditions are modified so that the weight is given a velocity downward of 10 ft/sec when it is at the equilibrium position. Find (a) the position and velocity at any time, (b) the maximum displacement of the weight from the equilibrium position.

3. A 3 lb weight on a spring stretches it 6 in. Assuming a damping force in pounds numerically equal to βv, where v is the instantaneous velocity in feet per second and $\beta > 0$, show that the motion is (a) critically damped if $\beta = 1.5$, (b) overdamped if $\beta > 1.5$, (c) oscillatory if $\beta < 1.5$.

B EXERCISES

1. A mass m is suspended vertically from a spring having constant k. The mass is pulled x_0 below its equilibrium position and given a velocity v_0 downward. A damping force, given by βv, where v is the instantaneous velocity and β is a positive constant, acts on the mass. Show that if the mass is chosen so that $m = \beta^2/4k$, then it will travel downward for a time given by

$$\frac{\beta^2 v_0}{2k(2kx_0 + \beta v_0)}$$

and then return gradually to the equilibrium position.

2. Interpret the results of Exercise 1 if $\beta v_0 = -2kx_0$.

C EXERCISES

1. A mass m is suspended vertically from a spring having constant k. At $t = 0$ the mass is struck so as to give it a velocity v_0 downward. A damping force βv, where v is the instantaneous velocity and β is a positive constant, acts on the mass. The damping is so large that $\beta > 2\sqrt{km}$. (a) Show that the instantaneous position of the mass at any time $t > 0$ is

$$x = \frac{v_0}{\gamma} e^{-\beta t/2m} \sinh \gamma t \quad \text{where} \quad \gamma = \frac{\sqrt{\beta^2 - 4km}}{2m}$$

measured from the equilibrium position. (b) Show that the mass travels downward for a time

$$\frac{1}{\gamma} \tanh^{-1} \frac{2m\gamma}{\beta}$$

and then gradually returns to the equilibrium position but never reaches it. Note that the time is independent of v_0. (c) Discuss the case $\gamma \to 0$ and compare with B Exercise 1.

2. Solve the previous problem in case the mass is pulled a distance x_0 below its equilibrium position and then given velocity v_0 downward.

4. The spring with external forces. In the previous paragraphs we discussed the problem of a spring where only restoring and damping forces were considered. We now consider cases where other external forces which depend on time may act. Such forces may occur, for example, when the support holding the spring is moved up and down in a prescribed manner such as in periodic motion, or when the weight is given a little push every time it reaches the lowest position. If we denote the external force by $F(t)$, the differential equation for motion of the spring is

$$\frac{W}{g} \cdot \frac{d^2x}{dt^2} = -kx - \beta \frac{dx}{dt} + F(t) \quad \text{or} \quad \frac{W}{g} \cdot \frac{d^2x}{dt^2} + \beta \frac{dx}{dt} + kx = F(t)$$

which may be written

$$a \frac{d^2x}{dt^2} + b \frac{dx}{dt} + cx = F(t) \tag{27}$$

(where $a = W/g$, $b = \beta$, $c = k$), an equation sometimes called the equation of *forced vibrations*.

ILLUSTRATIVE EXAMPLE 7

In Illustrative Example 3, page 192, assume that a periodic external force given by $F(t) = 24 \cos 8t$ is acting. Find x in terms of t, using the conditions given there.

Mathematical Formulation. The differential equation is

$$\frac{6}{32} \cdot \frac{d^2x}{dt^2} = -12x - 1.5 \frac{dx}{dt} + 24 \cos 8t$$

or

$$\frac{d^2x}{dt^2} + 8 \frac{dx}{dt} + 64x = 128 \cos 8t \tag{28}$$

and the initial conditions are $x = \frac{1}{3}$, $dx/dt = 0$ at $t = 0$.

Solution. From Illustrative Example 3, or directly, we see that the complementary solution of (28) is

$$x_c = e^{-4t} (A \cos 4\sqrt{3}\, t + B \sin 4\sqrt{3}\, t)$$

If we assume as particular solution $a \sin 8t + b \cos 8t$, we find $a = 2$, $b = 0$. Hence, the general solution of (28) is

$$x = e^{-4t}(A \cos 4\sqrt{3}\, t + B \sin 4\sqrt{3}\, t) + 2 \sin 8t$$

Using the initial conditions, we have $A = \frac{1}{3}$, $B = -11\sqrt{3}/9$ and, thus,

$$x = \frac{e^{-4t}}{9} (3 \cos 4\sqrt{3}\, t - 11\sqrt{3} \sin 4\sqrt{3}\, t) + 2 \sin 8t \tag{29}$$

The graph of (29) appears in Fig. 69. It will be observed that the terms in (29) involving e^{-4t} become negligible when t is large. These terms are called *transient terms* and are significant only when t is near zero. These transient

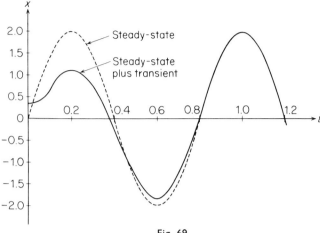

Fig. 69

terms in the solution, when they are significant, are sometimes called the *transient solution*. When the transient terms are negligible, the term 2 sin 8*t* remains. This is called the *steady-state term* or *steady-state solution*, since it indicates the behavior of the system when conditions have become steady. It is seen that the steady-state solution (dashed curve in Fig. 69) is periodic and has the same period as that of the applied external force.

A EXERCISES

1. A vertical spring having constant 5 lb/ft has a 16 lb weight suspended from it. An external force given by $F(t) = 24 \sin 10t$, $t \geq 0$ is applied. A damping force given numerically in pounds by $4v$, where v is the instantaneous velocity of the weight in feet per second, is assumed to act. Initially the weight is at rest at its equilibrium position. (a) Determine the position of the weight at any time. (b) Indicate the transient and steady-state solutions. (c) Find the amplitude, period, and frequency of the steady-state solution.

2. A vertical spring having constant 8 lb/ft has a 64 lb weight suspended from it. A force given by $F(t) = 16 \cos 4t$, $t \geq 0$ is applied. Assuming that the weight, initially at the equilibrium position, is given an upward velocity of 10 ft/sec and that the damping force is negligible, determine the position and velocity of the weight at any time.

B EXERCISE

The motion of a mass on a certain vertical spring is described by

$$\frac{d^2x}{dt^2} + 100x = 36 \cos 8t, \quad x = 0, \quad \frac{dx}{dt} = 0 \quad \text{at} \quad t = 0$$

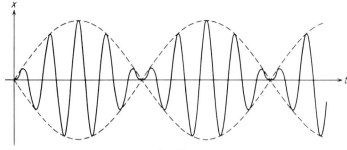

Fig. 70

where x is the instantaneous distance of the mass from the equilibrium position, downward being taken as the positive direction. (a) Give a physical interpretation to the problem. (b) Show that the solution may be written $x = 2 \sin t \sin 9t$. (c) Show that the graph of x as a function of t is similar to that of Fig. 70.

The solution may be written $x = \mathcal{A}(t) \sin 9t$, where $\mathcal{A}(t) = \sin t$ is called the time-varying amplitude and is a slowly varying function (period $= 2\pi$) in comparison with the wave $\sin 9t$ (period $= 2\pi/9$). The wave $\sin 9t$ is said to be *amplitude modulated*. In the theory of acoustics these fluctuations of amplitude are called *beats*, the loud sounds corresponding to the large amplitudes. Beats may occur when two tuning forks having nearly equal frequencies are set into vibration simultaneously. A practical use of this is in tuning of pianos (or other instruments) where successful tuning is marked by adjusting the frequency of a note to that of a standard note until beats are eliminated. The phenomenon is also important in the theories of optics and electricity.

C EXERCISE

A spring (having constant k) with an attached mass m is suspended from a support which oscillates about line OP (Fig. 71) in such a way that the instantaneous distance of the support from OP is $A \cos \omega t$, $t \geq 0$, where A is constant. Let x represent the instantaneous stretch of the spring.

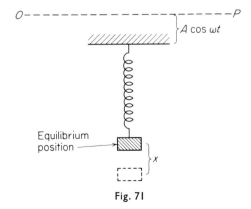

Fig. 71

(a) Show that the differential equation of motion of the mass is

$$m\frac{d^2x}{dt^2} + kx = mA\omega^2 \cos \omega t$$

if damping is negligible.

(b) If at $t = 0$, $x = 0$ and $dx/dt = 0$, and if ω is nearly equal to $\sqrt{k/m}$, show that beats are produced which have very large amplitudes these becoming larger the closer ω is to $\sqrt{k/m}$.

(c) Discuss the case $\omega = \sqrt{k/m}$.

5. The phenomenon of mechanical resonance. When the frequency of a periodic external force applied to a mechanical system is related in a simple way, which will be described, to the natural frequency of the system, mechanical resonance may occur which builds up the oscillations to such tremendous magnitudes that the system may fall apart. A company of soldiers marching in step across a bridge may in this manner cause the bridge to collapse even though it would have been strong enough to carry many more soldiers had they marched out of step. In an exactly analogous manner, it may be possible for a musical note of proper characteristic frequency to shatter a glass. Because of the great damages which may thus occur, mechanical resonance is in general something which needs to be avoided, especially by the engineer in designing structures or vibrating mechanisms. The special case given in the following example will indicate what may be the consequences of resonance.

ILLUSTRATIVE EXAMPLE 8

Suppose an external force given by $3 \cos 8t$ is applied to the spring of Illustrative Example 1, page 186. Describe the motion which ensues if it is assumed that initially the weight is at the equilibrium position ($x = 0$) and that its initial velocity is zero.

Mathematical Formulation. The differential equation is

$$\frac{6}{32} \cdot \frac{d^2x}{dt^2} = -12x + 3 \cos 8t \quad \text{or} \quad \frac{d^2x}{dt^2} + 64x = 16 \cos 8t \quad (30)$$

and the initial conditions are $x = 0$, $dx/dt = 0$ at $t = 0$.

Solution. The complementary solution of (30) is

$$x_c = A \cos 8t + B \sin 8t$$

For particular solution we must assume

$$x_p = t(a \cos 8t + b \sin 8t)$$

Substituting in the differential equation, we find $a = 0$, $b = 1$. Thus, the general solution is

$$x = A \cos 8t + B \sin 8t + t \sin 8t$$

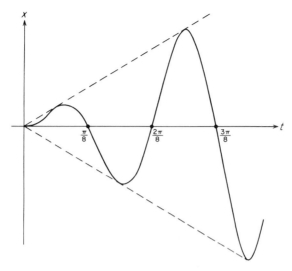

Fig. 72

Using the initial conditions, it is readily found that $A = B = 0$. Hence

$$x = t \sin 8t \tag{31}$$

The graph of (31) lies between the graphs of $x = t$ and $x = -t$ as shown in Fig. 72. It is seen from the graph that the oscillations build up without limit. Naturally, the spring is bound to break within a short time.

It should be noted that in this example damping was neglected and resonance occurred because the *frequency of the applied external force was equal to the natural frequency of the undamped system.* This is a general principle. In the case where damping occurs, the oscillations do not build up without limit but may nevertheless become very large. Resonance in this case occurs when the frequency of the applied external force is slightly smaller than the natural frequency of the system. For further discussion of this see B Exercise 1.

A EXERCISES

1. A vertical spring having constant 4 lb/ft has a 32 lb weight attached to it. A force given by $F(t) = 16 \sin 2t$, $t \geq 0$ is applied. Assuming that at $t = 0$ the weight is at rest at the equilibrium position and that the damping force is negligible, (a) set up a differential equation and conditions describing the motion; (b) determine the position and velocity of the weight at any time; (c) show that the motion is one of resonance.

2. In the previous problem suppose that at $t = 0$ the weight is 6 in. below the equilibrium position and is struck so as to give it a velocity of 4 ft/sec upward. Determine the position and velocity of the weight at any time. Is the motion still one of resonance?

B EXERCISES

1. The equation of forced vibration of a mass on a vertical spring is

$$m\frac{d^2x}{dt^2} + \beta\frac{dx}{dt} + kx = A\cos\omega t \qquad t \geq 0$$

where x is the displacement of the mass from its equilibrium position and m, β, k, A, and ω are positive constants. (a) Show that a steady-state oscillation is given by

$$x = \frac{A}{\sqrt{(m\omega^2 - k)^2 + \beta^2\omega^2}}\cos(\omega t + \phi)$$

(b) Show that maximum oscillations (resonance) will occur if ω is so chosen that

$$\omega = \sqrt{\frac{k}{m} - \frac{\beta^2}{2m^2}}$$

provided $\beta^2 < 2km$. (c) Show that at resonance, the amplitude of the oscillation varies inversely as the damping constant β.

2. Discuss Exercise 1 if $\beta^2 \geq 2km$.

C EXERCISES

1. A mass on a spring undergoes a forced vibration given by

$$m\frac{d^2x}{dt^2} + kx = A\cos^3\omega t \qquad t \geq 0$$

where m, k, A, and ω are constants. Show that there are two values of ω at which resonance occurs and determine them.

2. A mass on a spring undergoes a forced vibration given by

$$m\frac{d^2x}{dt^2} + kx = \sum_{n=1}^{M} a_n\cos\frac{2\pi nt}{T} \qquad t \geq 0, a_n \neq 0$$

(a) Show that the least period of the external force is T. (b) Show that resonance will occur if T has any one of the M values $2\pi n\sqrt{m/k}$, where $n = 1, 2, \ldots, M$.

It can be shown that a suitable function $F(t)$ defined in the interval $0 \leq t < T$ and which is such that $F(t + T) = F(t)$ outside the interval [i.e., $F(t)$ has period T] can be expanded in a series

$$A + \sum_{n=1}^{\infty}\left(a_n\cos\frac{2\pi nt}{T} + b_n\sin\frac{2\pi nt}{T}\right)$$

Such series are called *Fourier series*. Conditions under which such expansion is possible and determination of the constants A, a_n, b_n are presented in Chapter 11.

3. If $m\, d^2x/dt^2 + kx = F(t)$, $t \geq 0$ such that $x = 0$, $dx/dt = 0$ at $t = 0$, show that

$$x = \frac{1}{\sqrt{km}} \int_0^t F(u) \sin\sqrt{\frac{k}{m}}\,(t - u)\, du$$

Find x if

$$F(t) = \begin{cases} t, & 0 \leq t \leq T \\ 0, & t > T \end{cases}$$

and discuss a possible physical interpretation.

4. Solve the previous problem if

$$F(t) = \begin{cases} F_0/\epsilon, & 0 \leq t \leq \epsilon \\ 0, & t > \epsilon \end{cases}$$

where F_0 and ϵ are constants. Discuss the case $\epsilon \to 0$ and interpret the problem physically.

II. Electric Circuit Problems

In Chapter 3, Section II, the student learned how to formulate differential equations arising from certain problems involving electric circuits. The case where a resistor, capacitor, and inductor were connected in series with a battery or generator was not considered. In this section we shall treat this case.

Consider the series circuit of Fig. 73. When the key or switch K is closed, an instantaneous current will flow. If we call Q the instantaneous charge on the capacitor C, then by Kirchhoff's law,

$$L\frac{dI}{dt} + RI + \frac{Q}{C} = E(t) \qquad (1)$$

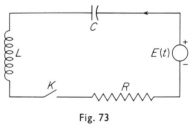

Fig. 73

where $E(t)$, the emf, may depend on time, but where we assume L, R, C are constants. Since $I = dQ/dt$, (1) becomes

$$L\frac{d^2Q}{dt^2} + R\frac{dQ}{dt} + \frac{Q}{C} = E(t) \qquad (2)$$

Upon comparison with the general equation of forced vibrations [see equation (27), page 199] we notice the striking analogy between the mechanical and electrical quantities.

Charge Q corresponds to *position* x.
Inductance L corresponds to *mass* m or W/g.
Resistance R corresponds to *damping constant* β.
Inverse capacitance $1/C$ corresponds to *spring constant* k.
Electromotive force $E(t)$ corresponds to *applied external force* $F(t)$.
Current $I = dQ/dt$ corresponds to *velocity* $v = dx/dt$.

Because of the remarkable analogy between these mechanical and electrical quantities, which holds in even more complicated cases, most of the statements made for mechanical systems apply to electric systems and vice versa. In fact, the analogy is often made use of in industry in studying a mechanical system which may be too complicated or too expensive to build, or when perhaps the consequences may be too dangerous.

In particular, the phenomenon of resonance occurs in electric systems. However, contrary to the dangerous effects which may result in mechanical resonance, the effects of electrical resonance are mainly very useful. The fields of radio, television, radar, and communications would virtually be impossible were it not for electrical resonance. In such instances the current and consequently the power generated may build up to the large amounts necessary in these fields. It is because of electrical resonance that we need to tune our radio to the frequency of the transmitting radio station in order to get reception.

Illustrative Example

An inductor of 0.5 henry is connected in series with a resistor of 6 ohms, a capacitor of 0.02 farad, a generator having alternating voltage given by 24 sin 10t, $t \geq 0$, and a switch K (Fig. 74).

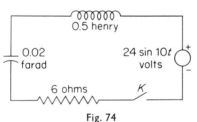

(a) Set up a differential equation for the instantaneous charge on the capacitor.

(b) Find the charge and current at time t if the charge on the capacitor is zero when the switch K is closed at $t = 0$.

Fig. 74

Mathematical Formulation: Voltage drop across resistor is $6I$. Voltage drop across inductor is $0.5 \, dI/dt$. Voltage drop across capacitor is $Q/0.02 = 50Q$.

Hence, by Kirchhoff's law,

$$6I + 0.5 \frac{dI}{dt} + 50Q = 24 \sin 10t$$

or since $I = dQ/dt$,

$$0.5 \frac{d^2Q}{dt^2} + 6 \frac{dQ}{dt} + 50Q = 24 \sin 10t$$

or

$$\frac{d^2Q}{dt^2} + 12 \frac{dQ}{dt} + 100Q = 48 \sin 10t \tag{3}$$

The conditions are $Q = 0$ and $I = dQ/dt = 0$ at $t = 0$.

Solution. The complementary solution of (3) is

$$e^{-6t}(A \cos 8t + B \sin 8t)$$

Assuming the particular solution $a \sin 10t + b \cos 10t$, we find $a = 0$, $b = -\frac{2}{5}$. Hence, the general solution of (3) is

$$Q = e^{-6t}(A \cos 8t + B \sin 8t) - \tfrac{2}{5} \cos 10t$$

From the initial conditions we find $A = \frac{2}{5}$, $B = \frac{3}{10}$. Hence, the required solution is

$$Q = \tfrac{1}{10}e^{-6t}(4 \cos 8t + 3 \sin 8t) - \tfrac{2}{5} \cos 10t$$

It will be noted that the term with e^{-6t} is the *transient solution*; it soon becomes negligible. The term $-\frac{2}{5} \cos 10t$ is the *steady-state solution*; it remains after the transient term has virtually disappeared. The student should compare this with the example and graph on pages 199 and 200.

A EXERCISES

1. An emf of 500 v is in series with a 20 ohm resistor, a 4 henry inductor, and a 0.008 farad capacitor. At $t = 0$, the charge Q and current I are zero. (a) Find Q and I at any time $t \geq 0$. (b) Indicate the transient and steady-state terms in Q and I. (c) Find the charge and current after a long time.

2. A capacitor of 10^{-3} farads is in series with an emf of 20 volts and an inductor of 0.4 henries. At $t = 0$, $Q = 0$, and $I = 0$. (a) Find the natural frequency and period of the electric oscillations. (b) Find the maximum charge and current.

3. A 0.1 henry inductor, a 4×10^{-3} farad capacitor, and a generator having emf given by $180 \cos 40t$, $t \geq 0$, are connected in series. Find the instantaneous charge Q and current I if $I = Q = 0$ at $t = 0$.

4. A resistor of 50 ohms, an inductor of 2 henries and a 0.005 farad capacitor are in series with an emf of 40 volts and an open switch. Find the instantaneous charge and current after the switch is closed at $t = 0$, assuming that at that time the charge on the capacitor is 4 coulombs.

B EXERCISES

1. An inductor L, capacitor C, and resistor R are connected in series. At $t = 0$, the charge on the capacitor is Q_0, while the current is zero. Show that the charge Q and current I will be oscillatory if $R < 2\sqrt{L/C}$ and will be given by

$$Q = \frac{Q_0}{2\omega L} e^{-Rt/2L} \sqrt{R^2 + 4\omega^2 L^2} \sin(\omega t + \phi)$$

$$I = -\frac{Q_0(R^2 + 4\omega^2 L^2)}{4\omega L^2} e^{-Rt/2L} \sin \omega t$$

where

$$\omega = \sqrt{\frac{1}{LC} - \frac{R^2}{4L^2}}, \qquad \phi = \arctan \frac{2\omega L}{R}$$

What is the quasi period of the oscillations (see page 193)?

2. If $R = 0$ in Exercise 1, show that the natural period of the oscillations is $2\pi\sqrt{LC}$. If $L = 0.5$ henries and $C = 4$ microfarads, find the natural frequency.

3. Discuss Exercise 1 if $R \geq 2\sqrt{L/C}$, showing the analogue of critically damped and overdamped motion in mechanical systems.

4. An inductor of 0.5 henries is connected in series with a resistor of 5 ohms, and a capacitor of 0.08 farads. At $t = 0$ the current is 10 amp, and the charge on the capacitor is zero. Show that the charge builds up to a maximum in 0.2 sec and determine the value of the maximum.

C EXERCISES

1. An inductor L, resistor R, and capacitor C are connected in series with an a-c generator having voltage given by $E_0 \cos \omega t$, $t \geq 0$. If L, R, C, E_0, and ω are given constants:

   (a) Show that the differential equation of the circuit is

$$L\frac{d^2I}{dt^2} + R\frac{dI}{dt} + \frac{I}{C} = \frac{d}{dt}(\text{Re }E_0 e^{i\omega t}) \quad t \geq 0$$

where I is the instantaneous current and Re denotes "real part of."

   (b) Let $I = \text{Re }(Ae^{i\omega t})$, where A is a constant complex number and show that

$$A = \frac{E_0}{R + i(\omega L - 1/\omega C)} = \frac{E_0}{R + iX}$$

Write $R + iX = Ze^{i\phi}$, so that $Z = \sqrt{R^2 + X^2}$, $\phi = $ arc tan X/R. Hence, show that

$$I = \frac{E_0}{Z}\cos(\omega t - \phi)$$

is the steady-state current. The quantity Z is called the *impedance* of the circuit, the quantity X is called the *reactance*.

   (c) Prove that the current becomes very large (electrical resonance) when the frequency of the applied voltage is given by $f = 1/(2\pi\sqrt{LC})$, whereas the charge on the capacitor is a maximum when

$$f = \frac{1}{2\pi}\sqrt{\frac{1}{LC} - \frac{R^2}{2L^2}}$$

2. Show that there are two frequencies, one below and one above the resonant frequency, at which the amplitudes are $1/n$th of the amplitude at resonance. Prove that the difference of these frequencies is independent of the capacitance and is given by $R\sqrt{n^2 - 1}/2\pi L$. The ratio of this difference to the resonant frequency $f = \omega/2\pi$ is $R\sqrt{n^2 - 1}/\omega L$. The quantity $Q = \omega L/R$ is called the "Q of the circuit." If Q is large, resonance is "sharp," and we say that we have "sharp tuning." This is important in radio, television, and communications. For practical purposes n is usually taken as 2.

III. Miscellaneous Problems

In this section we consider various illustrative problems which lead to linear differential equations with constant coefficients.

ILLUSTRATIVE EXAMPLE 1

A cubical box 10 ft on a side floats in still water (density 62.5 lb/ft³). It is observed that the box oscillates up and down with a period of $\frac{1}{2}$ sec. What is the weight of the box?

Mathematical Formulation. Figure 75 shows the cube in its equilibrium position, indicated by *ABC*. Figure 76 shows the cube nearly all submerged

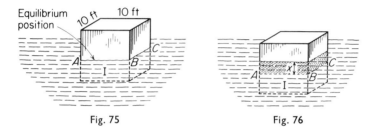

Fig. 75   Fig. 76

in water. In this position there is a force tending to push the box up again. To determine this force we need the physical law known as:

ARCHIMEDES' PRINCIPLE. *An object partially or totally submerged in a fluid is buoyed up by a force equal to the weight of the fluid displaced.*

From this principle it is clear that the weight of the cube equals the weight of the water occupied by that portion of the cube below the surface in Fig. 75, which is indicated by I. The region I needed to balance the weight of the cube is also shown in Fig. 76. From Fig. 76 it is evident that there is an additional unbalanced force equal to the weight of the water which would occupy the shaded region in that figure. Since the dimensions of the shaded region are x feet by 10 ft by 10 ft, and since the water weighs 62.5 lb/ft³, the weight of the water normally occupying such a region would be 62.5 × x × 10 × 10 lb, or 6250x lb. This is numerically the net force acting to move the cube. It is analogous to the restoring force of the vibrating spring. Denoting the weight of the box in pounds by W, which we have to find, we have by Newton's law,

$$\frac{W}{g} \cdot \frac{d^2x}{dt^2} = -6250x \quad \text{or} \quad \frac{d^2x}{dt^2} + \frac{200{,}000x}{W} = 0 \tag{1}$$

taking $g = 32$.

Solution. The general solution of (1) is

$$x = A \cos \sqrt{\frac{200{,}000}{W}}\, t + B \sin \sqrt{\frac{200{,}000}{W}}\, t$$

from which it is clear that the period is

$$T = \frac{2\pi}{\sqrt{200,000/W}} \quad \text{or} \quad T = \frac{2\pi\sqrt{W}}{200\sqrt{5}}$$

Equating this to $\frac{1}{2}$ sec, we find $W = 1270$ lb approximately.

ILLUSTRATIVE EXAMPLE 2

A simple pendulum consists of a particle of mass m supported by a wire (or inelastic string) of length l and of negligible mass. Assuming that the wire is always straight and that the system is free to vibrate in a vertical plane, find the period of vibration.

Mathematical Formulation. Let AB (Fig. 77) denote the wire, A being the fixed point of support, B the other end of the wire at which is attached mass m.

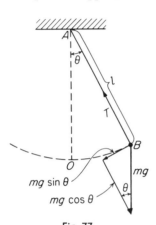

Fig. 77

Let θ denote the angle which the wire makes with the vertical AO at any instant. While the mass m is in motion there are two forces acting on it, the tension T in the string and the weight mg of the mass. Resolving the weight mg into two components, one parallel to the path of motion and one perpendicular to it, we see that the component perpendicular to the path is balanced by the tension. The magnitude of the net force acting tangent to the path is $mg \sin \theta$. We choose signs so that $\theta > 0$ when the mass is on the right in the figure and $\theta < 0$ when it is on the left. This means essentially that we are choosing directions along the arc to the right as positive and to the left as negative. When $\theta > 0$, the resulting force is to the left, and when $\theta < 0$, the resulting force is to the right. The net force in magnitude and direction is thus given by $-mg \sin \theta$. Since the arc length is given by $s = l\theta$, we have by Newton's law,

$$m \frac{d^2s}{dt^2} = ml \frac{d^2\theta}{dt^2} = -mg \sin \theta \quad \text{or} \quad \frac{d^2\theta}{dt^2} = -\frac{g}{l} \sin \theta \quad (2)$$

Equation (2) cannot be solved exactly in terms of elementary functions (however, see C Exercises 3, 4, 5). In order to proceed further we make an approximation. For small angles (roughly between $-5°$ and $+5°$) we may write $\sin \theta = \theta$, where θ is in radians. Thus within the range of our approximation (2) can be written

$$\frac{d^2\theta}{dt^2} + \frac{g\theta}{l} = 0 \quad (3)$$

Solution. The roots of the auxiliary equation corresponding to (3) are $\pm i\sqrt{g/l}$. Hence, its general solution is

$$\theta = A \sin \sqrt{g/l}\, t + B \cos \sqrt{g/l}\, t$$

From this it is clear that the period T is given by

$$T = \frac{2\pi}{\sqrt{g/l}} \quad \text{or} \quad T = 2\pi\sqrt{l/g} \tag{4}$$

a formula familiar in elementary physics.

It should be noted that to find the period here, as in Illustrative Example 1, initial conditions were not needed. It should also be noted that our approximation of $\sin\theta$ by θ is equivalent to assuming that the motion is that of simple harmonic motion.

A EXERCISES

1. A cube 5 ft on a side and weighing 500 lb floats in still water. It is pushed down slightly and released so that oscillations take place. Find the period and frequency of the vibrations.

2. The small oscillations of a simple pendulum have a period of 2 sec. Determine the length of the pendulum. Find the corresponding length of a simple pendulum which has twice this period.

3. A cylinder 4 ft in radius and 6 ft in altitude, weighing 1000 lb, vibrates in still water with its axis vertical. Find the frequency and period of the vibrations.

4. The bob of a simple pendulum of length 2 ft is displaced so that the pendulum rod makes an angle of 5° with the vertical. If the pendulum is released from this position: (a) Find the angle θ which the rod makes with the vertical at any time. (b) Determine the frequency of the vibration. (c) Calculate the distance traveled by the pendulum bob during one period. (d) Find the velocity and acceleration of the bob at the center of its path.

B EXERCISES

1. A cylinder of radius r and height h and having weight W floats with its axis vertical in a liquid of density ρ. If it is set into vibration, show that the period is

$$\frac{2}{r}\sqrt{\frac{\pi W}{\rho g}}.$$

2. A cylinder vibrates with its axis vertical in a certain liquid. It is found that the frequency of the vibrations in the liquid is half of the corresponding frequency in water. Determine the density of the liquid.

3. A simple pendulum vibrates in a medium in which the damping is proportional to the instantaneous velocity. If the pendulum bob passes through the equilibrium position $\theta = 0$ at $t = 0$ with velocity v_0, show that the angle θ which the pendulum rod makes with the vertical is

$$\theta = \frac{v_0}{\omega l}e^{-\beta t}\sin\omega t, \qquad \omega = \sqrt{\frac{g}{l} - \beta^2}$$

where β is the damping constant and l is the length of the pendulum. Find β if the distance traveled during one complete cycle is half the previous one. What is the quasi period and frequency?

C EXERCISES

1. A sphere of radius R floats half submerged in a liquid. It is set into vibration. If x denotes the instantaneous displacement of the diametral plane of the sphere from the equilibrium position, show that

$$\frac{d^2x}{dt^2} = -\frac{3g}{2}\left[\frac{x}{R} - \frac{1}{3}\left(\frac{x}{R}\right)^3\right]$$

Hence, show that for small vibrations the sphere vibrates with frequency equal to that of a simple pendulum of length $2R/3$.

2. If the sphere of the previous problem is pushed down until it is just barely under the liquid and is then released, show that the velocity of the sphere at the instant when the diametral plane coincides with the surface is $\frac{1}{2}\sqrt{5gR}$.

3. The instantaneous angle θ which the rod of a vibrating simple pendulum makes with the vertical is given by

$$\frac{d^2\theta}{dt^2} = -\frac{g}{l}\sin\theta$$

where l is the length of the pendulum. If initially the pendulum bob is displaced so that $\theta = \theta_0$ at $t = 0$ and is then released, show that

$$\left(\frac{d\theta}{dt}\right)^2 = \frac{2g}{l}(\cos\theta - \cos\theta_0)$$

Thus, show that the period T is given by

$$T = 2\sqrt{\frac{2l}{g}}\int_0^{\theta_0}\frac{d\theta}{\sqrt{\cos\theta - \cos\theta_0}}$$

4. Use the identity $\cos u = 1 - 2\sin^2 u/2$ to show that

$$T = 2\sqrt{\frac{l}{g}}\int_0^{\theta_0}\frac{d\theta}{\sqrt{\sin^2\dfrac{\theta_0}{2} - \sin^2\dfrac{\theta}{2}}}$$

Then by letting $\sin\dfrac{\theta}{2} = \sin\dfrac{\theta_0}{2}\sin\phi$, where ϕ is a new variable, show that

$$T = 4\sqrt{\frac{l}{g}}\int_0^{\pi/2}\frac{d\phi}{\sqrt{1 - k^2\sin^2\phi}}, \qquad k = \sin\frac{\theta_0}{2}$$

This integral is called an *elliptic integral of the first kind*.

5. By using the result

$$\frac{1}{\sqrt{1-x}} = 1 + \frac{1}{2}x + \frac{1 \cdot 3}{2 \cdot 4}x^2 + \frac{1 \cdot 3 \cdot 5}{2 \cdot 4 \cdot 6}x^3 + \cdots \qquad |x| < 1$$

where $x = k^2 \sin^2 \phi$, show that

$$T = 2\pi \sqrt{\frac{l}{g}} \left[1 + \left(\frac{1}{2}\right)^2 k^2 + \left(\frac{1 \cdot 3}{2 \cdot 4}\right)^2 k^2 + \left(\frac{1 \cdot 3 \cdot 5}{2 \cdot 4 \cdot 6}\right)^2 k^6 + \cdots \right]$$

assuming the term by term integration to be valid.

Hint: Use the result $\displaystyle\int_0^{\pi/2} \sin^{2n} \phi \, d\phi = \frac{1 \cdot 3 \cdots (2n-1)}{2 \cdot 4 \cdots 2n} \cdot \frac{\pi}{2}.$

   Find the period of a pendulum when the rod makes a maximum angle of $30°$, $60°$ with the vertical.

6. If the sphere of Exercise 1 is pushed down until the diametral plane is a distance $p(0 < p \leq R)$ below the surface of the liquid and is then released, show that the period T of the resulting vibrations is

$$T = 8R \sqrt{\frac{R}{g(6R^2 - p^2)}} \int_0^{\pi/2} \frac{d\phi}{\sqrt{1 - k^2 \sin^2 \phi}}, \qquad k^2 = \frac{p^2}{6R^2 - p^2}$$

Use the result of Exercise 5 to calculate T in the case where $p = R$. Determine T when p is near zero. Compare with Exercise 1. Does the result hold when $p = 0$?

Chapter Six

SIMULTANEOUS DIFFERENTIAL EQUATIONS

AND THEIR APPLICATIONS

I. Solutions of Simultaneous Differential Equations

1. Introduction. Up to now we have studied differential equations involving one independent and one dependent variable. Often in applications one encounters equations containing one independent but two or more dependent variables. For example,

$$\frac{dx}{dt} + 3\frac{dy}{dt} + y = e^t \tag{1}$$

involves the single independent variable t (with respect to which one obtains derivatives) and the two dependent variables x and y, dependent on t. We ask the

Question. What shall we mean by a solution of (1)?

Clearly if we can find x and y in terms of t, which when substituted in (1) reduce it to an identity, we shall certainly want to call the pair of functions x and y a solution. Such pairs are easy to find. For example, if we let $y = t^2$ in (1), we find

$$\frac{dx}{dt} = e^t - 6t - t^2 \quad \text{so that} \quad x = e^t - 3t^2 - \frac{t^3}{3} + c$$

upon integration. Certainly we can find an unlimited number of such pairs.

We can limit the number of possible pairs by having another differential equation similar to (1), for example,

$$\frac{dy}{dt} - x = y \tag{2}$$

Our problem now is to determine pairs x and y which satisfy simultaneously equations (1) and (2). For this reason we call the pair (1) and (2) *simultaneous differential equations.*

We have encountered a similar situation in algebra. Given the linear equation $x + 2y = 6$, for example, there are infinitely many pairs of solutions. Thus $x = 6$, $y = 0$; $x = 3$, $y = \frac{3}{2}$, etc. are solutions. If, however, we impose another condition, say $2x + y = 3$, the pair $x = 0$, $y = 3$ is the only simultaneous solution.

2. Determination of a solution of simultaneous differential equations. In algebra we were taught to solve two simultaneous equations in two unknowns by eliminating one of the unknowns between the two equations. A single equation having only one unknown is thus obtained from which we may deduce the value or values of the unknown. Finally, we substitute in either of the original equations and find values for the other unknown. Solutions to simultaneous differential equations are obtained in an analogous manner. The process is demonstrated in the following

ILLUSTRATIVE EXAMPLE 1

Solve simultaneously

$$\text{(a) } \frac{dx}{dt} + 3\frac{dy}{dt} + y = e^t, \qquad \text{(b) } \frac{dy}{dt} - x = y$$

Solution. From equation (b), $x = (dy/dt) - y$. Substituting in (a),

$$\frac{d}{dt}\left(\frac{dy}{dt} - y\right) + 3\frac{dy}{dt} + y = e^t \quad \text{or} \quad \frac{d^2y}{dt^2} + 2\frac{dy}{dt} + y = e^t \qquad (3)$$

an equation involving y but not x. The general solution of (3) is

$$y = c_1e^{-t} + c_2te^{-t} + \tfrac{1}{4}e^t \qquad (4)$$

Thus, we find

$$x = \frac{dy}{dt} - y = -2c_1e^{-t} + c_2e^{-t} - 2c_2te^{-t} \qquad (5)$$

The pair (4) and (5) constitutes the simultaneous solution. The student should check to see that these do indeed satisfy (a) and (b).

Remark: If the value (4) for y were substituted in (a) instead, we would have obtained

$$\frac{dx}{dt} = e^t - 3\frac{dy}{dt} - y = 2c_1e^{-t} - 3c_2e^{-t} + 2c_2te^{-t}$$

from which we get upon integrating,

$$x = -2c_1e^{-t} + c_2e^{-t} - 2c_2te^{-t} + c_3 \qquad (6)$$

Thus, we might believe that (4) and (6) constituted a solution. Upon substitution of these supposed solutions into the original equations we would find that $c_3 = 0$. Because of the possibility of obtaining *too many arbitrary constants*, the solution should *always* be checked in the original equations.

In Illustrative Example 1 it was easy to eliminate one of the dependent variables. Sometimes though, it may not be so obvious. Consider

ILLUSTRATIVE EXAMPLE 2

Solve simultaneously

$$\text{(a)} \quad \frac{d^2x}{dt^2} + \frac{dy}{dt} + x = y, \qquad \text{(b)} \quad \frac{d^2y}{dt^2} + 3\frac{dx}{dt} + 2y = x$$

Solution. We shall try to eliminate y from the two equations. Differentiating (a), we find

$$\frac{d^3x}{dt^3} + \frac{d^2y}{dt^2} + \frac{dx}{dt} = \frac{dy}{dt}$$

Subtracting (b), we eliminate d^2y/dt^2, so that

$$\frac{d^3x}{dt^3} - 2\frac{dx}{dt} - 2y = \frac{dy}{dt} - x \tag{7}$$

We must still eliminate y and dy/dt. From (a) we have

$$\frac{dy}{dt} = y - x - \frac{d^2x}{dt^2} \tag{8}$$

Substituting in (7) and arranging terms,

$$\frac{d^3x}{dt^3} + \frac{d^2x}{dt^2} - 2\frac{dx}{dt} + 2x = 3y \tag{9}$$

Only y needs to be eliminated. Solving for y in (9) and substituting in (8) yields

$$\frac{d^4x}{dt^4} + 4\frac{dx}{dt} + x = 0 \tag{10}$$

an equation involving x alone. From this point we proceed as in Illustrative Example 1, the only difference being the complexity of (10).

 It will be noted that the method of elimination was tedious and a shorter approach is certainly welcome. We show one such approach.

3. The use of operators in eliminating unknowns. Using the notation of the symbolic operator $D \equiv d/dt$, equations (a) and (b) of Illustrative Example 2 can be written in the form

$$(D^2 + 1)x + (D - 1)y = 0 \tag{11}$$

$$(3D - 1)x + (D^2 + 2)y = 0 \tag{12}$$

The temptation to eliminate x or y by treating D as nothing more than an algebraic symbol is great. If we should yield to this urge realizing that in so doing there still remains the task of justification we would proceed as follows: "Multiply" (11) by $(D^2 + 2)$ and (12) by $(D - 1)$ to obtain

$$(D^2 + 2)(D^2 + 1)x + (D^2 + 2)(D - 1)y = 0$$

$$(D - 1)(3D - 1)x + (D - 1)(D^2 + 2)y = 0$$

Subtracting, assuming $(D^2 + 2)(D - 1)y \equiv (D - 1)(D^2 + 2)y$, we have

$$(D^2 + 2)(D^2 + 1)x - (D - 1)(3D - 1)x = 0$$

i.e.,

$$(D^4 + 4D + 1)x = 0$$

which is the same equation as (10), which we obtained with more labor.

To justify this procedure, all we must realize is that "multiplication" by $(D^2 + 2)$, for example, merely means that a certain operation is to be performed. Thus $(D^2 + 2)Y$ says: (1) Take the second derivative of Y. (2) Multiply Y by 2. (3) Add the results of (1) and (2). In a similar manner we can show that

$$(D^2 + 2)(D - 1)y \equiv (D - 1)(D^2 + 2)y$$

For

$$(D^2 + 2)(D - 1)y \equiv \left(\frac{d^2}{dt^2} + 2\right)\left(\frac{dy}{dt} - y\right)$$

$$= \frac{d^2}{dt^2}\left(\frac{dy}{dt} - y\right) + 2\left(\frac{dy}{dt} - y\right)$$

$$= \frac{d^3y}{dt^3} - \frac{d^2y}{dt^2} + 2\frac{dy}{dt} - 2y$$

$$(D - 1)(D^2 + 2)y \equiv \left(\frac{d}{dt} - 1\right)\left(\frac{d^2y}{dt^2} + 2y\right)$$

$$= \frac{d}{dt}\left(\frac{d^2y}{dt^2} + 2y\right) - \left(\frac{d^2y}{dt^2} + 2y\right)$$

$$= \frac{d^3y}{dt^3} - \frac{d^2y}{dt^2} + 2\frac{dy}{dt} - 2y$$

Thus, the use of the operator notation is essentially a short cut.

To show its use in another example, consider

ILLUSTRATIVE EXAMPLE 3

Solve simultaneously

$$\text{(a) } \frac{dx}{dt} - 3x - 6y = t^2, \qquad \text{(b) } \frac{dy}{dt} + \frac{dx}{dt} - 3y = e^t$$

Solution. Write the equations in operator form.

$$\text{(c) } (D - 3)x - 6y = t^2, \qquad \text{(d) } Dx + (D - 3)y = e^t$$

"Multiply" (c) by D, (d) by $(D - 3)$, to find

$$D(D - 3)x - 6Dy = Dt^2 = \frac{d}{dt}(t^2) = 2t$$

$$(D - 3)Dx + (D - 3)^2y = (D - 3)e^t = De^t - 3e^t$$

$$= \frac{d}{dt}e^t - 3e^t = -2e^t$$

Hence, by subtraction, we have after simplifying,

$$(D^2 + 9)y = -2e^t - 2t$$

whose general solution is

$$y = c_1 \cos 3t + c_2 \sin 3t - \frac{1}{5}e^t - \frac{2t}{9} \tag{13}$$

Two alternatives are possible: we may substitute y into either of the given equations or we may eliminate y between the two given equations to produce an equation involving x alone. We choose the latter. "Multiplying" equation (c) by $(D - 3)$ and equation (d) by 6 and subtracting, we find

$$(D^2 + 9)x = 6e^t - 3t^2 + 2t$$

the general solution of which is

$$x = c_3 \cos 3t + c_4 \sin 3t + \tfrac{3}{5}e^t - \tfrac{1}{3}t^2 + \tfrac{2}{9}t + \tfrac{2}{27} \tag{14}$$

We must now check to see whether we have too many arbitrary constants (usually we do). Substituting x and y from (13) and (14) into either of the given equations, say (c), we find

$$(\sin 3t)(-3c_3 - 3c_4 - 6c_2) + (\cos 3t)(3c_4 - 3c_3 - 6c_1) + t^2 = t^2$$

This must be an identity, and so we must have

$$-3c_3 - 3c_4 - 6c_2 = 0, \qquad 3c_4 - 3c_3 - 6c_1 = 0 \tag{15}$$

Equations (15) yield

$$c_1 = \tfrac{1}{2}c_4 - \tfrac{1}{2}c_3, \qquad c_2 = -\tfrac{1}{2}c_3 - \tfrac{1}{2}c_4$$

Using these in (13), we have as the required simultaneous solution,

$$x = c_3 \cos 3t + c_4 \sin 3t + \frac{3}{5}e^t - \frac{1}{3}t^2 + \frac{2}{9}t + \frac{2}{27}$$

$$y = \left(\frac{1}{2}c_4 - \frac{1}{2}c_3\right)\cos 3t + \left(-\frac{1}{2}c_3 - \frac{1}{2}c_4\right)\sin 3t - \frac{1}{5}e^t - \frac{2t}{9}$$

These will also check in the other given equation as is easily verified.

Remark 1: It is clear that the operator method is available without fresh complications only where the two simultaneous equations can be written in the form

$$F_1(D)x + F_2(D)y = f(t) \atop F_3(D)x + F_4(D)y = g(t) \Bigg\}$$

(16)

where $F_1(D)$, $F_2(D)$, $F_3(D)$, and $F_4(D)$ are polynomial operators with constant coefficients. Such equations are *simultaneous linear differential equations*.

Remark 2: One can show that the *total* number of arbitrary constants which are to be present in the simultaneous solution of Equations (16) is the same as the degree of the polynomial operator obtained from the determinant of the coefficients of x and y in (16), i.e.,

$$\begin{vmatrix} F_1(D) & F_2(D) \\ F_3(D) & F_4(D) \end{vmatrix}$$

(17)

Thus in Illustrative Example 3, the determinant is

$$\begin{vmatrix} D-3 & -6 \\ D & D-3 \end{vmatrix} = (D-3)(D-3) - (-6)(D) = D^2 + 9$$

which is of second degree, and so the total number of arbitrary constants should be two, as we have, in fact, found.

A EXERCISES

Find the simultaneous solution of each system subject to any given conditions.

1. $\dfrac{dy}{dt} = x,\ \dfrac{dx}{dt} = -y;\ y(0) = 0,\ x(0) = 1.$

2. $\dfrac{du}{dx} = 2v - 1,\ \dfrac{dv}{dx} = 1 + 2u.$

3. $\dfrac{dx}{dt} = x + y,\ \dfrac{dy}{dt} = x - y.$

4. $\dfrac{d^2x}{dt^2} = -x,\ \dfrac{d^2y}{dt^2} = y.$

5. $\dfrac{d^2y}{dt^2} = x - 2,\ \dfrac{d^2x}{dt^2} = y + 2.$

6. $\dfrac{dy}{dt} + 6y = \dfrac{dx}{dt},\ 3x - \dfrac{dx}{dt} = 2\dfrac{dy}{dt};\ x = 2,\ y = 3$ at $t = 0.$

7. $\begin{cases} (D+2)x + (D-1)y = -\sin t, \\ (D-3)x + (D+2)y = 4\cos t. \end{cases}$

B EXERCISES

1. Solve
$$\begin{cases} \dfrac{d^2x}{dt^2} + \dfrac{dy}{dt} + x = y + \sin t, \\[2mm] \dfrac{d^2y}{dt^2} + \dfrac{dx}{dt} - y = 2t^2 - x, \end{cases}$$

subject to $x = 2$, $dx/dt = -1$, $y = -\frac{9}{2}$, $dy/dt = -\frac{7}{2}$ at $t = 0$.

2. Solve

(a) $\dfrac{dx}{yz} = \dfrac{dy}{xz} = \dfrac{dz}{xy}$.

(b) $\dfrac{dx}{xy} = \dfrac{dy}{y^2 + 1} = \dfrac{dz}{z}$.

3. Solve the system
$$\begin{cases} x^2y'' + xz' + z = x \\ xy' + z = \ln x \end{cases}$$

by first making the transformation $x = e^t$. Compare with the Euler equation, p. 180.

4. Solve the system
$$\frac{dx}{dt} = y, \qquad \frac{dy}{dt} = z, \qquad \frac{dz}{dt} = x$$

C EXERCISES

1. The probability $P_n(t)$ of exactly n nuclear particles (such as appear in cosmic rays) registering in a counter (such as a Geiger counter) in a time t is determined from the system of differential equations,

$$P_n'(t) = \lambda[P_{n-1}(t) - P_n(t)], \qquad n \neq 0; \qquad P_0'(t) = -\lambda P_0(t)$$

where λ is a positive constant. Using suitable conditions, solve for $P_n(t)$, $n = 0, 1, 2, \ldots$. From your results, show that

$$\sum_{n=0}^{\infty} P_n(t) = 1$$

What is the probability interpretation of this?

2. Solve the system
$$\frac{dx}{y + z} = \frac{dy}{z + x} = \frac{dz}{x + y}$$

II. Applications to Mechanics

1. The flight of a projectile. Suppose that a projectile is fired from a cannon which is inclined at an angle θ_0 with the horizontal and which imparts to the projectile a muzzle velocity v_0 feet per second. Assuming no air resistance and a flat stationary earth, let it be required to describe the subsequent flight.

Mathematical Formulation. Let the cannon be located at the origin O of an xy coordinate system (Fig. 78). The dashed curve shown indicates the path of the projectile; OV represents the muzzle velocity, a vector having

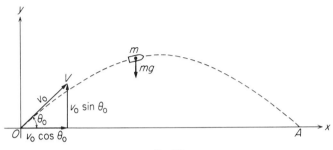

Fig. 78

magnitude v_0 and a direction in the xy plane making an angle θ_0 with the positive x axis. The components of the velocity in the x and y directions have magnitudes $v_0 \cos \theta_0$ and $v_0 \sin \theta_0$, respectively. Since there is no force of air resistance, the only force acting on the projectile of mass m is its weight mg. Let us take "up" and "right" as the positive directions. According to Newton's law we have:

net force in x direction = mass times acceleration in x direction

net force in y direction = mass times acceleration in y direction

which we may write as $F_x = ma_x$, $F_y = ma_y$. Since the net force in the x direction is zero and $a_x = d^2x/dt^2$, we have

$$m\frac{d^2x}{dt^2} = 0 \quad \text{or} \quad \frac{d^2x}{dt^2} = 0 \tag{1}$$

Since the net force in the y direction is $-mg$ (because "down" is the negative direction) and since $a_y = d^2y/dt^2$, we have

$$m\frac{d^2y}{dt^2} = -mg \quad \text{or} \quad \frac{d^2y}{dt^2} = -g \tag{2}$$

Furthermore, from the conditions of the problem we have

$$x = 0, \quad y = 0, \quad \frac{dx}{dt} = v_0 \cos \theta_0, \quad \frac{dy}{dt} = v_0 \sin \theta_0, \quad \text{at} \quad t = 0 \tag{3}$$

Our complete mathematical formulation consists of the differential equations (1) and (2) subject to the conditions (3). From the differential equations it is seen that the motion does not depend on m, and hence on the size of the projectile, provided there is no air resistance.

Solution. Upon integration of (1) we have $dx/dt = c_1$. Applying the condition that $dx/dt = v_0 \cos \theta_0$ at $t = 0$, we see that $c_1 = v_0 \cos \theta_0$, i.e., $dx/dt = (v_0 \cos \theta_0)$.* By another integration $x = (v_0 \cos \theta_0)t + c_2$, and since $x = 0$ at $t = 0$, $c_2 = 0$ and we have

$$x = (v_0 \cos \theta_0)t \tag{4}$$

In a similar manner, we have upon integration of (2)

$$\frac{dy}{dt} = -gt + c_3$$

and since $dy/dt = v_0 \sin \theta_0$ at $t = 0$, $c_3 = v_0 \sin \theta_0$, and we find

$$\frac{dy}{dt} = -gt + v_0 \sin \theta_0 \tag{5}$$

By another integration, using the fact that $y = 0$ at $t = 0$, we have

$$y = (v_0 \sin \theta_0)t - \tfrac{1}{2}gt^2 \tag{6}$$

The required solution is

$$x = (v_0 \cos \theta_0)t, \qquad y = (v_0 \sin \theta_0)t - \tfrac{1}{2}gt^2 \tag{7}$$

These equations give the position (x,y) of the projectile at any time t after firing. From them we can discuss anything concerning the motion. For example, suppose we choose to ask the following questions:

1. What is the total time of flight from O to A (Fig. 78)?
2. What is the range (distance OA along x axis)?
3. What is the maximum height reached?
4. What type of curve does the projectile describe?

Question 1 will be answered if we find the values of t which make $y = 0$. From (6) we see that this is so when

$$t\left[(v_0 \sin \theta_0) - \frac{1}{2}gt\right] = 0 \quad \text{or} \quad t = 0; \qquad t = \frac{2v_0 \sin \theta_0}{g}$$

The second value of t gives the time when the projectile is at A. Hence

$$\text{time of flight} = \frac{2v_0 \sin \theta_0}{g} \tag{8}$$

*Thus, the horizontal component of velocity remains constant.

To answer Question 2 we calculate the value of x when $t = $ time of flight. From the first of equations (7) we therefore have

$$\text{range} = \frac{(v_0 \cos \theta_0)(2v_0 \sin \theta)}{g} = \frac{v_0^2 \sin 2\theta_0}{g} \tag{9}$$

From (9) it is clear that the range is greatest when $2\theta_0 = 90°$, i.e., $\theta_0 = 45°$ and the maximum range is v_0^2/g.

To answer Question 3 we must find when y is a maximum, i.e., when $dy/dt = 0$. This amounts to saying that at the highest point the velocity in the y direction is zero. From the equation (5) we have

$$\frac{dy}{dt} = v_0 \sin \theta_0 - gt = 0 \quad \text{where} \quad t = \frac{v_0 \sin \theta_0}{g}$$

(Note that this is half the total time of flight, which seems logical.) Placing this value of t in the equation (6) for y, we find

$$\text{maximum height} = \frac{v_0^2 \sin^2 \theta_0}{2g} \tag{10}$$

Question 4 is actually answered by (7), which represents the parametric equations of a parabola. The path of the projectile is thus a portion of a parabola. By eliminating the parameter t we find

$$y = x \tan \theta_0 - \frac{gx^2}{2v_0^2} \sec^2 \theta_0 \tag{11}$$

which is another form for the parabola.

A EXERCISES

1. A projectile is fired from a cannon which makes an angle of 60° with the horizontal. If the muzzle velocity is 160 ft/sec: (a) Write a system of differential equations and conditions for the motion. (b) Find the position of the projectile at any time. (c) Find the range, maximum height, and time of flight. (d) Determine the position and velocity of the projectile after it is in flight for 2 and 4 sec.

2. Determine what would have been the maximum range of the "Big Bertha" cannon of World War I which had a muzzle velocity of 1 mile per second, had air resistance been negligible. For this maximum range, what is the height reached and the total time of flight?

3. A stone is thrown horizontally from a cliff 256 ft high with a velocity of 50 ft/sec. (a) Find the time of flight. (b) At what distance from the base of the cliff will the stone land?

B EXERCISES

1. A projectile fired from a cannon located on a horizontal plane has a range of 2000 ft and achieves a maximum height of 1000 ft. Determine its muzzle velocity and the time of flight.

2. A cannon having muzzle velocity v_0 and making an angle θ with the horizontal is to be fired so as to hit an object located on the same level as the cannon and at a distance d from it. Show that this is possible for two values of θ given by $\theta = \pi/4 \pm \phi$, where

$$\phi = \frac{1}{2} \arccos \frac{gd}{v_0^2}, \qquad d < \frac{v_0^2}{g}$$

Discuss the cases $d \gtrless v_0^2/g$.

3. A plane is inclined at an angle α with the horizontal. A cannon on this plane makes an angle θ with the horizontal. Show that the range of the projectile on the inclined plane is

$$R = \frac{2v_0^2 \cos \theta \sin (\theta - \alpha)}{g \cos^2 \alpha}$$

where v_0 is the muzzle velocity of the cannon. Hence show that the maximum range is obtained when $\theta = \alpha/2 + \pi/4$ and that its value is

$$R_{\max} = \frac{v_0^2}{g(1 + \sin \alpha)}$$

Discuss the case $\alpha = 0°, 90°$.

C EXERCISES

1. A gun is located at a horizontal distance R from the base of a cliff of height H. The gun, which has muzzle velocity v_0, is to be inclined at an angle θ with the horizontal and aimed so as to hit a target at the top of the cliff. Show that this will be possible for two values of θ given by

$$\theta = \frac{\pi}{4} + \frac{1}{2} \arctan \frac{`H}{R} \pm \frac{1}{2} \arccos \frac{H + gR^2/v_0^2}{\sqrt{R^2 + H^2}}$$

provided

$$\frac{H + gR^2/v_0^2}{\sqrt{R^2 + H^2}} \leq 1$$

Compare with B Exercise 2, where $H = 0$.

2. If in a given vertical plane projectiles are fired from a gun having muzzle velocity v_0 and located at O (Fig. 79), their paths will be parabolas as shown, one parabola corresponding to each angle of elevation (or depression) of the gun. (a) Determine the envelope of these parabolic trajectories, showing that this envelope is also a parabola. (b) If point O is at height H above a horizontal plane and the gun can be aimed in all possible directions, show that the volume over which

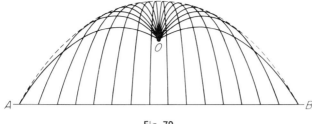

Fig. 79

the gun has "control" is

$$\frac{\pi v^2}{g}\left(H + \frac{v^2}{2g}\right)^2$$

3. Discuss the motion of a projectile in which air resistance proportional to the instantaneous velocity is taken into account.

2. An application to astronomy. According to Newton's famous universal law of gravitation, any two objects separated by a distance r and having masses M_1 and M_2, respectively, are attracted toward each other with a force having magnitude given by

$$F = \frac{GM_1M_2}{r^2} \qquad (12)$$

where G is a universal gravitation constant. It is interesting to make use of this law to describe the motion of planets in our solar system. We shall consider, in particular, the motion of the earth about the sun. In discussing this problem, we simplify our tasks tremendously by neglecting the effects of all other planets. Consequently the results are approximate but, nevertheless, they do represent to a high degree of accuracy, the true state of affairs as evidenced by experimental observations.

Mathematical Formulation. We assume the sun fixed at the origin of an xy coordinate system and that the earth is at point (x,y) at time t in its motion (Fig. 80). We take as positive directions of vector quantities the

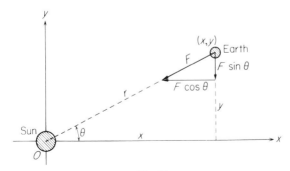

Fig. 80

$+x$ and $+y$ directions. From the figure, the force F acting on the earth is seen to have x and y components of magnitudes $F\cos\theta$ and $F\sin\theta$, respectively. Letting m_s and m_e be the respective masses of sun and earth, we have, making use of (12),

$$m_e \frac{d^2x}{dt^2} = -F\cos\theta = -\frac{Gm_em_s}{r^2}\cos\theta \tag{13}$$

$$m_e \frac{d^2y}{dt^2} = -F\sin\theta = -\frac{Gm_em_s}{r^2}\sin\theta \tag{14}$$

Since $\sin\theta = y/r$ and $\cos\theta = x/r$, equations (13) and (14) become

$$\frac{d^2x}{dt^2} = -\frac{kx}{r^3}, \quad \frac{d^2y}{dt^2} = -\frac{ky}{r^3} \tag{15}$$

where $k = Gm_s$. Since $r = \sqrt{x^2 + y^2}$, equations (15) can be written

$$\frac{d^2x}{dt^2} = -\frac{kx}{(x^2+y^2)^{3/2}}, \quad \frac{d^2y}{dt^2} = -\frac{ky}{(x^2+y^2)^{3/2}} \tag{16}$$

As initial conditions we assume that at $t = 0$, the earth is located on the x axis, a distance a from the sun, and is proceeding in the positive y direction with velocity v_0. Thus

$$x = a, \quad y = 0, \quad dx/dt = 0, \quad dy/dt = v_0 \quad \text{at} \quad t = 0 \tag{17}$$

If we can solve simultaneously equations (16) subject to conditions (17), we shall have the solution to our problem.

Solution. A little experimenting with equations (16) shows that it is difficult if not impossible to eliminate x or y. Upon noticing the combination $x^2 + y^2$, a change to polar coordinates seems advisable. This is further evidenced by the fact that the position of the earth relative to the sun is perhaps better described by coordinates (r,θ) than by (x,y). We therefore transform equations (16) to polar coordinates.

Since $x = r\cos\theta$ and $y = r\sin\theta$, we have, letting dots denote differentiations with respect to t,

$$\dot{x} = \dot{r}\cos\theta - (r\sin\theta)\dot{\theta}$$
$$\ddot{x} = \ddot{r}\cos\theta - 2(\dot{r}\sin\theta)\dot{\theta} - (r\sin\theta)\ddot{\theta} - (r\cos\theta)\dot{\theta}^2$$
$$\dot{y} = \dot{r}\sin\theta + (r\cos\theta)\dot{\theta}$$
$$\ddot{y} = \ddot{r}\sin\theta + 2(\dot{r}\cos\theta)\dot{\theta} + (r\cos\theta)\ddot{\theta} - (r\sin\theta)\dot{\theta}^2$$

Thus,

$$\left.\begin{aligned}\ddot{x} &= (\ddot{r} - r\dot{\theta}^2)\cos\theta - (2\dot{r}\dot{\theta} + r\ddot{\theta})\sin\theta \\ \ddot{y} &= (\ddot{r} - r\dot{\theta}^2)\sin\theta + (2\dot{r}\dot{\theta} + r\ddot{\theta})\cos\theta\end{aligned}\right\} \tag{18}$$

Equations (16) become, upon making use of equations (18),

$$(\ddot{r} - r\dot{\theta}^2) \cos\theta - (2\dot{r}\dot{\theta} + r\ddot{\theta}) \sin\theta = -\frac{k \cos\theta}{r^2} \tag{19}$$

$$(\ddot{r} - r\dot{\theta}^2) \sin\theta + (2\dot{r}\dot{\theta} + r\ddot{\theta}) \cos\theta = -\frac{k \sin\theta}{r^2} \tag{20}$$

Multiplying equation (19) by $\cos\theta$,equation (20) by $\sin\theta$, and adding,

$$\ddot{r} - r\dot{\theta}^2 = -\frac{k}{r^2} \tag{21}$$

Also multiplying (19) by $\sin\theta$, (20) by $\cos\theta$, and subtracting,

$$2\dot{r}\dot{\theta} + r\ddot{\theta} = 0 \tag{22}$$

The initial conditions (17) in rectangular form need to be replaced by corresponding conditions in polar form. Corresponding to the conditions (17), we have

$$r = a, \qquad \theta = 0, \qquad \dot{r} = 0, \qquad \dot{\theta} = \frac{v_0}{a} \quad \text{at} \quad t = 0 \tag{23}$$

We must now solve (21) and (22) simultaneously subject to conditions (23). A simplification results if we notice that the left side of (22) is $\dfrac{1}{r} \cdot \dfrac{d}{dt}(r^2\dot{\theta})$ as is easily verified. Thus (22) can be replaced by

$$\frac{d}{dt}(r^2\dot{\theta}) = 0 \quad \text{or} \quad r^2\dot{\theta} = c_1 \tag{24}$$

This equation has an interesting interpretation. Suppose an object moves from P to Q along arc PQ (Fig. 81). Let A be the area bounded by lines OP, OQ, and arc PQ. Then from elementary calculus,

$$A = \frac{1}{2}\int_0^\theta r^2\,d\theta \quad \text{or} \quad dA = \frac{1}{2}r^2\,d\theta$$

$$\text{or} \quad \frac{dA}{dt} = \frac{1}{2}r^2\frac{d\theta}{dt} = \frac{1}{2}r^2\dot{\theta}$$

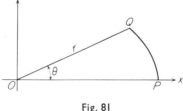

Fig. 81

The quantity dA/dt is called the *areal velocity*. Since $r^2\dot{\theta}$ is constant by (24), it follows that the areal velocity is constant. This is equivalent to saying that the object moves so that equal areas are described in equal times, or that the radius vector (line drawn from O to object) "sweeps" out equal areas in equal times. This *law of areas* is the first of Kepler's famous three laws.

These laws were based on deductions from the voluminous observations of the astronomer Tycho Brahe who spent many years in the compilation of data. We now list

KEPLER'S LAWS:

1. *Each of the planets moves in a plane curve about the sun, in such a way that the radius vector drawn from the sun to the planets describes equal areas in equal times.*

2. *The paths of the planets are ellipses, with the sun at one of the foci.*

3. *The squares of the periods (times for complete revolution about the sun) vary directly as the cubes of the major axes of the ellipses.*

It was essentially because of the work of Kepler in organizing the data of Tycho Brahe that Newton was able, with the aid of the calculus, to formulate his famous universal law of gravitation which is applied, not only to planets, but to all objects. In this section we have not used the historical approach but have instead started with Newton's universal law of gravitation, and deduced the first of Kepler's laws. In the remainder of this section we will deduce the second law. The third law is relegated to the C exercises for the interested student. In addition, in the C Exercise 4, the manner in which Newton was able rigorously to deduce his universal law of gravitation from Kepler's laws is indicated.

We now return to the solution of (21) and (22) subject to (23). From (23) we see that $r = a$, $\dot{\theta} = v_0/a$ at $t = 0$. Hence, from (24) $c_1 = av_0$. Thus, we may write $r^2\dot{\theta} = av_0$. From this, $\dot{\theta} = av_0/r^2$ and (21) becomes

$$\ddot{r} = \frac{a^2 v_0^2}{r^3} - \frac{k}{r^2} \tag{25}$$

an equation in which θ does not appear. Equation (25) does not involve t explicitly. Hence, letting $\dot{r} = p$ the equation may be written

$$\frac{dp}{dt} = \frac{dp}{dr} \cdot \frac{dr}{dt} = p \frac{dp}{dr} = \frac{a^2 v_0^2}{r^3} - \frac{k}{r^2} \quad \text{or} \quad p \frac{dp}{dr} = \frac{a^2 v_0^2}{r^3} - \frac{k}{r^2}$$

Separating the variables and integrating this last equation yields

$$\frac{p^2}{2} = \frac{k}{r} - \frac{a^2 v_0^2}{2r^2} + c_2 \tag{26}$$

From (26) since $p = \dot{r} = 0$ where $r = a$, we have

$$c_2 = \frac{v_0^2}{2} - \frac{k}{a}$$

Thus,

$$\frac{\dot{r}^2}{2} = \frac{k}{r} - \frac{a^2 v_0^2}{2r^2} + \frac{v_0^2}{2} - \frac{k}{a}$$

or

$$\frac{dr}{dt} = \sqrt{\left(v_0^2 - \frac{2k}{a}\right) + \frac{2k}{r} - \frac{a^2 v_0^2}{r^2}} \tag{27}$$

using the positive square root. From this we may obtain r as a function of t (see C Exercise 5). Of more interest, perhaps, is a description of the path taken by the earth in its motion. To determine this, we would want an equation containing r and θ. From (27) and $\dot{\theta} = a v_0 / r^2$, we have the simultaneous equations

$$\frac{dr}{dt} = \sqrt{\left(v_0^2 - \frac{2k}{a}\right) + \frac{2k}{r} - \frac{a^2 v_0^2}{r^2}}, \quad \frac{d\theta}{dt} = \frac{a v_0}{r^2} \tag{28}$$

The desired differential equation connecting r and θ but not containing t can be obtained by division of the equations in (28). We find

$$\frac{dr}{d\theta} = r\sqrt{Ar^2 + 2Br - 1} \quad \text{where} \quad A = \frac{1}{a^2} - \frac{2k}{a^3 v_0^2}, \quad B = \frac{k}{a^2 v_0^2} \tag{29}$$

Thus,

$$\int \frac{dr}{r\sqrt{Ar^2 + 2Br - 1}} = \int d\theta = \theta + c_3 \tag{30}$$

It is useful to make the substitution $r = 1/u$ in the integral on the left of (30), for we obtain

$$-\int \frac{du}{\sqrt{A + 2Bu - u^2}} = \theta + c_3,$$

$$-\int \frac{du}{\sqrt{A + B^2 - (u - B)^2}} = \theta + c_3$$

i.e.,

$$\text{arc cos} \frac{(u - B)}{\sqrt{A + B^2}} = \theta + c_3$$

Thus, it follows that

$$u = B + \sqrt{A + B^2} \cos(\theta + c_3) = B[1 + e \cos(\theta + c_3)]$$

where $e = \sqrt{A + B^2}/B = (a v_0^2 / k) - 1$. Since $u = 1/r$, we have

$$r = \frac{a^2 v_0^2 / k}{1 + e \cos(\theta + c_3)} \tag{31}$$

The quantity c_3 is determined from the condition $r = a$ where $\theta = 0$. If we had used the negative sign in (27) or (30) we would have obtained the same solution as (31) but with different arbitrary constant.

Interpretations. From analytic geometry, (31) is seen to be the polar form of a conic section having eccentricity e. It represents:

1. An *ellipse* if $e < 1$, i.e., $v_0^2 < 2k/a$;
2. A *hyperbola* if $e > 1$, i.e., $v_0^2 > 2k/a$;
3. A *parabola* if $e = 1$, i.e., $v_0^2 = 2k/a$;
4. A *circle* if $e = 0$, i.e., $v_0^2 = k/a$;

the sun being located at the focus in 1, 2, and 3, and the center in 4. Since the work done so far applies to any two objects (not only sun and earth) many things concerning the behavior of our universe are explained.

By astronomical observations one can show that for all planets in our solar system, the quantity v_0^2 is less than $2k/a$, so that all the planets have orbits which are ellipses with the sun at one focus. Also, orbits of the moon and man-made earth satellites ("baby moons") are ellipses. In most cases these ellipses are nearly circular, i.e., e is slightly greater than zero. This establishes Kepler's second law.

Recurring comets such as, for example, Halley's comet, have orbits which are elongated ellipses with eccentricities less than but close to one. The time for a comet to reappear near the earth depends on the eccentricity of its elliptical path. Halley's comet, for instance, appears once every 76 years approximately.*

Objects having hyperbolic or parabolic orbits would appear only once, theoretically, never to return. Before the understanding of such events the arrivals of such objects were probably classed as "miracles."

Experiments with particles of atomic dimensions performed in the cloud chambers in many of our universities show particles leaving "fog tracks" which are parabolic or hyperbolic in shape.

For further related subject matter, the student is referred to the exercises.

A EXERCISES

1. An object of mass m is attracted to a fixed point O with a force proportional to the instantaneous distance from O. Let O be the origin of a rectangular coordinate system and let (x,y) represent the position of the object at any time. (a) Set up differential equations describing the motion. (b) If the object starts on the x axis at distance a from O and is given an initial velocity v_0 in the positive y direction, show that the path is an ellipse with center at O. Under what conditions is the path a circle? (c) Show that the radius vector joining the mass and point O sweeps out equal areas in equal times, i.e., show that the areal velocity $\frac{1}{2}r^2\dot\theta$ is constant. What is the value of this constant?

* The last appearance of Halley's comet occurred in 1910; it is expected to appear next in 1986.

2. If the force in Exercise 1 is one of repulsion instead of attraction, show that the path is a portion of a hyperbola. Is the areal velocity constant in this case? Discuss the case where $v_0 = 0$.

3. Show that the areal velocity in rectangular coordinates is

$$\tfrac{1}{2}(x\dot{y} - y\dot{x})$$

B EXERCISES

1. An object of mass m moves so that it is attracted to a fixed point O (taken as origin of an xy coordinate system) with a force $F(r)$, where r is the instantaneous distance of the mass from O. Such a force depending only on r is called a *central force*. (a) Show that the equations of motion are (dots denote derivatives with respect to t)

$$m\ddot{x} = \frac{x}{r} F(r), \qquad m\ddot{y} = -\frac{y}{r} F(r)$$

(b) Prove that $x\ddot{y} - y\ddot{x} = 0$, and thus that $x\dot{y} - y\dot{x} = h$, where h is a constant. Using the result of A Exercise 3, show that the areal velocity is constant independent of the form of the central force.

2. Show that the differential equations of Exercise 1(a) may be replaced by

$$m(\ddot{r} - r\dot{\theta}^2) = -F(r), \qquad m(2\dot{r}\dot{\theta} + r\ddot{\theta}) = 0$$

Deduce that $r^2\dot{\theta} = h$ and thus show that the problem of central forces reduces to the solution of the differential equation

$$\ddot{r} - \frac{h^2}{r^3} = -\frac{F(r)}{m}$$

3. Problems involving central forces are simplified by use of the transformation $u = 1/r$. Show that this transformation yields the result

$$\ddot{r} = -h^2 u^2 \frac{d^2 u}{d\theta^2}$$

Thus transform the differential equation of Exercise 2 into

$$\frac{d^2 u}{d\theta^2} + u = \frac{G(u)}{mh^2 u^2}$$

where $F(1/u) \equiv G(u)$.

4. For a central force given by $F(r) = k/r^2$, show that the differential equation of Exercise 3 becomes

$$\frac{d^2 u}{d\theta^2} + u = \frac{k}{mh^2}$$

whose solution is

$$u = A \cos \theta + B \sin \theta + \frac{k}{mh^2}$$

Compare with the result of the text.

5. Using the differential equation of Exercise 3, discuss the motion of an object moving in a central force field given by $F(r) = k/r^3$, assuming that it starts at $(a,0)$, with initial velocity v_0 in the positive y direction. Show that if $k = mh^2 = ma^2v_0^2$, the mass spirals in toward the origin but never reaches it.

C EXERCISES

1. (a) Show that the ellipse defined by equation (31) of the text may be written

$$r = \frac{h^2/k}{1 + e \cos \theta}, \qquad 0 < e < 1$$

where the origin is one of the foci and the major axis lies along $\theta = 0$.
(b) Show that the equation of an ellipse whose major axis lies along $\theta = 0$ and which has the origin as one of the foci is

$$r = \frac{B^2/A}{1 + e \cos \theta}, \qquad e = \sqrt{1 - B^2/A^2}$$

where A and B are the respective lengths of the semimajor and semiminor axes. By comparison with (a) show that

$$h = B\sqrt{k/A}$$

2. The time T for a planet to make one complete revolution in its elliptical path is the "period" of the planet. Show that

$$T = \frac{\text{area of ellipse}}{\text{areal velocity}} = \frac{2\pi AB}{h} = \frac{2\pi A^{3/2}}{\sqrt{k}}$$

using the result of Exercise 1(b). Hence, prove Kepler's third law.

3. An object moves under the influence of a central force located at the origin of a coordinate system. If the path of the object is the circle $r = a \cos \theta$, determine the law of force. (*Hint:* Use the results of B Exercises 2 or 3.)

4. Show that in order for an object to move along the ellipse

$$r = \frac{l}{1 + e \cos \theta}$$

under the influence of a central force $F(r)$ located at the origin, we must have

$$F(r) \propto \frac{1}{r^2}$$

Historically, this is the manner in which Newton deduced from Kepler's law the "inverse square law" for planets and finally his universal law of gravitation for all objects.

5. Integrate equation (27) of the text and thus obtain the position of the earth (or other planet) with respect to the sun at any time.

3. The problem of the vibrating masses. A system consists of springs A, B and objects C, D attached in a straight line on a horizontal frictionless table RS [Fig. 82(a)], one end of spring A being fixed at O. The springs of negligible mass each have spring constant k, and the objects have equal mass M. The system is set into vibration by holding D in place, moving C to the left a distance $a > 0$ and then releasing both objects. The problem is to determine the positions of objects C and D at any time t thereafter.

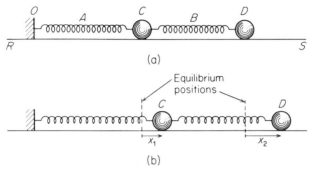

(a)

(b)

Fig. 82

Mathematical Formulation. To determine the differential equations of motion, let us see what conditions prevail at time t. At this time C and D may be removed from their equilibrium positions somewhat as shown in Fig. 82(b). Assume that at this time the masses are located at distances x_1 and x_2 from the respective equilibrium positions indicated by the dashed lines in the figure. We shall assume directions to the right are positive. Let us consider the forces on C and D at time t:

Spring A is exerting a force on C to the left of magnitude kx_1.
Spring B is exerting a force on C to the right of magnitude $k(x_2 - x_1)$. The net force to the right is $k(x_2 - x_1) - kx_1 = k(x_2 - 2x_1)$. Hence,

$$M \frac{d^2x_1}{dt^2} = k(x_2 - 2x_1) \tag{32}$$

by Newton's law. Similarly, spring A is exerting no direct force on D, but spring B is exerting a force on D to the left of magnitude $k(x_2 - x_1)$. The net force to the right is $0 - k(x_2 - x_1) = -k(x_2 - x_1)$. Hence,

$$M \frac{d^2x_2}{dt^2} = -k(x_2 - x_1) \tag{33}$$

by Newton's law. The initial conditions are given by

$$x_1 = -a, \quad x_2 = 0, \quad \frac{dx_1}{dt} = 0, \quad \frac{dx_2}{dt} = 0 \quad \text{at} \quad t = 0 \tag{34}$$

Our mathematical formulation consists of equations (32) and (33), which we must solve simultaneously subject to conditions (34).

Solution. Letting $\omega^2 = k/M$, equations (32) and (33) can be written

$$(D^2 + 2\omega^2)x_1 - \omega^2 x_2 = 0, \qquad -\omega^2 x_1 + (D^2 + \omega^2)x_2 = 0 \qquad (35)$$

where $D \equiv d/dt$. If we operate on the first equation with $(D^2 + \omega^2)$, multiply the second equation by ω^2, and add, we eliminate x_2 and find

$$(D^4 + 3\omega^2 D^2 + \omega^4)x_1 = 0 \qquad (36)$$

The auxiliary equation corresponding to this is $m^4 + 3\omega^2 m^2 + \omega^4 = 0$, from which $m^2 = (-3 \pm \sqrt{5})\omega^2/2$. Taking $\sqrt{5} = 2.24$, approximately, we obtain the four roots $m = \pm 0.62i\omega, \pm 1.62i\omega$.* The solution of (36) is, thus,

$$x_1 = c_1 \cos 0.62\omega t + c_2 \sin 0.62\omega t + c_3 \cos 1.62\omega t + c_4 \sin 1.62\omega t \quad (37)$$

In an exactly analogous manner we find, by eliminating x_1, the equation

$$(D^4 + 3\omega^2 D^2 + \omega^4)x_2 = 0$$

which is the same as (36) and, therefore, has the solution

$$x_2 = c_5 \cos 0.62\omega t + c_6 \sin 0.62\omega t + c_7 \cos 1.62\omega t + c_8 \sin 1.62\omega t \quad (38)$$

The determinant of the coefficients in equations (35) is

$$\begin{vmatrix} D^2 + 2\omega^2 & -\omega^2 \\ -\omega^2 & D^2 + \omega^2 \end{vmatrix} = D^4 + 3\omega^2 D^2 + \omega^4$$

a polynomial in D of fourth degree, so that there must be a total of four arbitrary constants. We have eight. If we substitute x_1 and x_2 in the original equations, we find the relations between the constants

$$1.62c_1 = c_5, \qquad 1.62c_2 = c_6, \qquad -0.62c_3 = c_7, \qquad -0.62c_4 = c_8$$

Hence, the solutions (37) and (38) become

$$x_1 = c_1 \cos 0.62\omega t + c_2 \sin 0.62\omega t + c_3 \cos 1.62\omega t + c_4 \sin 1.62\omega t$$
$$x_2 = 1.62c_1 \cos 0.62\omega t + 1.62c_2 \sin 0.62\omega t - 0.62c_3 \cos 1.62\omega t$$
$$- 0.62c_4 \sin 1.62\omega t$$

Using conditions (34), we find

$$c_1 = -0.28a, \qquad c_3 = -0.72a, \qquad c_2 = c_4 = 0$$

The required solution is, therefore,

$$x_1 = -a(0.28 \cos 0.62\omega t + 0.72 \cos 1.62\omega t)$$
$$x_2 = -a(0.45 \cos 0.62\omega t - 0.45 \cos 1.62\omega t)$$

* Actually $m = \pm \left(\dfrac{\sqrt{5} - 1}{2}\right) i\omega, \pm \left(\dfrac{\sqrt{5} + 1}{2}\right) i\omega.$

It is seen that there are two frequencies present, given approximately by

$$f_1 = \frac{0.62\omega}{2\pi} = 0.10\sqrt{k/M} \quad \text{and} \quad f_2 = \frac{1.62\omega}{2\pi} = 0.26\sqrt{k/M}$$

These are referred to as the *normal frequencies* associated with the system or frequencies corresponding to *normal modes of vibration*. When we dealt with simple vibrating systems as considered in Chapter 5, we found that the system had a single natural (or normal) frequency. When periodic external forces having frequency equal (or almost equal in case of damping) to the natural frequency were impressed on such systems, we found that great disturbances would be set up in the system, this phenomenon being called *resonance*. In the more complex system with two normal (or natural) frequencies, the phenomenon of resonance can occur if periodic external forces having either or both of these frequencies are impressed on the system. In more complicated systems, a larger number of normal frequencies may be present and the chance for resonance taking place is increased. This makes even more plausible why it could be dangerous for a group to "keep in step" when crossing a bridge, since a bridge is a complicated structure with many "natural frequencies" and exciting one of them may prove disastrous. Normal or natural frequencies are of great importance in science and technology. They appear in such seemingly unrelated fields as stress analysis (needed by civil and mechanical engineers in design of structures) and nuclear physics (where they are useful in explaining the theory of spectra as well as effects of atomic energy). They are also of great importance in electricity in connection with resonance. Here they act in more of a constructive manner and are to be desired rather than avoided.

A EXERCISES

1. Solve the problem of the text if the initial conditions are changed as follows: (a) C is held fixed while D is moved to the right a distance $a > 0$ and then both are released. (b) C and D are both pulled a distance a to the right and then released. (c) C is moved a distance a to the left while D is moved a distance a to the right and then both are released.

2. If the two springs A and B of the text have different spring constants k_1, k_2, while the masses of C and D are kept equal, show that the equations of motion are

$$M\ddot{x}_1 = k_2 x_2 - (k_1 + k_2)x_1, \qquad M\ddot{x}_2 = k_2 x_1 - k_2 x_2$$

Prove that there are two normal frequencies f_1 and f_2, where

$$f_1 = \frac{1}{2\pi}\sqrt{\frac{k_1 + 2k_2 + \sqrt{k_1^2 + 4k_2^2}}{2M}}$$

$$f_2 = \frac{1}{2\pi}\sqrt{\frac{k_1 + 2k_2 - \sqrt{k_1^2 + 4k_2^2}}{2M}}$$

3. If the springs in the problem of the text have the same spring constant, but the masses of C and D are changed so as to have ratio $3:2$, show that the normal frequencies have ratio $1:\sqrt{6}$.

B EXERCISES

1. A system consists of springs A, B, C and objects D and E attached in a straight line on a horizontal frictionless table RS (Fig. 83) the ends of the springs A and

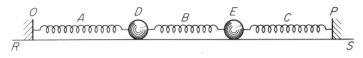

Fig. 83

C being fixed at O and P, respectively. The springs each have spring constant k and the objects have equal mass M. The system is set into vibration by holding D in place, moving E to the right a distance $a > 0$ and then releasing both. (a) Show that the differential equations describing the motion are

$$M\ddot{x}_1 = k(x_2 - x_1) - kx_1, \qquad M\ddot{x}_2 = k(x_1 - x_2) - kx_2$$

where x_1 and x_2 are the displacements of D and E from their equilibrium positions at time t. (b) Show that the system vibrates with normal frequencies

$$f_1 = \frac{1}{2\pi}\sqrt{\frac{k}{M}}, \qquad f_2 = \frac{1}{2\pi}\sqrt{\frac{3k}{M}}$$

(c) Determine the positions of D and E at any time.

2. A method often used in practice for determining the normal frequencies is to substitute $x_1 = A_1 e^{i\omega t}$, $x_2 = A_2 e^{i\omega t}$, where A_1, A_2, ω are undetermined constants, into the differential equations. Then one sets up a condition for the quantities to be different from zero. Show that for the problem of the text this method leads to the condition that the determinant (called the *secular determinant*),

$$\begin{vmatrix} \dfrac{2k}{M} - \omega^2 & -\dfrac{k}{M} \\[2ex] -\dfrac{k}{M} & \dfrac{k}{M} - \omega^2 \end{vmatrix} = 0$$

Hence, find the frequencies, using the fact that they are given by the values of $\omega/2\pi$.

3. Use the method of Exercise 2 to determine the normal frequencies of Exercise 1 (b). Can the method be employed to solve the differential equations?

4. If the springs of Exercise 1 are kept the same but the masses D and E are changed so as to have ratio $8:5$, show that the normal frequencies have ratio $\sqrt{3}:\sqrt{10}$.

C EXERCISES

1. A system is said to be vibrating in one of its "natural or normal modes of vibration" if the oscillation takes place with only one frequency, all others being absent. Referring to B Exercise 1: (a) Show that the mode of vibration corresponding to the lower frequency occurs when $x_1 = x_2$, i.e., when the masses move in the same direction. (b) Show that the mode of vibration corresponding to the higher frequency occurs when $x_1 = -x_2$, i.e., when the masses move in opposite directions.

2. Determine the normal modes for the vibrating masses discussed in the text.

3. (a) Show that the solutions x_1 and x_2 of B Exercise 1 can be written

$$x_1 = a_1 U + b_1 V, \qquad x_2 = a_2 U + b_2 V$$

where

$$U = A \cos \omega_1 t + B \sin \omega_1 t, \qquad \omega_1^2 = k/M,$$

$$V = C \cos \omega_2 t + D \sin \omega_2 t, \qquad \omega_2^2 = 3k/M$$

Determine the relations among the constants a_1, b_1, a_2, b_2. The quantities U and V each depend on only one frequency. They are *normal coordinates* and are frequently used in simplification of problems in the theory of vibrations. (b) Show that if initial conditions are chosen so that $A = B = 0$, i.e., $U = 0$ then $x_1 = -x_2$ while if $C = D = 0$, i.e., $V = 0$, then $x_1 = x_2$. These correspond to the lower and higher frequency modes of vibration, respectively. Compare with Exercise 1.

4. Arrive at the same results as in Exercise 3 by letting $U = \alpha e^{i\omega_1 t}$, $V = \beta e^{i\omega_2 t}$ where α, β are complex constants.

5. In B Exercise 1, assume two additional forces to act, a damping force proportional to the instantaneous velocity of each of the masses, and an external force acting on each and given by $A \cos \alpha t$, $t \geq 0$ where A and α are constants. (a) Find the steady-state solution. (b) Show that there are two frequencies of the external force for which resonance occurs. In view of the fact that the ends of springs A and C are fixed, what is the effect of the resonance? (c) Discuss the solution if there is no damping. For what value of α will resonance occur in this case?

6. A mass M_1 is hung from a vertical spring (of constant k) which is supported at O (Fig. 84). From M_1 is hung a simple pendulum having a bob of mass M_2. Assume that M_1 can vibrate only vertically and that all motion takes place in the vertical plane. (a) Set up differential equations for the motion. (b) Find the positions of M_1 and M_2 at any time, assuming small vibrations and arbitrary initial conditions. (c) Determine normal frequencies and modes if any.

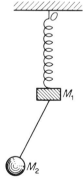

Fig. 84

III. Applications to Electric Networks

We have already seen in Chapters 3 and 5 how Kirchhoff's law was used to solve problems involving single-loop electric circuits. In advanced engineering work, it is often essential to consider electric networks which involve

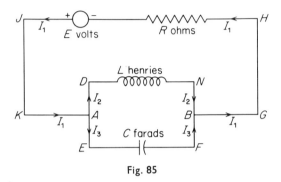

Fig. 85

more than one loop. An example of a two-loop network is shown in Fig. 85. In order to solve problems of electric networks involving two or more loops we need

KIRCHHOFF'S TWO LAWS:

1. *The algebraic sum of the currents travelling toward any branch point (A or B in Fig. 85) is equal to zero.*

2. *The algebraic sum of the potential drops (or voltage drops) around any closed loop is equal to zero.*

To enable us to apply these laws consistently we adopt the following

Conventions:

(a) If I is the current in one direction, $-I$ is the current in the opposite direction.

(b) In writing the algebraic sum of the potential drops around a closed loop, we consider a potential drop as *positive* if in describing the loop we travel in the *same* direction as the indicated current and negative if we travel in the opposite direction to the current.

(c) A potential rise (due to battery or generator for example) is considered to be the negative of a potential drop.

By using the above laws and conventions, we shall be able to formulate mathematically any problem in linear electric networks. To see the procedures involved, consider the network of Fig. 85 for example. There are three closed loops present, namely, *JHGBNDAKJ*, *JHGBFEAKJ*, and

NFEDN. The second of Kirchhoff's laws applied to these three loops yields three differential equations. These equations, however, are not independent, since, as we will find, one differential equation can be obtained from the other two. We may thus say that there are only two independent loops. In practice, it is logical to choose those loops which are simplest. At present, for practice, we consider all three loops.

The first thing to do in formulating mathematically a problem in electric networks is to label currents in the various parts. The direction adopted for current flow is in general immaterial so long as we are consistent. In Fig. 85 we have adopted the directions shown for I_1, I_2, and I_3. It is clear that if I_2 flows in a direction from A to D, then it will continue from D to N and from N to B as indicated. The situation seems quite logical when we reason that current I_1 separates at branch A into currents I_2 and I_3. At branch B, I_2 and I_3 combine to give I_1 again. Since I_1 splits into I_2 and I_3, it is clear that $I_1 = I_2 + I_3$.

Another way of arriving at the same result is from Kirchhoff's first law. Since I_2 is flowing *away* from A, then by convention (a), $-I_2$ is flowing *toward* A. Similarly the current $-I_3$ is flowing toward A. The algebraic sum of the currents flowing toward A is thus given by $I_1 - I_2 - I_3$, which when equated to zero yields $I_1 = I_2 + I_3$ as before.

Let us now consider the application of Kirchhoff's second law.

For the loop JHGBNDAKJ:

Voltage drop across R is $-I_1R$ by convention (b).
Voltage drop across L is $-L\, dI_2/dt$.
Voltage drop across battery E is $+E$ by convention (c).
Hence,
$$-I_1R - L\frac{dI_2}{dt} + E = 0 \tag{1}$$

For the loop JHGBFEAKJ:

Voltage drop across R is $-I_1R$.
Voltage drop across C is $-Q_3/C$ (where Q_3 is the charge on capacitor C supplied by current I_3).
Voltage drop across E is $+E$.
Hence,
$$-I_1R - \frac{Q_3}{C} + E = 0 \tag{2}$$

For the loop NFEDN:

Voltage drop across L is $L\, dI_2/dt$ by convention (b).
Voltage drop across C is $-Q_3/C$.
Hence,
$$L\frac{dI_2}{dt} - \frac{Q_3}{C} = 0 \tag{3}$$

It will be noted that, as mentioned before, equations (1), (2), and (3) are dependent. Thus, for instance, (3) is obtained by subtraction of (1) and (2). Realizing that only two differential equations are independent would have saved some labor. Also the loop $NFEDN$ is slightly simpler than the others as evidenced by the simpler differential equation (3). Since we have a choice. let us choose equations (2) and (3) together with the equation $I_1 = I_2 + I_3$, Since there are 3 equations and 4 unknowns, I_1, I_2, I_3, and Q_3, we need another equation. This is obtained by realizing that $I_3 = dQ_3/dt$. Using this value for I_3 and replacing I_1 by its equal $I_2 + I_3$, equations (2) and (3) can be written

$$-R\left(I_2 + \frac{dQ_3}{dt}\right) - \frac{Q_3}{C} + E = 0, \qquad L\frac{dI_2}{dt} - \frac{Q_3}{C} = 0$$

or in operator form with $D \equiv d/dt$,

$$RI_2 + \left(RD + \frac{1}{C}\right)Q_3 = E, \qquad LDI_2 - \frac{Q_3}{C} = 0 \tag{4}$$

These equations may be solved by methods already taken up. Let us, for example, consider $E = E_0 \sin \omega t$ an alternating voltage having frequency $\omega/2\pi$. Operating on the first of equations (4) with LD, multiplying the second equation by R, and subtracting, we find

$$\left(LRD^2 + \frac{L}{C}D + \frac{R}{C}\right)Q_3 = LE_0\omega \cos \omega t \tag{5}$$

an equation which can be solved for Q_3. From here the method proceeds as usual.

A EXERCISES

1. In the electric network of Fig. 86, $E = 60$ volts. Determine the currents I_1 and I_2 as functions of time t, assuming that at $t = 0$, when the key K is closed, $I_1 = I_2 = 0$. Find the steady-state currents.

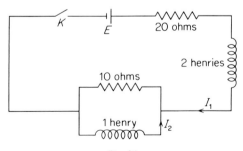

Fig. 86

2. Work Exercise 1 if $E = 150 \sin 10t$. Find the steady-state currents.

3. At $t = 0$ the charge on the capacitor in the circuit of Fig. 87 is 1 coulomb, while the current in the inductor is zero. Determine the charge on the capacitor and the currents in the various branches at any time.

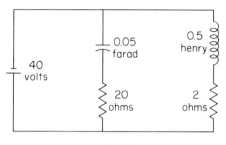

Fig. 87

4. Work Exercise 3 if the emf is $100 \sin 2t$.

5. Complete the problem of the text if $R = 10$ ohms, $C = 10^{-3}$ farads, $L = 0.4$ henries, $E_0 = 100$ volts, $\omega = 50$. Assume that the charge on the capacitor and the currents in the various branches are initially zero.

B EXERCISES

1. At $t = 0$ the capacitors in the network of Fig. 88 are charged to potential V_0, and the keys K_1 and K_2 are closed. Show that the potential across the capacitors of higher and lower capacitances are given, respectively, by

$$\frac{V_0}{3}\left(2\cos\frac{t}{2\sqrt{LC}} + \cos\frac{t}{\sqrt{LC}}\right) \quad \text{and} \quad \frac{V_0}{3}\left(4\cos\frac{t}{2\sqrt{LC}} - \cos\frac{t}{\sqrt{LC}}\right)$$

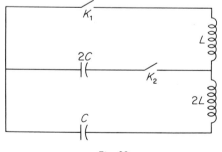

Fig. 88

2. Compare Exercise 1 with the problem of the vibrating masses on p. 233, pointing out the various analogies. What mechanical system might correspond to the network of Fig. 88?

C EXERCISES

1. In the circuit of Fig. 89 the capacitor C has a charge Q_0 at time $t = 0$, while the currents through the inductors are zero at that time. Show that at any time $t > 0$ the charge on the capacitor is given by

$$Q = Q_0 e^{-Rt/2L} \left(\cos \omega t + \frac{R}{2L\omega} \sin \omega t \right)$$

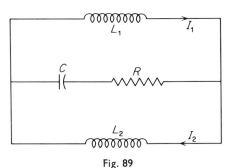

Fig. 89

where L is such that

$$\frac{1}{L} = \frac{1}{L_1} + \frac{1}{L_2}$$

and

$$\omega = \sqrt{\frac{1}{LC} - \frac{R^2}{4L^2}} \quad \text{if} \quad \frac{1}{LC} > \frac{R^2}{4L^2}$$

Show also that the currents I_1 and I_2 through L_1 and L_2 are

$$I_1 = -\frac{Q_0}{\omega CL_1} e^{-Rt/2L} \sin \omega t, \qquad I_2 = \frac{Q_0}{\omega CL_2} e^{-Rt/2L} \sin \omega t$$

2. Discuss the previous problem if $1/LC \leq R^2/4L^2$.

3. A radioactive element changes into another element at a rate proportional to the instantaneous mass present. Suppose that a radioactive element A_1 is changed successively into a radioactive element A_2 and then a stable element A_3. (a) Show that

$$\dot{x}_1 = -k_1 x_1, \qquad \dot{x}_2 = k_1 x_1 - k_2 x_2, \qquad \dot{x}_3 = k_2 x_2$$

where x_1, x_2, and x_3 are the instantaneous masses of A_1, A_2, and A_3, respectively, while k_1 and k_2 are constants. (b) If the masses of A_1, A_2, and A_3 are a_1, a_2, and a_3, respectively, at time $t = 0$, find the masses at $t > 0$. Discuss the case $a_2 = 0$, $a_3 = 0$.

4. Generalize Exercise 3 to the case of n elements $A_1, \ldots, A_n$.

5. A population P_1 having x_1 individuals at any time t is capable of continuously destroying members of a population P_2 which has x_2 individuals at time t. (a) Show that the equations describing the process are given by

$$\frac{dx_1}{dt} = \alpha x_1 x_2 - \beta x_1, \qquad \frac{dx_2}{dt} = \gamma x_2 - \delta x_1 x_2$$

where α, β, γ, and δ are positive constants. Discuss the physical significance of the two cases $\alpha = 0$ and $\delta = 0$. (b) Show by an appropriate change of variable that the equations in (a) can be written as

$$\frac{dX_1}{dt} = \beta(X_1 X_2 - X_1), \qquad \frac{dX_2}{dt} = \gamma(X_2 - X_1 X_2)$$

(c) Show that the steady-state solution of the equations in (b) is $X_1 = 1$, $X_2 = 1$ and thus find the steady-state populations of the two species. Discuss the physical significance.

6. (a) By eliminating t in the equations of Exercise 5(b) obtain the relationship between X_1 and X_2 and thus the populations x_1 and x_2. (b) By letting $X_1 = 1 + u$ and $X_2 = 1 + v$ in the equations of Exercise 5(b) obtain an approximate solution for u and v as functions of t assuming that u and v are small. Thus obtain an approximate solution to the equations of Exercise 5(a). (c) Show that in the neighborhood of the steady-state populations the locus of points (x_1,x_2) is an ellipse. Interpret physically.

7. (a) Discuss the solutions of the equations

$$\frac{dx}{dt} = a_1 x + b_1 y, \qquad \frac{dy}{dt} = a_2 x + b_2 y$$

as functions of t for different constants a_1, b_1, a_2, and b_2. (b) Show that $x = 0$ and $y = 0$ provides a steady-state solution to the equations of (a). Discuss the cases under which (x,y) approaches $(0,0)$ at t increases and the cases in which (x,y) does not approach $(0,0)$. Which cases would you be inclined to call cases of *stability*. (c) Can the results of (b) be obtained by examining the solution of

$$\frac{dy}{dx} = \frac{a_1 x + b_1 y}{a_2 x + b_2 y}$$

obtained by eliminating t in the equations of (a)? Explain. The xy plane is often called the *phase plane*.

8. (a) Discuss the relationship of Exercise 6 with Exercise 7. (b) Indicate how you might investigate the "stability" of solutions of the equations

$$\frac{dx}{dt} = M(x,y), \qquad \frac{dy}{dt} = N(x,y)$$

in the neighborhood of points where M and N are zero (the steady-state solutions). (c) Illustrate your procedure in (b) by considering the equations

$$\frac{dx}{dt} = x - x^3 y, \qquad \frac{dy}{dt} = xy - y$$

Chapter Seven

SOLUTION OF

LINEAR DIFFERENTIAL EQUATIONS BY

THE LAPLACE TRANSFORMATION

I. Introduction to the Laplace Transformation

In preceding chapters the student learned how to solve linear differential equations with constant coefficients subject to given conditions called boundary or initial conditions. It will be recalled that the method consists of finding the general solution of the equations in terms of a number of arbitrary constants and then determining these constants from the given conditions.

In this chapter we examine an important and powerful method called the *Laplace transformation method* or *method of Laplace transforms*, which can be used for solving such equations. This method has various advantages over other methods. First of all, by using the method, we can transform the given differential equations into algebraic equations.* Secondly, any given initial conditions are automatically incorporated into the algebraic problem so that no special consideration of them need be made. Finally, an appropriate use of tables of Laplace transforms can reduce the labor of obtaining solutions in much the same way thàt tables of logarithms reduce the labor of arithmetical calculations.†

1. Definition and examples of the Laplace transformation. Suppose that we are given a function $F(t)$ where $t > 0$. The *Laplace transformation* of $F(t)$ is defined as

$$f(s) = \mathcal{L}\{F(t)\} = \int_0^\infty e^{-st}F(t)dt \tag{1}$$

---

* This fact is reminiscent of the use of operator algebra for solving differential equations as seen in Chapter 4, pages 171-179.

† Although these advantages may alone be enough to warrant a study of the Laplace transformation, it should be emphasized that the transformation is useful in other connections as well as of interest in itself. See for example C Exercise 10, p. 336 where the method is applied to partial differential equations and also reference [4].

where s is a parameter which is assumed real.* The symbol $\mathcal{L}$ is called the *Laplace transformation operator* and $f(s) = \mathcal{L}\{F(t)\}$ is called the *Laplace transform* of $F(t)$.†

The improper integral in (1) is defined as

$$\lim_{M \to \infty} \int_0^M e^{-st}F(t)dt \tag{2}$$

and the Laplace transform is said to exist or not according as this limit exists or not. If (2) exists we say that the integral (1) converges. Conditions under which the Laplace transform exists are discussed on page 253.

Using definition (1) we can find the Laplace transform of various functions as indicated in the table on page 246 which will be useful for purposes of reference.‡

ILLUSTRATIVE EXAMPLE 1

Find

$$\text{(a) } \mathcal{L}\{1\} \qquad \text{(b) } \mathcal{L}\{e^{at}\}$$

Solution to (a).

$$\mathcal{L}\{1\} = \int_0^\infty e^{-st}(1)dt = \lim_{M \to \infty} \int_0^M e^{-st}\, dt = \lim_{M \to \infty} \frac{e^{-st}}{-s}\bigg|_0^M$$

$$= \lim_{M \to \infty} \frac{1 - e^{-sM}}{s} = \frac{1}{s} \quad \text{if } s > 0$$

Solution to (b).

$$\mathcal{L}\{e^{at}\} = \int_0^\infty e^{-st}(e^{at})dt = \lim_{M \to \infty} \int_0^M e^{-(s-a)t}\, dt$$

$$= \lim_{M \to \infty} \frac{e^{-(s-a)t}}{-(s-a)}\bigg|_0^M = \lim_{M \to \infty} \frac{1 - e^{-(s-a)M}}{s-a} = \frac{1}{s-a} \quad \text{if } s > a$$

These correspond to entries 1 and 5 of the table.

Note that from Illustrative Example 1, the existence of the Laplace transform of a function $F(t)$ depends on the values of s. Thus the Laplace transform of 1 exists if $s > 0$ but does not exist if $s \leq 0$. Similarly the Laplace transform of e^{at} exists if $s > a$ but does not exist if $s \leq a$. A similar

* In advanced theory of the Laplace transformation it is convenient to assume that s is a complex variable so that $f(s)$ is a function of a complex variable. The letter p is sometimes used in place of s, especially by some engineers and physicists. In another definition sometimes used, the integral in (1) is multiplied by s (or p).

† In general if functions are denoted by capital letters such as F, G their Laplace transforms are denoted by corresponding lowercase letters f, g. Alternatively an overbar may be used to denote the Laplace transform. For example $\mathcal{L}\{f(t)\} = \bar{f}(s)$.

‡ Note that the Laplace transform of zero is zero, as is clear from the definition, and has not been included in the table.

	$F(t)$	$f(s)$
1.	1	$\dfrac{1}{s}$ $s > 0$
2.	t	$\dfrac{1}{s^2}$ $s > 0$
3.	t^n $n = 1, 2, 3, \ldots$	$\dfrac{n!}{s^{n+1}}$ $s > 0$
4.	t^n $n > -1$	$\dfrac{\Gamma(n+1)}{s^{n+1}}$ $s > 0$
5.	e^{at}	$\dfrac{1}{s-a}$ $s > a$
6.	$\sin \omega t$	$\dfrac{\omega}{s^2 + \omega^2}$ $s > 0$
7.	$\cos \omega t$	$\dfrac{s}{s^2 + \omega^2}$ $s > 0$
8.	$\sinh \omega t$	$\dfrac{s}{s^2 - \omega^2}$ $s > |\omega|$
9.	$\cosh \omega t$	$\dfrac{\omega}{s^2 - \omega^2}$ $s > |\omega|$
10.	$e^{at} \sin \omega t$	$\dfrac{\omega}{(s-a)^2 + \omega^2}$ $s > a$
11.	$e^{at} \cos \omega t$	$\dfrac{s-a}{(s-a)^2 + \omega^2}$ $s > a$
12.	te^{at}	$\dfrac{1}{(s-a)^2}$ $s > a$
13.	$t \sin \omega t$	$\dfrac{2\omega s}{(s^2 + \omega^2)^2}$ $s > 0$
14.	$t \cos \omega t$	$\dfrac{s^2 - \omega^2}{(s^2 + \omega^2)^2}$ $s > 0$
15.	$Y'(t)$	$sy - Y(0)$ where $y = \mathcal{L}\{Y(t)\}$
16.	$Y''(t)$	$s^2 y - sY(0) - Y'(0)$
17.	$Y^{(n)}(t)$ $n = 1, 2, 3, \ldots$	$s^n y - s^{n-1} Y(0) - \cdots - Y^{(n-1)}(0)$
18.	$e^{at} F(t)$	$f(s-a)$
19.	$t^n F(t)$ $n = 1, 2, 3, \ldots$	$(-1)^n f^{(n)}(s)$
20.	$\displaystyle\int_0^t F(u)G(t-u)\,du$	$f(s)g(s)$
21.	$\displaystyle\int_0^t F(u)\,du$	$\dfrac{f(s)}{s}$
22.	$F(t-a)H(t-a) = \begin{cases} F(t-a) & t > a \\ 0 & t < a \end{cases}$	$e^{-as} f(s)$

situation arises in considering any Laplace transform.* It is not difficult to show that if the Laplace transform of a function exists for $s = \alpha$ then it will also exist for all $s > \alpha$. There are functions whose Laplace transforms do not exist for any values of s. Thus for example, since the integral

$$\int_0^\infty e^{-st} e^{t^2}\, dt$$

does not converge for any value of s, the Laplace transform of e^{t^2} does not exist. Further discussion of the existence of Laplace transforms is given on page 253.

ILLUSTRATIVE EXAMPLE 2

Find

(a) $\mathcal{L}\{\sin \omega t\}$ (b) $\mathcal{L}\{\cos \omega t\}$

Solutions. Although these can be obtained directly from the definition (see B Exercise 1) we shall resort to the following device. Replace a by $i\omega$ in part (b) of Illustrative Example 1. Then using Euler's formula $e^{i\omega t} = \cos \omega t + i \sin \omega t$ we have

$$\mathcal{L}\{e^{i\omega t}\} = \int_0^\infty e^{-st} e^{i\omega t}\, dt$$

$$= \int_0^\infty e^{-st} \cos \omega t\, dt + i \int_0^\infty e^{-st} \sin \omega t\, dt$$

$$= \mathcal{L}\{\cos \omega t\} + i\, \mathcal{L}\{\sin \omega t\}$$

$$= \frac{1}{s - i\omega} = \frac{1}{s - i\omega} \cdot \frac{s + i\omega}{s + i\omega} = \frac{s + i\omega}{s^2 + \omega^2}$$

$$= \frac{s}{s^2 + \omega^2} + i\, \frac{\omega}{s^2 + \omega^2}$$

Equating real and imaginary parts we obtain

$$\mathcal{L}\{\cos \omega t\} = \frac{s}{s^2 + \omega^2}, \qquad \mathcal{L}\{\sin \omega t\} = \frac{\omega}{s^2 + \omega^2}$$

which correspond to entries 6 and 7, respectively, in the table on page 246.†

---

* When writing Laplace transforms it may not always be convenient to indicate the actual range of values for which the Laplace transform exists, and we shall often omit it. One should of course be able to produce it on demand.

† It should be noted that the method is based on the equality

$$\int_0^\infty e^{-st} e^{i\omega t}\, dt = \frac{1}{s - i\omega}, \qquad s > 0$$

This can be justified using complex variable methods.

Since we have already hinted that Laplace transforms are useful in solving differential equations it should come as no surprise that we would be interested in finding Laplace transforms of derivatives. We can accomplish this directly from the definition. Thus we have

$$\mathcal{L}\{Y'(t)\} = \int_0^\infty e^{-st}Y'(t)dt = \lim_{M\to\infty}\int_0^M e^{-st}Y'(t)dt$$

$$= \lim_{M\to\infty}\left\{e^{-st}Y(t)\Big|_0^M + s\int_0^M e^{-st}Y(t)dt\right\}$$

$$= \lim_{M\to\infty}\left\{e^{-sM}Y(M) - Y(0) + s\int_0^M e^{-st}Y(t)dt\right\}$$

$$= s\int_0^\infty e^{-st}Y(t)dt - Y(0)$$

$$= sy(s) - Y(0)$$

where we have assumed that $\mathcal{L}\{Y(t)\} = y(s) = y$ and $\lim_{M\to\infty} e^{-sM}Y(M) = 0$.*

To find Laplace transforms of higher-order derivatives we can use the definition and integration by parts. However it is easier to employ the result which we have just obtained. To do this let $G(t) = Y'(t)$. Then

$$\mathcal{L}\{Y''(t)\} = \mathcal{L}\{G'(t)\} = s\,\mathcal{L}\{G(t)\} - G(0)$$

$$= s\,\mathcal{L}\{Y'(t)\} - Y'(0)$$

$$= s[sy(s) - Y(0)] - Y'(0)$$

$$= s^2y(s) - sY(0) - Y'(0)$$

The results correspond to entries 15 and 16 of the table. Generalizations to higher derivatives can similarly be obtained and are indicated by entry 17 of the table.

It is of interest and importance to note that the Laplace transformation operator $\mathcal{L}$ is a *linear operator* just as the operators $D, D^2, \ldots$, of Chapter 4, page 140. To prove this we need only show that

$$\mathcal{L}\{F(t) + G(t)\} = \mathcal{L}\{F(t)\} + \mathcal{L}\{G(t)\} = f(s) + g(s) \tag{3}$$

$$\mathcal{L}\{cF(t)\} = c\,\mathcal{L}\{F(t)\} = cf(s) \tag{4}$$

where $F(t)$ and $G(t)$ are functions having Laplace transforms $f(s)$ and $g(s)$, respectively, and c is any constant. The proof follows directly from the

---

* It is also assumed that $Y(t)$ is continuous at $t = 0$. For the case where this is not so see C Exercise 3, p. 258.

properties of integrals. Thus we have

$$\mathcal{L}\{F(t) + G(t)\} = \int_0^\infty e^{-st}\{F(t) + G(t)\}dt$$

$$= \int_0^\infty e^{-st}F(t)dt + \int_0^\infty e^{-st}G(t)dt$$

$$= \mathcal{L}\{F(t)\} + \mathcal{L}\{G(t)\}$$

$$= f(s) + g(s)$$

$$\mathcal{L}\{cF(t)\} = \int_0^\infty e^{-st}\{cF(t)\}dt$$

$$= c\int_0^\infty e^{-st}F(t)dt$$

$$= c\mathcal{L}\{F(t)\} = cf(s)$$

This *linear property* enables us to find Laplace transforms of sums as indicated in the following,

ILLUSTRATIVE EXAMPLE 3

Find

$$\mathcal{L}\{3 - 5e^{2t} + 4\sin t - 7\cos 3t\}.$$

Solution. Using the linear property we have

$$\mathcal{L}\{3 - 5e^{2t} + 4\sin t - 7\cos 3t\}$$

$$= \mathcal{L}\{3\} + \mathcal{L}\{-5e^{2t}\} + \mathcal{L}\{4\sin t\} + \mathcal{L}\{-7\cos 3t\}$$

$$= 3\mathcal{L}\{1\} - 5\mathcal{L}\{e^{2t}\} + 4\mathcal{L}\{\sin t\} - 7\mathcal{L}\{\cos 3t\}$$

$$= \frac{3}{s} - \frac{5}{s-2} + \frac{4}{s^2+1} - \frac{7s}{s^2+9} \qquad \text{if } s > 2$$

The results involving Laplace transforms of derivatives are often useful in finding Laplace transforms without direct use of the definition. Consider

ILLUSTRATIVE EXAMPLE 4

Find

$$\mathcal{L}\{t^n\} \qquad n = 1, 2, 3, \ldots$$

Solution. Let $Y(t) = t^n$ so that

$$Y'(t) = nt^{n-1}, \qquad Y(0) = 0$$

Then we have

$$\mathcal{L}\{Y'(t)\} = s\mathcal{L}\{Y(t)\} - Y(0)$$

or

$$\mathcal{L}\{nt^{n-1}\} = s\,\mathcal{L}\{t^n\}$$

Thus

$$\mathcal{L}\{t^n\} = \frac{n}{s}\mathcal{L}\{t^{n-1}\}$$

Putting $n = 1, 2, \ldots$, we find for $s > 0$

$$\mathcal{L}\{t\} = \frac{1}{s}\,\mathcal{L}\{1\} = \frac{1}{s^2}$$

$$\mathcal{L}\{t^2\} = \frac{2}{s}\,\mathcal{L}\{t\} = \frac{2}{s}\cdot\frac{1}{s^2} = \frac{2}{s^3}$$

$$\mathcal{L}\{t^3\} = \frac{3}{s}\,\mathcal{L}\{t^2\} = \frac{3\cdot 2}{s^4} = \frac{3!}{s^4}$$

and in general

$$\mathcal{L}\{t^n\} = \frac{n(n-1)\cdots 1}{s^{n+1}} = \frac{n!}{s^{n+1}} \tag{5}$$

2. Further properties of Laplace transforms. In constructing tables of Laplace transforms certain properties prove to be useful. To develop one such property let us write the definition

$$f(s) = \mathcal{L}\{F(t)\} = \int_0^\infty e^{-st}F(t)dt \tag{6}$$

and formally replace s by $s - a$. Then we find

$$f(s - a) = \int_0^\infty e^{-(s-a)t}F(t)dt = \int_0^\infty e^{-st}\{e^{at}F(t)\}dt$$

and so

$$\mathcal{L}\{e^{at}F(t)\} = f(s - a) \tag{7}$$

Another important property arises by differentiating both sides of (6) with respect to s. We find

$$\frac{df}{ds} = f'(s) = \frac{d}{ds}\int_0^\infty e^{-st}F(t)dt = \int_0^\infty -te^{-st}F(t)dt = -\mathcal{L}\{tF(t)\}$$

assuming the differentiation under the integral sign justifiable. Thus it follows that

$$\mathcal{L}\{tF(t)\} = -f'(s) \tag{8}$$

By further differentiation we have

$$\mathcal{L}\{t^2 F(t)\} = f''(s), \qquad \mathcal{L}\{t^3 F(t)\} = -f'''(s) \tag{9}$$

or in general

$$\mathcal{L}\{t^n F(t)\} = (-1)^n f^{(n)}(s) = (-1)^n \frac{d^n f}{ds^n} \tag{10}$$

The above results are summarized in the following

Theorem. If $\mathcal{L}\{F(t)\} = f(s)$ then

1. $\mathcal{L}\{e^{at}F(t)\} = f(s - a)$

2. $\mathcal{L}\{t^n F(t)\} = (-1)^n f^{(n)}(s)$ $n = 1, 2, 3, \ldots\,.$

To illustrate these results let us consider some examples.

ILLUSTRATIVE EXAMPLE 5

Find $\mathcal{L}\{e^{3t}\cos 4t\}$.

Solution. Since $\mathcal{L}\{\cos 4t\} = \dfrac{s}{s^2 + 16}$ we have

$$\mathcal{L}\{e^{3t}\cos 4t\} = \frac{s-3}{(s-3)^2 + 16} = \frac{s-3}{s^2 - 6s + 25}$$

Note that this is valid for $s > 3$. The result is a special case of entry 11 in the table on page 246.

ILLUSTRATIVE EXAMPLE 6

Find

$$\text{(a) } \mathcal{L}\{t\sin t\} \qquad \text{(b) } \mathcal{L}\{t^2\sin t\}$$

Solution. Since $\mathcal{L}\{\sin t\} = \dfrac{1}{s^2 + 1}$ we have

$$\mathcal{L}\{t\sin t\} = -\frac{d}{ds}\left(\frac{1}{s^2 + 1}\right) = \frac{2s}{(s^2 + 1)^2}$$

$$\mathcal{L}\{t^2\sin t\} = (-1)^2\frac{d^2}{ds^2}\left(\frac{1}{s^2 + 1}\right) = \frac{6s^2 - 2}{(s^2 + 1)^3}$$

which are valid for $s > 0$. Compare with entry 13 of the Laplace transform table.

We have indicated here two important theorems concerning properties of Laplace transforms. Other important theorems are discussed in the advanced exercises and it is suggested that the student read and understand the statements of these theorems even though a proof is not attempted.

3. The gamma function. We have already found (in Illustrative Example 4) that

$$\mathcal{L}\{t^n\} = \frac{n!}{s^{n+1}} \qquad s > 0, \qquad n = 1, 2, 3, \ldots \tag{11}$$

A natural question which arises is, How must (11) be modified if n is not a positive integer? To answer this let us first note that

$$\mathcal{L}\{t^n\} = \int_0^\infty e^{-st}t^n\, dt$$

Making the substitution $u = st$, $s > 0$ we find

$$\mathcal{L}\{t^n\} = \frac{1}{s^{n+1}}\int_0^\infty u^n e^{-u}\, du \tag{12}$$

If we now use the notation

$$\Gamma(n + 1) = \int_0^\infty u^n e^{-u}\, du \tag{13}$$

then (12) becomes

$$\mathcal{L}(t^n) = \frac{\Gamma(n + 1)}{s^{n+1}} \tag{14}$$

We call $\Gamma(n + 1)$ the *gamma function*. Let us consider this function a little more closely. On integrating by parts we find

$$\Gamma(n + 1) = \int_0^\infty u^n e^{-u}\, du$$

$$= (u^n)(-e^{-u}) \Big|_0^\infty - \int_0^\infty (nu^{n-1})(-e^{-u})du$$

$$= n\int_0^\infty u^{n-1} e^{-u}\, du$$

$$= n\,\Gamma(n)$$

The relation

$$\Gamma(n + 1) = n\Gamma(n) \tag{15}$$

is called a *recursion formula* for the gamma function. Since we have

$$\Gamma(1) = \int_0^\infty e^{-u}\, du = -e^{-u} \Big|_0^\infty = 1 \tag{16}$$

it follows that

$$\Gamma(2) = 1\Gamma(1) = 1, \qquad \Gamma(3) = 2\Gamma(2) = 2 \cdot 1 = 2!,$$

$$\Gamma(4) = 3\Gamma(3) = 3 \cdot 2! = 3!$$

and in general when n is a positive integer

$$\Gamma(n + 1) = n! \tag{17}$$

Thus (14) agrees with (11) for this case.

It follows that the gamma function is actually a generalization of the factorial. One interesting result is that

$$\Gamma(\tfrac{1}{2}) = \sqrt{\pi} \tag{18}$$

To indicate a proof of this let us first note that on letting $u = x^2$

$$I = \Gamma(\tfrac{1}{2}) = \int_0^\infty u^{-1/2} e^{-u}\, du = 2\int_0^\infty e^{-x^2}\, dx$$

We can then write

$$I^2 = \left(2\int_0^\infty e^{-x^2}\, dx\right)\left(2\int_0^\infty e^{-y^2}\, dy\right) = 4\int_0^\infty \int_0^\infty e^{-(x^2+y^2)}\, dx\, dy$$

By changing to polar coordinates (r, θ) this last integral can be transformed into

$$I^2 = 4 \int_{\theta=0}^{\pi/2} \int_{r=0}^{\infty} e^{-r^2} r \, dr \, d\theta$$

$$= 4 \int_{\theta=0}^{\pi/2} \left(-\frac{1}{2} e^{-r^2} \right) \Big|_0^{\infty} d\theta$$

$$= 4 \int_0^{\pi/2} \frac{1}{2} \, d\theta = \pi$$

from which $I = \Gamma(\frac{1}{2}) = \sqrt{\pi}$. Although this is a somewhat "hand-waving" approach, the method can be made mathematically rigorous by appropriate limiting procedures.

It is of interest to note that

$$\mathcal{L}\{t^{-1/2}\} = \frac{\Gamma(\frac{1}{2})}{s^{1/2}} = \sqrt{\frac{\pi}{s}}, \qquad s > 0$$

4. Remarks concerning existence of Laplace transforms. In the definition (1) of the Laplace transform, the factor e^{-st} is a "damping factor" which for any fixed positive value of s tends to decrease as t increases. Intuitively speaking, we would expect the integral to converge, and thus the Laplace transform to exist, provided that $F(t)$ does not "grow too rapidly" as t increases. The mathematician makes this more precise by defining a class of functions which are such that there exist constants K and α for which

$$|F(t)| < Ke^{\alpha t}$$

Such functions are said to be of *exponential order* α, or briefly of *exponential order*. The function $F(t) = t$ is certainly of exponential order since we have (for example)

$$t < e^t$$

The function e^{t^2} on the other hand is not of exponential order, i.e., it grows too rapidly to be of this type.

Another class of functions which the mathematician finds important is the class of *piecewise* or *sectionally continuous functions*. We call a function piecewise continuous in an interval if it has only a finite number of discontinuities in the interval and if the right- and left-hand limits at each discontinuity exist.* For example, the function

$$F(t) = \begin{cases} 1 & 0 \leq t < 2 \\ t & 2 \leq t \leq 5 \end{cases}$$

---

* The right-hand limit of a function $F(t)$ at the point t_0 is defined as $\lim_{\epsilon \to 0} F(t_0 + \epsilon)$ where ϵ approaches zero through positive values. Similarly, the left-hand limit of $F(t)$ at t_0 is $\lim_{\epsilon \to 0} F(t_0 - \epsilon)$ where ϵ approaches zero through positive values. To indicate that ϵ approaches zero through positive values we sometimes write $\lim_{\epsilon \to 0+} F(t_0 + \epsilon)$ and $\lim_{\epsilon \to 0+} F(t_0 - \epsilon)$ for the right- and left-hand limits, respectively.

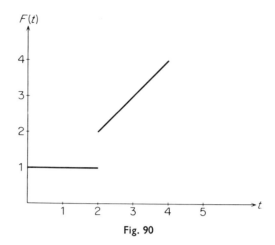

Fig. 90

whose graph is shown in Fig. 90 is piecewise continuous in the interval $0 \leq t \leq 5$ since there is only one discontinuity, $t = 2$, in the interval and the right- and left-hand limits at this discontinuity exist (and are equal to 2 and 1, respectively).

The following theorem is of fundamental importance.

> THEOREM. If $F(t)$ is of exponential order α and is piecewise continuous in every finite interval $0 \leq t < T$ then the Laplace transform of $F(t)$ exists for all $s > \alpha$.

It should be emphasized that the hypotheses of this theorem guarantee the existence of the Laplace transform. However if these conditions are not satisfied it does not follow that the Laplace transform does not exist. In fact it may or may not exist (see B Exercises 3 and 6). In situations such as these, the conditions are said to be *sufficient* but not *necessary* for the validity of the conclusions.

Let us illustrate the above theorem in the following

ILLUSTRATIVE EXAMPLE 7

Find the Laplace transform of

$$F(t) = \begin{cases} 3 & 0 \leq t < 2 \\ 0 & t > 2 \end{cases}$$

Solution. The function is piecewise continuous and of exponential order and so by the above theorem has a Laplace transform. This is given by

$$\mathcal{L}\{F(t)\} = \int_0^\infty e^{-st} F(t)dt$$

$$= \int_0^2 e^{-st}(3)dt + \int_2^\infty e^{-st}(0)dt$$

$$= 3\left(\frac{e^{-st}}{-s}\right)\Big|_0^2 = 3\left(\frac{1 - e^{-2s}}{s}\right)$$

5. The Heaviside unit step function. The function defined by

$$H(t - a) = \begin{cases} 1 & t > a \\ 0 & t < a \end{cases}$$

called the *Heaviside unit step function* or more briefly the *Heaviside function* or the *unit step function*, is often useful in applications. The graph of this function is shown in Fig. 91.

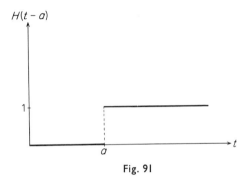

Fig. 91

The Laplace transform of this function is given by

$$\mathcal{L}\{H(t - a)\} = \int_0^\infty e^{-st}H(t - a)dt$$

$$= \int_0^a e^{-st}(0)dt + \int_a^\infty e^{-st}(1)dt$$

$$= \int_a^\infty e^{-st}\, dt$$

$$= \frac{e^{-as}}{s}$$

Various discontinuous functions can often be expressed in terms of the Heaviside function as indicated in the following

ILLUSTRATIVE EXAMPLE 8

Express the function $F(t) = \begin{cases} \sin t & t > \pi \\ \cos t & t < \pi \end{cases}$

in terms of the Heaviside unit step function.

Solution. The given function can be expressed as

$$F(t) = \cos t + \begin{cases} \sin t - \cos t & t > \pi \\ 0 & t < \pi \end{cases}$$

$$= \cos t + (\sin t - \cos t)\begin{cases} 1 & t > \pi \\ 0 & t < \pi \end{cases}$$

$$= \cos t + (\sin t - \cos t)H(t - \pi)$$

A EXERCISES

1. Using the definition, find the Laplace transform of each of the following functions. In each case specify the values of s for which the transform exists. Compare with results obtained from the table of Laplace transforms.

(a) $3t - 2$.   (b) $4 \sin 3t$.   (c) $5 \cos 2t$.
(d) $10e^{-5t}$.   (e) $2e^t - 3e^{-t} + 4t^2$.   (f) $3 \sin 5t - 4 \cos 5t$.
(g) $6 \cosh 3t - 2 \sinh 5t$.   (h) $t(e^{-3t} - t^2 + 1)$.

2. Given that $\mathcal{L}\{\sin \omega t\} = \dfrac{\omega}{s^2 + \omega^2}$ use entry 15 of the table on page 246 to find $\mathcal{L}\{\cos \omega t\}$.

3. Find the Laplace transform of each of the following.

(a) $t^2 e^{3t}$.   (b) $e^{-2t}(5 \sin 2t - 2 \cos 2t)$.   (c) $t(\sin t + e^{-t})$.
(d) $(t^2 + 1)^2$.   (e) $t(\cosh 2t - 2t)$.   (f) $8 \sinh^2 3t$.

4. Use the gamma function to find (a) $\mathcal{L}\{t^{3/2}\}$ (b) $\mathcal{L}\{(t^{1/4} + t^{-1/4})^2\}$ (c) $\mathcal{L}\{t^{2/3}\}$
(d) $\mathcal{L}\{\sqrt{t}\, e^t\}$.

5. (a) Explain how you can be sure that the function $F(t) = \begin{cases} t & 0 < t < 4 \\ 0 & t > 4 \end{cases}$ has a Laplace transform without actually finding it. (b) Find $\mathcal{L}\{F(t)\}$.

6. Verify entries 15 and 16 in the table for the functions

(a) $Y(t) = te^t$.   (b) $Y(t) = t^2 \sin 3t$.

7. Express each of the following functions in terms of Heaviside's unit step function and obtain their graphs.

(a) $F(t) = \begin{cases} 2 & t > 1 \\ 1 & t < 1. \end{cases}$ (b) $F(t) = \begin{cases} t^2 & t > 3 \\ 2t & t < 3. \end{cases}$ (c) $F(t) = \begin{cases} 0 & t > 2\pi \\ \cos t & t < 2\pi. \end{cases}$

8. Find (a) $\mathcal{L}\{tH(t - 1)\}$. (b) $\mathcal{L}\{e^t H(t - 2) - e^{-t} H(t - 3)\}$.

B EXERCISES

1. Obtain $\mathcal{L}\{\sin \omega t\}$ by (a) direct evaluation; (b) using the fact that $\sin \omega t$ satisfies the differential equation $Y'' + \omega^2 Y = 0$. Do the same for $\mathcal{L}\{\cos \omega t\}$.

2. Find $\mathcal{L}\{te^{-t} \sin t\}$.

3. Prove that $\mathcal{L}\{e^{\sqrt{t}}\}$ exists but $\mathcal{L}\{e^{e^t}\}$ does not exist.

4. If $\mathcal{L}\{F(t)\}$ exists for $s = \alpha$ prove that it also exists for all $s > \alpha$.

5. Find the Laplace transform of the periodic function shown in Fig. 92.

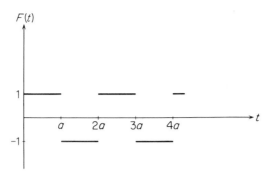

Fig. 92

6. Show that although the function $F(t) = t^{-1/2}$ does not satisfy the conditions of the theorem on page 254 it still has a Laplace transform. Is there any contradiction involved? Explain.

7. Express in terms of Heaviside's unit step function

$$F(t) = \begin{cases} 3 \sin t & t \leq \pi \\ t^2 & \pi < t \leq 2\pi \\ t - \cos t & t > 2\pi \end{cases}$$

8. The function

$$P(t) = \begin{cases} 0 & t < a \\ 1/\epsilon & a \leq t \leq a + \epsilon \\ 0 & t > a + \epsilon \end{cases}$$

where $\epsilon > 0$, whose graph is indicated in Fig. 93, is often called a *pulse function*.

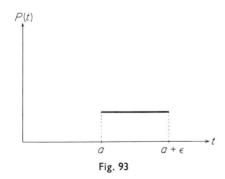

Fig. 93

(a) Express this function in terms of the Heaviside unit step function.
(b) Find the Laplace transform of this function.
(c) Show that the limit of the Laplace transform in (b) as $\epsilon \to 0$ exists and is equal to 1.

9. A function often used by physicists and engineers is called the *Dirac delta function* or *unit impulse function* and is denoted by $\delta(t - a)$. It has the property that for any "suitable function" $F(t)$ (for example a continuous function)

$$\int_{-\infty}^{\infty} F(t)\delta(t - a)dt = F(a)$$

(a) Show that according to this definition

$$\mathcal{L}\{\delta(t)\} = 1, \qquad \mathcal{L}\{\delta(t - a)\} = e^{-as}, \qquad a > 0$$

(b) Discuss the relationship if any with the pulse function of Exercise 8.
(c) Do you think that the Dirac delta function is a function in the usual sense? Explain.

C EXERCISES

1. Show that the functions $F(t) = 1$, $t > 0$ and $G(t) = \begin{cases} 1 & t = 3 \\ 5 & t \neq 3 \end{cases}$ have the same Laplace transforms, namely $1/s$, $s > 0$. Can you think of any other functions which have the same Laplace transform? Explain.

2. Let $F(t) = \begin{cases} 1 & t = 0 \\ t & t > 0 \end{cases}$. (a) Find $\mathcal{L}\{F(t)\}$ and $\mathcal{L}\{F'(t)\}$. (b) Is it true for this case that $\mathcal{L}\{F'(t)\} = s\mathcal{L}\{F(t)\} - F(0)$?

3. Prove that if $Y(t)$ has a discontinuity at $t = 0$ then we must replace entry 15 of the table by $sy - Y(0 +)$, where $Y(0 +)$ means $\lim_{\epsilon \to 0+} Y(t)$, i.e., the limit as $\epsilon \to 0$ through positive values. Using this, explain the discrepancy in Exercise 2.

4. (a) Prove that if $F(t)$ is continuous and of exponential order α then its Laplace transform $f(s)$ exists for $s > \alpha$. (b) Prove the theorem on page 254. *Hint:* For (a) use the fact that if $|F(t)| < Ke^{\alpha t}$ then

$$\left| \int_0^{\infty} F(t)e^{-st}\, dt \right| \leq \int_0^{\infty} |F(t)|\, e^{-st}\, dt$$

5. Let $F(t)$ be a periodic function of period P, starting at $t = 0$ (for example, see Fig. 92). (a) If $\mathcal{L}\{F(t)\}$ exists show that it is given by

$$\frac{\int_0^P e^{-st} F(t)dt}{1 - e^{-sP}}$$

(b) Use the result to obtain the Laplace transform of the function $F(t) = |\sin t|$ where the period is π.

6. Let $F(t) = e^t$. By using the series expansion

$$e^t = 1 + t + \frac{t^2}{2!} + \frac{t^3}{3!} + \cdots$$

and taking the Laplace transform term by term, verify formally that $\mathcal{L}\{e^t\} = 1/(s - 1)$, $s > 1$. How can you use this method to find (a) $\mathcal{L}\{\sin t\}$; (b) $\mathcal{L}\{\cos t\}$; (c) $\mathcal{L}\{e^{\sqrt{t}}\}$? Can you justify the method?

7. Show that (a) $\displaystyle\int_0^t H(u - a)du = (t - a)H(t - a)$ (b) $\displaystyle\int_0^t (u - a)^n H(u - a)du = \dfrac{(t - a)^{n+1}H(t - a)}{n + 1}$ where $a > 0$ and $n > -1$.

8. Show that the function illustrated graphically in Fig. 92 can be represented by

$$H(t) + \sum_{n=1}^{\infty} (-1)^n H(t - na)$$

II. Application of Laplace Transformation to Differential Equations

1. Solution of simple differential equations. Inverse Laplace transform. In order to see how the Laplace transformation can be used to find solutions to differential equations, let us consider the following

Problem for Discussion.

Solve

$$Y'' + 4Y = 16t, \quad Y(0) = 3, \quad Y'(0) = -6$$

If we take the Laplace transforms of both sides of the differential equation we find on using entry 16 and denoting $\mathcal{L}\{Y\}$ by y,

$$\mathcal{L}\{Y''\} + \mathcal{L}\{4Y\} = \mathcal{L}\{16t\}$$

$$s^2 y - sY(0) - Y'(0) + 4y = \frac{16}{s^2}$$

or

$$s^2 y - 3s + 6 + 4y = \frac{16}{s^2}$$

$$(s^2 + 4)y = 3s - 6 + \frac{16}{s^2}$$

$$y = \frac{3s - 6}{s^2 + 4} + \frac{16}{s^2(s^2 + 4)} \tag{1}$$

It seems logical now that if we can find the function whose Laplace transform is the right side of (1) then we would have the solution. To do this we write (1) in the form

$$y = \frac{3s}{s^2 + 4} - \frac{6}{s^2 + 4} + \frac{16}{4}\left(\frac{1}{s^2} - \frac{1}{s^2 + 4}\right)$$

$$= \frac{3s}{s^2 + 4} - \frac{10}{s^2 + 4} + \frac{4}{s^2}$$

Now we know that

The Laplace transform of cos 2t is $\dfrac{s}{s^2 + 4}$

The Laplace transform of sin 2t is $\dfrac{2}{s^2 + 4}$

The Laplace transform of t is $\dfrac{1}{s^2}$

It would seem therefore that the function sought is

$$Y(t) = 3 \cos 2t - 5 \sin 2t + 4t$$

This does indeed satisfy the given differential equation and conditions and so is the required solution.

In the problem just considered we needed to find a function $F(t)$ whose Laplace transform $f(s)$ is known. Such a function is called an *inverse Laplace transform* and is denoted by $\mathcal{L}^{-1}\{f(s)\}$ where $\mathcal{L}^{-1}$ is called the *inverse Laplace transformation operator*. From the fact that

$$\mathcal{L}\{F(t) + G(t)\} = f(s) + g(s)$$

$$\mathcal{L}\{cF(t)\} = cf(s)$$

it follows that

$$\mathcal{L}^{-1}\{f(s) + g(s)\} = F(t) + G(t) = \mathcal{L}^{-1}\{f(s)\} + \mathcal{L}^{-1}\{g(s)\} \qquad (2)$$

$$\mathcal{L}^{-1}\{cf(s)\} = cF(t) = c\,\mathcal{L}^{-1}\{f(s)\} \qquad (3)$$

which shows that $\mathcal{L}^{-1}$ is a linear operator.

In view of our previous experience regarding problems of existence and uniqueness (see page 8 for example) several questions arise.

1. *Existence.* Does the inverse Laplace transform of a given function $f(s)$ exist?

2. *Uniqueness.* If it does exist, is it unique?

3. *Determination.* How do we find it?

From the practical point of view, as we have already mentioned, number 3 seems most important. But the other two are also important. In what follows we shall investigate various methods by which inverse Laplace transforms can be found and at the same time shall show how to solve various differential equations using these methods. At the end of this section we shall consider the questions of existence and uniqueness.

2. Some methods for finding inverse Laplace transforms. From the above discussion problem, it is at once clear that proficiency in solving differential equations using Laplace transforms is practically synonymous with proficiency in determining inverse Laplace transforms. Several methods are available for finding inverse Laplace transforms. These are

(a) Use of Laplace transform tables
(b) Use of theorems on inverse Laplace transforms
(c) The method of partial fractions
(d) The method of convolutions
(e) Miscellaneous methods

We shall now treat examples illustrating each of these.

(a) *Use of Laplace Transform Tables*

Suppose that we wish to find $\mathcal{L}^{-1}\{f(s)\}$ where $f(s)$ is known. Then we need only look in the Laplace transform table (page 246) opposite $f(s)$. Let us consider for instance

ILLUSTRATIVE EXAMPLE 1

Solve

$$Y'' + Y = 16 \cos t, \qquad Y(0) = 0, \qquad Y'(0) = 0$$

Solution. Taking Laplace transforms we find

$$\{s^2 y - s Y(0) - Y'(0)\} + y = \frac{16s}{s^2 + 1}$$

$$(s^2 + 1)y = \frac{16s}{s^2 + 1}$$

Then

$$y = \frac{16s}{(s^2 + 1)^2}$$

Hence from entry 13 of the table, we have on letting $\omega = 1$ and dividing by 2 (justified by the linear property of Laplace transformation)

$$Y = 16\mathcal{L}^{-1}\left\{\frac{s}{(s^2 + 1)^2}\right\} = 8t \sin t$$

which is the required solution.

In some cases the inverse transform is not obtained directly from the table but it may be obtained by combinations of transforms which are in the table. Consider for instance

ILLUSTRATIVE EXAMPLE 2

Find

$$\mathcal{L}^{-1}\left\{\frac{2s - 3}{s^2 + 1}\right\}$$

Solution. The transform as given is not in the table. However by writing it as

$$2\mathcal{L}^{-1}\left\{\frac{s}{s^2 + 1}\right\} - 3\mathcal{L}^{-1}\left\{\frac{1}{s^2 + 1}\right\}$$

we see from entries 6 and 7 with $\omega = 1$ that the required result is

$$2 \cos t - 3 \sin t$$

It is quite evident that success in using tables depends on how extensive the tables are and also our ability to use the tables effectively.* In case we cannot find the required transform in the table other methods must be used.

(b) *Use of Theorems on Inverse Laplace Transforms*

Corresponding to each theorem developed for Laplace transforms there is a theorem on inverse Laplace transforms. For example corresponding to the theorem on page 250, we have

THEOREM. If $\mathcal{L}^{-1}\{f(s)\} = F(t)$

1. $\mathcal{L}^{-1}\{f(s - a)\} = e^{at} F(t)$.

2. $\mathcal{L}^{-1}\{f^{(n)}(s)\} = (-1)^n t^n F(t)$

As illustration consider

ILLUSTRATIVE EXAMPLE 3

Solve

$$Y'' + 2Y' + 5Y = 0, \qquad Y(0) = 3, \qquad Y'(0) = -7$$

Solution. Taking Laplace transforms we find

$$\{s^2 y - s Y(0) - Y'(0)\} + 2\{sy - Y(0)\} + 5y = 0$$
$$(s^2 + 2s + 5)y - 3s + 1 = 0$$

and so,

$$y = \frac{3s - 1}{s^2 + 2s + 5}$$

To find the inverse, let us complete the square in the denominator and rewrite as follows

$$y = \frac{3(s + 1) - 4}{(s + 1)^2 + 4} = 3\left\{\frac{s + 1}{(s + 1)^2 + 4}\right\} - 4\left\{\frac{1}{(s + 1)^2 + 4}\right\}$$

From the first part of the theorem we see that since

$$\mathcal{L}^{-1}\left\{\frac{s}{s^2 + 4}\right\} = \cos 2t, \qquad \mathcal{L}^{-1}\left\{\frac{s + 1}{(s + 1)^2 + 4}\right\} = e^{-t} \cos 2t$$

Also since

$$\mathcal{L}^{-1}\left\{\frac{1}{s^2 + 4}\right\} = \tfrac{1}{2} \sin 2t, \qquad \mathcal{L}^{-1}\left\{\frac{1}{(s + 1)^2 + 4}\right\} = \tfrac{1}{2} e^{-t} \sin 2t$$

Hence the required inverse transform is

$$3e^{-t} \cos 2t - \tfrac{4}{2} e^{-t} \sin 2t = e^{-t}(3 \cos 2t - 2 \sin 2t)$$

---

* As in the case of differentiation and integration in the calculus, the student should, for facility, become acquainted with certain basic Laplace transforms, for example entries 1–7 of the table.

(c) *The Method of Partial Fractions*

In many problems we arrive at a transform which is a rational function of s (i.e., a function having the form $P(s)/Q(s)$, where $P(s)$ and $Q(s)$ are polynomials and the degree of $P(s)$ is less than that of $Q(s)$). In such case it is often useful to express the given result as the sum of simpler fractions, called *partial fractions*. As an example consider

ILLUSTRATIVE EXAMPLE 4

Solve
$$Y'' - 3Y' + 2Y = 12e^{4t}, \qquad Y(0) = 1, \qquad Y'(0) = 0$$

Solution. Laplace transformation yields,
$$(s^2 - 3s + 2)y - s + 3 = \frac{12}{s - 4}$$

or
$$y = \frac{s^2 - 7s + 24}{(s - 1)(s - 2)(s - 4)} \tag{4}$$

To resolve this into partial fractions, two methods can be used.

First method. Assume
$$\frac{s^2 - 7s + 24}{(s - 1)(s - 2)(s - 4)} = \frac{A}{s - 1} + \frac{B}{s - 2} + \frac{C}{s - 4} \tag{5}$$

where A, B, C are undetermined constants. Multiplying by $(s - 1)(s - 2)$ $(s - 4)$ we obtain

$$s^2 - 7s + 24 = A(s - 2)(s - 4) + B(s - 1)(s - 4) + C(s - 1)(s - 2)$$
$$= (A + B + C)s^2 + (-6A - 5B - 3C)s + (8A + 4B + 2C)$$

Since this is an identity we have on equating coefficients of like powers of s,

$$A + B + C = 1, \qquad -6A - 5B - 3C = -7, \qquad 8A + 4B + 2C = 24$$

Solving these we find $A = 6$, $B = -7$, $C = 2$. Thus

$$Y = \mathcal{L}^{-1}\left\{ \frac{6}{s - 1} - \frac{7}{s - 2} + \frac{2}{s - 4} \right\} = 6e^t - 7e^{2t} + 2e^{4t}$$

Second method. Multiplying both sides of (5) by $s - 1$ we find

$$\frac{s^2 - 7s + 24}{(s - 2)(s - 4)} = A + \frac{B(s - 1)}{s - 2} + \frac{C(s - 1)}{s - 4}$$

Then letting $s \to 1$, we have

$$A = \frac{1 - 7 + 24}{(1 - 2)(1 - 4)} = 6$$

Similarly, multiplying (5) by $s - 2$ and letting $s \to 2$ yields $B = -7$ and multiplying (5) by $s - 4$ and letting $s \to 4$ yields $C = 2$. From here the method proceeds as in the first method.

ILLUSTRATIVE EXAMPLE 5

Find

$$\mathcal{L}^{-1}\left\{\frac{5s^2 - 7s + 17}{(s - 1)(s^2 + 4)}\right\}$$

Solution. Assume that

$$\frac{5s^2 - 7s + 17}{(s - 1)(s^2 + 4)} = \frac{A}{s - 1} + \frac{Bs + C}{s^2 + 4} \qquad (6)$$

First method. Multiplying by $(s - 1)(s^2 + 4)$ we have

$$5s^2 - 7s + 17 = (A + B)s^2 + (C - B)s + 4A - C$$

Then $A + B = 5,$ $C - B = -7,$ $4A - C = 17$

Thus $A = 3,\ B = 2,\ C = -5$ and we have

$$\mathcal{L}^{-1}\left\{\frac{3}{s - 1} + \frac{2s - 5}{s^2 + 4}\right\} = 3\mathcal{L}^{-1}\left\{\frac{1}{s - 1}\right\} + 2\mathcal{L}^{-1}\left\{\frac{s}{s^2 + 4}\right\} - 5\mathcal{L}^{-1}\left\{\frac{1}{s^2 + 4}\right\}$$

$$= 3e^t + 2\cos 2t - \frac{5}{2}\sin 2t$$

Second method. Multiplying (6) by $s - 1$ and letting $s \to 1$ yields $A = 3$. Thus

$$\frac{5s^2 - 7s + 17}{(s - 1)(s^2 + 4)} = \frac{3}{s - 1} + \frac{Bs + C}{s^2 + 4}$$

To determine C it is convenient to put $s = 0$ and obtain $C = -5$. Finally by placing $s = -1$ for example we find $B = 2$. The method then proceeds as before.

Note that in both examples, the first method is general but solution of the simultaneous equations can be tedious. The second method, although shorter, is most effective when the denominator can be factored into real distinct linear factors. More complicated cases are considered in the Exercises.

(d) *The Method of Convolutions*

We have already noted that if $f(s)$ and $g(s)$ are the Laplace transforms of $F(t)$ and $G(t)$, respectively, then

$$\mathcal{L}^{-1}\{f(s) + g(s)\} = F(t) + G(t), \qquad \mathcal{L}^{-1}\{f(s) - g(s)\} = F(t) - G(t)$$

It is of interest to ask whether there is some simple expression for the inverse Laplace transform of the product $f(s)g(s)$ in terms of $F(t)$ and $G(t)$. The answer is *yes* and the result is summarized in the following

THEOREM. If $\mathcal{L}^{-1}\{f(s)\} = F(t)$ and $\mathcal{L}^{-1}\{g(s)\} = G(t)$ then

$$\mathcal{L}^{-1}\{f(s)g(s)\} = \int_0^t F(u)G(t - u)du = F*G$$

where we call $F*G$ the *convolution* of F and G.

This theorem, which is often called the *convolution theorem*, is useful in obtaining inverse Laplace transforms. As an example of its use consider

ILLUSTRATIVE EXAMPLE 6

Find
$$\mathcal{L}^{-1}\left\{\frac{s}{(s^2+1)^2}\right\}.$$

Solution. We have

$$\mathcal{L}^{-1}\left\{\frac{s}{s^2+1}\right\} = \cos t, \qquad \mathcal{L}^{-1}\left\{\frac{1}{s^2+1}\right\} = \sin t$$

Hence by the convolution theorem

$$\mathcal{L}^{-1}\left\{\frac{s}{(s^2+1)^2}\right\} = \mathcal{L}^{-1}\left\{\frac{s}{s^2+1}\cdot\frac{1}{s^2+1}\right\} = \cos t * \sin t$$

$$= \int_0^t \cos u \sin(t-u)du$$

$$= \int_0^t \cos u[\sin t \cos u - \cos t \sin u]du$$

$$= \sin t \int_0^t \cos^2 u\, du - \cos t \int_0^t \sin u \cos u\, du$$

$$= \sin t[\tfrac{1}{2}t + \tfrac{1}{2}\sin t \cos t] - \cos t[\tfrac{1}{2}\sin^2 t]$$

$$= \tfrac{1}{2}t \sin t$$

Note that this agrees with entry 13. If we let $G(t) = 1$ in the convolution theorem we obtain

$$\mathcal{L}^{-1}\left\{\frac{f(s)}{s}\right\} = \int_0^t F(u)du \tag{7}$$

It follows that multiplying $f(s)$ by $1/s$ corresponds to integrating $F(t)$ from 0 to t. Similarly multiplying by $1/s^2$ corresponds to integrating twice, etc. The use of this is indicated in the following

ILLUSTRATIVE EXAMPLE 7

Find

$$\text{(a)}\ \mathcal{L}^{-1}\left\{\frac{1}{s(s^2+1)}\right\} \qquad \text{(b)}\ \mathcal{L}^{-1}\left\{\frac{1}{s^2(s^2+1)}\right\}$$

Solution to (a). Since $\mathcal{L}^{-1}\left\{\dfrac{1}{s^2+1}\right\} = \sin t$ we have using (7),

$$\mathcal{L}^{-1}\left\{\frac{1}{s(s^2+1)}\right\} = \int_0^t \sin u\, du = 1 - \cos t$$

Solution to (b). Since by (a) $\mathcal{L}^{-1}\left\{\dfrac{1}{s(s^2+1)}\right\} = 1 - \cos t$ we have using (7),

$$\mathcal{L}^{-1}\left\{\frac{1}{s^2(s^2+1)}\right\} = \int_0^t (1 - \cos u)du = t - \sin t$$

By letting $G(t) = e^{at}$ in the convolution theorem we find

$$\mathcal{L}^{-1}\left\{\frac{f(s)}{s-a}\right\} = \int_0^t F(t)e^{a(t-u)}du = e^{at}\int_0^t e^{-au}F(u)du \qquad (8)$$

Note that (7) is a special case of this with $a = 0$. From (8) we see there is a correspondence between

$$\frac{1}{s-a} \qquad \text{and} \qquad e^{at}\int_0^t e^{-au}(\ )du \qquad (9)$$

where the first can be considered as an operator acting on $f(s)$ while the second is considered as an operator acting on $F(t)$. The correspondence bears close resemblance to equation (16) in the section on operator methods on page 172. This provides a clue as to the connection between s and the operator D and thus the connection between Laplace transform methods and Heaviside's operational methods.

A proof of the convolution theorem is outlined in C Exercise 6.

(e) *Miscellaneous Methods*

Various special methods may also be useful in finding inverse Laplace transforms. As an illustration consider

ILLUSTRATIVE EXAMPLE 8

Find $\mathcal{L}^{-1}\{e^{-as}f(s)\}$ where $f(s) = \mathcal{L}\{F(t)\}$ and $a > 0$.
Solution. We have by definition

$$f(s) = \int_0^\infty e^{-st}F(t)dt$$

Then multiplying by e^{-as} we find

$$e^{-as}f(s) = \int_0^\infty e^{-s(t+a)}F(t)dt$$

With $t + a = u$ this last integral can be written as

$$e^{-as}f(s) = \int_a^\infty e^{-su}F(u-a)du = \int_0^a e^{-su}(0)du + \int_a^\infty e^{-su}F(u-a)du$$

$$= \mathcal{L}\{G(t)\}$$

where

$$G(t) = \begin{cases} 0 & t < a \\ F(t-a) & t > a \end{cases}$$

We thus have on taking inverse Laplace transforms,

$$\mathcal{L}^{-1}\{e^{-as}f(s)\} = \begin{cases} 0 & t < a \\ F(t-a) & t > a \end{cases}$$

This result can also be expressed in terms of the Heaviside unit function as

$$\mathcal{L}^{-1}\{e^{-as}f(s)\} = F(t-a)H(t-a)$$

The result of this Illustrative Example is important and we state it for future reference in the following

THEOREM. If $\mathcal{L}^{-1}\{f(s)\} = F(t)$ then

$$\mathcal{L}^{-1}\{e^{-as}f(s)\} = \begin{cases} 0 & t < a \\ F(t-a) & t > a \end{cases} = F(t-a)H(t-a)$$

3. Solution of simultaneous differential equations. The method of Laplace transformation can without any added difficulty be used to solve simultaneous linear differential equations with constant coefficients. The procedure is illustrated in the following

ILLUSTRATIVE EXAMPLE 9

Solve the simultaneous equations

$$Y' + 6Y = X', \qquad 3X - X' = 2Y', \qquad X(0) = 2, \qquad Y(0) = 3$$

where primes denote derivatives with respect to t.

Solution. Taking the Laplace transform of each differential equation and using the given conditions we have if $\mathcal{L}\{X\} = x$ and $\mathcal{L}\{Y\} = y$

$$\{sy - Y(0)\} + 6y = \{sx - X(0)\}$$
$$3x - \{sx - X(0)\} = 2\{sy - Y(0)\}$$

or

$$sx - (s + 6)y = -1$$
$$(3 - s)x - 2sy = -8$$

Solving for x and y, we have

$$x = \frac{2s + 16}{s^2 + s - 6} = \frac{2s + 16}{(s - 2)(s + 3)} = \frac{4}{s - 2} - \frac{2}{s + 3}$$

$$y = \frac{3s - 1}{s^2 + s - 6} = \frac{3s - 1}{(s - 2)(s + 3)} = \frac{1}{s - 2} + \frac{2}{s + 3}$$

Thus the required solution is

$$X = \mathcal{L}^{-1}\left\{\frac{4}{s - 2} - \frac{2}{s + 3}\right\} = 4e^{2t} - 2e^{-3t}$$

$$Y = \mathcal{L}^{-1}\left\{\frac{1}{s - 2} + \frac{2}{s + 3}\right\} = e^{2t} + 2e^{-3t}$$

4. Remarks concerning existence and uniqueness of inverse Laplace transforms. We have tacitly assumed above that there is only one function which has some given Laplace transform, i.e., we have assumed the inverse Laplace transform to be unique. That this is actually not so can be seen by noting that the function

$$G(t) = \begin{cases} 5 & t = 3 \\ 1 & t \neq 3 \end{cases} \tag{10}$$

differs from the function $F(t) = 1$, since the value of $G(t)$ at $t = 3$ is 5 while the value of $F(t)$ at $t = 3$ is 1. However the Laplace transform of *both* functions is given by $1/s$, $s > 0$. Thus the inverse Laplace transform of $1/s$ can be $F(t) = 1$ or the function $G(t)$ given in (10), or in fact any one of infinitely many functions.

A possible clue as to the reason why we do not get uniqueness is that the function $G(t)$ given in (10) is discontinuous at $t = 3$. As a matter of fact it can be shown that if we restrict ourselves to continuous functions then the inverse Laplace transform is unique. This theorem, which is rather difficult to prove, is called *Lerch's theorem.**

We can show (see C Exercise 3) that if $F(t)$ is piecewise continuous in every finite interval and of exponential order then $\lim_{s \to \infty} f(s) = 0$. If $\lim_{s \to \infty} f(s) \neq 0$ it follows that the inverse transform cannot be piecewise continuous and of exponential order. Thus the condition $\lim_{s \to \infty} f(s) = 0$ is a *necessary condition* for the existence of an inverse Laplace transform which is sectionally continuous and of exponential order.†

A EXERCISES

1. Find inverse Laplace transforms of the following functions.

(a) $\dfrac{4}{s + 2}$.

(b) $\dfrac{3s}{s^2 + 9}$.

(c) $\dfrac{15}{s^2 + 25}$.

(d) $\dfrac{6s - 10}{s^2 + 4} - \dfrac{3}{s - 4}$.

(e) $\dfrac{2 - s}{5 + s^2}$.

(f) $\dfrac{2 + 3s - s^2}{s^3}$.

* More generally *Lerch* has shown that if two functions have the same Laplace transform then they differ at most by a *null function*, i.e., a function $N(t)$ such that for all $t > 0$

$$\int_0^t N(u)du = 0$$

A practical significance of this is that, in a certain sense, the inverse Laplace transform is "essentially unique." For further discussion see C Exercise 10, page 270 and reference [4].

† The condition is not sufficient however. For sufficient conditions we must consider $f(s)$ as a function of the complex variable s. See [4].

2. Using theorems on inverse Laplace transforms find each of the following.

(a) $\mathcal{L}^{-1}\left\{\dfrac{1}{(s + 2)^3}\right\}$.

(b) $\mathcal{L}^{-1}\left\{\dfrac{2s - 10}{s^2 - 4s + 20}\right\}$.

(c) $\mathcal{L}^{-1}\left\{\dfrac{s + 1}{s^2 + s + 1}\right\}$.

(d) $\mathcal{L}^{-1}\left\{\dfrac{s}{(s - 1)^4}\right\}$.

(e) $\mathcal{L}^{-1}\left\{\dfrac{2s - 1}{4s^2 + 4s + 5}\right\}$.

3. Use the method of partial fractions to find inverse Laplace transforms of the following.

(a) $\dfrac{s + 17}{(s - 1)(s + 3)}$.

(b) $\dfrac{3s - 8}{s^2 - 16}$.

(c) $\dfrac{s - 11}{(s + 1)(s - 2)(s - 3)}$.

(d) $\dfrac{2s^2 + 15s + 7}{(s + 1)^2(s - 2)}$.

(e) $\dfrac{10}{s(s^2 - 2s + 5)}$.

(f) $\dfrac{s + 1}{(s^2 + 1)(s^2 + 4)}$.

4. Use the convolution method to find each of the following.

(a) $\mathcal{L}^{-1}\left\{\dfrac{1}{s^2 - 4}\right\}$.

(b) $\mathcal{L}^{-1}\left\{\dfrac{1}{s^2(s + 1)^2}\right\}$.

(c) $\mathcal{L}^{-1}\left\{\dfrac{1}{(s^2 + 1)^2}\right\}$.

5. Solve each of the following and check solutions.

(a) $Y'' - 4Y' + 3Y = 0$, $Y(0) = 3$, $Y'(0) = 5$.

(b) $Y'' + 2Y' = 4$, $Y(0) = 1$, $Y'(0) = -4$.

(c) $Y'' + 9Y = 20e^{-t}$, $Y(0) = 0$, $Y'(0) = 1$.

(d) $Y'' - 2Y' + Y = 12t$, $Y(0) = 4$, $Y'(0) = 1$.

(e) $Y'' + 8Y' + 25Y = 100$, $Y(0) = 2$, $Y'(0) = 20$.

6. Solve each of the following simultaneous systems of equations.

(a) $X' = Y$, $Y' = -X$, $X(0) = 2$, $Y(0) = -1$.

(b) $X' + X - 5Y = 0$, $Y' + 4X + 5Y = 0$, $X(0) = -1$, $Y(0) = 2$.

B EXERCISES

1. Use partial fractions to find $\mathcal{L}^{-1}\left\{\dfrac{11s^2 - 10s + 11}{(s^2 + 1)(s^2 - 2s + 5)}\right\}$

$\left(\text{Hint: Assume } \dfrac{11s^2 - 10s + 11}{(s^2 + 1)(s^2 - 2s + 5)} = \dfrac{As + B}{s^2 + 1} + \dfrac{Cs + D}{s^2 - 2s + 5}.\right)$

2. Find $\mathcal{L}^{-1}\left\{\dfrac{s^3 + 2s^2 + 4s + 5}{(s + 1)^2(s + 2)^2}\right\}$.

3. Solve $Y''' + 3Y'' + 3Y' + Y = 12e^{-t}$, $Y(0) = 1$, $Y'(0) = 0$, $Y''(0) = -3$.

4. Solve $X' = X + Y + Z$, $Y' = 2X + 5Y + 3Z$, $Z' = 3X + 9Y + 5Z$ subject to the conditions $X(0) = -2$, $Y(0) = -1$, $Z(0) = 3$.

5. Find (a) $\mathcal{L}^{-1}\{e^{-2s}/s^3\}$ (b) $\mathcal{L}^{-1}\{e^{-s}/(s + 1)^{3/2}\}$.

6. Solve $Y'' + Y = 0$, $Y(0) = 0$, $Y(\pi/2) = 4$. (*Hint:* Let $Y'(0) = C$ and find C).

7. Prove   (a) $F*G = G*F$.   (b) $F*(G*H) = (F*G)*H$.   Discuss.

C EXERCISES

1. Solve the integral equation

$$\int_0^t Y(u) \sin (t - u)du = Y(t) + \sin t - \cos t$$

2. Solve $t Y'' - t Y' + Y = 0$, $Y(0) = 0$, $Y'(0) = 1$.

3. If $F(t)$ is piecewise continuous in every finite interval and of exponential order, prove that $\lim\limits_{s \to \infty} f(s) = 0$.

4. Prove that $\mathcal{L}^{-1}\left\{\ln\left(1 + \dfrac{1}{s}\right)\right\} = \dfrac{1 - e^{-t}}{t}$.

5. Assuming that there is a function $\delta(t)$ (the *Dirac delta function* or *unit impulse function*, see B Exercise 9, page 258) having the property that

$$\mathcal{L}\{\delta(t)\} = \int_0^\infty e^{-st} \delta(t)dt = 1$$

what conclusions could you draw about $\delta(t)$ in view of Exercise 3.

6. Prove the convolution theorem. (*Hint:* Formally we have

$$f(s)g(s) = \left\{\int_0^\infty e^{-sx}F(x)dx\right\}\left\{\int_0^\infty e^{-sy}G(y)dy\right\}$$

$$= \int_0^\infty \int_0^\infty e^{-s(x+y)}F(x)G(y)dx\,dy$$

and making the transformation $x + y = t$, $x = u$ from the xy to the tu plane this becomes

$$\int_0^\infty e^{-st}\left\{\int_0^t F(u)G(t - u)du\right\}dt$$

The proof follows on using an appropriate limiting procedure.)

7. Let $p(s)$ and $q(s)$ be polynomials in s where the degree of $P(s)$ is less than the degree of $Q(s)$ and where $Q(s) = 0$ has distinct roots $a_1, a_2, \ldots, a_n$. Prove that

$$\mathcal{L}^{-1}\left\{\frac{p(s)}{q(s)}\right\} = \sum_{k=1}^{n} e^{a_k t}\frac{p(a_k)}{q'(a_k)}$$

This is often called *Heaviside's expansion formula*.

8. Use Exercise 7 to work (a) Illustrative Example 4, page 263; (b) Illustrative Example 5, page 264; (c) A Exercise 3(c).

9. Generalize the result of Exercise 7 to the case where the roots may not be distinct and illustrate by means of an example.

10. (a) Suppose that two functions $F_1(t)$ and $F_2(t)$ have the same Laplace transform. Show that they must differ by a function $N(t)$ such that

$$\int_0^\infty e^{-st}N(t)dt = 0$$

(b) If a and ϵ are any two positive numbers show that no matter how small ϵ is taken $F_1(t)$ cannot be different from $F_2(t)$ over the whole interval $a \leq t \leq a + \epsilon$ if $F_1(t)$ and $F_2(t)$ are continuous. (c) Discuss the significance of the result in (b).

III. Applications to Physical Problems

As we have already seen in preceding chapters a mathematical formulation of problems in mechanics, electricity, beams, etc., often leads to linear differential equations with constant coefficients. In this section we show how the Laplace transform is used to solve such problems.

ILLUSTRATIVE EXAMPLE 1

An electric circuit (see Fig. 94) consists of a resistor of resistance R ohms in series with a capacitor of capacitance C farads, a generator of E volts and a key. At time $t = 0$ the key is closed. Assuming that the charge on the condenser is zero at $t = 0$, find the charge and current at any later time. Assume that R, C, and E are constants.

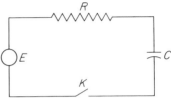

Fig. 94

Mathematical Formulation. If Q and $I = dQ/dt$ are the charge and current at any time t then by Kirchhoff's law we have

$$RI + \frac{Q}{C} = E \quad \text{or} \quad R\frac{dQ}{dt} + \frac{Q}{C} = E \tag{1}$$

with initial condition $Q(0) = 0$.

Solution. Taking Laplace transforms of both sides of (1) and using the initial condition, we have, if q is the Laplace transform of Q,

$$R\{sq - Q(0)\} + \frac{q}{C} = \frac{E}{s}$$

$$\left(Rs + \frac{1}{C}\right)q = \frac{E}{s}$$

$$q = \frac{CE}{S(RCs + 1)} = \frac{E/R}{s(s + 1/RC)}$$

$$= \frac{E/R}{1/RC}\left(\frac{1}{s} - \frac{1}{s + 1/RC}\right)$$

$$= CE\left(\frac{1}{s} - \frac{1}{s + 1/RC}\right)$$

Then taking the inverse Laplace transform we find,

$$Q = CE(1 - e^{-t/RC})$$

and so

$$I = \frac{dQ}{dt} = \frac{E}{R} e^{-t/RC}$$

Laplace transform methods prove to be of great value in problems involving piecewise continuous functions. In such cases the properties of the Heaviside unit function (page 255) are useful. As an illustration of the procedure let us consider

ILLUSTRATIVE EXAMPLE 2

Work Illustrative Example 1 for the case where the generator of E volts is replaced by a generator with voltage given as a function of time by

$$E(t) = \begin{cases} E_0 & 0 \leq t < T \\ 0 & t > T \end{cases}$$

where E_0 and T are positive constants.

Mathematical Formulation. Replacing E in Illustrative Example 1 by $E(t)$ we obtain the required differential equation

$$R\frac{dQ}{dt} + \frac{Q}{C} = E(t) \tag{2}$$

with initial condition

$$Q(0) = 0$$

The equation (2) can also be expressed in terms of the Heaviside unit function as

$$R\frac{dQ}{dt} + \frac{Q}{C} = E_0[1 - H(t - T)] \tag{3}$$

Solution. Taking Laplace transforms of both sides of (3) and using the initial condition we find

$$R\{sq - Q(0)\} + \frac{q}{C} = \frac{E_0(1 - e^{-sT})}{s}$$

$$\left(Rs + \frac{1}{C}\right)q = \frac{E_0(1 - e^{-sT})}{s}$$

$$q = \frac{E_0}{R} \frac{(1 - e^{-sT})}{s(s + 1/RC)}$$

$$= \frac{E_0}{Rs(s + 1/RC)} - \frac{E_0}{Rs(s + 1/RC)} e^{-sT}$$

$$= CE_0\left\{\frac{1}{s} - \frac{1}{s + 1/RC}\right\} - CE_0\left\{\frac{1}{s} - \frac{1}{s + 1/RC}\right\}e^{-sT}$$

Taking the inverse Laplace transforms of both sides using the result stated in the Theorem on page 250 we find

$$Q = CE_0(1 - e^{-t/RC}) - CE_0(1 - e^{-(t-T)/RC})H(t - T)$$

$$= \begin{cases} CE_0(1 - e^{-t/RC}) & t < T \\ CE_0(1 - e^{-t/RC}) - CE_0(1 - e^{-(t-T)/RC}) & t > T \end{cases}$$

$$= \begin{cases} CE_0(1 - e^{-t/RC}) & t < T \\ CE_0(e^{-(t-T)/RC} - e^{-t/RC}) & t > T \end{cases}$$

A EXERCISES

1. An electric circuit consists of a resistor of resistance R ohms in series with an inductor of inductance L henries and a generator of E volts where R, L, and E are constants. If the current is zero at time $t = 0$ find it at any later time.

2. An object of mass m is thrown vertically upward with initial speed v_0. Assuming that the acceleration due to gravity is constant and equal to g, and neglecting air resistance, determine the position and velocity of the object at any later time.

3. Work Exercise 1 if the generator has voltage given by

(a) $E(t) = \begin{cases} E_0 & 0 \le t \le T \\ 0 & t > T \end{cases}$.   (b) $E(t) = E_0 \sin \omega t$.

4. Work Illustrative Example 3, page 67.

5. Work A Exercise 3, page 81.

6. Work Illustrative Example 1, page 186.

B EXERCISES

1. A mass m at the end of a vertical vibrating spring of constant k undergoes vibrations about its equilibrium position according to the equation

$$m \frac{d^2X}{dt^2} + \beta \frac{dX}{dt} + kX = F_0 \cos \omega t$$

where β is a damping constant, and X is the displacement of the mass from its equilibrium position at any time t. (a) Solve this equation subject to the initial conditions $X(0) = X'(0) = 0$. (b) What is the steady-state solution? (c) Explain how the Laplace transform of the solution can be simplified so as to yield the steady-state solution.

2. Work Exercise 1 if the initial conditions are modified to read $X(0) = X_0$, $X'(0) = V_0$. Interpret the results physically.

3. Work Illustrative Example 8, page 202.

4. Work the Illustrative Example on page 206.

5. Work (a) A Exercise 1, page 207; (b) B Exercise 1, page 207.

6. Work Exercise 1 if the external force on the mass m is given by

(a) $F(t) = \begin{cases} F_0 & 0 < t < T \\ 0 & t > T \end{cases}$.   (b) $F(t) = F_0 t \cos \omega t$.

C EXERCISES

1. The vibrations of a mass m at the end of a vertical spring of constant k are given by

$$m\frac{d^2 X}{dt^2} + kX = F(t)$$

where $F(t)$ is the applied external force at any time t and X is the displacement of m from its equilibrium position at any time t. Suppose that the force is given by

$$F(t) = \begin{cases} F_0 & 0 < t < T \\ 2F_0 & T < t < 2T \\ 0 & t > 2T \end{cases}$$

(a) Find the displacement at any time t assuming that the initial displacement and velocity are zero. (b) Describe physically the vibrations of the mass.

2. Work Exercise 1 if a damping term $\beta\, dX/dt$ is taken into account.

3. Suppose that the force $F(t)$ in Exercise 1 is given by

$$F(t) = \begin{cases} F_0/\epsilon & 0 < t < \epsilon \\ 0 & t > \epsilon \end{cases}$$

(a) Find the displacement at any time t assuming that the initial displacement and velocity are zero. (b) Discuss the result in (a) for the limiting case where $\epsilon \to 0$ and give a physical interpretation. (c) How is your result in (b) related to the Dirac delta function of B Exercise 9, page 258 and C Exercise 5, page 270? (d) Could you obtain the result in (b) by letting $F(t) = \delta(t)$ in the equation of Exercise 1 and then taking Laplace transforms using $\mathcal{L}\{\delta(t)\} = 1$? Explain.

Chapter Eight

SOLUTION OF DIFFERENTIAL EQUATIONS

BY USE OF SERIES

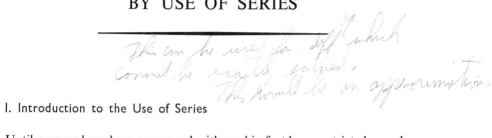

I. Introduction to the Use of Series

Until now we have been concerned with, and in fact have restricted ourselves to, differential equations which could be solved exactly and various applications which led to them. There are certain differential equations which are of extreme importance in higher mathematics and engineering or other scientific applications but which cannot be solved exactly in terms of elementary functions by any methods. For example, the innocent looking differential equations

$$y' = x^2 + y^2, \qquad xy'' + y' + xy = 0$$

cannot by solved exactly in terms of functions usually studied in elementary calculus, such as the rational algebraic, trigonometric and inverse trigonometric, exponential, and logarithmic functions. In such cases, short of recourse to higher transcendental functions, approximate methods provide the only alternative. It is the purpose of this chapter to describe some of these methods. Here, as before, we can supply only a few of the more important methods which are used, reserving other methods to the advanced exercises.

To motivate a discussion of one of these methods, consider the differential equation $y' = y$ subject to the condition that $y(0) = 1$. By separation of variables we easily discover that $y = e^x$ is the required solution. Now in the calculus we learned that many functions such as e^x, $\sin x$, $\cos x$, etc., possess series expansions of the type

$$a_0 + a_1 x + a_2 x^2 + a_3 x^3 + \cdots \tag{1}$$

We raise the following

Question. Let us assume that we could not solve the equation $y' = y$, supposing, for instance, that we were not yet acquainted with properties of exponential functions. What possible way could we proceed to find the required solution (assuming one existed)?

275

One of the possible ways in which we could begin would be to *assume* that the solution (if it exists) possesses a series expansion of the type (1), where a_0, a_1, . . . are at present undetermined. If (1) is to be a solution of $y' = y$, we must have

$$\frac{d}{dx}(a_0 + a_1x + a_2x^2 + a_3x^3 + \cdots) = a_0 + a_1x + a_2x^2 + a_3x^3 + \cdots$$

Now, *assuming* that term-by-term differentiation of infinite series is allowed, we have

$$a_1 + 2a_2x + 3a_3x^2 + 4a_4x^3 + \cdots = a_0 + a_1x + a_2x^2 + a_3x^3 + \cdots$$

Since this must be an identity, we must have coefficients of corresponding powers of x equal,* so that

$$a_1 = a_0, \qquad 2a_2 = a_1, \qquad 3a_3 = a_2, \qquad 4a_4 = a_3, \ldots$$

From these we find

$$a_1 = a_0, \qquad a_2 = \frac{a_1}{2} = \frac{a_0}{2}, \qquad a_3 = \frac{a_2}{3} = \frac{a_0}{3 \cdot 2} = \frac{a_0}{3!}, \qquad a_4 = \frac{a_3}{4} = \frac{a_0}{4!}, \ldots$$

the rule being apparent. Substituting these in the assumed solution, we have

$$y = a_0\left(1 + x + \frac{x^2}{2!} + \frac{x^3}{3!} + \frac{x^4}{4!} + \cdots\right)$$

Using the condition that $y = 1$ when $x = 0$, we find $a_0 = 1$, so that

$$y = 1 + x + \frac{x^2}{2!} + \frac{x^3}{3!} + \frac{x^4}{4!} + \cdots \tag{2}$$

Since we have found the result (2), assuming so many things, it is natural for us to ask whether this really is the required solution. Anyone acquainted with series knows that (2) is the series expansion for e^x, so that we really have obtained the required solution. In cases where we have nothing to check with we may really be in doubt. The solution in the form (2) is just as good as $y = e^x$, and in fact, for many purposes it is better. For example, if one wished to know the value of y when $x = 0.6$, it is true that the answer $e^{0.6}$ may be found in the tables, but as a matter of fact the tabular value was probably computed by use of the series (2) with x replaced by 0.6.

Although we have perhaps been unduly simple-minded in the above treatment, the general conclusions are applicable to many important cases. We must realize that we have not been rigorous because proofs of several steps have been omitted. We return to the question of rigor after the following

* Although this may appear obvious it needs and is capable of proof. However, we shall use the fact here. For a proof see [19], page 613.

ILLUSTRATIVE EXAMPLE

Find a solution of

$$xy'' + y' + xy = 0$$

Solution. We assume that a solution of the type (1) exists. Then

$$y = a_0 + a_1 x + a_2 x^2 + a_3 x^3 + a_4 x^4 + \cdots \qquad (3)$$
$$y' = a_1 + 2a_2 x + 3a_3 x^2 + 4a_4 x^3 + \cdots$$
$$y'' = 2a_2 + 6a_3 x + 12a_4 x^2 + \cdots$$

Hence,

$$xy = \quad a_0 x \ + a_1 x^2 \ + a_2 x^3 \ + a_3 x^4 \ + a_4 x^5 \ + \cdots$$
$$y' = a_1 + 2a_2 x + 3a_3 x^2 + 4a_4 x^3 + 5a_5 x^4 + 6a_6 x^5 + \cdots$$
$$xy'' = \quad 2a_2 x + 6a_3 x^2 + 12a_4 x^3 + 20a_5 x^4 + 30a_6 x^5 + \cdots$$

where we have arranged terms so that corresponding powers of x appear in the same column. It follows by addition that

$$xy'' + y' + xy = 0$$
$$= a_1 + (a_0 + 4a_2)x + (a_1 + 9a_3)x^2 + (a_2 + 16a_4)x^3 + \cdots$$

Since this must be an identity, we must have (setting each coefficient equal to zero)

$$a_1 = 0, \qquad a_2 = -\frac{a_0}{4}, \qquad a_3 = -\frac{a_1}{9} = 0$$

$$a_4 = -\frac{a_2}{16} = \frac{a_0}{4 \cdot 16}, \qquad a_5 = -\frac{a_3}{25} = 0, \qquad a_6 = -\frac{a_4}{36} = -\frac{a_0}{4 \cdot 16 \cdot 36}$$

Thus $a_1, a_3, a_5, \ldots$ are all zero, while $a_2, a_4, a_6, \ldots$ are given in terms of a_0. Using these in the assumed solution (3), we have

$$y = a_0 \left(1 - \frac{x^2}{4} + \frac{x^4}{4 \cdot 16} - \frac{x^6}{4 \cdot 16 \cdot 36} + \cdots \right)$$

If we write this in the form

$$y = a_0 \left(1 - \frac{x^2}{2^2} + \frac{x^4}{2^2 4^2} - \frac{x^6}{2^2 4^2 6^2} + \cdots \right) \qquad (4)$$

the rule by means of which successive terms of the series may be formed becomes apparent. This rule is also clear by a consideration of the general term.

Unlike the series for e^x, the student will not be blamed if he fails to recognize the series (4), for in truth none of the functions considered in elementary calculus has that series expansion. The fact that we do not recognize it, however, is no reason why we cannot use it, but before we do we must be sure that it means something. One important question which we should answer, for example, is whether the series is convergent. By the ratio test for series used in elementary calculus* the series is shown to be convergent

---

* See any text in the calculus, for example, [17] or [20].

for all values of x. There still remains the question of showing that it is a solution. This is indicated in the next section.

Just as we give people names when they are born in order to talk about them, so we give names to some series. The particular series in (4) apart from the constant a_0 will be known henceforth as $J_0(x)$. We can do just as much with $J_0(x)$ as with e^x. For example, after laborious calculations we can tabulate the results:

$$J_0(0) = 1, \qquad J_0(1) = 0.76, \qquad J_0(2) = 0.22,$$
$$J_0(3) = -0.26, \quad J_0(4) = -0.40, \quad J_0(5) = -0.18$$

We may graph $J_0(x)$ for $x \geq 0$ and obtain that shown in Fig. 95. The graph for $x < 0$ is easily obtained, since $J_0(x)$ is symmetric to the y axis.

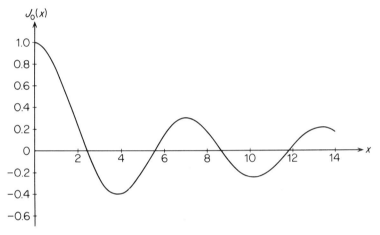

Fig. 95

It will be seen that the graph is oscillatory in character, resembling the graphs of the damped vibrations of Chapter 5. Many properties of the function $J_0(x)$ were discovered by an astronomer named Friedrich Wilhelm Bessel, and for this reason we call $J_0(x)$ a Bessel function, in particular of order zero. We say "order zero" and write subscript 0 because there were other functions, discovered by him, of orders 1, 2, 3, ..., and which are denoted by $J_1(x)$, $J_2(x)$, $J_3(x)$, ..., which also arise from differential equations of practical and theoretical importance. Further discussion of these is left to the advanced exercises.

It should be noted that although the differential equation which we started with was of second order, we have only one arbitrary constant present and hence do not have the general solution of the equation. A little considera-tion supplies the reason. In assuming the solution (3) we were looking for all solutions *having that particular form*. If we have not obtained a general solution, it means simply that the general solution was not *completely* of the form (3). One way to obtain the general solution is to proceed as in C Exercise 2. In some cases the assumption that the series has the form (3) fails completely and we do not get *any* result except the trivial one $y = 0$. In such cases we must look for a different form for the series. We consider this in Section III. In other cases we are very lucky and obtain the general solution as in A Exercise 5, for example.

II. A Question of Rigor

In the last section we obtained *formally* a series which we *hoped* would be a solution of a given differential equation. However, in obtaining this series, certain questionable operations were performed, such as, for example, the differentiation of a series term by term. Being scientists with a desire for truth, we do not want to be termed guilty of "blind manipulation" in producing a certain result. One way of proceeding is to attempt justification of each step as we proceed. Unfortunately this may be impossible. For example, how do we know that we can differentiate the series $a_0 + a_1 x + a_2 x^2 + \cdots$ if we do not know what the coefficients are? Clearly we have a vicious cycle. We cannot prove that we have a solution until we know $a_0, a_1, a_2, \ldots$ and we cannot honestly say that we have found the coefficients until we have justified the steps.

Fortunately there is another way to proceed, and this way turns out to be typical of much reasoning used in higher mathematics. We illustrate this by particularization to the case of the equation $xy'' + y' + xy = 0$, considered in the last section, and proceed as follows:

1. Assume that $y = a_0 + a_1 x + a_2 x^2 + \cdots$ is a solution and substitute it into the equation $xy'' + y' + xy = 0$, thus obtaining as in the last section the possible solution

$$1 - \frac{x^2}{2^2} + \frac{x^4}{2^2 4^2} - \frac{x^6}{2^2 4^2 6^2} + \cdots \tag{1}$$

   apart from the multiplicative arbitrary constant a_0.
2. Now that we have a possible solution, we try to verify that it is a solution.
3. If we can establish that it is a solution, we ask whether it is the only solution.
4. If it is not the only solution we ask what are other solutions.

The sequence is perfectly logical and leaves no gaps. In case we cannot prove certain things it is better to leave them in the form of a question, hoping that further investigations may throw light on the subject. This is basic to the scientific method.

Let us see how far we can get in our proof. The plan is to substitute the series (1) into $xy'' + y' + xy = 0$ and show that the latter is thereby reduced to an identity. To do this we must differentiate the series term by term and naturally the validity of this is questioned. Fortunately mathematicians have proved the following, which is important for our purpose.

THEOREM. If a power series $a_0 + a_1x + a_2x^2 + \cdots$ is differentiated term by term any given number of times, the resulting series obtained is convergent *within* the interval of convergence of the original series.

We illustrate this by a simple example. It is easy to show (using the ratio test) that the interval of convergence of the series

$$1 + x + \frac{x^2}{2} + \frac{x^3}{3} + \frac{x^4}{4} + \cdots$$

is $-1 \leq x < 1$. Term-by-term differentiation yields, successively,

$$1 + x + x^2 + x^3 + \cdots$$
$$1 + 2x + 3x^2 + 4x^3 + \cdots$$
$$2 + 6x + 12x^2 + 20x^3 + \cdots$$

all of which are found to have interval of convergence $-1 < x < 1$. Although we have lost the end point -1 in this interval by the successive differentiations, we can still say that each series converges *within* the interval of convergence of the original series as specified in the theorem. A proof of the theorem is not difficult and should be attempted by the student.

We now return to our original problem. Since the series (1) has interval of convergence $-\infty < x < \infty$, it follows by the theorem that the series may be differentiated term by term to obtain

$$y' = -\frac{x}{2} + \frac{x^3}{2^2 4} - \frac{x^5}{2^2 4^2 6} + \cdots, \quad y'' = -\frac{1}{2} + \frac{3x^2}{2^2 4} - \frac{5x^4}{2^2 4^2 6} + \cdots$$

which must also converge in $-\infty < x < \infty$. If we multiply the series for y and y'' each by x (which we can prove does not affect the convergence) and add to the series for y', we find

$$xy'' + y' + xy = \left(-\frac{x}{2} + \frac{3x^3}{2^2 4} - \frac{5x^5}{2^2 4^2 6} + \cdots \right)$$

$$+ \left(-\frac{x}{2} + \frac{x^3}{2^2 4} - \frac{x^5}{2^2 4^2 6} + \cdots \right) + \left(x - \frac{x^3}{2^2} + \frac{x^5}{2^2 4^2} - \cdots \right)$$

We should now like to show that all the terms in the series on the right cancel out to give zero. To do this we must group the terms according to powers of x. If we can do this we will obtain

$$\left(-\frac{x}{2} - \frac{x}{2} + x\right) + \left(\frac{3x^3}{2^2 4} + \frac{x^3}{2^2 4} - \frac{x^3}{2^2}\right) + \left(\frac{-5x^5}{2^2 4^2 6} - \frac{x^5}{2^2 4^2 6} + \frac{x^5}{2^2 4^2}\right) + \cdots$$

so that if *grouping is allowed* we do get zero. Once more the mathematician comes to the rescue with the following

> THEOREM. If $a_0 + a_1 x + a_2 x^2 + \cdots$ and $b_0 + b_1 x + b_2 x^2 + \cdots$ are two power series, both convergent in some interval of convergence, then the series
>
> $$(a_0 + b_0) + (a_1 + b_1)x + (a_2 + b_2)x^2 + \cdots$$
>
> converges at all points which lie in the interval of convergence of *both of the given series*. This may be extended to three or more power series.*

Upon applying this theorem, we see that (1) is indeed a solution. The method used in proving a series to be a solution will be found useful in the remainder of this chapter.

A EXERCISES

Find series solutions for each of the following and if possible find the sum of the series in closed form. Also try to verify that you have found the solution.

1. $y' = -y; y(0) = 1.$ **2.** $y' = xy; y(0) = 2.$

3. $y' = y - x.$ **4.** $y' = 2x - 3y.$

5. $y'' + y = 0.$ **6.** $y'' = y; y(0) = 1, y'(0) = 0.$

7. $y'' + y' = 0.$ **8.** $y'' - y' - 2y = 0.$

9. $x^2 y'' + xy' + (x^2 - 1)y = 0.$

10. $(1 - x^2)y'' - 2xy' + 6y = 0; y(1) = 1, y'(0) = 0.$

11. $xy'' + (1 - x)y' + 2y = 0.$

12. $(x^2 - 2x)y'' + (2 - 2x)y' + 2y = 0; y(0) = y(1) = 1.$

B EXERCISES

1. Obtain a series solution for $y' = x^2 + y^2$, given $y(0) = 1$. Find y when $x = 0.2$ accurate to three significant figures.

2. Show that $x^3 y'' = 1$ does not possess a Maclaurin series solution. By solving the equation exactly, account for this fact.

---

* This theorem can be extended to other operations with series, such as multiplication, for example. See [18], page 281.

3. Solve $y''' + y = 0$ by series. Compare with the exact solution.

4. How would you solve $y'' - y = e^x$, using series methods?

5. Solve $y'' + xy = \sin x$.

6. Solve Exercise 2 by assuming $y = a_0 + a_1(x - 1) + a_2(x - 1)^2 + \cdots$.

C EXERCISES

1. Given $y'' + P(x)y' + Q(x)y = 0$, show that if $y = Y(x)$ is a solution, then the general solution is

$$y = A Y(x) + B Y(x) \int \frac{e^{-\int P(x)dx}}{Y^2(x)} \, dx$$

(*Hint:* Let $y = v Y(x)$, where v is a new dependent variable; see the theorem on page 147.)

2. Using Exercise 1, show that the general solution of $xy'' + y' + xy = 0$ is $A J_0(x) + B Y_0(x)$, where

$$Y_0(x) = J_0(x) \int \frac{dx}{x J_0^2(x)}$$

The solution $Y_0(x)$ is called a *Bessel function of the second kind*, or *Neumann function*. Near $x = 0$ the function behaves like $\int dx/x = \ln |x|$. This explains why the assumption of a Maclaurin series failed to yield the general solution.

3. Find the general solution of $xy'' + 2y' + xy = 0$ by first assuming a Maclaurin series solution, recognizing the series as being associated with an elementary function, and then using the method of Exercise 1. Knowing the answer, can you think of a type of series which could have been used to yield the general solution?

4. The differential equation $x^2 y'' + xy' + (x^2 - n^2)y = 0$ is called *Bessel's general differential equation*. Its general solution may be written $y = A J_n(x) + B Y_n(x)$, where $J_n(x)$ is the *Bessel function of order n, first kind*, and $Y_n(x)$ is the *Bessel function of order n, second kind*, or *Neumann function of order n*. Using the method of Exercise 1, show that

$$Y_n(x) = J_n(x) \int \frac{dx}{x J_n^2(x)}$$

Some authors use other definitions of $Y_n(x)$.

5. A customary definition of $J_n(x)$ is

$$J_n(x) \equiv \frac{x^n}{2^n \, \Gamma(n + 1)} \left[1 - \frac{x^2}{2(2n + 2)} + \frac{x^4}{2 \cdot 4(2n + 2)(2n + 4)} \right.$$

$$\left. - \frac{x^6}{2 \cdot 4 \cdot 6(2n + 2)(2n + 4)(2n + 6)} + \cdots \right]$$

where $\Gamma(n + 1)$ is the *gamma function* (page 251) and reduces to $n!$ if $n = 1, 2, 3, \ldots$; also $0! = 1$. (a) Write the series for $J_1(x)$ and $J_2(x)$ and show that they are solutions of their corresponding differential equations. (b) Prove that $J_0'(x) = -J_1(x)$. (c) Show that $J_{1/2}(x) = \sqrt{2/\pi x} \sin x$, $J_{-1/2}(x) = \sqrt{2/\pi x} \cos x$.

6. The result

$$J_{n+1}(x) = \frac{2n}{x} J_n(x) - J_{n-1}(x)$$

enables one to determine $J_{n+1}(x)$, knowing $J_n(x)$ and $J_{n-1}(x)$, and is called a *recursion formula*. (a) Verify the result for $n = 1$ and $n = 2$. (b) Can you prove it for all values of n?

7. The equation

$$(1 - x^2)y'' - 2xy' + n(n + 1)y = 0$$

is of great importance in mathematics and physics, and is known as *Legendre's differential equation*. If n is zero or a positive integer, this equation has poly-nomial solutions, which are denoted by $P_n(x)$, $n = 0, 1, 2, \ldots$, and which have the property that $P_n(1) = 1$. (a) Determine $P_0(x)$, $P_1(x)$, $P_2(x)$, $P_3(x)$. What are the degrees of these polynomials? (b) Assuming that $y = P_n(x)$ is the poly-nomial solution of the given differential equation, use Exercise 1 to determine the general solution. Find another solution corresponding to $n = 1$ besides $P_1(x)$. What happens to this second solution for $x = \pm 1$?

8. The Legendre polynomials of Exercise 7 can be found from *Rodrigue's formula:*

$$P_n(x) = \frac{1}{2^n n!} \frac{d^n}{dx^n} (x^2 - 1)^n, \qquad n = 0, 1, 2, \ldots$$

Verify this for $n = 0, 1, 2, 3$.

9. Another differential equation of importance is $y'' - 2xy' + 2ny = 0$, which has polynomial solutions for $n = 0, 1, 2, 3, \ldots$ denoted by $H_n(x)$ and called *Hermite polynomials*. (a) Obtain apart from a multiplicative constant the first four polynomials. What are their degrees? (b) A formula for $H_n(x)$ is

$$H_n(x) = (-1)^n e^{x^2} \frac{d^n}{dx^n} (e^{-x^2}), \qquad n = 0, 1, 2, \ldots$$

Find $H_n(x)$ for $n = 0, 1, 2$, and 3 and compare with part (a).

10. The equation $xy'' + (1 - x)y' + ny = 0$, called *Laguerre's equation*, has poly-nomial solutions denoted by $L_n(x)$, $n = 0, 1, 2, 3 \ldots$. (a) Determine the first four polynomials apart from a multiplicative constant. (b) A formula for $L_n(x)$ is

$$L_n(x) = e^x \frac{d^n}{dx^n} (x^n e^{-x})$$

Compare values obtained from this formula with those of part (a).

III. Alternative Methods of Arriving at Series Solutions

In the last section we arrived at solutions of differential equations by assuming these solutions to have the form

$$a_0 + a_1 x + a_2 x^2 + a_3 x^3 + \cdots$$

In this section three other methods which yield series solutions are described. These are the method of Taylor series, a method of iteration due to Picard, and a method due to Frobenius.

1. The method of Taylor series. Let us suppose that $y(x)$ possesses a Taylor series expansion in an interval about $x = a$, i.e., that

$$y(x) = y(a) + y'(a)(x - a) + \frac{y''(a)(x - a)^2}{2!} + \frac{y'''(a)(x - a)^3}{3!} + \cdots \quad (1)$$

This enables us to write the solution $y(x)$ to a given differential equation when we can find the various derivatives $y'(a)$, $y''(a)$, ... from the differential equation.

ILLUSTRATIVE EXAMPLE 1

Solve

$$y' = x + y + 1$$

by the method of Taylor series.

Solution. We assume that $a = 0$ (for which the Taylor series becomes a Maclaurin series). From the differential equation we find

$$y' = x + y + 1, \qquad y'' = 1 + y',$$
$$y''' = y'', \qquad y^{(IV)} = y''', \ldots \quad (2)$$

Assuming $y = c$ when $x = 0$, we find from (2),

$$y'(0) = c + 1, \qquad y''(0) = c + 2, \qquad y'''(0) = c + 2, \ldots$$

Substituting into (1), we have

$$y(x) = c + (c + 1)x + \frac{(c + 2)x^2}{2!} + \frac{(c + 2)x^3}{3!} + \cdots$$

which may be written

$$y(x) = c + (c + 1)x + (c + 2)\left(\frac{x^2}{2!} + \frac{x^3}{3!} + \cdots\right)$$
$$= c + (c + 1)x + (c + 2)(e^x - 1 - x)$$
$$= (c + 2)e^x - x - 2$$

ILLUSTRATIVE EXAMPLE 2

Solve

$$y'' = xy$$

Solution. We assume $a = 0$. By differentiation of the given equation,

$$y''' = xy' + y, \qquad y^{(IV)} = xy'' + 2y',$$
$$y^{(V)} = xy''' + 3y'', \qquad y^{(VI)} = xy^{(IV)} + 4y''', \ldots$$

from which we obtain, assuming $y = c_1$ and $y' = c_2$ at $x = 0$,

$$y''(0) = 0, \qquad y'''(0) = c_1, \qquad y^{(IV)}(0) = 2c_2,$$
$$y^{(V)}(0) = 0, \qquad y^{(VI)}(0) = 4c_1, \ldots$$

Hence, the Taylor series is

$$y = c_1 + c_2 x + c_1 \frac{x^3}{3!} + \frac{2c_2 x^4}{4!} + \frac{4c_1 x^6}{6!} + \cdots$$

$$= c_1 \left(1 + \frac{x_3}{3!} + \frac{4x^6}{6!} + \cdots \right) + c_2 \left(x + \frac{2x^4}{4!} + \frac{10x^7}{7!} + \cdots \right)$$

The general term is not apparent. However, by taking further terms we find

$$y = c_1 \left(1 + \frac{x^3}{3!} + \frac{1 \cdot 4 x^6}{6!} + \frac{1 \cdot 4 \cdot 7 x^9}{9!} + \frac{1 \cdot 4 \cdot 7 \cdot 10 x^{12}}{12!} + \cdots \right)$$

$$+ c_2 \left(x + \frac{2x^4}{4!} + \frac{2 \cdot 5 x^7}{7!} + \frac{2 \cdot 5 \cdot 8 x^{10}}{10!} + \cdots \right)$$

The student may show that this is the general solution convergent for all x.

2. Picard's method of iteration. Picard's method is of particular use in obtaining solutions of first-order equations. However, its use may be extended to differential equations of higher order. We illustrate the method in

ILLUSTRATIVE EXAMPLE 3

Solve

$$y' = x + y + 1 \tag{3}$$

Solution. Assuming that $y = c$ when $x = 0$, we may integrate both sides of (3) with respect to x to obtain

$$y = c + \int_0^x (x + y + 1) \, dx \tag{4}$$

The integral on the right* cannot be performed since we do not know how y depends on x. In fact, that is what we are looking for. The method of

---

* Note that in this integral we are using the symbol x as a dummy symbol in the integration as well as the independent variable. We could of course have used a different symbol, for example u, to denote the dummy variable and written

$$\int_0^x (u + y + 1) \, du$$

However, no confusion should arise and since there are certain advantages to the symbolism in (4) we shall continue to use it.

Picard consists in assuming that $y = c$ is a first approximation to y. We denote this first approximation by $y_1 = c$. When this value is substituted for y in the integrand of (4), we denote the resulting value of y by y_2, which is a second approximation to y, i.e.,

$$y_2 = c + \int_0^x (x + y_1 + 1)dx = c + \int_0^x (x + c + 1)dx$$

$$= c + \frac{x^2}{2} + cx + x$$

Substituting this approximate value in the integrand of (4), we find the third approximation y_3, given by

$$y_3 = c + \int_0^x (x + y_2 + 1)dx = c + (c + 1)x + \frac{(c + 2)x^2}{2!} + \frac{x^3}{3!}$$

In a similar way we find

$$y_4 = c + (c + 1)x + \frac{(c + 2)x^2}{2!} + \frac{(c + 2)x^3}{3!} + \frac{x^4}{4!}$$

and, in general,

$$y_n = c + (c + 1)x + \frac{(c + 2)x^2}{2!} + \frac{(c + 2)x^3}{3!} + \cdots + \frac{(c + 2)x^{n-1}}{(n - 1)!} + \frac{x^n}{n!}$$

In the limiting case we see that

$$\lim_{n \to \infty} y_n = c + (c + 1)x + \frac{(c + 2)x^2}{2!} + \frac{(c + 2)x^3}{3!} + \cdots$$

That the series on the right is, in fact, the desired solution is seen by comparison with the results of Illustrative Example 1, where the same differential equation is solved. Thus we see that for this case $\lim_{n \to \infty} y_n = y$. For equations covered by the theorem on page 20, the sequence of approximations $y_1, y_2, y_3 \ldots$, can be shown to converge to the required solution.

Picard's method is unwieldy for some types of differential equations, since the successive approximations may become complicated due to the integrations which may have to be performed. However, in advanced mathematics the method of Picard is used extensively for theoretical purposes.*

In the general case, for the equation $y' = f(x,y)$, when it is desired to have $y = c$ where $x = a \neq 0$, we replace (4) by

$$y = c + \int_a^x f(x,y)dx$$

---

* For example, see [10].

A EXERCISES

1. Use the method of Taylor series to obtain series solutions of each of the following. Take $a = 0$ unless otherwise specified. Sum the series if possible.

(a) $y' = y$; $y(0) = 4$. (b) $y' = -xy$; $y(0) = 1$.
(c) $y' = 2x - y$. (d) $y'' + y = x$.
(e) $y'' = x^2 + 4y$; $y(0) = y'(0) = 0$. (f) $y'' + xy' + y = 0$.
(g) $x^2 y' = 1$; $y(1) = 1$ (use $a = 1$).
(h) $x^2 y'' = x + 1$; $y(1) = y'(1) = 0$ (use $a = 1$).

2. Use Picard's method to obtain solutions to each of the following. Find at least the fourth approximation to each solution.

(a) $y' = -3y$; $y(0) = 1$. (b) $y' = x^2 - y$; $y(0) = 0$.
(c) $y' = e^x + y$; $y(0) = 0$. (d) $2y' + xy - y = 0$.
(e) $y' = x + y$; $y(1) = 2$ (use $a = 1$).

B EXERCISES

1. Use the Taylor series method to solve $y'' + y = \sin x$, subject to the conditions $y(0) = y'(0) = 0$. Verify your answer by solving the equation exactly. Obtain $y(1)$ by both methods and compare.

2. Obtain the general solution of $y'' - 2by' + b^2 y = 0$ ($b = $ constant) and thus establish the rule for linear differential equations with constant coefficients concerning the case where the roots of the auxiliary equation are equal.

3. Use the method of Taylor series to obtain a solution of $y' = x^2 + y^2$, where $y(0) = 1$. Obtain the value of $y(0.2)$.

4. Solve $xy'' + y = 0$ by the method of Taylor series. (*Hint:* differentiate the equation as it stands with respect to x to find the various values of $y^{(n)}$ at zero.) Why isn't a general solution obtained?

5. Solve Exercise 4 by finding $y^{(n)}$ at $x = a$, where $a \neq 0$.

C EXERCISES

1. Use Picard's method to obtain a fourth approximation to the solution of $y' = x^2 + y^2$ if $y(0) = 1$. Is there any point in keeping terms beyond those involving x^4? Compare with B Exercise 3.

2. Can Picard's or Taylor's method be used for the equation $y' = e^{x^2} + y$?

3. If you were given the differential equation $y' = e^{-xy}$ subject to the condition $y(0) = 1$, how would you proceed to determine $y(0.2)$?

4. Can you extend Picard's method to differential equations of order higher than the first? If so, illustrate by an example.

3. The method of Frobenius. In the attempt to discover a series solution of a given differential equation, one may find that solutions of the type

$$y = a_0 + a_1 x + a_2 x^2 + a_3 x^3 + \cdots \tag{5}$$

do not exist. In such cases, one possibility is to assume a solution of another type. One such type is given by

$$y = x^c(a_0 + a_1 x + a_2 x^2 + a_3 x^3 + \cdots) \tag{6}$$

which is a generalization of (5), since (6) yields (5) when $c = 0$. For example, if a solution of a given differential equation were

$$x^{1/2} + x^{3/2} + x^{r/2} + x^{7/2} + \cdots \tag{7}$$

an assumption of type (5) would not yield this solution, but the assumption (6) should yield this solution, since (7) is a special case of (6) with $c = \frac{1}{2}$, $a_0 = a_1 = \cdots = 1$.

A series of type (6) is called a *Frobenius type* series. It is especially useful in finding solutions of

$$p(x)y'' + q(x)y' + r(x)y = 0$$

where p, q, r are polynomials, although it is applicable in other cases as well. Precise conditions under which such equations possess Frobenius type solutions will be taken up later in this section.

ILLUSTRATIVE EXAMPLE 4

Find Frobenius type solutions of

$$4xy'' + 2y' + y = 0$$

Solution. Assume that (6) is a solution and write it in the form

$$y = a_0 x^c + a_1 x^{c+1} + a_2 x^{c+2} + a_3 x^{c+3} + a_4 x^{c+4} + \cdots \tag{8}$$

Then

$$y' = ca_0 x^{c-1} + (c + 1)a_1 x^c + (c + 2)a_2 x^{c+1} + (c + 3)a_3 x^{c+2}$$
$$+ (c + 4)a_4 x^{c+3} + \cdots$$
$$y'' = c(c - 1)a_0 x^{c-2} + (c + 1)ca_1 x^{c-1} + (c + 2)(c + 1)a_2 x^c$$
$$+ (c + 3)(c + 2)a_3 x^{c+1} + \cdots$$

and so

$$4xy'' = 4c(c - 1)a_0 x^{c-1} + 4(c + 1)ca_1 x^c + 4(c + 2)(c + 1)a_2 x^{c+1} + \cdots$$
$$2y' = \quad\quad 2ca_0 x^{c-1} + 2(c + 1)\, a_1 x^c + \quad\quad 2(c + 2)a_2 x^{c+1} + \cdots$$
$$y = \quad\quad\quad\quad\quad\quad a_0 x^c + \quad\quad\quad\quad\quad a_1 x^{c+1} + \cdots$$

where terms are arranged so that like powers of x are in the same column.*

* The work involved here can be shortened by use of the Σ notation as shown in B Exercise 1.

Then by addition of these last three results we have

$$4xy'' + 2y' + y = 0$$

$$= [2ca_0 + 4c(c-1)a_0]x^{c-1} + [4(c+1)ca_1 + 2(c+1)a_1 + a_0]x^c$$

$$+ [4(c+2)(c+1)a_2 + 2(c+2)a_2 + a_1]x^{c+1} + \cdots$$

Since this is an identity, we must have

$$a_0[2c + 4c(c-1)] \hspace{4cm} = 0 \hspace{2cm} (9)$$

$$4(c+1)ca_1 + 2(c+1)a_1 + a_0 \hspace{1cm} = 0$$

$$4(c+2)(c+1)a_2 + 2(c+2)a_2 + a_1 = 0$$

etc.

We suppose that $a_0 \neq 0$, since otherwise the series (8) would start with a_1x^{c+1}. Hence, from (9) it follows that $2c + 4c(c-1) = 0$, i.e., $c = 0, \frac{1}{2}$. The equation for c, obtained by equating the coefficient of the lowest power of x to zero, is called the *indicial equation*, and the roots are called *indicial roots*. From the other equations,

$$a_1 = \frac{-a_0}{4(c+1)c + 2(c+1)},$$

$$a_2 = \frac{-a_1}{4(c+2)(c+1) + 2(c+2)}, \ldots$$

In general, we may show that

$$a_n = \frac{-a_{n-1}}{4(c+n)(c+n-1) + 2(c+n)}, \qquad n = 1, 2, 3, \ldots \qquad (10)$$

These are called *recursion relations*. Two cases are considered.

Case I, $c = 0$. For this case, equations (10) become

$$a_1 = -\frac{a_0}{2}, \qquad a_2 = -\frac{a_1}{12} = \frac{a_0}{24}, \qquad a_3 = -\frac{a_2}{30} = -\frac{a_0}{720}, \ldots$$

Using these values in (8), we find

$$y = x^0\left(a_0 - \frac{a_0 x}{2} + \frac{a_0 x^2}{24} - \frac{a_0 x^3}{720} + \cdots\right)$$

or

$$y = A\left(1 - \frac{x}{2!} + \frac{x^2}{4!} - \frac{x^3}{6!} + \cdots\right)$$

where we use A instead of a_0 to indicate the arbitrary constant.

Case II, $c = \frac{1}{2}$. For this case, equations (10) become

$$a_1 = -\frac{a_0}{6}, \qquad a_2 = -\frac{a_1}{20} = \frac{a_0}{120}, \qquad a_3 = -\frac{a_2}{42} = -\frac{a_0}{5040}, \ldots$$

Using these values in (8), we find

$$y = x^{1/2}\left(a_0 - \frac{a_0}{6}x + \frac{a_0}{120}x^2 - \frac{a_0}{5040}x^3 + \cdots\right)$$

or

$$y = B\left(x^{1/2} - \frac{x^{3/2}}{3!} + \frac{x^{5/2}}{5!} - \frac{x^{7/2}}{7!} + \cdots\right)$$

where we have used B instead of a_0 for the arbitrary constant. The general solution is thus

$$y = A\left(1 - \frac{x}{2!} + \frac{x^2}{4!} - \frac{x^3}{6!} + \cdots\right)$$

$$+ B\left(x^{1/2} - \frac{x^{3/2}}{3!} + \frac{x^{5/2}}{5!} - \frac{x^{7/2}}{7!} + \cdots\right) \quad (11)$$

The two series converge for all values of x, as is easily shown. The student acquainted with series expansions will see that (11) can be written in terms of elementary functions as

$$y = A\cos\sqrt{x} + B\sin\sqrt{x}$$

We are not always fortunate, however, in recognizing the series obtained.

ILLUSTRATIVE EXAMPLE 5

Obtain solutions of

$$y'' + xy' + y = 0$$

Solution. Substitution of (6) in the differential equation and simplifying yields

$$c(c-1)a_0x^{c-2} + c(c+1)a_1x^{c-1} + [a_0 + ca_0 + (c+2)(c+1)a_2]x^c$$

$$+ [a_1 + (c+1)a_1 + (c+3)(c+2)a_3]x^{c+1} + \cdots = 0$$

Thus,

$$c(c-1)a_0 = 0, \qquad c(c+1)a_1 = 0,$$

$$a_0 + ca_0 + (c+2)(c+1)a_2 = 0,$$

$$a_1 + (c+1)a_1 + (c+3)(c+2)a_3 = 0 \quad (12)$$

etc. From the first equation in (12), we obtain the indicial roots $c = 0, 1$.

Case I, $c = 0$. The fact that the second equation in (12) is automatically satisfied implies that a_1 may have any value, i.e., it is an arbitrary constant. The third and fourth equations yield $a_2 = -a_0/2$, $a_3 = -a_1/3$. From the form of the equations in (12) the general term is clear. For example, the next equation would be

$$a_2 + (c+2)a_2 + (c+4)(c+3)a_4 = 0$$

By continuing in this manner we find

$$a_2 = -\frac{a_0}{2}, \qquad a_3 = -\frac{a_1}{3}, \qquad a_4 = \frac{a_0}{2 \cdot 4},$$

$$a_5 = \frac{a_1}{3 \cdot 5}, \qquad a_6 = -\frac{a_0}{2 \cdot 4 \cdot 6}, \cdots$$

Substituting these in (6), we find

$$y = x^0 \left(a_0 + a_1 x - \frac{a_0}{2} x^2 - \frac{a_1}{3} x^3 + \frac{a_0}{2 \cdot 4} x^4 + \frac{a_1}{3 \cdot 5} x^5 - \frac{a_0}{2 \cdot 4 \cdot 6} x^6 + \cdots \right)$$

or

$$y = a_0 \left(1 - \frac{x^2}{2} + \frac{x^4}{2 \cdot 4} - \frac{x^6}{2 \cdot 4 \cdot 6} + \cdots \right)$$

$$+ a_1 \left(x - \frac{x^3}{3} + \frac{x^5}{3 \cdot 5 \cdot 7} - \cdots \right) \tag{13}$$

Here we have the general solution without having even considered the case where $c = 1$. If, however, we do consider this case, we obtain the second series in (13), as the student may verify.

From the above examples it is clear that different cases may arise. A more thorough investigation yields the following facts:

1. If the indicial roots differ by a constant which is not an integer or zero, the general solution is *always* obtained.
2. If the indicial roots differ by an integer not equal to zero, there are *two possibilities:*
   (a) The general solution is obtained by use of the smaller indicial root.*
   (b) No solution is obtained by using the smaller indicial root.
   However, in all cases a solution can be determined by using the *larger root.*
3. If the indicial roots differ by zero, i.e., are equal, only one solution is obtained.

It will be seen that the cases 1 and 2(a) provide no difficulty, since the general solution is obtained. In cases 2(b) and 3, only one solution (i.e., with one arbitrary constant) is obtained, and we must find another independent solution in order to determine the general solution. For methods by which this other independent solution can be obtained, see the C exercises.

---

* If the indicial roots are -2 and -1, for example, -2 is the smaller root.

4. Conditions for existence of a Frobenius type solution. Before we present sufficient conditions which will enable us to know in advance whether a solution of Frobenius type exists for the equation

$$p(x)y'' + q(x)y' + r(x)y = 0 \tag{14}$$

where $p(x)$, $q(x)$, $r(x)$ are polynomials, we shall need some definitions.

DEFINITION. $x = a$ is called an *ordinary point* of (14) if $p(a) \neq 0$. Thus $x = 1$, -1 or any number $\neq 0$ are ordinary points of $xy'' + y' + xy = 0$.

DEFINITION. If $p(a) = 0$ then $x = a$ is called a *singular point* of (14). Thus $x = 0$ is a singular point of $xy'' + y' + xy = 0$.

DEFINITION. If $p(a) = 0$ and if

$$\lim_{x \to a} (x - a)\frac{q(x)}{p(x)} \quad \text{and} \quad \lim_{x \to a} (x - a)^2\frac{r(x)}{p(x)}$$

both exist, then $x = a$ is called a *regular singular point*; otherwise it is called an *irregular singular point*.*

For the equation

$$xy'' + y' + xy = 0$$

$p(x) \equiv x$, $q(x) \equiv 1$, $r(x) \equiv x$, and

$$\lim_{x \to 0} \frac{x \cdot 1}{x} = 1, \quad \lim_{x \to 0} \frac{x^2 \cdot x}{x} = 0$$

exist. Hence, $x = 0$ is a regular singular point. It may be proved that the following theorem is true.

THEOREM. If $x = a$ is an ordinary point or a regular singular point of the differential equation (14), then a solution of the form

$$(x - a)^c[a_0 + a_1(x - a) + a_2(x - a)^2 + \cdots] \tag{15}$$

always exists. This is called a Frobenius series about $x = a$.†

If $x = a$ is an ordinary point, (15) with $c = 0$ yields the general solution. If $x = a$ is a regular singular point, (15) yields a solution or the general solution. If $x = a$ is an irregular singular point, solutions with form (15) may or may not exist.

If $a \neq 0$ in (15), the transformation $v = x - a$ is useful.

---

* The following definition of regular singular point is also used: $x = a$ is a regular singular point of $p(x)y'' + q(x)y' + r(x)y = 0$ if $(x - a)q(x)/p(x)$ and $(x - a)^2r(x)/p(x)$ are analytic at a, i.e., they possess Taylor series expansions about $x = a$. For the case where $p(x)$, $q(x)$, and $r(x)$ are polynomials, this definition and that given above are equivalent.

† If no mention of the value of a is made, it will be understood that we are taking $a = 0$.

ILLUSTRATIVE EXAMPLE 6

Show that the differential equations:

(a) $4xy'' + 2y' + y = 0$,
(b) $x^2 y'' + xy' + (x^2 - n^2)y = 0$,
(c) $y'' + xy' + y = 0$

possess solutions of Frobenius type (about $x = 0$), while

(d) $x^3 y'' + 3x^2 y' - 2y = 0$ may or may not.

Solution.

(a) $4xy'' + 2y' + y = 0$. Here $p(x) \equiv 4x$, $q(x) \equiv 2$, $r(x) \equiv 1$, $p(x) = 0$ where $x = 0$, i.e., $x = 0$ is a singular point. Now

$$\lim_{x \to 0} \frac{xq(x)}{p(x)} = \lim_{x \to 0} \frac{x \cdot 2}{4x} = \frac{1}{2}$$

$$\lim_{x \to 0} x^2 \frac{r(x)}{p(x)} = \lim_{x \to 0} x^2 \frac{1}{4x} = 0$$

Hence, $x = 0$ is a regular singular point and a solution of type $x^c(a_0 + a_1 x + a_2 x^2 + \cdots)$ exists.

(b) $x^2 y'' + xy' + (x^2 - n^2)y = 0$. Here $p(x) \equiv x^2$, $q(x) \equiv x$, $r(x) \equiv x^2 - n^2$, and $x = 0$ is a singular point. Furthermore,

$$\lim_{x \to 0} \frac{xq(x)}{p(x)} = \lim_{x \to 0} \frac{x \cdot x}{x^2} = 1$$

$$\lim_{x \to 0} \frac{x^2 r(x)}{p(x)} = \lim_{x \to 0} \frac{x^2(x^2 - n^2)}{x^2} = -n^2$$

Hence, $x = 0$ is a regular singular point, and a Frobenius type solution exists.

(c) $y'' + xy' + y = 0$. Here $p(x) \equiv 1$, $q(x) \equiv x$, $r(x) \equiv 1$.

There is no singularity since $p(x) \neq 0$. In particular, $x = 0$ is an ordinary point and hence a Frobenius type solution exists.

(d) $x^3 y'' + 3x^2 y' - 2y = 0$. Here $p(x) \equiv x^3$, $q(x) \equiv 3x^2$, $r(x) \equiv -2$ and $x = 0$ is a singular point. We have,

$$\lim_{x \to 0} \frac{xq(x)}{p(x)} = \lim_{x \to 0} \frac{x \cdot 3x^2}{x^3} = 3$$

but

$$\lim_{x \to 0} \frac{x^2 r(x)}{p(x)} = \lim_{x \to 0} \frac{x^2(-2)}{x^3}$$

does not exist. Hence, $x = 0$ is an irregular singular point, and so a solution of type (15) with $a = 0$ may or may not exist.

If $x = a$ is an ordinary point of equation (14), a general solution is always obtained by assuming a solution having form (15) with $c = 0$ (a Taylor series). In such cases the Taylor series method, p. 284, is often useful. Thus since $x = 1$ is an ordinary point of *all* equations in Illustrative Example 6, solutions of type (15) with $c = 0$ and $a = 1$ exist.

The following theorem is useful in predicting the interval of convergence of Frobenius type solutions when they exist.

> THEOREM. For the differential equation $p(x)y'' + q(x)y' + r(x)y = 0$, where $p(x)$, $q(x)$, and $r(x)$ are polynomials,* the Frobenius series
>
> $$(x - a)^c[a_1 + a_2(x - a) + a_3(x - a)^2 + \cdots]$$
>
> (if it exists) will converge:
>
> 1. For all values of x if $x = a$ is an ordinary point and no finite singular points exist.
> 2. For all values of x if $x = a$ is a regular singular point and no other finite singular points exist.
> 3. Within the interval $|x - a| < R$ if $x = a$ is an ordinary point or a regular singular point and where R is the distance to the nearest singularity. The series may also converge if $|x - a| = R$, but this needs investigation.

Thus in the equation $xy'' + y' + xy = 0$, $x = 0$ is a regular singular point and there are no other finite singular points. Hence the equation possesses a Frobenius type solution which converges for all x (as we have in fact seen in Section I).

For the equation $y'' + 2xy' - y = 0$ every point is an ordinary point, and so Frobenius type series about any point exist and converge for all x.

For the equation $(1 - x^2)y'' - 2xy' + n(n + 1)y = 0$, $x = \pm 1$ are singularities, and a Frobenius type series (about $x = 0$) will converge in the interval $|x| < 1$ and possibly when $|x| = 1$.

For the differential equation $(1 + x^2)y'' + 2y' + y = 0$, one might have the impression that there are no singularities, since $1 + x^2 \neq 0$ for any real value of x. However, it turns out that we must consider the singularities $x = \pm i$ in the complex plane. The distance from $x = 0$ to $x = \pm i$ is 1, and hence the Frobenius type series would converge for $|x| < 1$ and possibly for $|x| = 1$.†

---

* Analogous results hold when $p(x)$, $q(x)$ and $r(x)$ are not necessarily polynomials. See first footnote, page 292.

† The situation is analogous to the result

$$\frac{1}{1 + x^2} = 1 - x^2 + x^4 - x^6 + \cdots$$

The series converges only for $|x| < 1$ even though $1/(1 + x^2)$ does not have a singularity at $x = \pm 1$.

A EXERCISES

1. Find Frobenius type solutions (about $x = 0$ unless otherwise specified) for each of the following. Sum in closed form if possible.

(a) $xy'' + y = 0$.
(b) $x^2y'' + xy' + (x^2 - \frac{1}{4})y = 0$.
(c) $2xy'' + y' - xy = 0$.
(d) $(1 - x^2)y'' - 2xy' + 12y = 0$.
(e) $xy'' + 2y' + xy = 0$.
(f) $xy'' + y' + y = 0$.
(g) $x(1 - x)y'' + 2y' + 2y = 0$.
(h) $4x^2y'' - 4xy' + (3 - 4x^2)y = 0$.
(i) $x^2y'' + xy' + (x^2 - 4)y = 0$.
(j) $xy'' + (1 - x)y' + y = 0$.
(k) $y'' - 2xy' + 4y = 0$.
(l) $xy'' - y' + 4x^3y = 0$.

2. Show that the roots of the indicial equation may be found by letting $y = x^c$ in the given differential equation and determining c so that the coefficient of the lowest power of x is zero. Illustrate by working some of the above exercises.

B EXERCISES

1. In the method of Frobenius, the labor involved may be diminished by using the notation Σ for summation of series. As an illustration we work Illustrative Example 4 on page 288 by this method. The student should compare each step with the one in that example.

To solve

$$4xy'' + 2y' + y = 0$$

assume that

$$y = \sum_{-\infty}^{\infty} a_n x^{n+c} \quad \text{where we define } a_n = 0, \quad n < 0$$

Differentiating,

$$y' = \sum (n + c)a_n x^{n+c-1}$$
$$y'' = \sum (n + c)(n + c - 1)a_n x^{n+c-2}$$

where we omit the $-\infty$ and ∞ of the summation sign for convenience. Hence,

$$4xy'' = \sum 4(n + c)(n + c - 1)a_n x^{n+c-1} = \sum 4(n + c + 1)(n + c)a_{n+1}x^{n+c}$$
$$2y' = \sum 2(n + c)a_n x^{n+c-1} = \sum 2(n + c + 1)a_{n+1}x^{n+c}$$
$$y = \sum a_n x^{n+c}$$

where the terms have been written so that the coefficients of x^{n+c} are evident. The student should be sure he understands this step. By addition we have

$$4xy'' + 2y' + y = \sum [4(n + c + 1)(n + c)a_{n+1}$$
$$+ 2(n + c + 1)a_{n+1} + a_n]x^{n+c} = 0$$

or, since this is an identity,

$$4(n + c + 1)(n + c)a_{n+1} + 2(n + c + 1)a_{n+1} + a_n = 0$$

i.e.,

$$2(n + c + 1)(2n + 2c + 1)a_{n+1} + a_n = 0 \quad \text{for all } n. \tag{16}$$

Putting $n = -1$, we have, since $a_{-1} = 0$, $2c(2c - 1)a_0 = 0$. Thus $c = 0, \frac{1}{2}$, since $a_0 \neq 0$. For Case I, $c = 0$ we find putting $c = 0$ in (16),

$$a_{n+1} = \frac{-a_n}{(2n + 2)(2n + 1)} \quad \text{(recursion formula)}$$

Putting $n = 0, 1, 2, 3, \ldots$ we readily find

$$a_1 = -\frac{a_0}{2}, \qquad a_2 = -\frac{a_1}{3 \cdot 4} = \frac{a_0}{2 \cdot 3 \cdot 4} = \frac{a_0}{4!},$$

$$a_3 = -\frac{a_2}{5 \cdot 6} = -\frac{a_0}{4! \, 5 \cdot 6} = -\frac{a_0}{6!}, \ldots$$

Hence, a solution is

$$\sum a_n x^{n+c} = a_0\left(1 - \frac{x}{2!} + \frac{x^2}{4!} - \frac{x^3}{6!} + \cdots\right)$$

The student should complete the problem, treating Case II, $c = \frac{1}{2}$ and then finding the general solution.

2. Use the summation notation as in Exercise 1 to solve
   (a) $xy'' + 2y' - xy = 0$.   (b) $y'' + xy = 0$.

3. Work some of the A exercises by using the summation notation.

4. Is $x = 0$ a regular singular point for the equation $x^2 y'' + y' + xy = 0$? How would you find a solution of this equation?

5. How would you obtain the general solution of $y'' - xy' - y = 5\sqrt{x}$? (*Hint:* Assume a *particular solution* of the form $x^c(b_0 + b_1 x + b_2 x^2 + \cdots)$ and determine the constants so that the given equation is satisfied. Then solve $y'' - xy' - y = 0$ by assuming a Frobenius type solution and obtain the complementary solution.)

6. Solve $xy'' + 2y' + xy = 2x$.

C EXERCISES

1. If the method of Frobenius yields a series solution with only one arbitrary constant, procedures are available for determining the general solution. Two cases may arise: (A) roots of indicial equation are equal; (B) roots of indicial equation differ by an integer. The procedure will be indicated in an example illustrating each case.

ILLUSTRATIVE EXAMPLE 7 (Case A)

Find the general solution of

$$xy'' + y' + xy = 0$$

Solution. This is Bessel's equation of order zero. We proceed as usual, using the summation notation. Substituting $y = \sum_{-\infty}^{\infty} a_n x^{n+c}$ in the given equation, we find,

$$xy'' + y' + xy = \sum [a_{n-1} + (n + c + 1)^2 a_{n+1}] x^{n+c} \tag{17}$$

The customary procedure now is to say that

$$a_{n-1} + (n + c + 1)^2 a_{n+1} = 0$$

and, upon letting $n = -1$, obtain the indicial roots $c = 0, 0$. This yields the one solution which we have already obtained in Section I. We deviate from this usual procedure by considering for a moment that $c \neq 0$. However, we will assume that

$$a_{n-1} + (n + c + 1)^2 a_{n+1} = 0, \qquad n \geq 0$$

Thus,

$$a_{n+1} = -\frac{a_{n-1}}{(n + c + 1)^2}, \qquad n \geq 0$$

Putting $n = 0, 1, 2, 3, \ldots$, we have

$$a_1 = 0, \qquad a_2 = \frac{-a_0}{(c + 2)^2}, \qquad a_3 = 0,$$

$$a_4 = \frac{-a_2}{(c + 4)^2} = \frac{a_0}{(c + 2)^2 (c + 4)^2}$$

and, in general,

$$a_{2n-1} = 0, \qquad a_{2n} = \frac{(-1)^n a_0}{(c + 2)^2 (c + 4)^2 \cdots (c + 2n)^2}$$

Consider now

$$Y = \sum a_n x^{n+c} = a_0 x^c \left[1 - \frac{x^2}{(c + 2)^2} + \frac{x^4}{(c + 2)^2 (c + 4)^2} - \cdots \right]$$

It is clear from (17) or by direct substitution that

$$x Y'' + Y' + x Y = c^2 a_0 x^{c-1} \tag{18}$$

We now resort to the following device; differentiate (18) with respect to c.

$$\frac{\partial}{\partial c} (x Y'') + \frac{\partial}{\partial c} (Y') + \frac{\partial}{\partial c} (x Y) = 2c a_0 x^{c-1} + c^2 a_0 x^{c-1} \ln x$$

or

$$x \left(\frac{\partial Y}{\partial c} \right)'' + \left(\frac{\partial Y}{\partial c} \right)' + x \left(\frac{\partial Y}{\partial c} \right) = 2c a_0 x^{c-1} + c^2 a_0 x^{c-1} \ln x$$

assuming the interchange of order of differentiation is valid. It follows that $\left. \dfrac{\partial Y}{\partial c} \right|_{c=0}$ is a solution of the given differential equation. It is not difficult to show now that

$$\left. \frac{\partial Y}{\partial c} \right|_{c=0} = \frac{x^2}{2^2} - \frac{x^4}{2^2 4^2} \left(1 + \frac{1}{2} \right)$$

$$+ \frac{x^6}{2^2 4^2 6^2} \left(1 + \frac{1}{2} + \frac{1}{3} \right) - \cdots + \ln x \left(1 - \frac{x^2}{2^2} + \frac{x^4}{2^2 4^2} - \cdots \right)$$

is a solution besides the usual one $J_0(x)$. The general solution is

$$y = AJ_0(x) + B\left[J_0(x) \ln x + \frac{x^2}{2^2}\right.$$

$$\left. - \frac{x^4}{2^2 4^2}\left(1 + \frac{1}{2}\right) + \frac{x^6}{2^2 4^2 6^2}\left(1 + \frac{1}{2} + \frac{1}{3}\right) - \cdots\right]$$

The second solution may also be obtained from $J_0(x) \int \dfrac{dx}{x J_0^2(x)}$ (see C Exercise 2, p. 282).

ILLUSTRATIVE EXAMPLE 7 (Case B)

Find the general solution of

$$xy'' + y = 0$$

Solution. Letting $y = \Sigma\, a_n x^{n+c}$ as usual, we find

$$xy'' + y = \sum [(n + c + 1)(n + c)a_{n+1} + a_n] x^{n+c} \tag{19}$$

Normally we would write

$$(n + c + 1)(n + c)a_{n+1} + a_n = 0$$

and place $n = -1$ to find $c(c - 1) = 0$ or $c = 0, 1$. Considering these two cases, we find that the general solution is not obtained. Thus, we proceed as in the previous illustrative example. We assume that c is variable and that

$$(n + c + 1)(n + c)a_{n+1} + a_n = 0, \qquad n \geq 0$$

Then

$$a_1 = \frac{-a_0}{c(c + 1)}, \; a_2 = \frac{-a_1}{(c + 1)(c + 2)} = \frac{a_0}{c(c + 1)^2(c + 2)},$$

$$a_3 = \frac{-a_0}{c(c + 1)^2(c + 2)^2(c + 3)}, \ldots$$

Consider now

$$Y = \sum a_n x^{n+c} = a_0 x^c\left(1 - \frac{x}{c(c + 1)} + \frac{x^2}{c(c + 1)^2(c + 2)}\right.$$

$$\left. - \frac{x^3}{c(c + 1)^2(c + 2)^2(c + 3)} + \cdots\right) \tag{20}$$

It is clear from (19) or by actual substitution that

$$xY'' + Y = c(c - 1)a_0 x^{c-1} \tag{21}$$

A direct differentiation with respect to c as in the previous illustrative example fails to produce promising results. We note that the series for Y is meaningless where $c = 0$. By writing $a_0 = cp_0$, where p_0 is a new arbitrary constant, the factor c disappears, and hence the resulting series does have meaning when $c = 0$. For this value of a_0, (21) becomes

$$xY'' + Y = c^2(c - 1)p_0 x^{c-1}$$

Differentiation with respect to c now shows that

$$x\left(\frac{\partial Y}{\partial c}\right)'' + \frac{\partial Y}{\partial c} = (c^3 - c^2)p_0 x^{c-1} \ln x + (3c^2 - 2c)p_0 x^{c-1}$$

and thus $\left.\dfrac{\partial Y}{\partial c}\right|_{c=0}$ is a solution.

From (20), writing cp_0 in place of a_0, we have

$$Y = p_0 x^c\left(c - \frac{x}{c+1} + \frac{x^2}{(c+1)^2(c+2)} - \cdots\right)$$

The student may now show that the required general solution is

$$y = AZ(x) + B\left\{Z(x) \ln x - \left[1 + \frac{x}{1^2} - \left(\frac{1}{1^2 2^2} + \frac{2}{1^3 \cdot 2}\right)x^2\right.\right.$$
$$\left.\left. + \left(\frac{1}{1^2 2^2 3^2} + \frac{2}{1^3 \cdot 2^3 \cdot 3} + \frac{2}{1^2 \cdot 2^2 \cdot 3}\right)x^3 - \cdots\right]\right\}$$

where

$$Z(x) = \frac{x}{1} - \frac{x^2}{1^2 \cdot 2} + \frac{x^3}{1^2 \cdot 2^2 \cdot 3} - \frac{x^4}{1^2 \cdot 2^2 \cdot 3^2 \cdot 4} \cdots$$

The student may find it of interest to show that

$$Z(x) = \sqrt{x}\, J_1(2\sqrt{x}).$$

2. Find the general solutions of each of the following:

(a) $xy'' + y' + y = 0$.
(b) $xy'' + xy' + y = 0$.
(c) $x^2 y'' + xy' + (x^2 - 4)y = 0$.

3. (a) Show that Frobenius type solutions (about $x = 0$) do not exist for the equation $x^4 y'' + 2x^3 y' + y = 0$. (b) Letting $x = 1/u$ (often used for such cases), solve this equation and thus account for the result in (a).

4. Use the method of Exercise 3 to solve:

(a) $x^4 y'' + 2x^2(x + 1)y' + y = 0$.
(b) $4x^3 y'' + 10x^2 y' + (2x + 1)y = 0$.

5. (a) Find Frobenius type series solutions for the equation $(1 - x^2)y'' - 2xy' + 2y = 0$, and show that the result is valid only for $|x| < 1$.
(b) Use the transformation $x = 1/u$ to obtain solutions of the given equation valid for $|x| > 1$.
(c) By noticing that $y = x$ is a solution of the given equation, use the method of C Exercise 1, page 282, to obtain the general solution for $|x| \neq 1$. What relation has this solution with (a) and (b)?

6. The differential equation of Exercise 5 is a special case of Legendre's equation, $(1 - x^2)y'' - 2xy' + n(n + 1)y = 0$ (see C Exercise 7, p. 283). Obtain results for this equation similar to those obtained in Exercise 5.

7. Are the techniques of Exercises 5 and 6 valid for Bessel's equation $x^2 y'' + xy' + (x^2 - n^2)y = 0$?

8. The differential equation

$$x(1 - x)y'' + [\gamma - (\alpha + \beta + 1)x]y' - \alpha\beta y = 0$$

is called *Gauss's differential equation*, or the *hypergeometric differential equation*, and is quite useful. (a) Show that a solution is given by

$$y = 1 + \frac{\alpha \cdot \beta}{1 \cdot \gamma} x + \frac{\alpha(\alpha + 1)\beta(\beta + 1)}{1 \cdot 2 \cdot \gamma(\gamma + 1)} x^2 + \cdots$$

This is called the *hypergeometric series* and is denoted by $F(\alpha,\beta,\gamma;x)$. From the theorem on page 294, what interval of convergence is expected?
(b) Obtain a solution of

$$x(1 - x)y'' + (1 - 3x)y' - y = 0$$

by recognizing it as a special case of the hypergeometric equation. Can you find the general solution? Show that the solution is valid only for $|x| < 1$. How can you find a solution valid for $|x| > 1$?

9. How would you obtain series solutions of the Frobenius type for a differential equation such as

$$(\sin x)y'' + xy' + y = 0$$

Chapter Nine

THE NUMERICAL SOLUTION OF

DIFFERENTIAL EQUATIONS

In many fields of scientific investigation, the end product is a number or a table of values. Since differential equations play an important part in scientific investigations, it would naturally seem important to determine how differential equations can be solved numerically. This is of even greater importance when we realize that giant computing machines are now available which help extraordinarily in the laborious tasks of numerical work. Some of these machines compute tables of values and may even graph results in a very small percentage of the time that it would take an ordinary computer. The fact that machines lessen the labor, however, does not mean that the operator need know less about numerical methods. On the contrary he should know much about the various methods since he must know the most efficient way of "feeding" the mathematics into the machine.

A study of techniques of numerical analysis is an extensive field in itself. In a book such as this we can give but a brief introduction to this important subject.

I. Numerical Solution of $y' = f(x,y)$

In this section we restrict ourselves to a study of solving numerically the first-order differential equation* $y' = f(x,y)$. We ask the

Question. Given that a solution of $y' = f(x,y)$ is such that y is to equal c where $x = a$, how can we determine the value of y when $x = a + h$? By integration of the differential equation with respect to x we have†

$$y = c + \int_a^x f(x,y)dx \tag{1}$$

---

* We suppose that $f(x,y)$ satisfies the conditions of the fundamental existence and uniqueness theorem of page 20. If the solution does not exist or is not unique, there is no point in attempting a numerical solution.

† See footnote, page 285.

and it is clear that $y = c$ where $x = a$ so that (1) satisfies the required condition. The value of y when $x = a + h$ must be given by

$$y = c + \int_a^{a+h} f(x,y)dx \tag{2}$$

Unfortunately, since y occurs under the integral sign of (2), we cannot proceed further without some sort of approximation. Each type of approximation used in (2) determines one method of numerical analysis. We examine one of these methods which we call

1. The constant slope method. The simplest approximation to take in (2) is to assume that $f(x,y)$ is constant over the range $a \leq x \leq a + h$. Clearly this will be a good approximation only if h is small.* We may take the value of the constant to be $f(a,c)$, i.e., the value of the slope $f(x,y)$ at $x = a, y = c$. Thus from (2)

$$y = c + \int_a^{a+h} f(a,c)dx = c + hf(a,c) \tag{3}$$

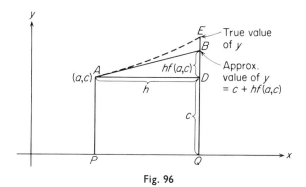

Fig. 96

The graphical interpretation of (3) is seen from Fig. 96.† The true solution is represented by the dashed curve AE. Since distance $AD = h$ it is easy to see that the value of y corresponding to (3) is represented by the ordinate QB. The error made is given by BE. This gets smaller as h gets smaller. If h is large, the error made is large.

In case h is large, this error may be reduced by going back to (2) and

---

* The degree of smallness evidently depends on the degree of accuracy desired. Hence the word "small" must necessarily be vague until further information is available.

† The result in (3) can also be obtained from the first two terms of the Taylor series for y. Thus we have

$$y(a + h) = y(a) + hy'(a) + \frac{h^2}{2!}y''(a) + \cdots$$

$$= c + hf(a,c) + \cdots$$

writing it as

$$y = c + \int_{a}^{a+(h/n)} f(x,y)dx + \int_{a+(h/n)}^{a+(2h/n)} f(x,y)dx + \cdots + \int_{a+(n-1)h/n}^{a+h} f(x,y)dx \quad (4)$$

where n is suitably chosen so that h/n is small. In this way we may write (4) as

$$y = c + \frac{h}{n}f(a,c) + \frac{h}{n}f\left(a + \frac{h}{n}, c_1\right) + \frac{h}{n}f\left(a + \frac{2h}{n}, c_2\right) + \cdots$$

$$+ \frac{h}{n}f\left(a + (n-1)\frac{h}{n}, c_{n-1}\right) \quad (5)$$

where c_k is the value of y when $x = a + \dfrac{kh}{n}$, $k = 1, \ldots, n - 1$.

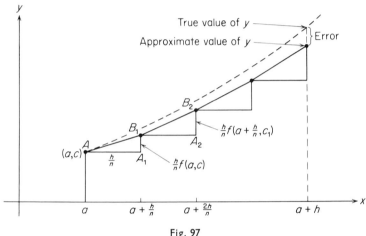

Fig. 97

The geometric interpretation of (5) is given in Fig. 97. By an application of (3) with h/n replacing h, we see that $A_1B_1 = \dfrac{h}{n} f(a,c)$, the ordinate of point B_1 being given by

$$c_1 = c + \frac{h}{n}f(a,c)$$

A new slope is now computed corresponding to point B_1, whose coordinates are $\left(a + \dfrac{h}{n}, c_1\right)$; the value of this slope is given by $f\left(a + \dfrac{h}{n}, c_1\right)$. Using this, we arrive at point B_2, the distance A_2B_2 given by $\dfrac{h}{n}f\left(a + \dfrac{h}{n}, c_1\right)$. Since the ordinate of B_2 is the ordinate of B_1 plus the distance A_2B_2, the ordinate of B_2 is

$$c_2 = c + \frac{h}{n}f(a,c) + \frac{h}{n}f\left(a + \frac{h}{n}, c_1\right)$$

Similarly, the ordinate of point B_k is

$$c_k = c + \frac{h}{n}f(a,c) + \frac{h}{n}f\left(a + \frac{h}{n}, c_1\right) + \cdots + \frac{h}{n}f\left(a + \frac{(k-1)h}{n}, c_{k-1}\right)$$

and in particular

$$c_n = c + \frac{h}{n}f(a,c) + \frac{h}{n}f\left(a + \frac{h}{n}, c_1\right) + \cdots + \frac{h}{n}f\left(a + \frac{(n-1)h}{n}, c_{n-1}\right)$$

is the ordinate of the point reached after n steps, which is the value of y given in (5).

This method, although quite simple, yields very good results, the accuracy becoming better in general as n is chosen larger and larger, provided no errors of other sorts are introduced. As n gets larger, however, although the accuracy may be greater, the computation becomes more laborious, and a compromise must thus be reached. The method is, however, well adapted for computing machines and is not difficult to set up. We shall illustrate the method by the following

ILLUSTRATIVE EXAMPLE

Given $y' = x + y$, find the value of y corresponding to $x = 1$ if $y = 1$ where $x = 0$.

Here $h = 1$. We would like to choose n so that h/n is small. It is convenient to choose $n = 10$ so that $h/n = 0.1$. The computation is conveniently arranged in the following table.

x	y	$y' = x + y$	Old y + 0.1 (slope) = New y
0.00	1.00	1.00	$1.00 + 0.1(1.00) = 1.10$
0.10	1.10	1.20	$1.10 + 0.1(1.20) = 1.22$
0.20	1.22	1.42	$1.22 + 0.1(1.42) = 1.36$
0.30	1.36	1.66	$1.36 + 0.1(1.66) = 1.53$
0.40	1.53	1.93	$1.53 + 0.1(1.93) = 1.72$
0.50	1.72	2.22	$1.72 + 0.1(2.22) = 1.94$
0.60	1.94	2.54	$1.94 + 0.1(2.54) = 2.19$
0.70	2.19	2.89	$2.19 + 0.1(2.89) = 2.48$
0.80	2.48	3.28	$2.48 + 0.1(3.28) = 2.81$
0.90	2.81	3.71	$2.81 + 0.1(3.71) = 3.18$
1.00	3.18		

The initial conditions $x = 0$, $y = 1$ determine a slope $y' = x + y$ (first line of table). Since the increment in x is 0.1, the new value of y is given by $1.00 + 0.1$ (slope) $= 1.00 + 0.1(1.00) = 1.10$. This value of y is then transferred to the second line of the table and the process is repeated. In the table we have kept three significant figures; the value obtained for y is 3.18. By solving exactly, it may be verified that the true value of y where $x = 1$ is 3.44; the error is thus about 8%. If we had used $n = 20$, the accuracy would have been considerably increased but there would be twice as much computation involved.

The method of this section is, as we have stated, only one of numerous methods which could have been used. We have presented it here, not because it is the best method (so far as amount of accuracy obtained with a given labor is concerned) but because it is very simple to understand and also is a very direct method. In the next section another method is indicated. The student who wishes to investigate the subject of numerical methods further will certainly find his efforts rewarding, the main reason being that in the physical sciences and in mathematics, the equations that arise are very often incapable of exact treatment.* This is perhaps to be expected as we progress further in theoretical researches.

A EXERCISES

For each of the following differential equations and conditions, determine the indicated value of y by using the specified number of subdivisions n. If possible compare with values obtained by solving the equation exactly.

1. $y' = 2x + y$; $y(0) = 0$. Find $y(0.5)$; use $n = 5$.

2. $y' = x^2 - y$; $y(1) = 0$. Find $y(1.6)$; use $n = 6$.

3. $y' = (y + 1)/x$; $y(2) = 3$. Find $y(2.8)$; use $n = 4$ and $n = 8$.

4. $y' = (x - y)/(x + y)$; $y(3) = 2$. Find $y(1)$; use $n = 5$ and $n = 10$.

5. $y' = x^2 + y^2$; $y(1) = 2$. Find $y(0.5)$; use $n = 5$ and $n = 10$.

6. $y' = \sqrt{x + y}$; $y(5) = 4$. Find $y(4)$; use $n = 5$ and $n = 10$.

7. $y' = y^2 + \sqrt{y}$; $y(0) = 0.5$. Find $y(1)$; use $n = 5$ and $n = 10$.

B EXERCISES

1. Given $y' = 1/(1 + x^2)$; $y(0) = 0$, find $y(1)$ numerically by choosing $n = 5$ and $n = 10$. How can you use your results to compute π?

2. Given $y' = y$; $y(0) = 1$, find $y(1)$ numerically by choosing $n = 2, 5, 10$. How can you use your results to compute e?

* See, for example, [9] or [14].

3. (a) The differential equation $y' = (x + y)^2$ is to be solved numerically for $y(2)$, given $y(0) = 0$. What are the numerical values obtained by choosing $n = 2, 5,$ 10? How can one be sure of a solution accurate to two decimal places? (b) Solve the differential equation of (a) exactly by using the transformation $x + y = v$. Thus find $y(2)$ exactly and compare with the results of (a).

4. Given $y' = e^{-xy}$; $y(0) = 1$, find $y(1)$ by using a handbook which tabulates the various values of e^u. Obtain accuracy to at least two decimal places.

5. Given $y' = y(x + y)$; $y(0) = 0.5$, find $y(0.5)$, using $n = 5$. Compare with the exact solution. What accuracy is obtained by using $n = 20$?

C EXERCISES

1. The method of this section was limited to the numerical solution of a first-order differential equation. The second-order differential equation $y'' = f(x,y,y')$ subject to the conditions $y = c_1$, $y' = c_2$ where $x = a$ may be written as two simultaneous first-order equations

$$y' = v, \qquad v' = f(x,y,v)$$

subject to the conditions $y = c_1$, $v = c_2$ where $x = a$. Can you devise a procedure for finding y and y' when $x = a + h$? If so, use the method on the equation $y'' = x + y$ subject to the conditions $y(0) = y'(0) = 0$ to obtain $y(1)$. Compare with the exact solution.

2. Use the method discovered in Exercise 1 to find $y(0.8)$ and $y'(0.8)$ for the differential equation $y'' = \sqrt{x + y}$ subject to the conditions $y(0) = 1$, $y'(0) = 0$. Can this equation be solved exactly by letting $x + y = v$?

3. Is it possible to improve accuracy in the constant slope method by an appropriate averaging process? Illustrate your suggested procedure by using it to work some of the above exercises.

2. The Runge-Kutta method. As we have already seen (page 302), if we are given the differential equation

$$\frac{dy}{dx} = f(x,y) \quad \text{where} \quad y(a) = c$$

then

$$y(a + h) = c + \int_a^{a+h} f(x,y)dx \tag{6}$$

Also from the Taylor series expansion we have

$$y(a + h) = y(a) + hy'(a) + \frac{h^2}{2!} y''(a) + \frac{h^3}{3!} y'''(a) + \cdots \tag{7}$$

By expressing the various derivatives indicated in (7) in terms of $f(x,y)$, Runge and Kutta were able to arrive at various formulas for approximating the series in (7). One such formula, which is found to agree with (7) up to and including the term involving h^4 is given by

$$y(a + h) = c + \tfrac{1}{6}(m_1 + 2m_2 + 2m_3 + m_4) \tag{8}$$

where
$$m_1 = hf(a,c)$$
$$m_2 = hf(a + \tfrac{1}{2}h, c + \tfrac{1}{2}m_1)$$
$$m_3 = hf(a + \tfrac{1}{2}h, c + \tfrac{1}{2}m_2)$$
$$m_4 = hf(a + h, c + m_3)$$

The verification of this formula, is tedious but not difficult [see C Exercise 3]. Another formula is given in C Exercise 2. To see an application of this *Runge-Kutta method*, as it is often called, let us consider the following

ILLUSTRATIVE EXAMPLE

Given $y' = x + y$, $y(0) = 1$, find $y(1)$.
    Solution. We have in this case $f(x,y) = x + y$, $a = 0$, $c = 1$. If we choose $h = 1$, we find
$$m_1 = hf(a,c) = f(0,1) = 1$$
$$m_2 = hf(a + \tfrac{1}{2}h, c + \tfrac{1}{2}m_1) = f(\tfrac{1}{2},\tfrac{3}{2}) = 2$$
$$m_3 = hf(a + \tfrac{1}{2}h, c + \tfrac{1}{2}m_2) = f(\tfrac{1}{2},2) = \tfrac{5}{2}$$
$$m_4 = hf(a + h, c + m_3) = f(1,\tfrac{7}{2}) = \tfrac{9}{2}$$

and so
$$y(a + h) = c + \tfrac{1}{6}(m_1 + 2m_2 + 2m_3 + m_4)$$
$$y(1) = 1 + \tfrac{1}{6}(1 + 4 + 5 + \tfrac{9}{2})$$
$$= 3.42$$

Since the true value is 3.44, the accuracy of this method is clearly indicated. Increased accuracy is obtained by using smaller values of h and applying the method more than once. The method should be compared with the constant slope method of the Illustrative Example on page 304 where the same differential equation is used.

A EXERCISES

For each of the following differential equations and conditions, determine the indicated value of y by using the Runge-Kutta method. If possible compare with values obtained by solving the equation exactly.

1. $y' = 2x + y$; $y(0) = 1$. Find $y(0.5)$.

2. $y' = x^2 - y$; $y(1) = 0$. Find $y(1.6)$.

3. $y' = (y + 1)/x$; $y(2) = 3$. Find $y(2.8)$.

4. $y' = x - y$; $y(1) = 2$. Find $y(0.5)$.

B EXERCISES

1. Explain how you could improve the accuracy of solution of a differential equation by successive applications of the Runge-Kutta method. Illustrate by use of A Exercise 1.

2. Use (a) two, (b) three, and (c) four applications of the Runge-Kutta method to solve A Exercise 2. What are the advantages of using successive applications of the method? How could you determine the number of applications?

3. Use two applications of the Runge-Kutta method to solve B Exercise 4 on page 306. Compare the accuracy of this method with that of the constant slope method.

4. (a) Using $h = 0.2$, find $y(1.2)$ by the Runge-Kutta method for the equation $y' = x + y$ subject to $y(1) = 0$. (b) Using $h = 0.1$, find $y(1.1)$ by the Runge-Kutta method for the equation in (a). Using this result, then compute $y(1.2)$. Compare with the accuracy of (a) and with the exact answer.

C EXERCISES

1. Show that if $|f(x,y)| > 1$ the Runge-Kutta method for the differential equation

$$\frac{dy}{dx} = f(x,y)$$

can be improved in accuracy by considering instead the differential equation

$$\frac{dx}{dy} = \frac{1}{f(x,y)}$$

where we consider x as the dependent and y as the independent variable. Illustrate by considering the differential equation

$$\frac{dy}{dx} = x + y, \qquad y(2) = 1$$

and finding $y(2.5)$.

2. Another method due to Runge consists in computing the following

$$m_1 = hf(a,c)$$
$$m_2 = hf(a + h, b + m_1)$$
$$m_3 = hf(a + h, b + m_2)$$
$$m_4 = hf(a + \tfrac{1}{2}h, b + \tfrac{1}{2}m_1)$$

and then using

$$y(a + h) = c + \tfrac{1}{6}(m_1 + 4m_4 + m_3)$$

By solving various differential equations using this method, for example the ones in the A and B Exercises above, decide whether this method is better or worse than the method given in the text. Can you give a possible explanation for your conjecture?

3. Derive the Runge-Kutta formula of the text. (*Hint:* Use Taylor's theorem for functions of two variables and the trapezoidal rule for approximating integrals. Then compare the terms of equations (6) and (7) of page 306 up to and including the terms involving h^4.)

4. Explain how the formula of Exercise 2 may be obtained.

II. Numerical Solution of Differential Equations Using Series

The use of series techniques should be classed as a very important basis for numerical methods. Thus, all the methods of Chapter 8 for obtaining solutions can be employed in the numerical solution of differential equations. The important thing to remember in using series is to make sure that the series obtained are convergent for those values of the variable which are being used. To illustrate the use of series in numerical computation, consider

ILLUSTRATIVE EXAMPLE 1

Given $y' = x + y$; $y(0) = 1$, find $y(1)$.
Solution. Assume a solution of the form

$$y = a_0 + a_1 x + a_2 x^2 + a_3 x^3 + \cdots$$

Since $y = 1$ where $x = 0$, we find $a_0 = 1$, so that

$$y = 1 + a_1 x + a_2 x^2 + a_3 x^3 + \cdots \tag{1}$$

Substituting (1) in the given differential equation, we have

$$a_1 + 2a_2 x + 3a_3 x^2 + 4a_4 x^3 + 5a_5 x^4 + \cdots = 1 + (a_1 + 1)x$$
$$+ a_2 x^2 + a_3 x^3 + a_4 x^4 + \cdots$$

and equating coefficients,

$$a_1 = 1, \quad 2a_2 = a_1 + 1 = 2 \quad \text{or} \quad a_2 = 1, \quad 3a_3 = a_2 \quad \text{or} \quad a_3 = \tfrac{1}{3},$$

$$a_4 = \frac{1}{3 \cdot 4}, \qquad a_5 = \frac{1}{3 \cdot 4 \cdot 5}, \cdots$$

Putting these into (1), we find

$$y = 1 + x + x^2 + \frac{x^3}{3} + \frac{x^4}{3 \cdot 4} + \frac{x^5}{3 \cdot 4 \cdot 5} + \cdots$$

which can be shown to be convergent for all values of x. If $x = 1$, we find

$$y = 1 + 1 + 1 + 0.333 + 0.083 + 0.017 + \cdots = 3.433$$

Further accuracy can be obtained by taking more terms in the series. The student should compare this method with that used in the Illustrative Example of the last section.

If the initial conditions involve values of x other than $x = 0$, we can proceed as in the following

ILLUSTRATIVE EXAMPLE 2

Given $y' = x + y$; $y(1) = 2$, find $y(1.5)$.
Solution. Assume a solution of the form

$$y = a_0 + a_1(x - 1) + a_2(x - 1)^2 + a_3(x - 1)^3 + \cdots$$

Since $y = 2$ when $x = 1$, we find $a_0 = 2$, so that

$$y = 2 + a_1(x - 1) + a_2(x - 1)^2 + \cdots \tag{2}$$

Substituting in the given differential equation and equating coefficients of the various powers of $(x - 1)$, we find

$$a_1 = 3, \qquad a_2 = 2, \qquad a_3 = \frac{2}{3}, \qquad a_4 = \frac{2}{3 \cdot 4}, \qquad a_5 = \frac{2}{3 \cdot 4 \cdot 5}, \cdots$$

and so (2) becomes

$$y = 2 + 3(x - 1) + 2(x - 1)^2 + \frac{2}{3}(x - 1)^3 + \frac{2}{3 \cdot 4}(x - 1)^4 + \cdots \tag{3}$$

which is convergent for all values of x. If $x = 1.5$ in particular,

$$y = 2 + 3(0.5) + 2(0.5)^2 + \frac{2}{3}(0.5)^3 + \frac{2}{3 \cdot 4}(0.5)^4 + \cdots = 4.09$$

The student should compare this with the exact value. It should be noted that the series (3) can also be obtained by the Taylor series method of Chapter 8. The computations are perhaps a little shorter. We have, using $y' = x + y$,

$$y'' = 1 + y', \qquad y''' = y'', \qquad y^{(IV)} = y''', \ldots$$

so that

$$y(1) = 2, \qquad y'(1) = 3, \qquad y''(1) = 4, \qquad y'''(1) = 4, \qquad y^{(IV)}(1) = 4, \ldots$$

Hence, by Taylor's theorem,

$$y = y(1) + y'(1)(x - 1) + \frac{y''(1)(x - 1)^2}{2!} + \frac{y'''(1)(x - 1)^3}{3!} + \cdots$$

$$= 2 + 3(x - 1) + 2(x - 1)^2 + \frac{2}{3}(x - 1)^3 + \cdots$$

as in (3). The student might also try Picard's method in this problem.

There are two remarks which should be made.

Remark 1: From the apparent accuracy of the results in this section by the use of series, the student may wonder why we even think of using the numerical methods described in the last section. One answer to this may be given by presenting the equation $y' = \sqrt{x^3 + y^4}$ subject to certain prescribed conditions. Although it is possible to use series methods on this equation, the labor is prohibitive. On the other hand, the method of the last section would yield results without too much labor, particularly if a computing machine (or slide rule) is handy.

Remark 2: Series methods may, of course, be applied to the numerical solution of differential equations of order higher than the first. In such cases, the method of Frobenius of Chapter 8 may be of value in case the equations do not possess Taylor or Maclaurin series solutions.

A EXERCISES

Solve numerically each of the following by use of series. Compare with the exact results, if possible. Use at least two decimal place accuracy.

1. $y' = 2x + y$; $y(0) = 1$. Find $y(0.5)$.

2. $y' = x^2 - y$; $y(1) = 0$. Find $y(1.6)$.

3. $y' = 2xy$; $y(0) = 1$. Find $y(1)$.

4. $y' = 3y - 2x$; $y(1) = 1$. Find $y(0)$ and $y(0.5)$.

5. $y' = y + \sin x$; $y(\pi/4) = 0$. Find $y(\pi/2)$.

6. $y' = x(x + y)$; $y(2) = 4$. Find $y(1.9)$ and $y(2.1)$.

7. $y'' = x - y$; $y(0) = 0$; $y'(0) = 2$. Find $y(1)$.

8. $y'' = 2x + y + 3y'$; $y(2) = 1$; $y'(2) = -1$. Find $y(2.2)$.

B EXERCISES

1. Given $y' = x^2 + y^2$, $y(1) = 2$. Find $y(0.8)$ and $y(1.2)$ to two decimal places by use of series.

2. The current I in an electric circuit is given by
$$I'(t) + 2I(t) = \sin t$$
If $I = 0$ at $t = 0$, use series to calculate I when $t = 0.5$. Compare the labor involved with the exact method of solution.

3. The displacement x of a vibrating mass from its equilibrium position $x = 0$ is given by the differential equation $x''(t) + 3x'(t) + 5x(t) = \cos 2t$, where $x = 0$ and $dx/dt = 4$ at $t = 0$. Find x and dx/dt at $t = 0.3$ by series.

C EXERCISES

1. Show that the differential equation
$$\frac{dy}{dx} = \frac{x^n + y}{x}$$
possesses a solution of the form $y = a_0 + a_1x + a_2x^2 + \cdots$ if and only if n is zero or an integer greater than 1, and prove that the series is finite in this case.

2. For the case $n = 1$ in the differential equation of Exercise 1, show that there is a solution of the form

$$y = a_0 + a_1(x - b) + a_2(x - b)^2 + \cdots, \qquad b \neq 0$$

and that this series converges in the interval $0 < x \leq 2b$. By choosing b suitably, evaluate $y(0.5)$, $y(1.5)$, given that $y(1) = 1$.

3. Solve the differential equation of Exercise 1 exactly for all n and compare with the results of Exercises 1 and 2.

4. Given the differential equation $xy'' - xy' + y = 0$, find $y(0.5)$, if y is bounded at $x = 0$ and $y(1) = 1$.

Chapter Ten

PARTIAL DIFFERENTIAL EQUATIONS

In the preceding nine chapters we have been concerned with ordinary differential equations involving derivatives of one or more dependent variables with respect to a single independent variable. We have learned how such differential equations arise, methods by which their solutions can be obtained, both exact and approximate, and have considered applications to various scientific fields.

We now do similar things with partial differential equations involving one dependent variable but two or more independent variables and their (partial) derivatives.* It may be added that the introduction of more independent variables makes the subject of partial differential equations even more complicated than that of ordinary differential equations and thus comparatively little is known concerning them. Nevertheless, the subject is so large that we shall be able to touch upon it but briefly in this book.

In this chapter we shall be concerned mainly with how partial differential equations may arise.

I. How Partial Differential Equations Arise
Mathematically

1. Elimination of arbitrary constants or arbitrary functions. It will be remembered that one way in which we arrived at ordinary differential equations was to start with a relation between the variables which contained, as well, certain arbitrary constants. By differentiating often enough and eliminating the arbitrary constants among the several relations thus obtained, a differential equation of order, in general, equal to the original number of arbitrary constants was found. This leads naturally to the

Question. Can a partial differential equation be arrived at by successive

---

* We could also talk about partial differential equations having two or more dependent variables. These are useful in connection with simultaneous partial differential equations. As in ordinary differential equations, such equations may be solved by elimination of all but one dependent variable.

differentiations of a relation involving one dependent variable, two or more independent variables, and several arbitrary constants?

The answer is *yes* as we shall indicate in the following

ILLUSTRATIVE EXAMPLE 1

Obtain a partial differential equation from the relation $z = ax^3 + by^3$, where a and b are arbitrary constants.

Solution. Taking z as a dependent variable, we have

$$\frac{\partial z}{\partial x} = 3ax^2, \qquad \frac{\partial z}{\partial y} = 3by^2$$

so that

$$a = \frac{1}{3x^2} \cdot \frac{\partial z}{\partial x}, \qquad b = \frac{1}{3y^2} \cdot \frac{\partial z}{\partial y}$$

Substituting these values of a and b in $z = ax^3 + by^3$, we find

$$x \frac{\partial z}{\partial x} + y \frac{\partial z}{\partial y} = 3z \tag{1}$$

which is the required partial differential equation.

If we had taken x as a dependent variable we would have on differentiation of $z = ax^3 + by^3$ with respect to y and z, respectively,

$$0 = 3ax^2 \frac{\partial x}{\partial y} + 3by^2, \qquad 1 = 3ax^2 \frac{\partial x}{\partial z}$$

Solving for a and b and substituting into the given relation yields

$$y \frac{\partial x}{\partial y} + 3z \frac{\partial x}{\partial z} = x \tag{2}$$

an equation which differs in form from that just obtained.

It will be remembered from Chapter 1 that a solution of a differential equation is a relation which reduces the differential equation to an identity. The student can easily show that the given relation is a solution of both (1) and (2).

ILLUSTRATIVE EXAMPLE 2

Obtain a partial differential equation from the relation $z = ax^2 + bxy + cy^2$ where a, b, and c are arbitrary constants.

Solution. Taking z as dependent variable, we have

$$\frac{\partial z}{\partial x} = 2ax + by, \qquad \frac{\partial z}{\partial y} = bx + 2cy \tag{3}$$

Then multiplying the first equation in (3) by x, the second equation by y, and adding we obtain the required equation,

$$x\frac{\partial z}{\partial x} + y\frac{\partial z}{\partial y} = 2z$$

Partial differential equations arise not only by elimination of arbitrary constants but by elimination of *arbitrary functions* as well.

A very simple example is obtained by considering the relation $z = f(x) + g(y)$, where $f(x)$ and $g(y)$ are any differentiable functions. By differentiation* of this relation with respect to y we have

$$\frac{\partial z}{\partial y} = g'(y) \tag{4}$$

the prime denoting derivative with respect to y. By differentiating (4) with respect to x, we now find

$$\frac{\partial^2 z}{\partial x\,\partial y} = 0$$

which is the required partial differential equation.

As a more complicated example, consider

Illustrative Example 3

Obtain a partial differential equation from the relation $z = F(x + 3y) + G(x - 3y)$, where F and G are arbitrary differentiable functions.

Solution. Upon letting $x + 3y = u$ and $x - 3y = v$ we have by differentiation with respect to x,

$$\frac{\partial z}{\partial x} = \frac{\partial F}{\partial u}\cdot\frac{\partial u}{\partial x} + \frac{\partial G}{\partial v}\cdot\frac{\partial v}{\partial x}$$

or

$$\frac{\partial z}{\partial x} = F'(u) + G'(v) \tag{5}$$

where $\partial F/\partial u$ and $\partial G/\partial v$ are denoted by $F'(u)$ and $G'(v)$, respectively. Similarly

$$\frac{\partial z}{\partial y} = \frac{\partial F}{\partial u}\cdot\frac{\partial u}{\partial y} + \frac{\partial G}{\partial v}\cdot\frac{\partial v}{\partial y}$$

or

$$\frac{\partial z}{\partial y} = 3F'(u) - 3G'(v) \tag{6}$$

---

* In performing the differentiations, we naturally assume that the functions are differentiable.

The relations (5) and (6) are insufficient in number to enable us to eliminate the arbitrary functions. To accomplish this we take second derivatives, as might well be expected since two arbitrary functions are involved. From (5) and (6) we have

$$\frac{\partial^2 z}{\partial x^2} = \frac{\partial F'}{\partial u} \cdot \frac{\partial u}{\partial x} + \frac{\partial G'}{\partial v} \cdot \frac{\partial v}{\partial x}$$

$$= F''(u) + G''(v) \tag{7}$$

$$\frac{\partial^2 z}{\partial x \, \partial y} = \frac{\partial^2 z}{\partial y \, \partial x} = \frac{\partial}{\partial y}\left(\frac{\partial z}{\partial x}\right)$$

$$= \frac{\partial F'}{\partial u} \cdot \frac{\partial u}{\partial y} + \frac{\partial G'}{\partial v} \cdot \frac{\partial v}{\partial y}$$

$$= 3F''(u) - 3G''(v)$$

$$\frac{\partial^2 z}{\partial y^2} = 3\frac{\partial F'}{\partial u} \cdot \frac{\partial u}{\partial y} - 3\frac{\partial G'}{\partial v} \cdot \frac{\partial v}{\partial y}$$

$$= 9F''(u) + 9G''(v) \tag{8}$$

The arbitrary functions $F''(u)$ and $G''(v)$ can now be eliminated, since it is observed that the right-hand side of (8) is nine times the right-hand side of (7). Thus the required differential equation is

$$\frac{\partial^2 z}{\partial y^2} = 9\frac{\partial^2 z}{\partial x^2}$$

More complicated examples appear in the advanced exercises.

A EXERCISES

1. Obtain partial differential equations (of least order) by eliminating the arbitrary constants in each relation given. Verify that the relation is a solution of the equation obtained. Use z as dependent variable unless otherwise stated.

(a) $z = ax^2 - by^2$. (b) $a \sin x + b \cos y = 2z$.
(c) $z = ax^2 + by^2 + a^2 + b^2$. (d) $ax^2 + by^2 + cz^2 = 1$.
(e) $z = x \cos \alpha + y \sin \alpha + \beta$. (f) $ax^2 + by^2 = cz + 1$.
(g) $a^2 e^x + a \sec y = b \ln z$ (take y as dependent).

2. Obtain partial differential equations (of least order) by eliminating the arbitrary functions in each given relation. In each case verify that the given relation is a solution of the equation obtained. Take z as dependent variable unless otherwise stated.

(a) $z = F(x - 2y)$. (b) $z = F(xy)$.
(c) $x = F(y/z)$ (let x be dependent). (d) $z = F(x^2 - y^2)$.
(e) $z = e^{3y}F(x - 2y)$. (f) $z = F(x + 3y) + G(2x - y)$.

B EXERCISES

1. Show directly that the partial differential equations

$$x\frac{\partial z}{\partial x} + y\frac{\partial z}{\partial y} = 3z, \qquad y\frac{\partial x}{\partial y} + 3z\frac{\partial x}{\partial z} = x$$

are equivalent (see Illustrative Example 1).

2. Considering $z = F(3x - 2y)$, it would seem that $3x - 2y = G(z)$, where F and G are inverse functions. Assuming this true, are the partial differential equations obtained from these two relations equivalent?

3. Obtain a partial differential equation with $z = F(x^2y) + G(xy^2)$, where F and G are arbitrary differentiable functions, as solution.

4. If a function $F(x,y)$ can be written $x^nG(y/x)$ it is called homogeneous of degree n. Show that any homogeneous function which is differentiable satisfies the partial differential equation

$$x\frac{\partial F}{\partial x} + y\frac{\partial F}{\partial y} = nF$$

This is called *Euler's theorem on homogeneous functions*.

5. Show that if $F = \sqrt{x^2 + y^2}$ arc tan y/x, then

$$x\frac{\partial F}{\partial x} + y\frac{\partial F}{\partial y} = F$$

6. Determine n so that

$$z = x^3 \text{ arc tan}\left(\frac{x^2 - xy + y^2}{x^2 + xy + y^2}\right) \quad \text{satisfies} \quad x\frac{\partial z}{\partial x} + y\frac{\partial z}{\partial y} = nz$$

7. Show that the function $V(x,y,z) = (x^2 + y^2 + z^2)^{-1/2}$ satisfies Laplace's partial differential equation

$$\frac{\partial^2 V}{\partial x^2} + \frac{\partial^2 V}{\partial y^2} + \frac{\partial^2 V}{\partial z^2} = 0$$

8. Taking z as dependent variable, obtain a partial differential equation of least order having solution

$$z = ax^6y^3 + bx^4y^2 + cx^2y + d$$

where a, b, c are arbitrary constants. Compare with the equation obtained from $z = F(x^2y)$, where F is an arbitrary function.

C EXERCISES

1. If $z = F(y/x) + xG(y/x)$ show that

$$x^2\frac{\partial^2 z}{\partial x^2} + 2xy\frac{\partial^2 z}{\partial x\,\partial y} + y^2\frac{\partial^2 z}{\partial y^2} = 0$$

2. (a) In the relation $F(u,v) = 0$, F is an arbitrary differentiable function of u and v, which are given differentiable functions of x, y, and z. By differentiation with respect to x and y, prove that

$$\frac{\partial F}{\partial u}\left(\frac{\partial u}{\partial x} + \frac{\partial u}{\partial z}\frac{\partial z}{\partial x}\right) + \frac{\partial F}{\partial v}\left(\frac{\partial v}{\partial x} + \frac{\partial v}{\partial z}\frac{\partial z}{\partial x}\right) = 0$$

$$\frac{\partial F}{\partial u}\left(\frac{\partial u}{\partial y} + \frac{\partial u}{\partial z}\frac{\partial z}{\partial y}\right) + \frac{\partial F}{\partial v}\left(\frac{\partial v}{\partial y} + \frac{\partial v}{\partial z}\frac{\partial z}{\partial y}\right) = 0$$

(b) By eliminating $\partial F/\partial u$ and $\partial F/\partial v$ from the equations of (a), show that the resulting partial differential equation has the form

$$P\frac{\partial z}{\partial x} + Q\frac{\partial z}{\partial y} = R$$

where P, Q, R are known functions of x, y, and z. Discuss any restrictions which must be imposed in performing this elimination. The result is the partial differential equation corresponding to $F(u,v) = 0$.

3. Using the method of Exercise 2, find partial differential equations corresponding to each of the following, where F is an arbitrary function.

(a) $F(2x + 3z, x - 2y) = 0$.   (b) $F(x^2 + y^2, yz) = 0$.
(c) $F(z \sin x, z \cos y) = 0$.   (d) $F(x - y - z, x^2 - 2xy) = 0$.
(e) $F(x^2 - y^2, xyz) = 0$.

4. (a) Show that the differential equation

$$\frac{\partial^3 z}{\partial x^3} + 3\frac{\partial^3 z}{\partial x^2\,\partial y} + 3\frac{\partial^3 z}{\partial x\,\partial y^2} + \frac{\partial^3 z}{\partial y^3} = 0$$

has solution $z = F(x - y) + xG(x - y) + x^2 H(x - y)$ where F, G, and H are arbitrary differentiable functions.
(b) Show that the differential equation of (a) also has solutions given by

$$z = F(x - y) + yG(x - y) + y^2 H(x - y),$$

$$z = F(x - y) + yG(x - y) + xyH(x - y)$$

Are all these solutions related? Explain.

II. How Partial Differential Equations Arise from Physical Problems

1. Boundary-value problems. From an applied point of view, perhaps the most important manner in which partial differential equations may arise is from a mathematical formulation of physical problems. Ordinary differential equations have the number of variables involved so restricted in number (one dependent and one independent variable) that they can describe only relatively simple applied problems.

Partial differential equations, on the other hand, can have any number of independent variables and so we might expect to be able to describe more complex applied problems. A simple example will illustrate this. Suppose a thin metal bar of length L is placed on the x axis of an xy coordinate system (Fig. 98). Suppose that the bar is immersed in boiling water so that it is at temperature 100°C. Then it is removed and the ends $x = 0$ and $x = L$ are kept in ice so that the ends are at temperature 0°C. We shall suppose that no heat escapes from the surface of the bar, i.e., the surface is

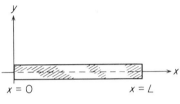

Fig. 98

insulated. We shall not be concerned here with how this can be accomplished physically. Let us inquire as to what the temperature will be at any place in the bar at any time. Denoting the temperature of the bar by U it is easily seen that U depends on the position x of the bar, as well as the time t (measured from time zero when the bar is at 100°C) of observation. We denote this dependence by $U(x,t)$. Thus we have the dependent variable U depending on the two independent variables x and t. As we shall see later, a mathematical formulation of the problem leads to a partial differential equation involving the various derivatives of U with respect to x and t.

In many instances the formulation of a partial differential equation from consideration of the physical situation is easy by comparison with the next problem, which is to find solutions subject to certain initial or boundary conditions just as in the case of ordinary differential equations. Sometimes solutions may be found, but it is difficult to satisfy the associated conditions. This is in contrast to ordinary differential equations where once the (general) solution has been obtained it is usually possible to satisfy the conditions. As in the case of ordinary differential equations, the problem of determining solutions of a partial differential equation subject to conditions is often called a *boundary-value problem*. Also as in ordinary differential equations, existence and uniqueness problems arise.

In other instances, the mathematical formulation of a physical problem is very difficult. Many problems now remain unsolved because of such difficulty. In many cases, crude approximations to reality are made in order to produce a formulation, the hope being that any errors thus arising will be small. The ingenious engineer or other scientist with a good knowledge of mathematics, no matter what his field, has before him much opportunity for the further development of his subject.

In the remainder of this chapter we shall see how partial differential equations and boundary conditions arise in a few simple instances. In the next chapter we shall see how solutions to these boundary-value problems may be obtained.

2. The problem of the vibrating string. As a first illustration, consider the following problem: A string (such as a violin string, for example) is tightly stretched between two fixed points $x = 0$ and $x = L$ on the x axis of Fig. 99(a). At time $t = 0$ the string is picked up at the middle [Fig. 99(b)], to a distance h. Then the string is released. The problem is to describe the motion which takes place.

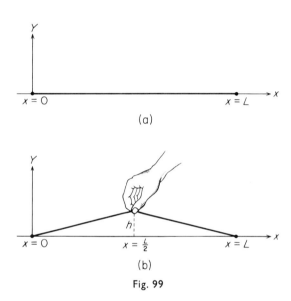

(a)

(b)

Fig. 99

Clearly many things could happen. The string could be so tightly stretched that when we lifted the middle a height h the string would break. This case is simple and we shall not consider it. It is more natural to assume that the string is perfectly flexible and elastic. Also, to simplify the problem, we assume that h is small compared with L. Other assumptions will be made as we proceed.

Mathematical Formulation. Let us suppose that at some instant t, the string has a shape as shown in Fig. 100. We shall call $Y(x,t)$ the displacement of point x on the string (measured from the equilibrium position which we take as the x axis) at the time t. The displacement, at time t, of the neighboring point $x + \Delta x$ will then be given by $Y(x + \Delta x, t)$.

In order to describe the motion which ensues, we consider the forces acting on the small element of string between x and $x + \Delta x$, shown considerably enlarged in Fig. 101. There will be two forces acting on the element, the tension $T(x)$ due to the portion of the string to the left, and the tension

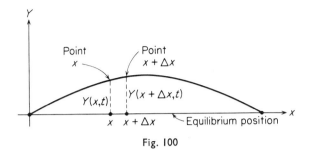

Fig. 100

$T(x + \Delta x)$ due to the portion to the right. Note that we have for the moment assumed that the tension depends on position. Resolving these forces into components gives

$$\left.\begin{array}{l} \text{net vertical force (upward)} = T(x + \Delta x) \sin \theta_2 - T(x) \sin \theta_1 \\[4pt] \text{net horizontal force (to right)} = T(x + \Delta x) \cos \theta_2 - T(x) \cos \theta_1 \end{array}\right\} \quad (1)$$

We now assume that there is no right and left motion of the string, i.e., to a high degree of approximation the net horizontal force is zero. This agrees with the physical situation.* The net vertical force in (1) produces an acceleration of the element. Assuming the string has density (mass per unit length) ρ, the mass of the element is $\rho \, \Delta s$. The vertical acceleration of the string is given approximately by $\partial^2 Y / \partial t^2$.† Hence,

$$T(x + \Delta x) \sin \theta_2 - T(x) \sin \theta_1 = \rho \, \Delta s \frac{\partial^2 Y}{\partial t^2} \quad (2)$$

to a high degree of accuracy. If θ is the angle which the tangent at any point of the element makes with the positive x axis, then θ is a function of position

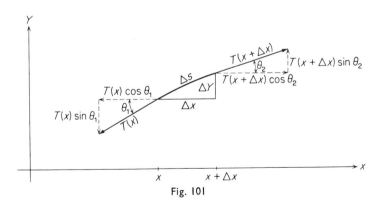

Fig. 101

* Actually this consequence follows from some of the other assumptions which we make.

† More exactly it is $(\partial^2 Y / \partial t^2) + \epsilon$ where $\epsilon \to 0$ as $\Delta x \to 0$.

and we write $\theta_1 = \theta(x)$, $\theta_2 = \theta(x + \Delta x)$. Substitution into (2) and dividing by Δx yields

$$\frac{T(x + \Delta x) \sin \theta(x + \Delta x) - T(x) \sin \theta(x)}{\Delta x} = \rho \frac{\Delta s}{\Delta x} \cdot \frac{\partial^2 Y}{\partial t^2} \tag{3}$$

We now make the assumption that only motions will be considered for which the slope of the tangent at any point on the string is small.* It follows that $\Delta s / \Delta x$ is very close to unity and that $\sin \theta(x)$ and $\sin \theta(x + \Delta x)$ can be replaced with high accuracy by $\tan \theta(x)$ and $\tan \theta(x + \Delta x)$, respectively. In view of these approximations we may write (3) as

$$\frac{T(x + \Delta x) \tan \theta(x + \Delta x) - T(x) \tan \theta(x)}{\Delta x} = \rho \frac{\partial^2 Y}{\partial t^2} \tag{4}$$

to a high degree of accuracy. In the limit as $\Delta x \to 0$, (4) becomes

$$\frac{\partial}{\partial x} [T(x) \tan \theta(x)] = \rho \frac{\partial^2 Y}{\partial t^2} \quad \text{or} \quad \frac{\partial}{\partial x}\left[T(x) \frac{\partial Y}{\partial x} \right] = \rho \frac{\partial^2 Y}{\partial t^2} \tag{5}$$

since $\tan \theta(x) = \partial Y / \partial x$. Equation (5) is called the vibrating string equation or more generally the *wave equation*. If $T(x) = T$, a constant, the equation can be written

$$T \frac{\partial^2 Y}{\partial x^2} = \rho \frac{\partial^2 Y}{\partial t^2} \quad \text{or} \quad \frac{\partial^2 Y}{\partial t^2} = a^2 \frac{\partial^2 Y}{\partial x^2} \tag{6}$$

where $a^2 \equiv T/\rho$. We shall in this book take the tension as constant.

Let us now see what the boundary conditions are. Since the string is fixed at points $x = 0$ and $x = L$, we have

$$Y(0,t) = 0, \qquad Y(L,t) = 0 \quad \text{for} \quad t \geq 0 \tag{7}$$

These state that the displacements at the ends of the string are always zero. Referring to Fig. 99(b) it is seen that

$$Y(x,0) = \begin{cases} \dfrac{2hx}{L} & 0 \leq x \leq \dfrac{L}{2} \\[2ex] \dfrac{2h}{L}(L - x) & \dfrac{L}{2} \leq x \leq L \end{cases} \tag{8}$$

This merely gives the equations of the two straight line portions of that figure. $Y(x,0)$ denotes the displacement of any point x at $t = 0$. Since the string is released from rest, its initial velocity everywhere is zero. Denoting by Y_t the velocity $\partial Y / \partial t$ we may write

$$Y_t(x,0) = 0 \tag{9}$$

which says that the velocity at any place x at time $t = 0$ is zero.

---

* The degree of smallness depends, of course, on accuracy desired.

The differential equation (6) together with the boundary conditions (7), (8), and (9) constitute our boundary-value problem.

3. The problem of heat conduction in a metal bar. On page 319 we raised a question concerning temperatures in a thin metal bar at any place and at any time, given that the bar is initially at 100°C, that the ends $x = 0$ and $x = L$ are kept at 0°C and that the surface of the bar is insulated so that no heat can escape. We shall now formulate this problem mathematically, showing how it leads to a partial differential equation.

Let us consider a bar of constant cross section A (as in Fig. 102 where the cross section is rectangular, although it could be any shape). Consider the element of volume of the bar included between two neighboring planes,

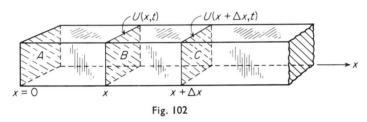

Fig. 102

parallel to A and denoted by B and C at distances x and $x + \Delta x$, respectively, from A. Denote the temperature in plane B at time t by $U(x,t)$; the temperature in plane C at time t will be then given by $U(x + \Delta x, t)$. To proceed further we shall need the following two physical laws concerning heat transfer.*

1. *The amount of heat necessary to raise the temperature of an object of mass m by an amount ΔU is ms ΔU, where s is a constant dependent on the material used, and is called the specific heat.*

2. *The amount of heat flowing across an area (such as B or C) per unit time is proportional to the rate of change of temperature with respect to distance perpendicular to the area (i.e., normal distance x).*

Taking the direction from left to right in Fig. 102 as positive, we may write the second law as

$$Q = -KA\,\Delta t\,\frac{\partial U}{\partial x} \qquad (10)$$

where Q is the quantity of heat flowing to the right, Δt is the length of time during which the flow takes place, and K is the constant of proportionality called the *thermal conductivity*, which depends on the material. The minus sign in (10) shows that Q is positive (i.e., flow is to the right) when $\partial U/\partial x$ is negative (i.e., when the temperature is decreasing as we go to the right).

* A discussion of heat transfer is given in Chapter 3, p. 94.

Similarly Q is negative when $\partial U/\partial x$ is positive. This is in agreement with the physical facts. Using (10), we may say that the amount of heat flowing from left to right across plane B (Fig. 102) is $-KA\,\Delta t\,\dfrac{\partial U}{\partial x}\bigg|_{x}$. Similarly, the amount which flows from left to right across plane C is

$$-KA\,\Delta t\,\frac{\partial U}{\partial x}\bigg|_{x+\Delta x}$$

The net amount of heat which accumulates in the volume between B and C is the amount that flows in at B minus the amount that flows out at C, i.e.,

$$\left[-KA\,\Delta t\,\frac{\partial U}{\partial x}\bigg|_{x}\right] - \left[-KA\,\Delta t\,\frac{\partial U}{\partial x}\bigg|_{x+\Delta x}\right] = KA\,\Delta t\left[\frac{\partial U}{\partial x}\bigg|_{x+\Delta x} - \frac{\partial U}{\partial x}\bigg|_{x}\right] \quad (11)$$

This amount of accumulated heat raises or lowers the temperature of the volume element depending on whether (11) is $+$ or $-$. By law 1, then

$$KA\,\Delta t\left(\frac{\partial U}{\partial x}\bigg|_{x+\Delta x} - \frac{\partial U}{\partial x}\bigg|_{x}\right) = ms\,\Delta U = \rho A\,\Delta x\,s\,\Delta U \quad (12)$$

since the mass of the volume element is the density ρ times the volume $A\,\Delta x$. It should be stated that (12) is only approximately true, the degree of the approximation being better, the smaller the values of Δx, ΔU, and Δt. Dividing both sides of (12) by $A\,\Delta x\,\Delta t$ and letting Δx and Δt approach zero, we obtain

$$K\frac{\partial^2 U}{\partial x^2} = \rho s\frac{\partial U}{\partial t} \quad \text{or} \quad \frac{\partial U}{\partial t} = \kappa\frac{\partial^2 U}{\partial x^2} \quad (13)$$

where $\kappa \equiv K/\rho s$ is called the *diffusivity* of the material. This equation is called the *one-dimensional heat flow or heat conduction equation*.

It should be noted that if the surface were not insulated we should have had to consider an extra term in (12), namely, the amount of heat escaping from (or flowing into) the element (see B Exercise 1).

Taking the special case where the ends are kept at 0°C and where the initial temperature of the bar is 100°C, the following boundary conditions result:

$$\left.\begin{array}{l} U(0,t) = 0, \qquad U(L,t) = 0 \quad \text{for} \quad t > 0 \\[6pt] U(x,0) = 100 \quad \text{for} \quad 0 < x < L \end{array}\right\} \quad (14)$$

The first two express the fact that the temperatures at $x = 0$ and $x = L$ are zero for all time. The third expresses the fact that the temperature at any place x between 0 and L at time zero is 100°C.

In this section we have derived only two of the numerous partial differential equations which can arise in physics and applied mathematics. Extensions of these and derivations of other equations which arise in various fields are considered in the exercises.

A EXERCISES

1. A string vibrates in a vertical plane. Show that the differential equation describing the small vibrations of the string if gravitation is considered is

$$\frac{\partial^2 Y}{\partial t^2} = a^2 \frac{\partial^2 Y}{\partial x^2} + g$$

where the tension T and density ρ are constants, $a^2 = T/\rho$, and g is the acceleration due to gravity.

2. The string of Exercise 1 vibrates in a viscous medium, and a damping force proportional to the instantaneous velocity is assumed to act. Write a partial differential equation describing the motion.

3. Show that the quantity a in the wave equation (6) has dimensions of velocity.

4. If the ends of the bar in the heat-flow problem of the text are insulated instead of being kept at 0°C, express mathematically the new boundary conditions. Can you think of the solution to the boundary-value problem by physical reasoning?

B EXERCISES

1. The surface of a thin metal bar is not insulated but, instead, radiation can take place into the surroundings. Assuming Newton's law of cooling (page 99) is applicable, show that the heat equation becomes

$$\frac{\partial U}{\partial t} = \kappa \frac{\partial^2 U}{\partial x^2} - c(U - U_0),$$

where c is a constant and U_0 is the temperature of the surroundings.

2. Consider a three-dimensional region as in Fig. 103, which may represent a continuous distribution of electric charges (or a continuous distribution of mass). Let ρ, which may vary from point to point, denote the charge per unit volume (or mass per unit volume). The quantity ρ is thus the charge density (or mass density). The electric potential at P due to charge q at Q (or gravitational potential at P due to mass m at Q) is defined to be q/r (or m/r), where r is the distance

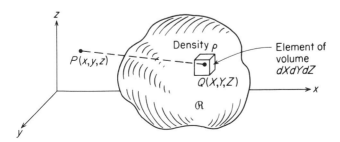

Fig. 103

from P to Q given by

$$r = \sqrt{(x - X)^2 + (y - Y)^2 + (z - Z)^2}$$

(a) Show that the electric potential V at point P due to the entire charge distribution in the region $\mathcal{R}$ (or gravitational potential due to the mass distribution) is

$$V = \iiint\limits_{\mathcal{R}} \frac{\rho(X,Y,Z)dX\,dY\,dZ}{\sqrt{(x - X)^2 + (y - Y)^2 + (z - Z)^2}}$$

(b) Show that V must satisfy the equation

$$\frac{\partial^2 V}{\partial x^2} + \frac{\partial^2 V}{\partial y^2} + \frac{\partial^2 V}{\partial z^2} = 0$$

which is called *Laplace's equation* and is of great importance.

C EXERCISES

1. In applied mathematics and physics it is important to determine the equation of heat conduction in three dimensions. To do this, consider an element of

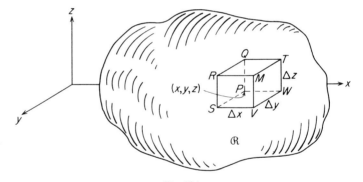

Fig. 104

volume within a region $\mathcal{R}$ (Fig. 104). This element is taken as a parallelepiped and is shown considerably enlarged in the figure. Show that the heat equation is

$$\frac{\partial U}{\partial t} = \kappa\left(\frac{\partial^2 U}{\partial x^2} + \frac{\partial^2 U}{\partial y^2} + \frac{\partial^2 U}{\partial z^2}\right)$$

where the various symbols have the same meaning as in the text. (*Hint:* The net amount of heat which accumulates in the volume element is the sum of the amounts of heat entering through the faces $PQRS$, $PQTW$, $PSVW$ minus the sum of the amounts which leave through faces $WTMV$, $SRMV$, $QRMT$.)

2. Show that if U depends only on x and t, the one-dimensional heat flow equation of the text results from the general heat equation of Exercise 1. Show also that the steady-state temperature satisfies Laplace's equation of B Exercise 2.

Chapter Eleven

SOLUTIONS OF BOUNDARY-VALUE

PROBLEMS AND FOURIER SERIES

I. Introduction

In the last chapter we saw how partial differential equations might arise, both mathematically from relations containing arbitrary constants or arbitrary functions, and physically from a statement of an applied problem. As has already been pointed out, the formulations of partial differential equations and boundary conditions may sometimes be difficult, sometimes impossible. If a boundary-value problem is formulated, there remains the task of finding a solution of this boundary-value problem, i.e., finding a solution of the given partial differential equation which satisfies the given boundary conditions. Sometimes it is easy to find a solution, in fact many solutions, of the partial differential equation, but difficult or even impossible to find that solution which satisfies the given conditions.

Suppose we do succeed in formulating a boundary-value problem. How do we proceed to find a solution? As in ordinary differential equations there are, logically, three questions which we as scientists should *ask* even though we may not be able to *answer*.

1. *Does a solution to our problem exist?* If in any way we can show that a solution does not exist there is clearly no point in looking for it. Mathematicians have succeeded in proving that certain types of boundary-value problems have solutions. Theorems guaranteeing the existence of solutions are called *existence theorems* and are very valuable.

2. *If a solution exists, is it unique?* If it is not unique, i.e., if we have two possible answers to a given physical problem it might prove utterly embarrassing. Theorems guaranteeing the uniqueness of solutions are called *uniqueness theorems.*

3. *If a solution does exist and is unique, what is this solution?* In many cases the scientist obtains a solution and does not bother to ask whether it is the only one. Perhaps if he tried again, using some other technique, he might find another solution. The answer is that he usually does not try again, for

he is happy to have been able to find one solution. Clearly this is contrary to the scientific method, and anyone who is able to produce a solution and not have any ideas as to whether it is unique, and who perhaps may not even be aware of the question, might better be labeled *magician* than *scientist*. It is far better to be aware of such problems and to leave them in the form of questions than to be smug in the belief that a particular problem has been completely solved. To answer such questions requires a great deal of further study, and all that we can hope to do is to make the student aware of the existence of these questions and to hope that he may become interested enough to go on and find their answers.

II. Solutions to Some Simple Boundary-Value Problems

As an illustration of how we may obtain solutions of boundary-value problems consider the following

ILLUSTRATIVE EXAMPLE 1

Find a solution of the boundary-value problem

$$\frac{\partial^2 U}{\partial x^2} = xe^y; \qquad U(0,y) = y^2, \qquad U(1,y) = \sin y$$

Solution. We may write the equation as

$$\frac{\partial}{\partial x}\left(\frac{\partial U}{\partial x}\right) = xe^y$$

Integrating with respect to x (keeping y constant), we have

$$\frac{\partial U}{\partial x} = \frac{x^2 e^y}{2} + F(y)$$

where $F(y)$ is an arbitrary function of y. Another integration yields

$$U = \frac{x^3 e^y}{6} + xF(y) + G(y)$$

where $G(y)$ is another arbitrary function of y. From the first condition

$$U(0,y) = G(y) = y^2$$

so that the solution thus far is

$$U(x,y) = \frac{x^3 e^y}{6} + xF(y) + y^2$$

The second condition yields

$$U(1,y) = \frac{e^y}{6} + F(y) + y^2 = \sin y, \qquad F(y) = \sin y - y^2 - \frac{e^y}{6}$$

so that the solution becomes

$$U(x,y) = \frac{x^3 e^y}{6} + x\left(\sin y - y^2 - \frac{e^y}{6}\right) + y^2$$

It is easy to check that this satisfies the differential equation and the conditions and therefore that it is a solution. However we have not shown that it is the only solution (see B Exercise 1).

ILLUSTRATIVE EXAMPLE 2

Find a solution of the boundary-value problem

$$\frac{\partial^2 U}{\partial x \, \partial y} = \frac{\partial U}{\partial x} + 2, \qquad U(0,y) = 0, \qquad U_x(x,0) = x^2$$

Solution. Writing the equation as

$$\frac{\partial}{\partial x}\left(\frac{\partial U}{\partial y} - U\right) = 2$$

and integrating with respect to x yields

$$\frac{\partial U}{\partial y} - U = 2x + F(y)$$

which is a linear equation having integrating factor e^{-y}. Hence,

$$\frac{\partial}{\partial y}(e^{-y}U) = 2xe^{-y} + e^{-y}F(y)$$

or, by integrating and solving for U,

$$U(x,y) = -2x + e^y \int e^{-y}F(y)dy + e^y G(x)$$

where $G(x)$ is arbitrary. Writing

$$H(y) \equiv e^y \int e^{-y}F(y)dy,$$

we have

$$U(x,y) = -2x + H(y) + e^y G(x) \tag{1}$$

From $U(0,y) = 0$ we find $H(y) = -G(0)e^y$, so (1) becomes

$$U(x,y) = -2x - G(0)e^y + e^y G(x)$$

Differentiating with respect to x and placing $y = 0$, we find

$$U_x(x,0) = -2 + G'(x) = x^2 \quad \text{or} \quad G(x) = \frac{x^3}{3} + 2x + c$$

Hence,

$$\cdot \; U(x,y) = -2x - G(0)e^y + e^y\left(\frac{x^3}{3} + 2x + c\right)$$

Since $c = G(0)$, we may write the result as

$$U(x,y) = \frac{x^3 e^y}{3} + 2xe^y - 2x$$

ILLUSTRATIVE EXAMPLE 3

(a) Assuming that a solution of the form

$$U(x,t) = X(x)T(t)$$

(where $X(x)$ is a real function of x alone and $T(t)$ is a real function of t alone) exists for the boundary-value problem

$$\frac{\partial U}{\partial t} = \frac{\partial^2 U}{\partial x^2}$$

$$U(0,t) = 0, \qquad U(10,t) = 0, \qquad U(x,0) = 50 \sin \frac{3\pi x}{2} \qquad (2)$$

find a solution.

(b) What would be a solution if the condition for $U(x,0)$ of (2) is replaced by

$$U(x,0) = 50 \sin \frac{3\pi x}{2} + 20 \sin 2\pi x$$

Solution. Substituting $U = XT$ in the differential equation, we have

$$\frac{\partial}{\partial t}(XT) = \frac{\partial^2}{\partial x^2}(XT) \quad \text{or} \quad XT' = X''T \qquad (3)$$

where X'' means $d^2 X/dx^2$ and T' means dT/dt. Writing (3) as

$$\frac{T'}{T} = \frac{X''}{X} \qquad (4)$$

we see that one side depends only on t, while the other side depends only on x. Since x and t are independent variables, they do not depend on each other and, hence, (4) can be true if and only if each member is the same constant, which we call c. From (4) we have, therefore,

$$T' = cT, \qquad X'' = cX \qquad (5)$$

Three cases arise, $c < 0$, $c = 0$, $c > 0$.*

Case I, $c < 0$. It is convenient to write $c = -\lambda^2$ where λ is a real number. Thus (5) becomes

$$T' + \lambda^2 T = 0, \qquad X'' + \lambda^2 X = 0$$

which have solutions

$$T = C_1 e^{-\lambda^2 t}, \qquad X = A_1 \cos \lambda x + B_1 \sin \lambda x$$

It follows that a solution is given by

$$U(x,t) = XT = e^{-\lambda^2 t}(A \cos \lambda x + B \sin \lambda x)$$

where $A = A_1 C_1$, $B = B_1 C_1$. From the first of conditions (2)

$$U(0,t) = e^{-\lambda^2 t} A = 0 \quad \text{or} \quad A = 0$$

_____

* We can say this by virtue of the assumption that X and T are real; otherwise we would have to consider the case where c is complex.

Hence, the solution so far is

$$U(x,t) = Be^{-\lambda^2 t} \sin \lambda x \qquad (6)$$

The second of conditions (2) yields

$$U(10,t) = Be^{-\lambda^2 t} \sin 10\lambda = 0$$

so that either $B = 0$ or $\sin 10\lambda = 0$, since $e^{-\lambda^2 t}$ is never zero. If $B = 0$, the solution is identically zero and we can never hope to satisfy the last of conditions (2). Hence, the only possibility is

$$\sin 10\lambda = 0, \quad \text{i.e.,} \quad 10\lambda = m\pi \quad \text{or} \quad \lambda = \frac{m\pi}{10}$$

where $m = 0, \pm 1, \pm 2, \ldots$ and (6) becomes

$$U(x,t) = Be^{-m^2\pi^2 t/100} \sin \frac{m\pi x}{10} \qquad (7)$$

The last condition of (2) yields

$$U(x,0) = 50 \sin \frac{3\pi x}{2} = B \sin \frac{m\pi x}{10}$$

which is satisfied if $B = 50$, $m = 15$, for which the solution (7) becomes

$$U(x,t) = 50e^{-2.25\pi^2 t} \sin \frac{3\pi x}{2}$$

Case II, $c = 0$. In this case, equations (5) become

$$T' = 0, \qquad X'' = 0$$

from which we obtain $T = C_1$, $X = A_1 x + B_1$ so that

$$U(x,t) = C_1(A_1 x + B_1) = Ax + B$$

is a solution. To satisfy the first of conditions (2) we must have $B = 0$, so that $U(x,t) = Ax$. Similarly from the second condition we have $A = 0$. Thus we cannot find a solution by taking $c = 0$. Similarly the student should show that the assumption $c > 0$ fails to yield a solution.

To answer part (b) we see that all the steps up to equation (7) hold as before. Thus all that we have to do is try to satisfy the new boundary condition. This is seen to be impossible, since

$$U(x,0) = B \sin \frac{m\pi x}{10} = 50 \sin \frac{3\pi x}{2} + 20 \sin 2\pi x \qquad (8)$$

can never be satisfied for any choice of constants m and B. We do not give up, however, and perhaps after some time we may come to realize the following fact. If U_1 and U_2 are two solutions of the differential equation, then $a_1 U_1 + a_2 U_2$, where a_1 and a_2 are any constants, is a solution. The proof is simple and follows immediately. In like manner we may show that if U_1, U_2, ..., U_n are solutions, then $a_1 U_1 + a_2 U_2 + \cdots + a_n U_n$ is a solution. We have seen a theorem corresponding to this in the case of linear ordinary differential equations. In fact, our equation is an example of a *linear partial differential equation.*

It follows from the above that if m_1 and m_2 are any of the numbers $0, \pm 1, \pm 2, \ldots$, then

$$B_1 e^{-m_1^2 \pi^2 t/100} \sin \frac{m_1 \pi x}{10} \quad \text{and} \quad B_2 e^{-m_2^2 \pi^2 t/100} \sin \frac{m_2 \pi x}{10}$$

are solutions, and so also is

$$U(x,t) = B_1 e^{-m_1^2 \pi^2 t/100} \sin \frac{m_1 \pi x}{10} + B_2 e^{-m_2^2 \pi^2 t/100} \sin \frac{m_2 \pi x}{10} \tag{9}$$

Furthermore, (9) automatically satisfies the first and second of conditions (2), and we have only to see if it satisfies (8). We have

$$U(x,0) = B_1 \sin \frac{m_1 \pi x}{10} + B_2 \sin \frac{m_2 \pi x}{10}$$

$$= 50 \sin \frac{3 \pi x}{2} + 20 \sin 2 \pi x$$

It is seen that this is satisfied if

$$B_1 = 50, \quad m_1 = 15, \quad B_2 = 20, \quad m_2 = 20$$

Thus, the required solution is

$$U(x,t) = 50 e^{-2.25 \pi^2 t} \sin \frac{3 \pi x}{2} + 20 e^{-4 \pi^2 t} \sin 2 \pi x$$

The process of building up solutions to linear ordinary or linear partial differential equations is known in engineering and other scientific endeavors as *superposition of solutions,* and the principle is often referred to as the *principle of superposition.* It is of extreme importance in obtaining solutions, as we have seen in this example, and as we shall see later. The method of assuming solutions of the type $U(x,t) = X(x)T(t)$ is often referred to as the method of "separation of variables." It is of great importance in many problems of physics and applied mathematics.

A EXERCISES

1. Obtain solutions to the following boundary-value problems:

(a) $\dfrac{\partial U}{\partial x} = \sin y$; $U(0,y) = 0$.

(b) $\dfrac{\partial^2 U}{\partial y^2} = x^2 \cos y$; $U(x,0) = 0$, $U\left(x, \dfrac{\pi}{2}\right) = 0$.

(c) $\dfrac{\partial^2 V}{\partial x\, \partial y} = 0;\ V(0,y) = 3\sin y,\ V_x(x,1) = x^2.$

(d) $\dfrac{\partial^2 U}{\partial x\, \partial y} = 4xy + e^x;\ U_y(0,y) = y,\ U(x,0) = 2.$

(e) $\dfrac{\partial^2 Z}{\partial x\, \partial y} = 3\dfrac{\partial Z}{\partial y} + 2y;\ Z_y(0,y) = y^2 - 2y,\ Z(x,0) = x + 3e^{-x}.$

2. Use the method of "separation of variables" to obtain solutions to each of the following boundary-value problems.

(a) $\dfrac{\partial U}{\partial x} = \dfrac{\partial U}{\partial y}\ ;\ U(0,y) = e^{2y}.$

(b) $\dfrac{\partial U}{\partial x} + U = \dfrac{\partial U}{\partial y}\ ;\ U(x,0) = 4e^{-3x}.$

(c) $\dfrac{\partial U}{\partial x} + \dfrac{\partial U}{\partial y} = U;\ U(0,y) = 2e^{-y} + 3e^{-2y}.$

(d) $4\dfrac{\partial Y}{\partial t} + \dfrac{\partial Y}{\partial x} = 3Y;\ Y(x,0) = 4e^{-x} - e^{-5x}.$

(e) $\dfrac{\partial U}{\partial t} = 4\dfrac{\partial^2 U}{\partial x^2}\ ;\ U(0,t) = 0,\ U(10,t) = 0,\ U(x,0) = 5\sin 2\pi x.$

(f) $2\dfrac{\partial U}{\partial t} = \dfrac{\partial^2 U}{\partial x^2}\ ;\ U(0,t) = 0,\ U(\pi,t) = 0,\ U(x,0) = 2\sin 3x - 5\sin 4x.$

(g) $\dfrac{\partial^2 Y}{\partial t^2} = \dfrac{\partial^2 Y}{\partial x^2}\ ;\ Y(0,t) = 0,\ Y(20,t) = 0,\ Y_t(x,0) = 0,\ Y(x,0) = 10\sin\dfrac{\pi x}{2}.$

(h) $\dfrac{\partial^2 Y}{\partial t^2} = 4\dfrac{\partial^2 Y}{\partial x^2}\ ;\ Y(0,t) = 0,\ Y(10,t) = 0,\ Y_t(x,0) = 0,$

$$Y(x,0) = 3\sin 2\pi x - 4\sin\dfrac{5\pi x}{2}.$$

(i) $9\dfrac{\partial^2 Y}{\partial t^2} = \dfrac{\partial^2 Y}{\partial x^2}\ ;\ Y(0,t) = 0,\ Y(\pi,t) = 0,\ Y_t(x,0) = 2\sin x - 3\sin 2x,$

$$Y(x,0) = 0.$$

(j) $\dfrac{\partial U}{\partial t} = \dfrac{\partial^2 U}{\partial x^2} + U;\ U(0,t) = 0,\ U(10,t) = 0,\ U(x,0) = 5\sin 2\pi x - \sin 4\pi x.$

3. Give a physical interpretation to the boundary-value problems of Exercises 2(e), (f), (g), (h), and (i).

B EXERCISES

1. The uniqueness of a solution to a boundary-value problem is often difficult to establish. However, for some simple problems it is relatively easy. The method consists in assuming that there are two solutions U_1 and U_2, where $U_1 \not\equiv U_2$.

One then tries to prove that the difference $U_1 - U_2$ has to be zero. Referring to Illustrative Example 1 of the text show that if U_1 and U_2 are two functions satisfying the differential equation and the boundary conditions and if

$$U_1(x,y) - U_2(x,y) \equiv V(x,y)$$

then

$$\frac{\partial^2 V}{\partial x^2} = 0, \qquad V(0,y) = 0, \qquad V(1,y) = 0$$

Show that the only possible solution is $V \equiv 0$, proving the uniqueness.

2. Establish the uniqueness of a few of the boundary-value problems in A Exercise 1.

3. In seeking solutions to partial differential equations, an alternative to the method of separation of variables is to assume solutions of the type e^{ax+by}, where a and b are constants. Apply this method to (a) A Exercise 2(c); (b) A Exercise 2(h). Can the method be applied to the equation

$$x\frac{\partial U}{\partial x} + \frac{\partial U}{\partial y} = 0$$

Could the separation of variables method be applied here? To what types of partial differential equations do you think the method can be applied? (The student should compare the assumption e^{ax+by} to the assumption e^{mx} used in ordinary linear differential equations with constant coefficients.)

C EXERCISES

1. (a) Show that the partial differential equation

$$A\frac{\partial^2 U}{\partial x^2} + B\frac{\partial^2 U}{\partial x \, \partial y} + C\frac{\partial^2 U}{\partial y^2} = 0$$

where A, B, and C are constants, has solutions of the form e^{ax+by}. Show that if $A \neq 0$, then $a = m_1 b$ and $a = m_2 b$ so that $e^{b(y+m_1x)}$ and $e^{b(y+m_2x)}$ are solutions, where b is arbitrary. (b) By actual substitution show that $F(y + m_1x)$ and $G(y + m_2x)$, where F and G are arbitrary functions, are also solutions. Hence, show that $U = F(y + m_1x) + G(y + m_2x)$ is a solution. This is called a *general solution* if $m_1 \neq m_2$. (c) Discuss any modifications in Parts (a) and (b) if $A = 0$.

2. Show how Exercise 1 may be used to find general solutions of each of the following:

(a) $\dfrac{\partial^2 U}{\partial x^2} - 3\dfrac{\partial^2 U}{\partial x \, \partial y} + 2\dfrac{\partial^2 U}{\partial y^2} = 0.$ (b) $\dfrac{\partial^2 U}{\partial x^2} + \dfrac{\partial^2 U}{\partial y^2} = 0.$

(c) $\dfrac{\partial^2 Y}{\partial t^2} = a^2\dfrac{\partial^2 Y}{\partial x^2}.$ (d) $\dfrac{\partial^2 U}{\partial x^2} + 4\dfrac{\partial^2 U}{\partial x \, \partial y} = 0.$

(e) $2\dfrac{\partial^2 U}{\partial x \, \partial y} - 3\dfrac{\partial^2 U}{\partial y^2} = 0.$

3. If m_1 and m_2 of Exercise 1 are equal, then $F(y + m_1x)$ is a solution. Show that $xG(y + m_1x)$ or $yG(y + m_1x)$ is also a solution, and hence that $F(y + m_1x) + xG(y + m_1x)$ is a general solution. Use this to obtain general solutions of each of the following:

(a) $\dfrac{\partial^2 U}{\partial x^2} - 4\dfrac{\partial^2 U}{\partial x\, \partial y} + 4\dfrac{\partial^2 U}{\partial y^2} = 0.$ (b) $4\dfrac{\partial^2 Y}{\partial t^2} - 12\dfrac{\partial^2 Y}{\partial x\, \partial t} + 9\dfrac{\partial^2 Y}{\partial x^2} = 0$

(Compare with the case of repeated roots in the auxiliary equation in connection with linear ordinary differential equations.)

4. Show that if U_1 is a general solution of

$$A\frac{\partial^2 U}{\partial x^2} + B\frac{\partial^2 U}{\partial x\, \partial y} + C\frac{\partial^2 U}{\partial y^2} = 0$$

and if U_2 is any (particular) solution of

$$A\frac{\partial^2 U}{\partial x^2} + B\frac{\partial^2 U}{\partial x\, \partial y} + C\frac{\partial^2 U}{\partial y^2} = F(x,y) \tag{10}$$

then a general solution of (10) is $U = U_1 + U_2$.
(Compare with a theorem of ordinary differential equations.)

5. Use Exercise 4 to obtain a general solution of

$$\frac{\partial^2 Z}{\partial x^2} + 4\frac{\partial^2 Z}{\partial x\, \partial y} + 3\frac{\partial^2 Z}{\partial y^2} = 4e^{2x+3y}$$

(*Hint:* Assume a particular solution ae^{2x+3y} and determine a.)

6. Find a general solution of

$$\frac{\partial^2 U}{\partial x^2} + 2\frac{\partial^2 U}{\partial x\, \partial y} + \frac{\partial^2 U}{\partial y^2} = 3\sin(x - 4y) + x^2.$$

7. Find a general solution of

$$\frac{\partial^2 U}{\partial x^2} + 2\frac{\partial^2 U}{\partial x\, \partial y} - 3\frac{\partial^2 U}{\partial y^2} = 6e^{y-3x} + \cos(x - 2y).$$

(*Hint:* Corresponding to the term $6e^{y-3x}$, assume particular solution axe^{y-3x} or aye^{y-3x} and determine a.)

8. Apply the techniques of Exercises 1–7 to determine general solutions of:

(a) $\dfrac{\partial^3 U}{\partial x^3} - 2\dfrac{\partial^3 U}{\partial x^2\, \partial y} - \dfrac{\partial^3 U}{\partial x\, \partial y^2} + 2\dfrac{\partial^3 U}{\partial y^3} = 0.$

(b) $\dfrac{\partial^4 Z}{\partial x^4} + 2\dfrac{\partial^4 Z}{\partial x^2\, \partial y^2} + \dfrac{\partial^4 Z}{\partial y^4} = 0.$

(c) $3\dfrac{\partial^3 U}{\partial x^3} - 4\dfrac{\partial^3 U}{\partial x\, \partial y^2} = 3e^y - 2\sin(x + 2y).$

9. (a) If the system of equations,

$$\frac{dx}{P} = \frac{dy}{Q} = \frac{dz}{R}$$

where P, Q, and R are functions of x, y, and z, has solution $u(x,y,z) = c_1$, $v(x,y,z) = c_2$, show that the partial differential equation

$$P\frac{\partial z}{\partial x} + Q\frac{\partial z}{\partial y} = R$$

has solution $F(u,v) = 0$, where F is an arbitrary differentiable function. Compare with C Exercise 2 page 318.
(b) Use the result of (a) to find a solution of

$$x\frac{\partial z}{\partial x} + (x - y)\frac{\partial z}{\partial y} = y$$

10. (a) Given the function $U(x,t)$. Assuming suitable restrictions, find the Laplace transform of $\partial U/\partial t$ with respect to the variable t, showing that

$$\mathcal{L}\left\{\frac{\partial U}{\partial t}\right\} = su - U(x,0)$$

where $u = u(x,s) = \mathcal{L}\{U(x,t)\}$.

(b) Show that $\mathcal{L}\left\{\dfrac{\partial^2 U}{\partial t^2}\right\} = s^2 u - sU(x,0) - U_t(x,0)$.

(c) Show that $\mathcal{L}\left\{\dfrac{\partial U}{\partial x}\right\} = \dfrac{du}{dx}$, $\mathcal{L}\left\{\dfrac{\partial^2 U}{\partial x^2}\right\} = \dfrac{d^2 u}{dx^2}$.

(d) Show how Laplace transforms can be used to solve the boundary-value problem

$$\frac{\partial U}{\partial t} = \frac{\partial^2 U}{\partial x^2}, \quad U(0,t) = 0, \quad U(1,t) = 0, \quad U(x,0) = 8\sin 2\pi x$$

(*Hint:* Take Laplace transforms of the first two boundary conditions.)

11. Use the method of Laplace transforms as in Exercise 10 to obtain solutions to
(a) A Exercise 2(g); (b) A Exercise 2(h); (c) A Exercise 2(j).

12. Can you use Laplace transform methods to solve the boundary-value problem

$$\frac{\partial U}{\partial t} = \frac{\partial^2 U}{\partial x^2}, \quad U(0,t) = 0, \quad U(1,t) = 0, \quad U(x,0) = x(1 - x)?$$

Explain.

III. An Attempt to Solve the Problem of Fourier

In the last chapter, we arrived at the boundary-value problem,

$$\frac{\partial U}{\partial t} = \kappa \frac{\partial^2 U}{\partial x^2} \tag{1}$$

$$U(0,t) = 0, \qquad U(L,t) = 0, \qquad U(x,0) = 100 \tag{2}$$

by a consideration of heat conduction in an insulated bar of length L which was initially at $100°C$ and had its ends kept at temperature $0°C$. In Illustrative Example 3 of the last section we dealt with a similar problem, the only difference being that there $\kappa = 1$, $L = 10$, and the last boundary condition of (2) was different.

Fourier, a French mathematician of the 19th century, was led to a problem similar to that given above in his researches on heat.

In view of our success in solving the Illustrative Example 3 of last section, let us see whether we have similar luck in this boundary-value problem. As before, we seek a solution $U(x,t) = X(x)T(t)$. Substituting into (1) and separating the variables, we have

$$\frac{T'}{\kappa T} = \frac{X''}{X} \tag{3}$$

Since one side of (3) depends on x, while the other depends on t, it follows that each side is constant. Calling this constant c and considering the cases $c < 0$, $c = 0$, $c > 0$, we may, as in Illustrative Example 3 of the last section, show that only $c < 0$ yields anything.* Hence, we assume that $c = -\lambda^2$ and obtain from (3),

$$T' + \kappa\lambda^2 T = 0, \qquad X'' + \lambda^2 X = 0$$

whose solutions are given by

$$T = C_1 e^{-\kappa\lambda^2 t}, \qquad X = A_1 \cos \lambda x + B_1 \sin \lambda x$$

As before, then, a solution is

$$U(x,t) = e^{-\kappa\lambda^2 t}(A \cos \lambda x + B \sin \lambda x)$$

To satisfy the first of conditions (2), we have $A = 0$, and the solution thus far is

$$U(x,t) = Be^{-\kappa\lambda^2 t} \sin \lambda x$$

To satisfy the second of conditions (2), we must have $\sin \lambda L = 0$, $\lambda L = m\pi$, where m is any integer, so that the solution thus far is

$$U(x,t) = Be^{-\kappa m^2 \pi^2 t/L^2} \sin \frac{m\pi x}{L} \tag{4}$$

---

* This can be seen physically by observing that as $t \to \infty$ the temperature becomes unbounded if $c > 0$, thus violating a fundamental physical fact. Also, if $c = 0$ the temperature is independent of time.

We now consider the last boundary condition of (2). This yields

$$U(x,0) = B \sin \frac{m\pi x}{L} = 100$$

Here we are apparently stuck, and probably so was Fourier. In the previous section we saw that the *principle of superposition* helped us out of our difficulty in part (b) of Illustrative Example 3. Can it help us out of the difficulty here too? Fourier attempted this. He reasoned that the sum of solutions of the type (4) satisfied the given differential equation and the first and second boundary conditions of (2). Since a finite number of terms in this solution still did not appear to help in the satisfaction of the last condition of (2), he reasoned that perhaps an infinite number of terms would help. However, when dealing with an infinite number of terms we must naturally worry about things like convergence, etc. Assuming for the present that such questions are put aside, the assumption leads to

$$U(x,0) = 100$$

$$= b_1 \sin \frac{\pi x}{L} + b_2 \sin \frac{2\pi x}{L} + \cdots + b_n \sin \frac{n\pi x}{L} + \cdots \qquad (5)$$

The more we look at the requirement (5), the stranger it appears. It states that an infinite number of sinusoidal terms must be so combined as to give a constant for *all* values of x within the range $0 \leq x \leq L$. We see at once, however, that when $x = 0$ and $x = L$ the right-hand side is zero, and so (5) cannot possibly be true at the end points. If it is true at all, it can only hold for $0 < x < L$.

The problem Fourier faced was the determination of the constants b_1, $b_2, \ldots$ so that (5) would be true. That he succeeded in solving the problem and opened up whole new fields in mathematics and applied science is now a matter of history. Suffice it to say that when he did publish his results many mathematicians and scientists thought it pure nonsense, for it was not at that time placed on a rigorous basis. Now mathematicians have developed the theory of *Fourier series* [one example of which is the right-hand side of (5)] to such an extent that whole volumes have been written concerning it. We shall touch on this important topic just enough so that we may be able to obtain some understanding of the use of Fourier series in obtaining solutions to some of the boundary-value problems which we have formulated.

1. The Fourier series concept. Let us consider the series

$$A + a_1 \cos \frac{\pi x}{L} + a_2 \cos \frac{2\pi x}{L} + a_3 \cos \frac{3\pi x}{L} + \cdots$$

$$+ b_1 \sin \frac{\pi x}{L} + b_2 \sin \frac{2\pi x}{L} + b_3 \sin \frac{3\pi x}{L} + \cdots \qquad (6)$$

The case where $A, a_1, a_2, \ldots$ were zero arose in our attempt to solve Fourier's problem. The series (6) is thus a generalization of that series to include an additive constant A and terms which involve cosines as well as sines. In equation (5) we were faced with the problem of determining b_1, b_2, ... so that the given series on the right would equal 100. In the generalization, we shall ask for the determination of the constants A, a_1, a_2, ..., b_1, b_2, ... so that the series (6) will equal a given function, say $f(x)$. Now $\sin(\pi x/L)$ and $\cos(\pi x/L)$ have periods $2\pi/(\pi/L) = 2L$, or $4L$, $6L$, ... Similarly, $\sin(2\pi x/L)$ and $\cos(2\pi x/L)$ have periods $2\pi/(2\pi/L) = L$, or $2L$, $3L$, ... In general, the student should notice that each of $\sin(n\pi x/L)$ and $\cos(n\pi x/L)$ has a period equal to $2\pi/(n\pi/L) = 2L/n$, or $4L/n$, $6L/n$, ..., $2nL/n = 2L$, ... It will be seen that *all* the terms have a common period $2L$. This is the least period for all the terms. We may say, then, that if the infinite series (6) is equal to $f(x)$ where x lies in an interval of length $2L$, it will hold in any other interval, provided $f(x)$ has period $2L$. We shall restrict ourselves often to the interval $(-L,L)$, although our results will be capable of extension to any other interval of length $2L$.

Fourier arrived at an ingenious way of determining the constants in (6) for which that series is supposed to equal $f(x)$. How he arrived at the method is, as they say, a long story and we cannot enter into it here.* The final method is, however, very simple. It consists of the following steps:

1. Assume

$$A + a_1 \cos \frac{\pi x}{L} + a_2 \cos \frac{2\pi x}{L} + \cdots + b_1 \sin \frac{\pi x}{L} + b_2 \sin \frac{2\pi x}{L} + \cdots = f(x)$$

$$\tag{7}$$

To find A, integrate both sides of (7) from $-L$ to L.

$$\int_{-L}^{L} A\, dx + \int_{-L}^{L} a_1 \cos \frac{\pi x}{L}\, dx + \cdots + \int_{-L}^{L} b_1 \sin \frac{\pi x}{L}\, dx + \cdots = \int_{-L}^{L} f(x)dx$$

Then

$$\int_{-L}^{L} A\, dx = 2LA = \int_{-L}^{L} f(x)dx \quad \text{or} \quad A = \frac{1}{2L}\int_{-L}^{L} f(x)dx$$

since all the other integrals are zero.

2. To find a_k, $k = 1, 2, \ldots$, multiply both sides of (7) by $\cos(k\pi x/L)$ and then integrate from $-L$ to L, i.e.,

$$\int_{-L}^{L} A \cos \frac{k\pi x}{L}\, dx + \int_{-L}^{L} a_1 \cos \frac{\pi x}{L} \cos \frac{k\pi x}{L}\, dx + \cdots$$

$$+ \int_{-L}^{L} a_k \cos^2 \frac{k\pi x}{L}\, dx + \cdots + \int_{-L}^{L} b_1 \sin \frac{\pi x}{L} \cos \frac{k\pi x}{L}\, dx + \cdots$$

$$+ \int_{-L}^{L} b_k \sin \frac{k\pi x}{L} \cos \frac{k\pi x}{L}\, dx + \cdots = \int_{-L}^{L} f(x) \cos \frac{k\pi x}{L}\, dx \quad (8)$$

* For an interesting account see [13]. Also see [8].

Two typical integrals which arise are

$$\int_{-L}^{L} \cos \frac{m\pi x}{L} \cos \frac{k\pi x}{L} \, dx \quad \text{and} \quad \int_{-L}^{L} \sin \frac{m\pi x}{L} \cos \frac{k\pi x}{L} \, dx$$

where m and k are integers. We can show that*

$$
\left.
\begin{aligned}
\int_{-L}^{L} \cos \frac{m\pi x}{L} \cos \frac{k\pi x}{L} \, dx &= \begin{cases} 0 & \text{if } m \neq k \\ L & \text{if } m = k \end{cases} \\
\int_{-L}^{L} \sin \frac{m\pi x}{L} \cos \frac{k\pi x}{L} \, dx &= 0
\end{aligned}
\right\} \quad (9)
$$

Using these, it follows that all the terms on the left of (8) with one exception are zero, and we find

$$a_k = \frac{1}{L} \int_{-L}^{L} f(x) \cos \frac{k\pi x}{L} \, dx, \qquad k = 1, 2, 3, \dots$$

3. To find b_k, multiply both sides of (7) by $\sin (k\pi x/L)$ and integrate from $-L$ to L. We find that

$$b_k = \frac{1}{L} \int_{-L}^{L} f(x) \sin \frac{k\pi x}{L} \, dx, \qquad k = 1, 2, 3, \dots$$

The method is referred to so much that we write it in the form of a

Summary. If

$$A + a_1 \cos \frac{\pi x}{L} + a_2 \cos \frac{2\pi x}{L} + \cdots + b_1 \sin \frac{\pi x}{L} + b_2 \sin \frac{2\pi x}{L} + \cdots = f(x) \quad (10)$$

and if we assume that the operations performed above are legitimate, we are led to the conclusion that†

$$
\left.
\begin{aligned}
A &= \frac{1}{2L} \int_{-L}^{L} f(x) dx \\
a_k &= \frac{1}{L} \int_{-L}^{L} f(x) \cos \frac{k\pi x}{L} \, dx \\
b_k &= \frac{1}{L} \int_{-L}^{L} f(x) \sin \frac{k\pi x}{L} \, dx
\end{aligned}
\right\} \quad (11)
$$

* To show this use the trigonometric formulas

$$\sin A \cos B = \tfrac{1}{2}[\sin (A + B) + \sin (A - B)]$$
$$\cos A \cos B = \tfrac{1}{2}[\cos (A + B) + \cos (A - B)]$$

† It should be remarked that A may be obtained by formally placing $k = 0$ in the expression for a_k and noticing that $A = a_0/2$. For this reason one often writes the series (10) with A replaced by $a_0/2$.

2. Remarks concerning the rigor of the preceding results. When we discussed series solutions of differential equations, we assumed a form for the series and then proceeded to determine coefficients of terms of the series. It was only after we had obtained these coefficients that we could verify rigorously that the result actually was a solution.

A similar situation prevails in the determination of the coefficients of the terms in the series (10). We have assumed that certain operations (such as term by term integration of an infinite series) were legitimate, and it is quite natural for us to look upon the results perhaps with some suspicion. Now that we have obtained the coefficients (11) we adopt the following attitude:

1. Consider the hypothesis that the coefficients (11) are valid.

2. Use these coefficients in the series

$$A + a_1 \cos \frac{\pi x}{L} + a_2 \cos \frac{2\pi x}{L} + \cdots + b_1 \sin \frac{\pi x}{L} + b_2 \sin \frac{2\pi x}{L} + \cdots$$

and see whether the series converges.

3. If it does converge and in particular, if it converges to $f(x)$, the function we started out with, then (10) is proved if the coefficients (11) are used.

4. In order to be completely rigorous we must, of course, show that the coefficients (11) are unique, i.e., they are the only coefficients which have the desired property.

The first three steps in the procedure above were carried out by a mathematician named Dirichlet, and the conditions which he discovered are known as the *Dirichlet conditions*. Briefly, they are as follows:

DIRICHLET CONDITIONS. (a) Let $f(x)$ be a single-valued function defined in the interval $(-L,L)$ and defined by periodic extension outside of this interval by the relation $f(x + 2L) = f(x)$, i.e., $f(x)$ has period $2L$. (b) Let $f(x)$ be piecewise continuous* in $(-L,L)$. (c) Let $f'(x)$ be piecewise continuous in $(-L,L)$.

Then it can be proved† that the series (10) with coefficients (11) converges to $f(x)$ if x is a point of continuity and converges to $\frac{1}{2}[f(x + 0) + f(x - 0)]$ if x is a point of discontinuity, the latter representing the mean of the limits of $f(x)$ from both sides of the point of discontinuity. The preceding theorem

---

* A function is said to be *piecewise continuous* in an interval if the function has only a finite number of discontinuities in the interval and if the right- and left-hand limits at each discontinuity exist. Such functions have already been discussed in connection with Laplace transforms (see page 253).

† See [2] or [3], for example.

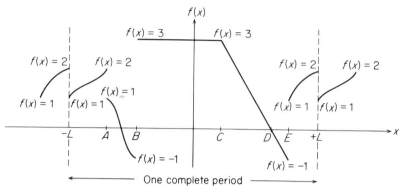

Fig. 105

is of great value, since it guarantees that a function such as that shown in Fig. 105 possesses a convergent Fourier series. If the function sketched in the graph is used to arrive at a Fourier series, it would be found that the resulting series converges to the following values:

At A the series would converge to $\dfrac{2+1}{2} = 1.5$.

At B the series would converge to $\dfrac{3+(-1)}{2} = 1$.

At C the series would converge to 3, since x is a point of continuity.

At D the series would converge to 0.

At E the series would converge to $\dfrac{1+(-1)}{2} = 0$.

At $-L$ and $+L$ the series would converge to $\dfrac{2+1}{2} = 1.5$.

Note that the graph from $-L$ to L is assumed to be repeated to the right and left of the dashed lines shown in the figure.

3. Examples of the expansion of functions in Fourier series. We shall now illustrate the process of finding the Fourier series corresponding to certain given functions. There is absolutely nothing difficult about the process since all we have to do is calculate the "Fourier coefficients" and substitute these into the series. We summarize the procedure as follows:

1. Determine the period (equal to $2L$) of the given function and thus find L.

2. Evaluate the Fourier coefficients.*

$$A = \frac{1}{2L} \int_{c}^{c+2L} f(x)dx$$

$$a_k = \frac{1}{L} \int_{c}^{c+2L} f(x) \cos \frac{k\pi x}{L} \, dx \qquad (12)$$

$$b_k = \frac{1}{L} \int_{c}^{c+2L} f(x) \sin \frac{k\pi x}{L} \, dx$$

where we have made use of the periodicity of the function in integrating from c to $c + 2L$ (an interval of length $2L$). For $c = -L$ this reduces as a special case to the formulas (11), page 340.

3. Substitute the Fourier coefficients from step 2 in the series

$$A + a_1 \cos \frac{\pi x}{L} + a_2 \cos \frac{2\pi x}{L} + \cdots + b_1 \sin \frac{\pi x}{L} + b_2 \sin \frac{2\pi x}{L} + \cdots \quad (13)$$

4. The result (13) is the Fourier series corresponding to $f(x)$.

Before going on to the examples, it is worthwhile to consider a case in which the labor of the above procedure is considerably reduced. This is the case where the Fourier series (13) contains only sine terms (i.e., $A = a_1 = a_2 = \cdots = 0$) or only cosine terms ($b_1 = b_2 = \cdots = 0$). In case only sine terms appear, we have a *Fourier sine series:*

$$f(x) = b_1 \sin \frac{\pi x}{L} + b_2 \sin \frac{2\pi x}{L} + \cdots \qquad (14)$$

Upon replacing x by $-x$ in (14) and realizing that $\sin(-A) = -\sin A$, (14) becomes

$$f(-x) = -\left(b_1 \sin \frac{\pi x}{L} + b_2 \sin \frac{2\pi x}{L} + \cdots\right) = -f(x) \qquad (15)$$

or $f(-x) = -f(x)$. A function which has this property is called an *odd function.*† Examples of graphs of odd functions are shown in Fig. 106. It will be seen that in each of these graphs, the value of the function at place x [i.e., $f(x)$] is equal to the negative of the value of the function at $-x$ [i.e., $-f(-x)$].

If only cosine terms are present, i.e., if we have a *Fourier cosine series,* then

$$f(x) = A + a_1 \cos \frac{\pi x}{L} + a_2 \cos \frac{2\pi x}{L} + \cdots \qquad (16)$$

and upon replacing x by $-x$ (realizing that $\cos(-A) = \cos A$), we would find $f(-x) = f(x)$. A function having this property is called an *even function.* Examples of even functions are shown in Fig. 107.

---

* See the second footnote on p. 340.

† The terminology probably arises from the fact that $(-x)^n = -x^n$ if n is an odd integer.

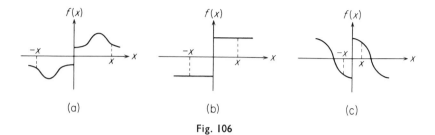

(a)   (b)   (c)

Fig. 106

Comparison of Figs. 106 and 107 shows that even functions are symmetric with respect to the y axis, while odd functions are skew-symmetric.

Conversely, we may show that odd functions have corresponding Fourier sine series, while even functions have corresponding Fourier cosine series. In view of these remarks we see that in the case of odd or even functions our labor is reduced by half. For if we know that a function is odd we know that A and all the a_k's are zero, and, hence, we have only to evaluate the b_k's. Similarly if a function is even, we need only evaluate A and the a_k's. The formulas for the coefficients in such cases can be slightly modified. Considering the interval to be $(-L,L)$ we may write the coefficients (12) as

$$A = \frac{1}{2L} \int_{-L}^{L} f(x)dx$$

$$a_k = \frac{1}{L} \int_{-L}^{L} f(x) \cos \frac{k\pi x}{L} \, dx$$

$$b_k = \frac{1}{L} \int_{-L}^{L} f(x) \sin \frac{k\pi x}{L} \, dx$$

If $f(x)$ is even, then so also is $f(x) \cos (k\pi x/L)$ even while $f(x) \sin (k\pi x/L)$ is odd. It follows that

$$A = \frac{2}{2L} \int_{0}^{L} f(x)dx = \frac{1}{L} \int_{0}^{L} f(x)dx,$$

$$a_k = \frac{2}{L} \int_{0}^{L} f(x) \cos \frac{k\pi x}{L} \, dx, \qquad b_k = 0$$

(17)

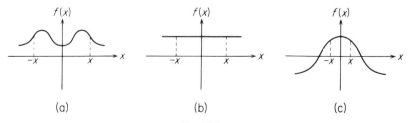

(a)   (b)   (c)

Fig. 107

where the integration is from 0 to L instead of $-L$ to L. Similarly, if $f(x)$ is odd, we may show that

$$A = 0, \qquad a_k = 0, \qquad b_k = \frac{2}{L} \int_0^L f(x) \sin \frac{k\pi x}{L} \, dx \qquad (18)$$

We shall make use of results (17) and (18) any time that we have odd or even functions to simplify our work. When we have functions which are neither odd nor even we shall use the general results (12).

Let us consider some illustrations.

ILLUSTRATIVE EXAMPLE 1

Find a Fourier series for the function

$$f(x) = \begin{cases} -1, & -2 < x < 0 \\ 1, & 0 < x < 2 \end{cases}$$

and having period 4.

Solution. The graph of this function appears in Fig. 108. It is seen that the function is odd. Hence we expect a Fourier sine series. Since the period is 4, we have $2L = 4$, $L = 2$. Hence from (18),

$$A = a_k = 0$$

$$b_k = \frac{2}{2} \int_0^2 f(x) \sin \frac{k\pi x}{2} \, dx = \int_0^2 (1) \sin \frac{k\pi x}{2} \, dx$$

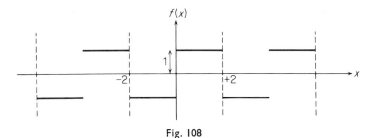

Fig. 108

Integration yields

$$b_k = -\frac{2}{k\pi} \cos \frac{k\pi x}{2} \Big|_0^2 = \frac{2}{k\pi} (1 - \cos k\pi)$$

from which we obtain

$$b_1 = 4/\pi, \qquad b_2 = 0, \qquad b_3 = 4/3\pi, \ldots$$

Thus, the required Fourier series is

$$\frac{4}{\pi} \sin \frac{\pi x}{2} + \frac{4}{3\pi} \sin \frac{3\pi x}{2} + \frac{4}{5\pi} \sin \frac{5\pi x}{2} + \cdots$$

which could also have been written, using the summation notation, as

$$\sum_{k=1}^{\infty} \frac{2}{k\pi} (1 - \cos k\pi) \sin \frac{k\pi x}{2}$$

It should be noted that the series converges to zero at $x = 0$ or $x = 2$, as would be expected from the Dirichlet conditions, since these are points of discontinuity. At a place such as $x = 1$ which is a point of continuity, the series should converge to the value of $f(x)$ when $x = 1$, which is 1. It follows that

$$\frac{4}{\pi}\left(1 - \frac{1}{3} + \frac{1}{5} - \frac{1}{7} + \cdots\right) = 1$$

from which we obtain the interesting result,

$$1 - \frac{1}{3} + \frac{1}{5} - \frac{1}{7} + \cdots = \frac{\pi}{4}$$

which may be established in another way (see B Exercise 6).

ILLUSTRATIVE EXAMPLE 2

Expand the function defined by

$$f(x) = \begin{cases} 0.1x. & 0 \leq x \leq 10 \\ 0.1(20 - x) & 10 \leq x \leq 20 \end{cases}$$

in a Fourier sine series.

Solution. In the statement of this problem there is apparently nothing to indicate the period of the function. Since the function is defined in the interval $0 \leq x \leq 20$, one might consider taking the period to be 20. In such a case the graph would appear as in Fig. 109. From this graph it is clear that the function is an even function and cannot possibly have a Fourier sine series expansion. To obtain a sine series we would need an odd function. One way to do this is to assume period 40 and construct the graph of Fig. 110. It follows that $2L = 40$, $L = 20$. Then

$$b_k = \frac{2}{L}\int_0^L f(x)\sin\frac{k\pi x}{L}\,dx = \frac{2}{20}\int_0^{20} f(x)\sin\frac{k\pi x}{20}\,dx$$

$$= \frac{1}{10}\int_0^{10} 0.1x\sin\frac{k\pi x}{20}\,dx + \frac{1}{10}\int_{10}^{20} 0.1(20 - x)\sin\frac{k\pi x}{20}\,dx$$

After integration by parts, we find

$$b_1 = \frac{8}{\pi^2}, \quad b_2 = 0, \quad b_3 = -\frac{8}{3^2\pi^2}, \quad b_4 = 0, \quad b_5 = \frac{8}{5^2\pi^2}, \cdots$$

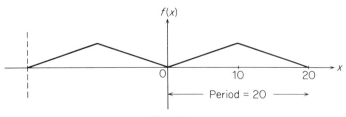

Fig. 109

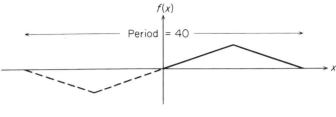

Fig. 110

Thus, the Fourier series is

$$\frac{8}{\pi^2}\left(\sin\frac{\pi x}{20} - \frac{1}{3^2}\sin\frac{3\pi x}{20} + \frac{1}{5^2}\sin\frac{5\pi x}{20} - \cdots\right)$$

At $x = 10$ the series converges to 1. Thus, we have

$$1 + \frac{1}{3^2} + \frac{1}{5^2} + \frac{1}{7^2} + \cdots = \frac{\pi^2}{8}$$

an interesting result which is difficult to establish otherwise.

ILLUSTRATIVE EXAMPLE 3

Expand $f(x) = x$, $0 < x < 2\pi$ in a Fourier series if $f(x)$ has period 2π.

Solution. Since the period is 2π, we have $2L = 2\pi$, $L = \pi$. The graph of $f(x)$ appears in Fig. 111. Since the function is neither even nor odd, we expect both sines and cosines in the Fourier expansion. Using (12) with $c = 0$ and $L = \pi$, we find

$$A = \frac{1}{2\pi}\int_0^{2\pi} x\,dx = \pi$$

$$a_k = \frac{1}{\pi}\int_0^{2\pi} x\cos kx\,dx = 0, \qquad b_k = \frac{1}{\pi}\int_0^{2\pi} x\sin kx\,dx = -\frac{2}{k}$$

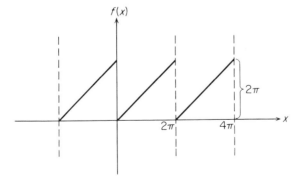

Fig. 111

Thus, the Fourier series is

$$\pi - 2\left(\sin x + \frac{\sin 2x}{2} + \frac{\sin 3x}{3} + \cdots\right)$$

It may be noticed that only sine terms are present except for the constant π. The reason for this is explained by noting that if we had shifted the x axis upward a distance π in Fig. 111, which would have amounted to graphing $f(x) - \pi$ instead of $f(x)$, the result would have been an odd function. As a check we note that at $x = \pi/2$ the series should converge to $\pi/2$. Thus we have

$$\pi - 2\left(1 - \frac{1}{3} + \frac{1}{5} - \cdots\right) = \frac{\pi}{2} \quad \text{or} \quad 1 - \frac{1}{3} + \frac{1}{5} - \cdots = \frac{\pi}{4}$$

which is correct.

A EXERCISES

1. Obtain Fourier series expansions corresponding to each of the following functions defined in the indicated interval and having indicated period outside that interval. Graph the function in each case and state whether it is even or odd.

(a) $f(x) = \begin{cases} 2, & -\pi < x < 0 \\ -2, & 0 < x < \pi \end{cases}$ Period 2π

(b) $f(x) = 1, \ -2 < x < 2$ Period 4

(c) $f(x) = \begin{cases} 0, & -3 < x < 0 \\ 2, & 0 < x < 3 \end{cases}$ Period 6

(d) $f(x) = \begin{cases} 0, & -1 < x < 0 \\ x, & 0 < x < 1 \end{cases}$ Period 2

(e) $f(x) = \begin{cases} -x, & -\pi < x < 0 \\ x, & 0 < x < \pi \end{cases}$ Period 2π

(f) $f(x) = \begin{cases} 3, & 0 < x < 4 \\ -3, & 4 < x < 8 \end{cases}$ Period 8

(g) $f(x) = 4x - x^2, \ 0 < x < 4$ Period 4

(h) $f(x) = \begin{cases} 1, & 0 < x < 2\pi/3 \\ 0, & 2\pi/3 < x < 4\pi/3 \\ -1, & 4\pi/3 < x < 2\pi \end{cases}$ Period 2π

2. Expand each function defined in the indicated interval into Fourier sine or Fourier cosine series as indicated.

(a) $f(x) = 5, \ 0 < x < 3$ sine series

(b) $f(x) = \begin{cases} 1, & 0 < x < \pi/2 \\ 0, & \pi/2 < x < \pi \end{cases}$ cosine series

(c) $f(x) = \begin{cases} x, & 0 < x < 5 \\ 0, & 5 < x < 10 \end{cases}$ sine series

(d) $f(x) = 2$, $0 < x < 1$ cosine series

(e) $f(x) = 4x - x^2$, $0 < x < 4$ sine series

(f) $f(x) = \begin{cases} -1, & 0 < x < 2 \\ 1, & 2 < x < 4 \end{cases}$ cosine series

B EXERCISES

1. Show that
$$x^2 = \frac{\pi^2}{3} - 4\left(\cos x - \frac{\cos 2x}{2^2} + \frac{\cos 3x}{3^2} - \cdots\right), \qquad -\pi < x < \pi$$

Show by Dirichlet's theorem that the equality holds at $x = \pm\pi$ and, hence, that
$$\frac{1}{1^2} + \frac{1}{2^2} + \frac{1}{3^2} + \cdots = \frac{\pi^2}{6}$$

2. Show that if $a \neq 0, \pm1, \pm2, \ldots$,
$$\frac{\pi \cos ax}{2a \sin a\pi} = \frac{1}{2a^2} + \frac{\cos x}{1^2 - a^2} - \frac{\cos 2x}{2^2 - a^2} + \frac{\cos 3x}{3^2 - a^2} - \cdots \qquad -\pi < x < \pi$$

Show that the equality holds for $x = \pm\pi$ and hence prove that
$$\frac{1}{1^2 - a^2} + \frac{1}{2^2 - a^2} + \frac{1}{3^2 - a^2} + \cdots = \frac{1}{2a^2} - \frac{\pi}{2a}\cot \pi a$$

3. Expand
$$f(x) = \begin{cases} -x^2, & -L < x < 0 \\ x^2, & 0 < x < L \end{cases}$$

in a Fourier series of period $2L$. What happens at $x = \pm L$?

4. Show that
$$e^x = \frac{e^{2\pi} - 1}{\pi}\left(\frac{1}{2} + \sum_{n=1}^{\infty} \frac{\cos nx - n \sin nx}{n^2 + 1}\right), \qquad 0 < x < 2\pi$$

5. (a) By replacing x by $2\pi - x$ in Exercise 4, show that
$$\frac{\pi}{2} \cdot \frac{\cosh(\pi - x)}{\sinh \pi} = \frac{1}{2} + \sum_{n=1}^{\infty} \frac{\cos nx}{n^2 + 1}$$

(b) Prove that the equality holds for $x = 0$, and hence evaluate
$$\sum_{n=1}^{\infty} \frac{1}{n^2 + 1}$$

6. (a) Show that
$$\frac{1}{1 + x^2} = 1 - x^2 + x^4 - x^6 + \cdots, \qquad |x| < 1$$

(b) Integrate the result in (a) and show that
$$\frac{\pi}{4} = 1 - \frac{1}{3} + \frac{1}{5} - \frac{1}{7} + \cdots$$

What assumptions do you have to make? Can you prove them?

C EXERCISES

1. An inductor L and a capacitor C are in series with an emf of period $2T$ given by

$$E(t) = \begin{cases} E_0, & 0 < t < T \\ -E_0, & T < t < 2T \end{cases}$$

If the charge on the capacitor and the current are zero at $t = 0$ and if L, C, E_0, T are constants, show that the charge is given by

$$Q = \frac{4E_0}{\pi L \omega} \sum_{n=1}^{\infty} \frac{\omega \sin \omega_n t - \omega_n \sin \omega t}{(2n-1)(\omega^2 - \omega_n^2)}$$

where $\omega_n = (2n-1)\pi/T$, $\omega = 1/\sqrt{LC}$. Determine the current at any time. What happens when $\omega_n = \omega$ for some n?

2. Assuming

$$S_M(x) = \frac{a_0}{2} + \sum_{n=1}^{M} (a_n \cos nx + b_n \sin nx) \tag{19}$$

prove that

$$\frac{1}{\pi} \int_{-\pi}^{\pi} S_M^2(x)dx = \frac{a_0^2}{2} + \sum_{n=1}^{M} (a_n^2 + b_n^2)$$

One might thus suspect that if $\lim_{M \to \infty} S_M(x) = f(x)$, then the series on the right of (19) as $M \to \infty$ represents the Fourier series of $f(x)$ and that

$$\frac{1}{\pi} \int_{-\pi}^{\pi} [f(x)]^2 \, dx = \frac{a_0^2}{2} + \sum_{n=1}^{\infty} (a_n^2 + b_n^2) \tag{20}$$

where

$$a_n = \frac{1}{\pi} \int_{-\pi}^{\pi} f(x) \cos nx \, dx, \qquad b_n = \frac{1}{\pi} \int_{-\pi}^{\pi} f(x) \sin nx \, dx, \qquad n = 0, 1, \ldots$$

The result (20) can be established under very general conditions on $f(x)$. For example, it may be shown that the theorem holds if $f(x)$ is bounded in the interval $-\pi < x < \pi$ and if $\int_{-\pi}^{\pi} f(x)dx$ exists.* The theorem is called *Parseval's identity*. Apply it to B Exercise 1 and thus show that

$$\frac{1}{1^4} + \frac{1}{2^4} + \frac{1}{3^4} + \cdots = \frac{\pi^4}{90}$$

IV. Solutions to Boundary-value Problems Requiring Use of Fourier Series

In Section III we found that an investigation of a heat conduction problem led quite naturally to a need for the study of Fourier series. We now have

---

* See [24], pages 180–182.

enough background to complete that problem at least formally. It will be recalled that we had to solve the boundary-value problem

$$\frac{\partial U}{\partial t} = \kappa \frac{\partial^2 U}{\partial x^2} \tag{1}$$

$$U(0,t) = 0, \qquad U(L,t) = 0, \qquad U(x,0) = 100 \tag{2}$$

By applying the principle of superposition of solutions, we arrived at

$$U(x,t) = b_1 e^{-\kappa \pi^2 t/L^2} \sin \frac{\pi x}{L} + b_2 e^{-4\kappa \pi^2 t/L^2} \sin \frac{2\pi x}{L} + \cdots \tag{3}$$

and it remained only to satisfy the last boundary condition of (2), which yielded

$$100 = b_1 \sin \frac{\pi x}{L} + b_2 \sin \frac{2\pi x}{L} + \cdots$$

from which we should have liked to obtain $b_1, b_2, \ldots$. Now we realize that to do this we must expand the function $f(x) = 100$ in a Fourier sine series, the period being $2L$. The coefficients b_k are given by

$$b_k = \frac{2}{L} \int_0^L 100 \sin \frac{k\pi x}{L} \, dx = \frac{200}{k\pi} (1 - \cos k\pi) \tag{4}$$

Thus (3) becomes

$$U(x,t) = \frac{400}{\pi} \left(e^{-\kappa \pi^2 t/L^2} \sin \frac{\pi x}{L} + \frac{1}{3} e^{-9\kappa \pi^2 t/L^2} \sin \frac{3\pi x}{L} \right.$$

$$\left. + \frac{1}{5} e^{-25\kappa \pi^2 t/L^2} \sin \frac{5\pi x}{L} + \cdots \right) \tag{5}$$

This is only a formal solution, since we still have to show that it satisfies the given differential equation and boundary conditions, and also we have to show that if it is a solution it is unique. All these can be shown, but the details are difficult and are omitted here.*

We now consider some other boundary-value problems.

ILLUSTRATIVE EXAMPLE 1

A metal bar 100 cm long has ends $x = 0$ and $x = 100$ kept at 0°C. Initially, half of the bar is at 60°C, while the other half is at 40°C. Assuming a diffusivity of 0.16 cgs units and that the surface of the bar is insulated, find the temperature everywhere in the bar at time t.

* See [3].

Mathematical Formulation. The heat conduction equation is

$$\frac{\partial U}{\partial t} = 0.16 \frac{\partial^2 U}{\partial x^2} \tag{6}$$

where $U(x,t)$ is the temperature at place x and time t. The boundary conditions are

$$U(0,t) = 0, \qquad U(100,t) = 0, \qquad U(x,0) = \begin{cases} 60, & 0 < x < 50 \\ 40, & 50 < x < 100 \end{cases} \tag{7}$$

Solution. Assuming a solution $U = XT$, we find

$$XT' = 0.16X''T \qquad \text{or} \qquad \frac{T'}{0.16T} = \frac{X''}{X}$$

Setting these equal to a constant which, as our previous experience indicated was negative, and which we therefore denote by $-\lambda^2$, we find

$$T' + 0.16\lambda^2 T = 0, \qquad X'' + \lambda^2 X = 0$$

and are thus led to the solution

$$U(x,t) = e^{-0.16\lambda^2 t}(A \cos \lambda x + B \sin \lambda x) \tag{8}$$

The first two of conditions (7) show that $A = 0$, $\lambda = m\pi/100$. To satisfy the last condition we use the superposition of solutions to obtain

$$U(x,t) = b_1 e^{-16.10^{-6}\pi^2 t} \sin \frac{\pi x}{100} + b_2 e^{-64.10^{-6}\pi^2 t} \sin \frac{2\pi x}{100} + \cdots \tag{9}$$

Assuming $t = 0$, we see that

$$b_1 \sin \frac{\pi x}{100} + b_2 \sin \frac{2\pi x}{100} + \cdots = U(x,0)$$

Thus, we have

$$b_k = \frac{2}{100} \int_0^{100} U(x,0) \sin \frac{k\pi x}{100}\, dx$$

$$= \frac{2}{100} \int_0^{50} (60) \sin \frac{k\pi x}{100}\, dx + \frac{2}{100} \int_{50}^{100} (40) \sin \frac{k\pi x}{100}\, dx$$

$$= \frac{120}{k\pi}\left(1 - \cos \frac{k\pi}{2}\right) + \frac{80}{k\pi}\left(\cos \frac{k\pi}{2} - \cos k\pi\right)$$

Thus $b_1 = 200/\pi$, $b_2 = 40/\pi$, . . . , and (9) becomes

$$U(x,t) = \frac{200}{\pi} e^{-16.10^{-6}\pi^2 t} \sin \frac{\pi x}{100} + \frac{40}{\pi} e^{-64.10^{-6}\pi^2 t} \sin \frac{2\pi x}{100} + \cdots \tag{10}$$

which can be shown to be a unique solution.

ILLUSTRATIVE EXAMPLE 2

A string of length of 2 ft weighs 4 oz and is stretched until the tension throughout is 1 lb force. The center of the string is picked up $\frac{1}{4}$ in. above the equilibrium position and then released. Find the subsequent displacement of the string as a function of time.

Mathematical Formulation. The equation for the vibrating string (see Chapter 10, Section II) is

$$\frac{\partial^2 Y}{\partial t^2} = a^2 \frac{\partial^2 Y}{\partial x^2}, \qquad a^2 = \frac{T}{\rho} \qquad (11)$$

where $Y(x,t)$ denotes the displacement from the equilibrium position of point x of the string at time t, T is the tension, and ρ is the mass per unit length. We have

$$\rho = \frac{\text{mass}}{\text{length}} = \frac{m}{l} = \frac{W}{lg} = \frac{\frac{1}{4}}{2g} = \frac{1}{256}$$

Hence, $a^2 = T/\rho = 1/\rho = 256$.

Thus, the required equation is

$$\frac{\partial^2 Y}{\partial t^2} = 256 \frac{\partial^2 Y}{\partial x^2}$$

The boundary conditions are given by

$$Y(0,t) = 0, \qquad Y(2,t) = 0, \qquad Y_t(x,0) = 0,$$
$$Y(x,0) = \begin{cases} \frac{1}{48}x, & 0 < x < 1 \\ \frac{1}{48}(2 - x), & 1 < x < 2 \end{cases} \qquad (12)$$

the last conditions being obtained as in Chapter 10, Section II.

Solution. Letting $Y = XT$ and proceeding as usual, we find

$$\frac{T''}{256T} = \frac{X''}{X} = -\lambda^2$$

Hence a solution is given by

$$Y(x,t) = (A_1 \cos \lambda x + B_1 \sin \lambda x)(C_1 \cos 16\lambda t + D_1 \sin 16\lambda t)$$

The first of conditions (12) yields

$$Y(0,t) = A_1(C_1 \cos 16\lambda t + D_1 \sin 16\lambda t) = 0$$

so that $A_1 = 0$, since the second factor is not zero without having the solution identically zero. Thus,

$$Y(x,t) = \sin \lambda x(B \cos 16\lambda t + C \sin 16\lambda t) \qquad (13)$$

where we have written $B_1 C_1 \equiv B$, $B_1 D_1 \equiv C$.

From the second condition in (12) we find

$$Y(2,t) = \sin 2\lambda(B \cos 16\lambda t + C \sin 16\lambda t) = 0$$

and we must have $\sin 2\lambda = 0$, $2\lambda = m\pi$, $\lambda = m\pi/2$. The solution is thus

$$\cdot\; Y(x,t) = \sin \frac{m\pi x}{2} (B \cos 8m\pi t + C \sin 8m\pi t) \qquad (14)$$

By differentiation with respect to t and using the third condition in (12) we find $C = 0$, so that the solution is

$$Y(x,t) = B \sin \frac{m\pi x}{2} \cos 8m\pi t \qquad (15)$$

To satisfy the last boundary condition of (12) we use the principle of super-position and write formally

$$Y(x,t) = b_1 \sin \frac{\pi x}{2} \cos 8\pi t + b_2 \sin \frac{2\pi x}{2} \cos 16\,\pi t + \cdots$$

$$Y(x,0) = b_1 \sin \frac{\pi x}{2} + b_2 \sin \frac{2\pi x}{2} + \cdots$$

Hence we have

$$b_k = \frac{2}{2} \int_0^2 Y(x,0) \sin \frac{k\pi x}{2}\, dx = \frac{1}{6k^2\pi^2} \sin \frac{k\pi}{2}$$

Finally,

$$Y(x,t) = \frac{1}{6\pi^2}\left(\sin \frac{\pi x}{2} \cos 8\pi t - \frac{1}{3^2} \sin \frac{3\pi x}{2} \cos 24\pi t \right.$$
$$\left. + \frac{1}{5^2} \sin \frac{5\pi x}{2} \cos 32\pi t - \cdots \right) \quad (16)$$

which may be shown to represent the unique solution.

There is a physical significance to the various terms of (16). Each term represents a particular *mode* in which the system vibrates. The first term, apart from the constant factor is $\sin(\pi x/2)\cos 8\pi t$, which represents the first mode of vibration. At $t = 0$ the graph of the string is shown in Fig. 112, where the vertical scale has been enlarged. As t varies, the tendency is for the string in this first mode of vibration to oscillate about the equilibrium position (x axis) with frequency (determined from $\cos 8\pi t$) given by 4 cycles per second. This lowest frequency is called the *fundamental frequency* or *first harmonic*. Since $b_2 = 0$ in (16), the term corresponding to the second mode of vibration is missing. The third mode present has a frequency of 12 cycles per second, which is called the third harmonic (or sometimes the second overtone). Similarly the fifth harmonic frequency is 20 cycles per second.

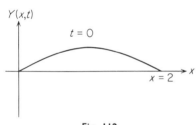

Fig. 112

It is found that in the case of the vibrating string all the harmonic frequencies are integer multiples of the fundamental frequency. Thus 12, 20, ... are integer multiples of 4. Whenever this occurs we say that we have music, as for example, in the violin string. In the string of our example the sound produced is of such very low frequency that it is not in the audible range. As we increase the tension we increase the frequency and the result is a musical tone. The various coefficients of the terms in (16) have physical significance. They measure the intensity of the various modes. Thus the higher frequencies correspond to lower intensities.

It can be shown (see A Exercises 2 and 3, page 361) that a vibrating circular drumhead also has various modes of vibration and corresponding frequencies. However, these frequencies are not integer multiples of a fundamental, and as a consequence noise is heard instead of music.

A EXERCISES

1. A metal bar 100 cm long has its ends $x = 0$ and $x = 100$ kept at 0°C. Initially, the right half of the bar is at 0°C, while the other half is at 80°C. Assuming a diffusivity of 0.20 cgs units and an insulated surface, find the temperature at any position of the bar at any time.

2. If the bar of the previous exercise has initial temperature $f(x)$ given by

$$f(x) = \begin{cases} 0, & 0 < x < 40 \\ 100, & 40 < x < 60 \\ 0, & 60 < x < 100 \end{cases}$$

calculate the temperature of the bar at any time.

3. A metal bar 40 cm long with a diffusivity of 0.20 cgs units has its surface insulated. If the ends are kept at 20°C and the initial temperature is 100°C, find the temperature of the bar at any time. (*Hint:* Lower all temperature readings by 20°C.)

4. A string of length 4 ft weighs 2 oz and is stretched until the tension throughout is 4 lb force. The string is assumed to lie along the x axis with one end fixed at $x = 0$ and the other at $x = 4$. If at $t = 0$ the string is given a shape $f(x)$ and then released, determine the subsequent displacement of the string as a function of time for the cases

(a) $f(x) = 0.25 \sin \dfrac{\pi x}{4}$.

(b) $f(x) = 0.1 \sin \pi x - 0.02 \sin 3\pi x$.

(c) $f(x) = \begin{cases} 0.02x, & 0 \le x \le 2 \\ 0.02(4 - x), & 2 \le x \le 4 \end{cases}$

B EXERCISES

1. Solve the boundary-value problem

$$\frac{\partial U}{\partial t} = \kappa \frac{\partial^2 U}{\partial x^2}, \qquad U(0,t) = T_1, \qquad U(L,t) = T_2, \qquad U(x,0) = f(x)$$

where κ, L, T_1, T_2 are given constants and $f(x)$ is a given function. (*Hint:* Let $U(x,t) = V(x,t) + \psi(x)$, where $\psi(x)$ is an undetermined function. Choose $\psi(x)$ so that the differential equation and conditions for $V(x,t)$ are simplified. Physically the interpretation is that the temperature $U(x,t)$ has been separated into a term dependent on time and a steady-state term $\psi(x)$ independent of time.)

2. A metal bar 50 cm long whose surface is insulated is at temperature 60°C. At $t = 0$ a temperature of 30°C is applied at one end and a temperature of 80°C to the other end, and these temperatures are maintained. Determine the temperature of the bar at any time assuming $\kappa = 0.15$ cgs unit.

3. (a) A bar of diffusivity κ whose surface is insulated and whose ends are located at $x = 0$ and $x = L$ has an initial temperature distribution $f(x)$. Assuming that the ends of the bar are insulated, determine the temperature of the bar at any time. (b) Find the temperature of the bar if

$$f(x) = \begin{cases} \dfrac{2Tx}{L} & 0 < x \le \dfrac{L}{2} \\ \dfrac{2T}{L}(L - x) & \dfrac{L}{2} \le x < L \end{cases}$$

4. Work Exercise 3(a) if one end is insulated, the other at constant temperature T_0.

5. If the surface of a metal bar is not insulated but instead radiates heat into a medium of constant temperature U_0 according to Newton's law of cooling, the differential equation for heat flow becomes

$$\frac{\partial U}{\partial t} = \kappa \frac{\partial^2 U}{\partial x^2} - c(U - U_0)$$

Assuming the ends of the bar of length L are kept at 0°C and the initial temperature distribution is $f(x)$, while $U_0 = 0$°C, find $U(x,t)$.

6. If gravitation is taken into account, the vibrating string equation is

$$\frac{\partial^2 Y}{\partial t^2} = a^2 \frac{\partial^2 Y}{\partial x^2} + g$$

Find $Y(x,t)$, assuming the ends of the string are fixed at $x = 0$ and $x = L$ and that the string initially has shape $f(x)$ and is released with initial velocity zero. (*Hint:* Assume $Y(x,t) = V(x,t) + \psi(x)$ as in Exercise 1.)

7. A vibrating string has ends fixed at $x = 0$ and $x = L$. At $t = 0$ the shape is given by $f(x)$ and the velocity distribution by $g(x)$. Show that

$$Y(x,t) = \frac{1}{2}[f(x - at) + f(x + at)] + \frac{1}{2a}\int_{x-at}^{x+at} g(u)du$$

8. Discuss the vibration of a string in a viscous medium where the force of resistance is proportional to the instantaneous velocity.

C EXERCISES

1. A semi-infinite plate bounded by $x = 0$, $x = L$, and the x axis has its plane faces insulated. If sides $x = 0$ and $x = L$ are kept at temperature zero while the side lying on the x axis is kept at constant temperature T, show that the steady-state

temperature is given by

$$U(x,y) = \frac{4T}{\pi}\left(e^{-\pi y/L}\sin\frac{\pi x}{L} + \frac{1}{3}e^{-3\pi y/L}\sin\frac{3\pi x}{L} + \frac{1}{5}e^{-5\pi y/L}\sin\frac{5\pi x}{L} + \cdots\right)$$

(*Hint:* See C Exercise 2 page 326. Note that the temperature must be bounded as $y \to \infty$.)

2. A square of side a has three sides at temperature zero and the fourth at constant temperature T. If the plane faces are insulated, find the steady-state temperature. From this try to determine the steady-state temperature if the sides are kept at constant temperatures T_1, T_2, T_3, and T_4. (The problem of finding a solution to Laplace's equation in a region R which takes on certain prescribed values on the boundary of R is often called a *Dirichlet problem*. This exercise is a Dirichlet problem where the region R is a square.)

3. Solve the boundary-value problem

$$\frac{\partial^2 U}{\partial r^2} + \frac{1}{r}\frac{\partial U}{\partial r} + \frac{1}{r^2}\frac{\partial^2 U}{\partial \theta^2} = 0, \qquad 0 \le r \le a, \qquad 0 \le \theta < 2\pi$$

$$U(a,\theta) = f(\theta), \qquad 0 \le \theta < 2\pi, \qquad U(r,\theta) \text{ is bounded}$$

4. A circular plate of radius a has its plane faces insulated. If half the circumference is kept at constant temperature T_1 and the other half at constant temperature T_2, find the steady-state temperature. (*Hint:* In C Exercise 2, page 326, change the steady-state equation in rectangular coordinates given by

$$\frac{\partial^2 U}{\partial x^2} + \frac{\partial^2 U}{\partial y^2} = 0$$

to polar coordinates (r,θ) to obtain

$$\frac{\partial^2 U}{\partial r^2} + \frac{1}{r}\frac{\partial U}{\partial r} + \frac{1}{r^2}\frac{\partial^2 U}{\partial \theta^2} = 0$$

Then use Exercise 3.) Note that this is a *Dirichlet problem* for a circle (see Exercise 2).

5. Work Exercise 4 if $\partial U/\partial r = a_1$ on half the circumference and a_2 on the other half. Interpret physically. (The determination of solutions to Laplace's equation with normal derivative specified on the boundary is called a *Neumann problem*.)

V. Fourier-Bessel Series, Orthogonal Functions and Applications

The concepts of Fourier series and their applications to boundary-value problems can be extended. To see this consider the following

Problem. A circular conducting plate of unit radius (see Fig. 113) has its plane faces insulated. Find the temperature U at any point distant r from the center at any time if the initial temperature is $f(r)$ and the boundary temperature is kept at zero.

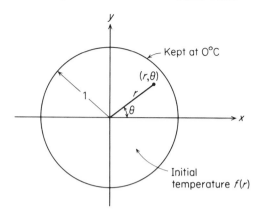

Fig. 113

Mathematical Formulation. The heat conduction equation for U is

$$\frac{\partial U}{\partial t} = \kappa\left(\frac{\partial^2 U}{\partial x^2} + \frac{\partial^2 U}{\partial y^2}\right) \quad \text{or} \quad \frac{\partial U}{\partial t} = \kappa\left(\frac{\partial^2 U}{\partial r^2} + \frac{1}{r}\frac{\partial U}{\partial r} + \frac{1}{r^2}\frac{\partial^2 U}{\partial \theta^2}\right)$$

in polar coordinates (r,θ). From symmetry U is independent of θ, i.e., $U = U(r,t)$, and we arrive at the boundary-value problem

$$\frac{\partial U}{\partial t} = \kappa\left(\frac{\partial^2 U}{\partial r^2} + \frac{1}{r}\frac{\partial U}{\partial r}\right) \tag{1}$$

$$U(1,t) = 0, \quad U(r,0) = f(r), \quad U(r,t) \text{ is bounded} \tag{2}$$

Solution. Letting $U = R(r)T(t) = RT$ in (1) and separating variables,

$$\frac{T'}{\kappa T} = \frac{R''}{R} + \frac{1}{r}\frac{R'}{R} = -\lambda^2$$

Thus

$$T' + \kappa\lambda^2 T = 0, \qquad rR'' + R' + \lambda^2 rR = 0 \tag{3}$$

Substituting $\lambda r = x$, the second equation becomes Bessel's equation

$$x\frac{d^2 R}{dx^2} + \frac{dR}{dx} + xR = 0$$

with solution (see C Exercise 2, page 282)

$$R = aJ_0(x) + bY_0(x) = aJ_0(\lambda r) + bY_0(\lambda r)$$

Since $Y_0(\lambda r)$ is unbounded at $r = 0$ we let $b = 0$. Also from the first of equations (3), $T = ce^{-\kappa\lambda^2 t}$. Then a possible solution is

$$U(r,t) = RT = ac\, e^{-\kappa\lambda^2 t}J_0(\lambda r) = Ae^{-\kappa\lambda^2 t}J_0(\lambda r) \tag{4}$$

Using the first of conditions (2) in (4) we require that

$$J_0(\lambda) = 0$$

This has positive roots* λ_1, λ_2, ... so that possible solutions are

$$A_1 e^{-\kappa \lambda_1^2 t} J_0(\lambda_1 r), \quad A_2 e^{-\kappa \lambda_2^2 t} J_0(\lambda_2 r), \ldots$$

Using the superposition principle, as in Fourier series, we are led to

$$U(r,t) = \sum_{n=1}^{\infty} A_n e^{-\kappa \lambda_n^2 t} J_0(\lambda_n r) \tag{5}$$

as a possible solution. The second condition in (2) leads to

$$f(r) = \sum_{n=1}^{\infty} A_n J_0(\lambda_n r) \tag{6}$$

a problem similar to that of Fourier. It develops that there is an analogous procedure for determining the values A_n. To show this note that $R_m = J_0(\lambda_m r)$ and $R_n = J_0(\lambda_n r)$ are respective solutions of

$$rR_m'' + R_m' + \lambda_m^2 r R_m = 0 \quad \text{and} \quad rR_n'' + R_n' + \lambda_n^2 r R_n = 0$$

Multiplying the first equation by R_n, the second by R_m and subtracting,

$$r[R_m'' R_n - R_n'' R_m] + [R_m' R_n - R_n' R_m] = (\lambda_n^2 - \lambda_m^2) r R_m R_n$$

or

$$r \frac{d}{dr} [R_m' R_n - R_n' R_m] + [R_m' R_n - R_n' R_m] = (\lambda_n^2 - \lambda_m^2) r R_m R_n$$

i.e.,

$$\frac{d}{dr} \{r[R_m' R_n - R_n' R_m]\} = (\lambda_n^2 - \lambda_m^2) r R_m R_n$$

Integration, using

$$R_m = J_0(\lambda_m r), \ R_n = J_0(\lambda_n r), \ R_m' = \lambda_m J_0'(\lambda_m r), \ R_n' = \lambda_n J_0'(\lambda_n r)$$

yields, apart from a constant of integration,

$$(\lambda_n^2 - \lambda_m^2) \int r J_0(\lambda_m r) J_0(\lambda_n r) dr = r[\lambda_m J_0'(\lambda_m r) J_0(\lambda_n r) - \lambda_n J_0'(\lambda_n r) J_0(\lambda_m r)] \tag{7}$$

In particular, integrating from 0 to 1 we find if $\lambda_m \neq \lambda_n$, $J_0(\lambda_m) = 0$, $J_0(\lambda_n) = 0$,

$$\int_0^1 r J_0(\lambda_m r) J_0(\lambda_n r) dr = 0 \qquad m \neq n \tag{8}$$

This result, analogous to (9) page 340 for Fourier series enables us to proceed further. Thus multiplying (5) by $r J_0(\lambda_m r)$ and integrating from 0 to 1 using (8) yields

$$\int_0^1 r f(r) J_0(\lambda_m r) dr = \sum_{n=1}^{\infty} A_n \int_0^1 r J_0(\lambda_m r) J_0(\lambda_n r) dr$$

$$= A_m \int_0^1 r [J_0(\lambda_m r)]^2 \, dr$$

* These are 2.40, 5.52, 8.65, 11.79, ... approximately.

from which

$$A_m = \frac{\int_0^1 rf(r)J_0(\lambda_m r)dr}{\int_0^1 r[J_0(\lambda_m r)]^2 dr} \qquad (9)$$

Using these coefficients in (5) we have a formal solution. We can show (see B Exercise 1) that the denominator in (9) is

$$\int_0^1 r[J_0(\lambda_m r)]^2 dr = \tfrac{1}{2}[J_1(\lambda_m)]^2 \quad \text{where} \quad J_1(\lambda_m) = -J_0'(\lambda_m) \qquad (10)$$

As in Fourier series the above must be justified. The following theorem is fundamental.

THEOREM. If $f(r)$ satisfies the Dirichlet conditions on page 341 (except for the periodic extension) then the series $\sum\limits_{n=1}^{\infty} A_n J_0(\lambda_n r)$ with coefficients (9) converges to $f(r)$ at a point of continuity and to $\tfrac{1}{2}[f(r+0) + f(r-0)]$ at a point of discontinuity. The series is called a *Fourier-Bessel series*.

It will be apparent that both Fourier series and Fourier-Bessel series involve sets of functions $\phi_1(x)$, $\phi_2(x)$, . . . having the property that

$$\int_a^b \phi_m(x)\phi_n(x)dx = 0 \qquad m \neq n \qquad (11)$$

Such functions are said to be *orthogonal* in the interval (a,b). If furthermore the functions are such that

$$\int_a^b \phi_m(x)\phi_n(x)dx = 1 \qquad m = n \qquad (12)$$

they are said to be *orthonormal* in (a,b). Other examples of orthogonal functions are considered in the exercises. An important question involves the existence of an expansion

$$f(x) = \sum_{n=1}^{\infty} A_n \phi_n(x) \qquad (13)$$

in terms of orthonormal functions. On multiplying (13) by $\phi_m(x)$ and formally integrating term by term using (11) and (12) we find

$$A_m = \int_a^b f(x)\phi_m(x)dx \qquad (14)$$

Here too, justification is required. We call series such as (13) with coefficients (14) *orthogonal series* or *generalized Fourier series*. For further discussion see the exercises.

A EXERCISES

1. Solve the problem in the text if (a) $f(r) = 50J_0(\lambda_1 r)$; (b). $f(r) = 20J_0(\lambda_1 r) - 10J_0(\lambda_2 r)$.

2. The displacement Z of a circular membrane or drumhead of unit radius is determined from the boundary-value problem

$$\frac{\partial^2 Z}{\partial t^2} = a^2 \left(\frac{\partial^2 Z}{\partial r^2} + \frac{1}{r} \frac{\partial Z}{\partial r} \right) \qquad 0 \leq r < 1, \quad t > 0$$

$$Z(1,t) = 0, \quad Z(r,0) = f(r), \quad Z_t(r,0) = 0, \quad Z(r,t) \text{ is bounded}$$

Solve this problem and interpret physically.

3. Solve Exercise 2 if (a) $f(r) = .05J_0(\lambda_1 r)$; (b) $f(r) = .20J_0(\lambda_1 r) - .15J_0(\lambda_3 r)$. Would you expect a musical note? Explain.

4. Solve and interpret physically the boundary-value problem

$$\frac{\partial^2 V}{\partial r^2} + \frac{1}{r} \frac{\partial V}{\partial r} + \frac{\partial^2 V}{\partial z^2} = 0 \qquad 0 \leq r < 1, \quad 0 < z < 1$$

$$V(1,z) = 0, \quad V(r,0) = 0, \quad V(r,1) = f(r), \quad V(r,z) \text{ is bounded}$$

Hint: Use the fact that in *cylindrical coordinates* (r,θ,z), as indicated in Fig. 114, Laplace's equation [see B Exercise 2, page 326] is

$$\frac{\partial^2 V}{\partial r^2} + \frac{1}{r} \frac{\partial V}{\partial r} + \frac{1}{r^2} \frac{\partial^2 V}{\partial \theta^2} + \frac{\partial^2 V}{\partial z^2} = 0$$

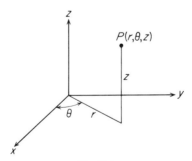

Fig. 114

5. Solve

$$\frac{\partial^2 U}{\partial r^2} + \frac{1}{r} \frac{\partial U}{\partial r} + \frac{\partial^2 U}{\partial z^2} = 0, \quad U(r,0) = f(r), \quad U(1,z) = 0, \quad U(r,z) \text{ is bounded}$$

for $0 \leq r < 1, \ z \geq 0$.

B EXERCISES

1. Derive the result (10), page 360. (*Hint:* Let $\lambda_n \to \lambda_m$ in (7).)

2. Solve the problem in the text if $U_r(1,t) = 0$ replaces $U(1,t) = 0$.

3. (a) Show that $r^2 R'' + rR' + (r^2 - p^2)R = 0$, Bessel's equation, has a bounded solution $R = J_p(r)$ where $J_p(x)$ is given in C Exercise 5, page 282. (b) If $\lambda_1, \lambda_2, \ldots$ are the positive roots of $J_p(\lambda) = 0$, show that

$$\int_0^1 r J_p(\lambda_m r) J_p(\lambda_n r) dr = 0 \qquad m \neq n$$

4. Show that (a) $J_0'(x) = -J_1(x)$; (b) $\dfrac{d}{dx}\{x^p J_p(x)\} = x^p J_{p-1}$.

5. Show that for $0 < r < 1$, $\frac{1}{2} = \sum_{n=1}^{\infty} \dfrac{J_0(\lambda_n r)}{\lambda_n J_1(\lambda_n)}$ where $J_0(\lambda_n) = 0$.

6. Solve the problem in the text for (a) $f(r) = 100$; (b) $f(r) = 50r$.

7. Solve Exercise 2 if (a) $f(r) = .05(1 - r)$; (b) $f(r) = .15r(1 - r)$.

8. Show that

$$\int_0^1 r[J_p(\lambda_n r)]^2 \, dr = \frac{\lambda_n^2 [J_p'(\lambda_n)]^2 + (\lambda_n^2 - p^2)[J_p(\lambda_n)]^2}{2\lambda_n^2}$$

C EXERCISES

1. Let $\phi_1(x), \phi_2(x), \ldots$ be orthonormal in $a \leq x \leq b$. (a) Use the inequality

$$\int_a^b [f(x) - \sum_{k=1}^{n} c_k \phi_k(x)]^2 \, dx \geq 0 \quad \text{where} \quad c_k = \int_a^b f(x) \phi_k(x) dx$$

under suitable integrability conditions to establish *Bessel's inequality*

$$c_1^2 + c_2^2 + \cdots \leq \int_a^b [f(x)]^2 \, dx$$

(b) Prove that $\lim\limits_{n \to \infty} c_n = 0$.

2. The functions of Exercise 1 are called *complete* in $a \leq x \leq b$ if

$$\lim_{n \to \infty} \int_a^b [f(x) - \sum_{k=1}^{n} c_k \phi_k(x)]^2 \, dx = 0$$

Show that this is equivalent to *Parseval's identity* (compare C Exercise 2, page 350)

$$c_1^2 + c_2^2 + \cdots = \int_a^b [f(x)]^2 \, dx$$

3. Interpret Exercises 1 and 2 in terms of mean square error between $f(x)$ and $\sum_{k=1}^{n} c_k \phi_k(x)$. If Exercise 2 holds we say that $\sum_{k=1}^{n} c_k \phi_k(x)$ *converges in mean* to $f(x)$ as $n \to \infty$.

4. Write Parseval's identity for Fourier-Bessel series and B Exercise 5 to show that

$$\sum_{k=1}^{\infty} \frac{1}{\lambda_k^2} = \frac{1}{4}$$

5. A Sturm-Liouville boundary-value problem is defined by

$$\frac{d}{dx}\left\{p(x)\frac{dy}{dx}\right\} + \{q(x) + \lambda r(x)\}y = 0$$

$$a_1 y(a) + a_2 y'(a) = 0, \qquad b_1 y(b) + b_2 y'(b) = 0$$

(a) Show that if $p(x) = 1$, $q(x) = 0$, $r(x) = 1$, $a = 0$, $b = 1$, $a_1 = 1$, $a_2 = 0$, $b_1 = 1$, $b_2 = 0$, there are infinitely many non-zero solutions, called *eigenfunctions* corresponding to values of λ, called *eigenvalues*.
(b) Discuss the case $p(x) = x$, $q(x) = -1/x$, $r(x) = x$, $a = 0$, $b = 1$, $a_1 = 1$, $a_2 = 0$, $b_1 = 1$, $b_2 = 0$.
(c) If y_m and y_n are eigenfunctions corresponding to λ_m and λ_n show that

$$\int_a^b r(x)y_m(x)y_n(x)dx = 0 \qquad m \neq n$$

How is this related to orthogonality and C Exercises 11–13, page 182?

6. Let $P_m(x)$, $H_m(x)$, and $L_m(x)$, $m = 1, 2, \ldots$, be the *Legendre, Hermite,* and *Laguerre polynomials* (C Exercises 7–10, page 283).
(a) Prove that for $m \neq n$

$$\int_0^1 P_m(x)P_n(x)dx = 0, \quad \int_{-\infty}^{\infty} e^{-x^2} H_m(x)H_n(x)dx = 0, \quad \int_0^{\infty} e^{-x} L_m(x)L_n(x)dx = 0$$

(b) Show how to expand $f(x) = 2x^3 - 4x + 3$ in terms of these polynomials.

7. (a) Show that in spherical coordinates (Fig. 115) Laplace's equation is

$$\nabla^2 V = \frac{1}{r^2}\left[\frac{\partial}{\partial r}\left(r^2 \frac{\partial V}{\partial r}\right) + \frac{\partial^2 V}{\partial \theta^2} + \cot\theta \frac{\partial V}{\partial \theta} + \csc^2\theta \frac{\partial^2 V}{\partial \phi^2}\right] = 0$$

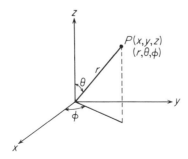

Fig. 115

(b) Show that a solution independent of ϕ is

$$V = \{Ar^n + Br^{-(n+1)}\}P_n(\cos \theta)$$

8. Use Exercise 7 to find the potential (a) inside and (b) outside a unit sphere if the potential on the sphere is $V = \cos^3 \theta$.

VI. Prologue to the Future

In this book an attempt has been made to present a brief introduction to the vast subject of differential equations, both ordinary and partial, and to some of their applications. We have endeavored to show that mathematics can be of interest for its own sake, as well as a necessary language in the formulation and, hence, understanding of scientific problems. In many instances we have been forced, for lack of time, to stop in our mathematical or scientific pursuits just when they may have been getting interesting or important or both. For example, we have not been able to examine in detail the convergence of Fourier series, of Fourier-Bessel series or of orthogonal series in general. Instead we had to be content with but a brief statement, for example the Dirichlet conditions. Similarly, we have not been able to explore in more detail various important aspects of convergence of series solutions of differential equations with singular points or of the advanced theory of Laplace transformation, which cannot be treated adequately without the theory of complex variables.

Although we have not been able to pursue these and other topics, it is hoped that the student will take advanced work in such fields or read some of the extensive literature which is available.

BIBLIOGRAPHY

[1] Byerly, W. E., *Fourier's Series and Spherical Harmonics*, Ginn, 1893.
[2] Carslaw, H. S., *Introduction to the Theory of Fourier's Series and Integrals*, 3rd edition, Dover, 1952.
[3] Churchill, R. V., *Fourier Series and Boundary Value Problems*, 2nd edition, McGraw-Hill, 1963.
[4] Churchill, R. V., *Operational Mathematics*, 2nd edition, McGraw-Hill, 1958.
[5] Cohen, A., *Elementary Treatise on Differential Equations*, 2nd edition, Heath, 1933.
[6] Davis, H. T., *The Theory of Linear Operators*, Principia Press, 1936.
[7] Forsyth, A. R., *A Treatise on Differential Equations*, 6th edition, St. Martins Press, 1954.
[8] Fourier, J., *The Analytical Theory of Heat*, Dover, 1955.
[9] Hildebrand, F. B., *Introduction to Numerical Analysis*, McGraw-Hill, 1956.
[10] Ince, E. L., *Ordinary Differential Equations*, 4th edition, Dover, 1953.
[11] Jackson, D., *Fourier Series and Orthogonal Polynomials*, Carus Monograph No. 6, Open Court, 1941.
[12] Kármán, T. von and Biot, M. A., *Mathematical Methods in Engineering*, McGraw-Hill, 1940.
[13] Langer, R. E., *Fourier's Series, The Genesis and Evolution of a Theory*, Slaught Memorial Paper No. 1, American Math. Monthly, 1947.
[14] Levy, H. and Baggott, E. A., *Numerical Solutions of Differential Equations*, Dover, 1950.
[15] Margenau, H. and Murphy, G. M., *Mathematics of Physics and Chemistry*, 2nd edition, Van Nostrand, 1956.
[16] McLachlan, N. W., *Bessel Functions for Engineers*, 2nd edition, Oxford, 1955.
[17] Sherwood, G. E. F. and Taylor, A. E., *Calculus*, 3rd edition, Prentice-Hall, 1954.
[18] Sokolnikoff, I. S., *Advanced Calculus*, McGraw-Hill, 1939.
[19] Taylor, A. E., *Advanced Calculus*, Blaisdell, 1955.
[20] Thomas, G. B., Jr., *Calculus and Analytic Geometry*, Addison-Wesley, 2nd edition, 1953.
[21] Timoshenko, S., *Strength of Materials*, Vol. 1, Van Nostrand, 1955.
[22] Watson, G. N., *Theory of Bessel Functions*, Cambridge, 1922.
[23] Webster, A. G., *Partial Differential Equations of Mathematical Physics*, Dover, 1956.
[24] Whittaker, E. T. and Watson, G. N., *Modern Analysis*, American edition, Cambridge, 1943.

ANSWERS TO EXERCISES

CHAPTER I

REVIEW EXERCISES, p. 3

1. (a) $4x^3 - 6x + 1$. (b) $2x - \frac{3}{2}x^{-3/2} - \frac{4}{3}(4x)^{-2/3} - 10x^{-6}$.

(c) $3x^{-1/2} \cos 3x - \frac{1}{2}x^{-3/2} \sin 3x + 3 \sin 3x$. (d) $4x \cos 4x + 3 \sin 4x$.

(e) $\dfrac{2xe^x}{x^2 + 1} + e^x \ln (x^2 + 1) + 2e^{-2x}$.

(f) $e^{-3x}[(4A - 3B) \cos 4x - (3A + 4B) \sin 4x]$.

(g) $-4(x^2 + 3x - 2)^{1/2} \csc 4x \cot 4x + (x + \frac{3}{2})(x^2 + 3x - 2)^{-1/2} \csc 4x$
    $+ 6 \sec 2x \tan 2x$.

(h) $3 \sec 3x$. (i) $\sqrt{1 - x^2}$. (j) $\dfrac{2xe^{\text{arc tan } x^2}}{1 + x^4} - \dfrac{6 \cos (2 \text{ arc cos } x)}{(1 - x^2)^{1/2}}$.

(k) $\dfrac{c - 2x}{2y}$. (l) $\dfrac{8x - 3x^2y}{x^3 - 4y^3}$. (m) $\dfrac{3y \sin 3x - \sin y}{x \cos y + \cos 3x}$.

(n) $\sqrt{1 - 4y^2}\left(\dfrac{3y - 2x \text{ arc sin } 2y}{2x^2 - 3x \sqrt{1 - 4y^2}}\right)$. (o) $\dfrac{(2 - 2xye^{x^2y})(1 + x^2y^2) - y}{x^2(1 + x^2y^2)e^{x^2y} + x}$.

(p) $-\sqrt{\dfrac{1 - y^2}{1 - x^2}}$. (q) $\dfrac{6x(x + y) + 2(x + y) \sin (x + y) - y}{y + (x + y) \ln (x + y) - 2(x + y) \sin (x + y)}$.

(r) $\dfrac{y(\ln y)^3 - 6y^2 \sin 3x \cos 3x}{y \sin^2 3x - 3x(\ln y)^2}$.

(s) $\dfrac{1 - \sqrt{2x + 1} \sec y + 2y \sqrt{2x + 1} \tan x \sec^2 x}{\sqrt{2x + 1} (x \sec y \tan y - \tan^2 x)}$.

(t) $\dfrac{y \sqrt{x^2 + y^2} - x^2 \sqrt{x^2 - y^2}}{x \sqrt{x^2 + y^2} + xy \sqrt{x^2 - y^2}}$.

2. (a) $16 \cos 2x - 12 \sin 2x$. (b) $2e^{-x}(\sin x - \cos x)$. (c) $y[(\ln y)^2 - 1]/x^2$.

(d) $\frac{1}{3}x^{-4/3}y^{-1/3}$.

3. (a) $\dfrac{3t^2 + 1}{4t - 1}, \dfrac{12t^2 - 6t - 4}{(4t - 1)^3}$.   (b) $-\tan t, -\frac{1}{3}\sec^3 t$.

(c) $\dfrac{\sin \theta}{1 - \cos \theta}, \dfrac{-1}{a(1 - \cos \theta)^2}$.   (d) $\dfrac{e^u - e^{-u}}{e^u + e^{-u}}, \dfrac{8}{(e^u + e^{-u})^3}$.

5. (a) $2\cos(x + 3y), 6\cos(x + 3y), -2\sin(x + 3y), -18\sin(x + 3y)$,

$-6\sin(x + 3y), -6\sin(x + 3y), -18\cos(x + 3y)$.

(b) $-\lambda^2 e^{-\lambda y}\sin \lambda x, \lambda^2 e^{-\lambda y}\sin \lambda x$.   (c) $\dfrac{2x}{8z + y}, \dfrac{-z}{8z + y}, \dfrac{8z^2 + 2yz}{(8z + y)^3}$.

(d) $\dfrac{10z + 1}{4x^3 y}, -\dfrac{x}{4y}$.   (e) $\dfrac{2(y^2 + z^2 - x^2)}{(x^2 + y^2 + z^2)^2}, \dfrac{2(x^2 + z^2 - y^2)}{(x^2 + y^2 + z^2)^2}, \dfrac{2(x^2 + y^2 - z^2)}{(x^2 + y^2 + z^2)^2}$.

6. (a) $(2x + 3)^{-1}, -2(2x + 3)^{-3}$; x dependent, y independent.

(b) $9e^{-3x+y}, -3e^{-3x+y}$; V dependent, x and y independent.

(c) $\dfrac{x^4 - 3z^2 y}{z^3 - 1}, \dfrac{4x^3 z}{z^3 - 1}$; y dependent, x and z independent.

(d) $\dfrac{2\cos 2\theta + r\sin \theta}{\cos \theta - e^{-r}}$; r dependent, θ independent.

A EXERCISES, p. 11

Differential Equation	Ordinary or Partial	Order	Degree	Independent Variables	Dependent Variables
(a)	ordinary	1	1	x	y
(b)	ordinary	2	1	x	y
(c)	partial	2	1	x, y, t	U
(d)	ordinary	3	2	t	s
(e)	ordinary	1	1	θ	r
(f)	ordinary	2	1	y	x
(g)	partial	2	3	x, y	V
(h)	ordinary	1	1	x or y	y or x
(i)	ordinary	2	not defined	x	y
(j)	partial	2	1	x, y, z	T

B EXERCISES, p. 12

1. (c) $y = e^{-4x} + 4e^x$.

2. $m = 1, \frac{1}{2}, -2$.   (a) $y = c_1 e^x + c_2 e^{x/2} + c_3 e^{-2x}$.   (b) $y = 3e^x + 8e^{x/2} - e^{-2x}$.

3. (a) $m = \pm 2$.

A EXERCISES, p. 22

1. (a) $y' + 2y = 6x(x + 1)$.   (b) $y' = 1 + (y - x) \cot x$.

   (c) $(x^2 - 1)y' = xy$.   (d) $xy' \ln x = y(\ln x - 1)$.

   (e) $y'' + 16y = 16x$.   (f) $\dfrac{d^2 I}{dt^2} + 2\dfrac{dI}{dt} + I = 12 \cos 3t - 16 \sin 3t$.

   (g) $2xyy' = y^2 - x^2$.   (h) $x^3 y''' - 3x^2 y'' + 6xy' - 6y = 0$.

   (i) $y''' - 3y'' - 10y' + 24y = 0$.

   (j) $\theta^2(1 - \ln \theta)\dfrac{d^3 r}{d\theta^3} + \theta\dfrac{d^2 r}{d\theta^2} - \dfrac{dr}{d\theta} = 0$.

2. Particular solutions are (a) $y = -4 \cos x$.   (b) $y = 3e^x - e^{-x} - 4x$.

   (c) $x^2 - y^2 + 2xy = -17$.   (d) $y = 1 - 2x + 3x^2$.   (e) $xy^2 = 13x - 36$.

3. $yy' + x = 0$.   (b) $2xy' = y$.   (c) Let (c,c) be any point on $y = x$. Then the required circle is $(x - c)^2 + (y - c)^2 = c^2$. The required differential equation is $(x - y)^2[1 + (y')^2] = (x + yy')^2$.

   (d) $xyy'' - yy' + x(y')^2 = 0$.

B EXERCISES, p. 23

3. $A = B = 0$ gives the required particular solution.

4. (b) $x^3 - y^3 + 3x - 12y + 13 = 0$.

5. (a) $y = 4e^{x^2/2}$.   (b) $x^2 + y^2 + x^2 y^2 = 1$.

C EXERCISES, p. 23

2. (a) $y'' - y' - 6y = 0$.   (b) $(y''' + y')(x^3 + 12x) = (y'' + y)(4x^2 + 24)$.

9. (a) $y = cx + 1 + c^2$; $y = 1 - x^2/4$.

   (b) $y = cx + \tan c$; $x = -\sec^2 c, y = \tan c - c \sec^2 c$.

CHAPTER 2

A EXERCISES, p. 34

1. (a) $3x^2 + 4y^2 = c$.   (b) $x^2 - 2xy - y^2 = c$.   (c) $3xy^2 - x^3 = c$.

   (d) Not exact.   (e) $x^2 - y^2 - 2y \sin x = c$.   (f) $r^2 \cos \theta - r = c$.

   (g) $ye^{-x} - \cos x + y^2 = c$.   (h) $x^3 + 3y \ln x + 3y^2 = c$.

   (i) $ye^x - xy^2 = c$.   (j) Not exact.

2. (a) $x^2 - xy + y^2 = 3$. (b) $x^2y + y + 6 = 0$. (c) $x^2 - x \sin y = 4$.

(d) $2x \tan y + \cos 2x = 2\pi + 1$. (e) $x^2y + y^2e^{2x} = 1$.

3. (a) $x^2y^2 + x^4 = c$. (b) $6xy^4 - y^6 = c$. (c) $y \cos^2 x + 3 \sin x = c$.

(d) $\dfrac{1}{2} \ln (x^2 + y^2) + \arctan \dfrac{y}{x} = c$.

B EXERCISES, p. 34

1. $x + y^2 - x^2 = c(x + y)$.

4. $N(x,y) = -\cos x + \dfrac{x^3}{3} - \dfrac{x^2}{2} \sec y \tan y + F(y)$,

$\frac{1}{3}x^3y - y \cos x - \frac{1}{2}x^2 \sec y + \int F(y)\,dy = c$.

5. $x^2 \left(\sin \dfrac{y}{x} + \tan \dfrac{y}{x} \right) = c$.

C EXERCISES, p. 35

2. $y^4(3 - xy^5) = cx^2$.

A EXERCISES, p. 38

1. (a) $x^2 + y^2 = 5$. (b) $xy = 3$. (c) $(x^2 + 2)^3(y^2 + 1) = c$.

(d) $2e^{3x} + 3 \ln y = c$. (e) $x^2 - 4 \ln (1 + y^2) = 1$.

(f) $\ln r - \arctan \theta = c$. (g) $\tan x \tan y = 1$.

(h) $\sqrt{1 + x^2} - \sqrt{1 + y^2} = c$. (i) $y^3 \sin^2 x = 8$. (j) $y = ce^{4x^2+3x}$.

(k) $I = 2(1 - e^{-5t})$. (l) $x^{-2} - y^2 - 2 \ln y = c$.

2. $(x^2 + 2)(y^2 + 3) = 24$.

B EXERCISES, p. 38

1. $(x - 1)(y + 3)^5 = c(y - 1)(x + 3)^5$.

2. $2 \arctan (e^r) + \arctan (\cos \theta) = \dfrac{\pi}{2}$.

3. $25(3x^2 - 1)e^{3x^2} + 9(5y^2 + 1)e^{-5y^2} = c$.

C EXERCISES, p. 38

2. (a) $\dfrac{2y}{x} + \sin \dfrac{2y}{x} = 4 \ln |x| + c$. (b) $(x + y)^5 = c(x - 2y)^2$.

3. $x - \arctan (x + y) = c$. **4.** (a) $4y - 2x + \sin (2x + 4y) = c$.

(b) $6\sqrt{2x + 3y} - 4 \ln (3\sqrt{2x + 3y} + 2) - 9x = c$.

$y=x^3$ LIKE THE RIGHT ANS.
$y=x^3$ SEEMS

A EXERCISES, p. 42

1. (a) $x^3 + x^2y^2 = c$.　(b) $y = 2x - x^3$.　(c) $y^2 - x = y(c - \sin x)$.

(d) $x^2(c + \cos 2y) = 2y$.　(e) $x = \left(\dfrac{\pi}{2} - y\right)\sin y$.　(f) $y = (x + c)\cos^2 x$.

DIDN'T AGREE, SAY - HERE

(g) $6x^4y - x^6 = c$.　(h) $6xy^3 - y^6 = c$.　(i) $I = 1 - \dfrac{1}{\sqrt{t^2 + 1}}$.

(j) $y^3e^x + ye^{2x} = c$.

2. $y = x \ln\left(\dfrac{x}{3}\right)$.

B EXERCISES, p. 42

1. $y^2 + \sin^2 x = c\sin^3 x$.　**2.** $x^2 + y^2 + 1 = ce^{y^2}$.　**3.** $e^{x^3}(1 + xy) = c$.

4. $(x^2 + y^2)\sqrt{1 + y^2} = c$.

C EXERCISES, p. 42

2. $e^{xy}(x + y) = c$.　**3.** $x^2y^4 + x^4y^3 = c$.

A EXERCISES, p. 45

1. (a) $x^2 - 2xy = c$.　(b) $x^5 - 5x^3y = c$.　(c) $xy = y^2 + \ln y + c$.

(d) $x^2\cos 3x + 3y = cx^2$.　(e) $I = e^{-2t} + 4e^{-3t}$.　(f) $2y\sin x - \sin^2 x = c$.

(g) $x - 3y - 3 = ce^y$.　(h) $7r = 3\theta^2 + 4\theta^{-1/3}$.　**2.** $I = 10te^{-2t}$.

B EXERCISES, p. 45

3. $y = (1 - x + ce^{-x})^{-1}$.　**4.** $2x^2 - 3y = cx^2y^3$.　**5.** $y = c_1x^4 - \frac{4}{3}x^3 + c_2$.

C EXERCISES, p. 46

2. $\ln y = 2x^2 + cx$.

A EXERCISES, p. 48

1. $y = x\ln x + cx$.　**2.** $x = y - y\ln x$.　**3.** $y = cx^3 - x$.

4. $x^3 - 3xy^2 = c$.　**5.** $x^2 + 4xy + y^2 = c$.　**6.** $1 + \ln x = \tan\dfrac{y}{x}$.

7. $y + \sqrt{x^2 + y^2} = c$.　**8.** $x + 3y = cy^2$.　**9.** $y^3 = 3x^3\ln x$.

10. $x^2 - y^2 = cx$.

B EXERCISES, p. 48

1. $y^2 + y\sqrt{x^2 + y^2} + x^2\ln(y + \sqrt{x^2 + y^2}) - 3x^2\ln x = cx^2$.

2. $(x + y)^3 = c(2x + y)^4$.　**3.** $(y - x)(y - 3x)^9 = c(y - 2x)^{12}$.

4. $\ln[(x - 1)^2 + (y + 1)^2] - 3\arctan\left(\dfrac{y + 1}{x - 1}\right) = c$.

5. $y - 2x + 7 = c(x + y + 1)^4$.　**6.** $\ln(2x + 3y + 2) = 2y - x + c$.

7. $2x + y - 3 \ln (x + y + 2) = c.$

9. (a) 0. (b) Not homogeneous. (c) 2. (d) 4. (e) -3.

C EXERCISES, p. 49

1. $x + \sqrt{x^2 - y^2} = c.$ **2.** $x^2 \cos \dfrac{y}{x^2} + y \sin \dfrac{y}{x^2} = cx^3.$

3. $\frac{1}{2} \ln (x^6 + y^4) + \arctan \dfrac{x^3}{y^2} = c.$ **4.** Choose $n = \frac{3}{4}$, $2 + 5xy^2 = cx^{5/2}.$

6. $(Y - \alpha X)^{2+\sqrt{2}}(Y - \beta X)^{2-\sqrt{2}} = c(Y - X)^2$ where $\alpha = 3 + 2\sqrt{2}$,
$\beta = 3 - 2\sqrt{2}$, $X = x - 2$, $Y = y + 1.$

7. $v^2 + 2v - v\sqrt{v^2 - 1} + \ln (v + \sqrt{v^2 - 1}) = 4x + c$ where $v = x + y.$

8. $xy + \ln (x/y) = c.$

A EXERCISES, p. 51

1. $xy^2 - y = cx.$ **2.** $y^3 + 2x = cy.$ **3.** $x^2 - 2\arctan \dfrac{y}{x} = c.$

4. $\sqrt{x^2 + y^2} = x + y + c.$ **5.** $x^3 + xy^2 - 2y = cx.$

6. $x + y - \arctan \dfrac{y}{x} = c.$ **7.** $\ln (x^2 + y^2) + 2y - 2x = c.$

8. $\ln (x^2 + y^2) = 2xy + c.$

B EXERCISES, p. 51

1. $(x^2 + y^2)^{3/2} - 3xy = c.$ **2.** $3x^2 + 3y^2 + 2(xy)^{-3} = c.$

3. $x^2 - y^2 + \ln \left| \dfrac{x - y}{x + y} \right| = c.$

C EXERCISES, p. 51

1. $\ln (x^2 + 2y^2) = x^2 + y^2 + c.$ **2.** $x^3 - x^2y - y = cx^2.$

3. $x^2 - 2 \ln (y^2 + \sin^2 x) = c.$

A EXERCISES, p. 55

1. $y = \dfrac{x^3}{3} + 10x.$ **2.** $y = \dfrac{x^5}{360} + c_1x^3 + c_2x^2 + c_3x + c_4.$

3. $y = 3 \cos x + \dfrac{x^2}{2} - 2.$ **4.** $y = \dfrac{e^x - e^{-x}}{2} - \dfrac{x^3}{6} - x.$

5. $I = \dfrac{t^4}{12} + \dfrac{t^2}{2} + 3t + 2.$ **6.** $y = \dfrac{x^2}{2} - \ln x + \dfrac{1}{2}.$

7. $y = \frac{1}{2} \ln x + \frac{8}{3}x^{1/2} + c_1x^2 + c_2x + c_3.$

8. $y = \dfrac{(2x + 1)^{3/2}}{3} + \dfrac{14}{3}$.   **9.** $y = 3 \cos 2x + \sin 2x$.

10. $y = \dfrac{c_1}{x} + c_2$.   **11.** $y = c_1 e^x + c_2 e^{-x}$.

12. $x = \int dy/(\ln y + c_1) + c_2$, $y = c_3$.   **13.** $y = \ln \cosh (x + c_1) + c_2$.

14. $y + 1 = c_1 \tan \frac{1}{2}(x + c_2)$.   **15.** $y = x + c_1 - c_2 \int e^{-x^2/2}\, dx$.

B EXERCISES, p. 55

1. $y = \dfrac{x^4}{24} \ln x - \dfrac{25x^4}{288} + \dfrac{x^3}{6} - \dfrac{x^2}{8} + \dfrac{x}{18} - \dfrac{1}{96}$.

2. $y = \dfrac{x^5}{240} - \dfrac{x^4}{96} + \dfrac{x^3}{48} - \dfrac{x^2}{32} + \dfrac{x}{32} - \dfrac{1}{64} + \dfrac{e^{-2x}}{64}$.

3. $y = \dfrac{x^2}{2} + c_1 x \ln x + c_2 x + c_3$.   **4.** $y = -4 \ln (x + c_1) + c_2 x + c_3$.

5. $y = c_1 e^x + c_2 e^{-x} + c_3$.   **6.** $(x + c_1)^2 + y^2 = c_2^2$

7. $y = (x + c_1) \ln x + c_2$.

C EXERCISES, p. 55

1. $\pm \sqrt{15}$.   **2.** (a) $(x + c_1)^2 + y^2 = c_2^2$.

2. $c_1 \arcsin \left(\dfrac{y - c_1}{c_1}\right) - \sqrt{2c_1 y - y^2} = \pm x + c_2$ or, in parametric form,

$y = A(1 - \cos \theta)$, $\pm x = A(\theta - \sin \theta) + B$, a family of cycloids.

3. $(x - A)^2 + (y - B)^2 = 1$.

MISCELLANEOUS EXERCISES, CHAPTER 2

A EXERCISES, p. 55

1. $x - x^{-1} = \frac{1}{3} \ln (y^3 - 1) + c$.   **2.** $x^2 y + y^2 x = c$.

3. $x^2 + xy + y^2 = c(x + y)$.   **4.** $5x^2 y = x^5 + c$.   **5.** $(3 - y)^2 = 4x$.

6. $y = 2x - x^2 + c$.   **7.** $2s^3 + 3t^2 + 24 \ln t = c$.   **8.** $x^3 + 3xy^2 = c$.

9. $3ye^x - 2x^3 = c$.   **10.** $xy = x + \ln x + c$.

11. $\ln x = \displaystyle\int \dfrac{dv}{\arctan v} + c$, where $v = \dfrac{y}{x}$.   **12.** $x + y + 1 = ce^x$.

13. $y = x^2 - 2 + ce^{-x^2/2}$.   **14.** $\frac{1}{2}x^2 y^2 + 4x - 3y = c$.

15. $r^2 \cos \theta + 10r = c$.   **16.** $y = ce^{2x} - \dfrac{x^2}{2} - \dfrac{x}{2} - \dfrac{1}{4}$.   **17.** $x^2 y^{-3} - x = c$.

18. $x^2 + y^2 - 2x + 2 = 6e^{-x}$.   **19.** $3xy^2 + x^3 - 9y = c$.

20. $y^2 \ln y - x = cy^2$.   **21.** $u^3v^{-3} - 3 \ln v = c$.   **22.** $x \cot y - \sin x = c$.

23. $x^2 - y^2 + 4xy = c$.   **24.** $y = (x + c) \sin x$.   **25.** $x^2 + y^2 = cx$.

26. $2x^3 - 3ye^x = c$.   **27.** $y - \ln (x + y + 1) = c$.   **28.** $x^3 + 3x^2y = c$.

29. $y^2 - 2x \sin y = c$.   **30.** $e^{-y/x} + \ln x = c$.   **31.** $\cos x \cos y = c$.

32. $y = x^3 + cx^2$.   **33.** $x^3y^2 + x^2 = c$.   **34.** $xy^{-1} + 2y = c$.

35. $y = c_1e^x - x^2 - 2x + c_2$.   **36.** $2y^{1/2} + \frac{2}{3}y^{3/2} = \dfrac{x^2}{2} + c$.

37. $\sec x(\csc y - \cot y)^3 = c$.   **38.** $\sec \dfrac{y}{x} + \tan \dfrac{y}{x} = cx$.

39. $(1 - s)^{3/2} - (1 - t)^{3/2} = 1$.   **40.** $x^2y + x^3 = c$.   **41.** $y^3(1 + x^3) = c$.

42. $2xy + 2 \cos y + 2x^2 = \pi + 2$.   **43.** $N = N_0e^{-\alpha t}$.   **44.** $xye^{x/y} = c$.

45. $I = ce^{-t} + \frac{1}{2}e^t$.   **46.** $3xy = x^3 + 5$.   **47.** $xy^2 - 2y = cx$.

48. $e^{p^2} - e^{q^2} = c$.   **49.** $y^3 \cos x + y^2 + 48 = 0$.   **50.** $y + \sin y = cx$.

51. $y = ce^{-2x} - \frac{3}{2}x - \frac{3}{4}$.   **52.** $y^2 = x(c - y)$.

53. $2 \ln r + (\ln r)^2 = 2 \ln \theta + (\ln \theta)^2 - 5$.

54. $U = 100t - \dfrac{100}{a} (1 - e^{-at})$.   **55.** $(u - 1)v = cu^2$.

56. $I = 3 \sin t - \cos t + e^{-3t}$.   **57.** $s - \ln (s + t + 2) = c$.

58. $y^2 = c_1x + c_2$.   **59.** $\sqrt{1 - x^2} + \sqrt{1 - y^2} = c$.

60. $2y \sin x + \cos^2 x = c$.   **61.** $(y + 3)^{-1} = (4x)^{-1} + c$.

62. $y = cx^3 - x^3e^{-x}$.   **63.** $\ln \sin y + \cos x = c$.

64. $y^2 = 2x^2 \ln x + cx^2$.   **65.** $2xy^3 - 3y = cx$.   **66.** $\ln y = cx + \ln x$.

67. $xy - x^2 = c$.   **68.** $y = x + c_1 \ln x + c_2$.   **69.** $t^3I^{-3} + 3 \ln I = c$.

70. $x = ye^y - 3 + ce^y$.   **71.** $r = \frac{1}{4}e^\theta + \frac{3}{4}e^{-3\theta}$.   **72.** $y = ae^{bx}$.

73. $6xy = c_1x^3 + c_2x^2 + c_3x + 1$.

74. $\ln (x^2 + 2xy + 3y^2) = 2\sqrt{2} \arctan \left(\dfrac{x + 3y}{x\sqrt{2}} \right) + c$.

75. $y(\sec x - \tan x) = 2 \ln (1 + \sin x) - 2 \sin x + c$.   **76.** $e^{4x} + 2e^{2y} = c$.

77. $r^4 = a^4 \sin (4\theta + c)$.   **78.** $2x^3 - 3ye^x = c$.

79. $x^2y = (x^2 - 2) \sin x + 2x \cos x + c$.

80. $2\sqrt{1 + x^3} = 3 \ln (y + 1) + c$.   **81.** $x^3y^2 + x^4y = c$.

B EXERCISES, p. 58

1. $x^2y^2 = 2 \sin x - 2x \cos x + c.$ **4.** $x + 2y + 1 = ce^{y/2}.$

5. $\sqrt{y + \sin x} = \dfrac{x}{2} + c.$ **6.** $\sin (x + y) + \cos (x + y) = ce^{x-y}.$

7. $3e^{4x} + 4e^{3x-3y} = c.$ **8.** $y = \dfrac{3}{4} e^{2x} + \dfrac{1}{4} - \dfrac{3x}{2} - \dfrac{3x^2}{2} - x^3 - \dfrac{x^4}{2}.$

10. (a) $y = cx + c^2, y = -x^2/4.$ (b) $y = 2vx + \ln v$, where $v^2x + v = c.$

13. $xy + 2 \ln (x/y) - (xy)^{-1} = c.$ **14.** $(y - ce^{-3x})(y - x^2 - c) = 0.$

C EXERCISES, p. 59

1. $\ln |x| = \ln |u^2 + 1| - \frac{16}{31} \ln |2u - 1| - \frac{23}{31} \ln |3u^2 + 4u + 5|$

$$- \frac{68}{31\sqrt{11}} \text{ arc tan} \left(\frac{3v + 2}{\sqrt{11}} \right), \text{ where } u = \sqrt{\frac{5x - 6y}{5x + 6y}}.$$

4. $5x^{12}y^{12} + 12x^{10}y^{15} = c.$ **5.** $x^2 + cxy + y^2 = 1.$

15. $y = x + e^{-x^2}[c_1 + \int e^{-x^2} dx]^{-1}.$

CHAPTER 3

A EXERCISES, p. 71

1. (b) 4410 cm, 2940 cm/sec. (c) 3430 cm, 4410 cm.

2. (a) 2940 cm, 490 cm/sec upward after 2 sec.
    1960 cm, 1470 cm/sec downward after 4 sec.

   (b) 3062.5 cm above starting point (assuming $g = 980$ cm/sec^2 and answers accurate to at least five significant figures), 2.5 sec.

   (c) 2940 cm, 4165 cm.

3. 9.08 sec, 290.7 ft/sec.

4. (a) $v = 49(1 - e^{-20t}), x = 49t + 2.45e^{-20t} - 2.45.$ (b) 49 cm/sec.

5. (a) 25 ft/sec. (b) $v = 25(1 - e^{-2t/15}), x = 25t + \frac{375}{2}e^{-2t/15} - \frac{375}{2}.$

6. (a) 50 ft/sec. (b) $v = 50 - 10e^{-0.64t}, x = 50t + \frac{125}{8}e^{-0.64t} - \frac{125}{8}.$

7. (a) $v = 16(1 - e^{-2}) = 13.8$ ft/sec. (b) $t = \frac{1}{2} \ln 16 = 2 \ln 2 = 1.39$ sec.

8. (a) $v = 16\left(\dfrac{e^{4} - 1}{e^4 + 1}\right) = 15.4$ ft/sec. (b) $t = \frac{1}{4} \ln 31 = 0.86$ sec.

9. (a) $2\sqrt{3}$ ft/sec toward or away from $O.$

   (b) Amplitude $= 1$ ft, Period $= \dfrac{\pi}{2}$ sec, Frequency $= \dfrac{2}{\pi}$ cycles per second.

   (c) $\sqrt{2}/2$ ft from O, $2\sqrt{2}$ ft/sec toward O, $8\sqrt{2}$ ft/sec^2 toward $O.$

10. (a) $20\sqrt{3}$ cm/sec toward or away from O, 40 cm/sec² toward O.

(b) Amplitude $= 20$ cm, Period $= \pi$ sec, Frequency $= 1/\pi$ cycles per sec.

(c) 10 cm from O, $20\sqrt{3}$ cm/sec away from O, 40 cm/sec² toward O.

(d) After $\dfrac{\pi}{4}$ sec, $\dfrac{3\pi}{4}$ sec, $\dfrac{5\pi}{4}$ sec, etc.

11. 2 ft/sec.

12. (a) $x = \pm 4 \sin 5t$, $v = \pm 20 \cos 5t$, $a = \mp 100 \sin 5t$ (the choice of sign depends on the direction of motion of the particle at $t = 0$.)

(b) Amplitude $= 4$ cm, Period $= 2\pi/5$ sec, Frequency $= 5/2\pi$ cycles per sec.

(c) Magnitude of force $= 100\sqrt{2}$ dynes.

B EXERCISES, p. 73

4. (b) $v = p\left[\dfrac{(p + v_0)e^{\alpha t} - (p - v_0)}{(p + v_0)e^{\alpha t} + (p - v_0)}\right]$ where $p = V\sqrt{\dfrac{W}{F}}$, $\alpha = \dfrac{2g}{V}\sqrt{\dfrac{F}{W}}$,

limiting velocity $= p = V\sqrt{\dfrac{W}{F}}$. If $v_0 = 0$, $v = p\left[\dfrac{e^{\alpha t} - 1}{e^{\alpha t} + 1}\right]$

$= p \tanh\dfrac{\alpha t}{2}$ using hyperbolic functions.

(c) $v = \sqrt{p^2 - (p^2 - v_0^2)e^{-2kx}}$ where $p = V\sqrt{W/F}$, $k = Fg/WV^2$.

5. 37.5 ft, 8 ft/sec.

6. (a) $v = 100\sqrt{1 - e^{-0.0064x}}$.

(b) $v = 100\left(\dfrac{e^{0.64t} - 1}{e^{0.64t} + 1}\right) = 100 \tanh (0.32t)$.

(c) 97.9 ft/sec.   (d) 100 ft/sec.   (e) 784 ft

7. (a) $x = 4 \cos 2t - 3 \sin 2t$, $v = -8 \sin 2t - 6 \cos 2t$.

(b) Amplitude $= 5$ cm, Period $= \pi$ sec, Frequency $= 1/\pi$ cycles per sec. [*Hint*: $4 \cos 2t - 3 \sin 2t = 5(\frac{4}{5} \cos 2t - \frac{3}{5} \sin 2t) = 5 \cos (2t + \phi)$ where $\cos \phi = \frac{4}{5}$, $\sin \phi = -\frac{3}{5}$. Thus the maximum value of x, i.e. the amplitude, is 5. This can also be found by calculus.]

(c) Maximum velocity $= 10$ cm/sec, maximum acceleration $= 20$ cm/sec².

11. (a) 85 min.   (b) 4.9 mi/sec.   **12.** (a) $\frac{1}{4}$ mi.   (b) 9 sec.

C EXERCISES, p. 74

1. (b) 200 ft, 80 ft/sec, 16 ft/sec².   **5.** 130.8 ft, 52.3 ft/sec, 10.5 ft/sec².

7. $v = \dfrac{cFt}{\sqrt{F^2t^2 + m_0^2c^2}}$, $x = \dfrac{c}{F}\sqrt{F^2t^2 + m_0^2c^2} - \dfrac{m_0c^2}{F}$.

8. (a) $x = \frac{5}{2}t^2$.   (b) $x = \dfrac{c^2}{5}(\sqrt{1 + 25t^2/c^2} - 1)$.

A EXERCISES, p. 81

1. $I = \frac{1}{2}(1 - e^{-20t})$.   **2.** $I = 2 \sin 10t - \cos 10t + e^{-20t}$.

3. $I = 20e^{-4t}$.   **4.** $Q = \frac{1}{4}(1 - e^{-8t})$, $I = 2e^{-8t}$.

5. $Q = 0.16 \cos 6t + 0.12 \sin 6t - 0.16e^{-8t}$,

    $I = 0.72 \cos 6t - 0.96 \sin 6t + 1.28e^{-8t}$.

6. $Q = 0.05e^{-10t}$, $I = -0.5e^{-10t}$.   **7.** $I(t) = 2e^{-4t} \sin 50t$.

B EXERCISES, p. 81

3. (a) $Q = 10 - 5(1 + 0.01t)^{-1000}$, $I = 50(1 + 0.01t)^{-1001}$.   (b) 10 coulombs.

4. (a) $I(t) = 4 - 4(1 + 0.02t)^{-10,000}$.   (b) 4 amp.

5. $Q = 0.99CEe^{-t/RC}$.

C EXERCISES, p. 82

1. $I(t) = \begin{cases} 1 - e^{-100t}, & 0 \le t \le 5 \\ (1 - e^{-500})e^{-100(t-5)}, & t \ge 5. \end{cases}$

2. $Q = CE_0(e^{-T/RC} - e^{-2T/RC} + e^{-3T/RC} - e^{-4T/RC})$.

A EXERCISES, p. 87

1. (a) $2xy' = y$.   (b) $yy' = -2x$, $2x^2 + y^2 = c_1$.   **2.** $3x^2 + 2y^2 = c_1$.

3. (a) $e^{x^2+y^2} = c_1 x^2$; $x^2 - 3y^2 = 1$, $4e^{x^2+y^2-5} = x^2$.

    (b) $x^3 + 3xy^2 = c_1$; $x^2 + 8y = y^2$, $x^3 + 3xy^2 = 36$.

    (c) $4y^2 - 8y + \sin^2 2x = c_1$; $y = 1 - \tan 2x$, $8y^2 - 16y + 2 \sin^2 2x = 1$.

    (d) $9x - 3y + 5 = c_1 e^{-6y}$; $y = 3e^{-2x} + 3x$, $9x - 3y + 5 = -4e^{6(3-y)}$.

    (e) $e^{-x^2-y^2} = c_1 x^2$; $y^2 = 5(1 + x^2)$, $4e^{29-x^2-y^2} = x^2$.

B EXERCISES, p. 87

1. $a = \frac{1}{3}$.   **4.** (a) $y^2 = \dfrac{2x^{2-p}}{2 - p} - x^2 + c_1$ if $p \ne 2$; $e^{x^2+y^2} = c_1 x^2$ if $p = 2$.

    (b) $x^2 - y^2 = c_1 e^{x^2+y^2}$.

C EXERCISES, p. 88

1. $2 \arctan (y/x) + \ln (x^2 + y^2) = c$, or in polar coordinates $r = ae^{-\theta}$.

2. $\ln (x^2 + y^2) \pm 2\sqrt{3} \arctan (y/x) = \pm 2\pi \sqrt{3}/3$ or $r = e^{\pm\sqrt{3}(\theta-\pi/3)}$.

3. $\pm y \tan \alpha + \sec^2 \alpha \ln |y \mp \tan \alpha| = x + c_1$.

5. $r = c_1 \sin \theta$.   **6.** $(\ln r)^2 + \theta^2 = c_1$.   **7.** $r = c_1(1 + \cos \theta)$.

A EXERCISES, p. 91

1. (b) $x = 24 - 22e^{-t/2}$.   (c) 3 lb/gal approx.   (d) 24 lb.

2. (a) $x = 40(1 - e^{-t/20})$.   (b) 13.9 min.   **3.** 20.8 min.

4. 34.7 min, 184.5 min.   **5.** (a) 5.1 lb, 6.6 lb, 7.6 lb.   (b) 3 hr 53 min.

6. (a) $x = \dfrac{300[(18/17)^t - 1]}{3(18/17)^t - 2}$.   (b) 26.6 lb.   (c) 100 lb.

B EXERCISES, p. 91

1. (a) $x = 1.5(10 - t) - 0.0013(10 - t)^4, 0 \leq t \leq 10$.   (b) 1.5 lb/gal.

2. (a) $3[1 - (1 - t/120)^4], 0 \leq t \leq 120$.   (b) 2.81 lb/gal.   (c) None.

(d) 96.3 lb.

3. (a) 2.33 lb.   (b) 1.12 lb/gal.   (c) 10.3 hr.

C EXERCISES, p. 93

4. (a) 1.44×10^{-2} liters moles^{-1} min^{-1}.

(b) 127 g sodium acetate, 71 g ethyl alcohol.

A EXERCISES, p. 97

1. (a) $741 \ln r - 2120$.   (b) 265°C.   (c) 4.2×10^7 cal/min.

2. (a) $548 - 216 \ln r$ or $200 - 216 \ln (r/5), 5 \leq r \leq 10$.

(b) 112°C.   (c) 1.96×10^7 cal/min.

3. (a) $0.08x + 25$.   (b) 144 cal/hr.

A EXERCISES, p. 102

1. (a) 65.3°C.   (b) 52 min, 139 min.   **2.** (a) 34.1°C, 37.4°C.   (b) 8.5 min.

3. 98%, 96%, 92%.   **4.** About 24 years.   **5.** 64.5 days.   **6.** 79 min.

7. 1.35 hr, 1.98 hr.

B EXERCISES, p. 102

3. $1492, 4.92%.

C EXERCISES, p. 103

2. 22,400 years.

A EXERCISES, p. 107

1. Taking x axis horizontal, with origin at P, $y = x^2/500, -100 \leq x \leq 100$.

2. $y = x^2/625, -250 \leq x \leq 250$; absolute value of slope $= 0.8$.

3. $y = 2.0 \times 10^{-3}x^2 + 8.3 \times 10^{-10}x^4, -100 \leq x \leq 100$, taking x axis horizontal with origin at P.

B EXERCISES, p. 107

1. (a) 15.6 lb.   (b) $y = 31.2[\cosh (x/31.2) - 1]$, choosing the minimum point at $(0,0)$.

C EXERCISES, p. 108

2. (a) 66 ft.   (b) 34 lb.   3. (a) 55 ft.   (b) 16.4 lb.   (c) 21.4 lb.

A EXERCISES, p. 112

3. 18 hr, 50 hr.

B EXERCISES, p. 112

3. At 50 ft/sec, heights are 39 ft; at 6 mi/sec, heights are 2970 miles, assuming constant gravitational acceleration and 11,500 miles otherwise.

A EXERCISES, p. 115

1. $V = b \ln \left(\dfrac{M_0}{M_0 - at} \right) - gt, 0 \le t < M_0/a.$

2. $x = bt - \dfrac{b}{a} (M_0 - at) \ln \left(\dfrac{M_0}{M_0 - at} \right) - \dfrac{1}{2} gt^2, 0 \le t < M_0/a.$

B EXERCISES, p. 115

1. (a) 220 meters/sec, 448 meters/sec, 350 meters/sec.   (b) 445 meters.

A EXERCISES, p. 122

1. (a) 18 hr.   (b) 30 hr.   2. (a) 23.8 min.   (b) 2.16 hr.

B EXERCISES, p. 122

4. Elliptical shape.

A EXERCISES, p. 127

1. $y = x(1 + \ln x).$ 2. $y = ce^{x/2} - 4x - 8.$ 3. $x^2 + y^2 - 4y = 9.$

4. $y = \frac{1}{3}(x + 1).$ 6. $\ln (x^2 + y^2) + 2 \arctan (x/y) = \ln 2 + \pi/2.$

B EXERCISES, p. 127

1. $x(\sqrt{x^2 + y^2} + x)/y^2 + \ln |(\sqrt{x^2 + y^2} + x)/y^3| = \frac{3}{2} - 3 \ln 2$

   or $x(\sqrt{x^2 + y^2} - x)/y^2 + \ln |(\sqrt{x^2 + y^2} + x)/y^3| = \frac{3}{8} - 3 \ln 2.$

3. $\sqrt{y^2 + 1} + \ln (\sqrt{y^2 + 1} - 1) = \pm x + c$

   or $\sqrt{y^2 + 1} - \ln (\sqrt{y^2 + 1} + 1) = \pm x + c.$

5. The straight line $y = a\sqrt{2m} - mx$ or the hyperbola $xy = a^2/2.$

6. The straight line $y = am/\sqrt{1 + m^2} - mx$ or the hypocycloid $x^{2/3} + y^{2/3} = a^{2/3}.$

C EXERCISES, p. 128

2. $r = \pm a/(\theta + c)$ where a is the constant length.

3. $r = a \sin(\theta + c)$, where a is the constant length.

5. $r = \sqrt{3}(\csc \theta - \cot \theta)$ or $r = (\sqrt{3}/3)(\csc \theta + \cot \theta)$.

6. (b) $x \cos c + y \sin c = a$ and the envelope $x^2 + y^2 = a^2$.

A EXERCISES, p. 135

1. $y = \dfrac{S}{6EI}(3Lx^2 - x^3),\, 0 \leq x \leq L, \dfrac{SL^3}{3EI}$.

2. $y = \dfrac{S}{48EI}(3L^2x - 4x^3),\, 0 \leq x \leq L/2, \dfrac{SL^3}{48EI}, \dfrac{SL^2}{16EI}$ (y for $L/2 \leq x \leq L$ is obtained by symmetry.)

3. (a) $y = \dfrac{S}{6EI}(3Lx^2 - x^3) + \dfrac{w}{24EI}(x^4 - 4Lx^3 + 6L^2x^2)$.   (b) $\dfrac{SL^3}{3EI} + \dfrac{wL^4}{8EI}$.

4. (a) $y = \dfrac{w}{24EI}(x^4 - 2Lx^3 + L^3x) + \dfrac{S}{48EI}(3L^2x - 4x^3),\quad 0 \leq x \leq L/2$ (y for $L/2 \leq x \leq L$ is obtained by symmetry.)

  (b) $\dfrac{5wL^4}{384EI} + \dfrac{SL^3}{48EI}$.

5. $y = \dfrac{w}{384EI}(16x^4 - 12Lx^3 + L^3x),\, 0 \leq x \leq L/2$ (y for $L/2 \leq x \leq L$ is obtained by symmetry.)

6. $y = \begin{cases} \dfrac{S}{12EI}(3Lx^2 - 2x^3),\, 0 \leq x \leq L/2. \\[2mm] \dfrac{SL^2}{48EI}(6x - L),\, L/2 \leq x \leq L. \end{cases}$ $\dfrac{5SL^2}{48EI}$.

7. $y = \begin{cases} \dfrac{w}{24EI}(x^4 - 4Lx^3 + 6L^2x^2) + \dfrac{S}{12EI}(3Lx^2 - 2x^3),\, 0 \leq x \leq \dfrac{L}{2}. \\[2mm] \dfrac{w}{24EI}(x^4 - 4Lx^3 + 6L^2x^2) + \dfrac{SL^2}{48EI}(6x - L),\, \dfrac{L}{2} \leq x \leq L. \end{cases}$

B EXERCISES, p. 136

1. $y = \dfrac{w}{24EI}(x^4 - 2Lx^3 + L^2x^2),\, 0 \leq x \leq L/2, \dfrac{wL^4}{384EI}$ (y for $L/2 \leq x \leq L$ is obtained by symmetry.)

2. $y = \begin{cases} \dfrac{1}{48EI}[(3SL + 2wL^2)x^2 - 4(wL + S)x^3 + 2wx^4], \ 0 \leq x \leq L/2. \\ \dfrac{1}{48EI}[(3SL + 2wL^2)(L - x)^2 - 4(wL + S)(L - x)^3 + 2w(L - x)^4], \end{cases}$

$L/2 \leq x \leq L.$

Maximum deflection $= \dfrac{L^3}{384EI}(2S + wL)$. (Note that this is valid only for $S \geq 0$; for $S < 0$ the maximum deflection need not occur at $x = L/2$.)

3. (a) $y = \dfrac{w}{48EI}(2x^4 - 5Lx^3 + 3L^2x^2)$.

C EXERCISES, p. 136

6. (a) $y = \dfrac{k}{360EI}(3x^5 - 10L^2x^3 + 7L^4x), \ 0 \leq x \leq L$.

(b) $y = \dfrac{k}{360EI}(x^6 - 5L^3x^3 + 4L^5x), \ 0 \leq x \leq L$.

(k is the constant of proportionality in each case.)

CHAPTER 4

A EXERCISES, p. 143

1. (a) $(D^2 + 3D + 2)y = x^3$. (b) $(3D^4 - 5D^3 + 1)y = e^{-x} + \sin x$.
(c) $(D^2 + \beta D + \omega^2)s = 0$, $D = d/dt$. (d) $(x^2D^2 - 2xD - 1)y = 1$.

2. (a) $x^3 + 6x^2 - 12x - 6 - 2e^{-x}$. (b) $48 \sin 2x - 16 \cos 2x$.
(c) $6x^2 - 6x - 6 - 2e^{-x} - 8 \cos 2x - 16 \sin 2x$.
(d) $26x^3 - 36x^2 + (4x^2 - 12x - 8)e^{-x} + (12x^2 + 54x + 6) \sin 2x$
$\qquad\qquad\qquad\qquad\qquad + (36x^2 - 18x + 18) \cos 2x$.

B EXERCISES, p. 143

1. $(D - 1)(x^3 + 2x) = -x^3 + 3x^2 - 2x + 2$.
$(D - 2)(D - 1)(x^3 + 2x) = 2x^3 - 9x^2 + 10x - 6$.
$(D^2 - 3D + 2)(x^3 + 2x) = 2x^3 - 9x^2 + 10x - 6$.

C EXERCISES, p. 144

1. $(D - x)(2x^3 - 3x^2) = -2x^4 + 3x^3 + 6x^2 - 6x$.
$(D + x)(D - \dot{x})(2x^3 - 3x^2) = -2x^5 + 3x^4 - 2x^3 + 3x^2 + 12x - 6$.
$(D^2 - x^2)(2x^3 - 3x^2) = -2x^5 + 3x^4 + 12x - 6$.
$(D - x)(D + x)(2x^3 - 3x^2) = -2x^5 + 3x^4 + 2x^3 - 3x^2 + 12x - 6$.

5. $y = c_1e^x + c_2e^{2x} + \dfrac{x}{2} + \dfrac{3}{4}$.

6. (a) $y = c_1 e^{-2x} + c_2 e^x - \frac{1}{2} e^{-x}.$

   (b) $y = c_1 e^{3x} + c_2 e^{-2x} + c_3 e^x - \frac{1}{2} x e^x - \frac{1}{3}.$

   (c) $y = c_1 e^x + c_2 x e^x + 1.$ **(d)** $y = c_1 e^{-x} + c_2 e^{-x} \int e^{(x^2/2) + x} \, dx - 1.$

A EXERCISES, p. 146

1. (a) $y = c_1 e^x + c_2 e^{-5x}.$ **(b)** $y = c_1 e^{5x/2} + c_2 e^{-5x/2}.$ **(c)** $y = c_1 e^{2x} + c_2 e^{-2x}.$

   (d) $y = c_1 e^{2x} + c_2 e^{x/2} + c_3.$ **(e)** $I = c_1 e^{(2 + \sqrt{2})t} + c_2 e^{(2 - \sqrt{2})t}.$

   (f) $y = c_1 e^{-x} + c_2 e^{-3x} + c_3 e^{2x}.$

2. (a) $y = -\frac{1}{2} e^x + \frac{5}{2} e^{-x}.$ **(b)** $y = e^{2x} - 2e^x.$ **(c)** $y = \frac{1}{2}(e^{4x} + e^{-4x}) - 1.$

B EXERCISES, p. 146

1. $y = c_1 e^{-3x} + c_2 e^{(\sqrt{5}-1)x} + c_3 e^{-(\sqrt{5}+1)x}.$

C EXERCISES, p. 147

1. $y = c_1 e^{(2 - \sqrt{6})x} + c_2 e^{(2 + \sqrt{6})x} + c_3 e^{-(2 - \sqrt{6})x} + c_4 e^{-(2 + \sqrt{6})x}.$

2. $y = c_1 e^{(3 + \sqrt{3})x} + c_2 e^{(3 - \sqrt{3})x} + c_3 e^{-(2 + \sqrt{2})x} + c_4 e^{-(2 - \sqrt{2})x}.$

A EXERCISES, p. 148

1. (a) $y = c_1 e^{2x} + c_2 x e^{2x}.$ **(b)** $y = c_1 e^{x/4} + c_2 x e^{x/4}.$ **(c)** $I = c_1 e^{3t/2} + c_2 t e^{3t/2}.$

   (d) $y = c_1 + c_2 x + c_3 x^2 + c_4 x^3 + c_5 e^{2x} + c_6 e^{-2x}.$

   (e) $y = c_1 + c_2 x + c_3 e^x + c_4 x e^x.$

   (f) $y = c_1 e^{\sqrt{5/2}x} + c_2 x e^{\sqrt{5/2}x} + c_3 e^{-\sqrt{5/2}x} + c_4 x e^{-\sqrt{5/2}x}.$

2. (a) $y = e^x - 3x e^x.$ **(b)** $y = 1.$ **(c)** $s = -4t e^{-8t}.$

C EXERCISES, p. 149

1. $y = c_1 x + c_2 [x \int e^{x^2/2} \, dx - e^{x^2/2}].$ **2.** $p = -1, y = c_1 x^{-1} + c_2 x^{-1} \ln x.$

3. $y = c_1 \left[\dfrac{x}{2} \ln \left(\dfrac{1 + x}{1 - x} \right) - 1 \right] + c_2 x.$

   $y = c_1 \left[\dfrac{x}{2} \ln \left(\dfrac{1 + x}{1 - x} \right) - 1 \right] + c_2 x - \dfrac{x}{6} \ln (1 - x^2).$

A EXERCISES, p. 152

1. (a) $y = c_1 \sin 2x + c_2 \cos 2x.$ **(b)** $y = e^{-2x}(c_1 \sin x + c_2 \cos x).$

   (c) $s = c_1 \sin \dfrac{3t}{2} + c_2 \cos \dfrac{3t}{2}.$ **(d)** $y = e^x \left(c_1 \sin \dfrac{\sqrt{3}}{2} x + c_2 \cos \dfrac{\sqrt{3}}{2} x \right).$

   (e) $y = c_1 + c_2 x + c_3 \sin 4x + c_4 \cos 4x.$

   (f) $y = c_1 e^x + e^{-x}(c_2 \sin x + c_3 \cos x).$

2. (a) $y = 4 \cos x.$ **(b)** $U = \sin 4t.$ **(c)** $I = e^{-t}(\sin 2t + 2 \cos 2t).$

B EXERCISES, p. 152

1. $y = c_1 e^{-2x} + c_2 e^{2x} + e^x(c_3 \sin \sqrt{3}x + c_4 \cos \sqrt{3}x)$
$$+ e^{-x}(c_5 \sin \sqrt{3}x + c_6 \cos \sqrt{3}x).$$

3. $y = (c_1 \sin \sqrt{2}x + c_2 \cos \sqrt{2}x) + x(c_3 \sin \sqrt{2}x + c_4 \cos \sqrt{2}x).$

C EXERCISES, p. 152

1. $y = e^x(c_1 \sin x + c_2 \cos x) + e^{-x}(c_3 \sin x + c_4 \cos x).$

2. $y = e^x(c_1 \sin 2x + c_2 \cos 2x) + e^{-x}(c_3 \sin 2x + c_4 \cos 2x).$

MISCELLANEOUS REVIEW EXERCISES

A EXERCISES, p. 152

1. (a) $y = c_1 e^{3x} + c_2 e^{-x}$. (b) $y = c_1 e^{4x} + c_2 + c_3 e^{-2x}$.

(c) $y = c_1 e^{2x} + c_2 x e^{2x} + c_3 x^2 e^{2x} + c_4 + c_5 x$.

(d) $y = c_1 e^{-x} + c_2 \sin x + c_3 \cos x + c_4 e^{-2x}$.

(e) $y = e^{2x}(c_1 \sin 3x + c_2 \cos 3x) + e^{-x}(c_3 \sin 2x + c_4 \cos 2x) + c_5 e^{5x} + c_6 e^{-x}$.

(f) $y = e^x(c_1 \sin \sqrt{3}x + c_2 \cos \sqrt{3}x) + c_3 e^{-2x} + c_4 x e^{-2x} + c_5 + c_6 e^{-x}$.

(g) $y = c_1 e^{-x} + c_2 x e^{-x} + c_3 e^x + c_4 x e^x + c_5 + c_6 e^{-2x}$
$$+ e^{-x}(c_7 \sin 2x + c_8 \cos 2x).$$

(h) $y = e^x(c_1 \sin x + c_2 \cos x) + x e^x(c_3 \sin x + c_4 \cos x).$

(i) $y = c_1 e^{\sqrt{3}x} + c_2 e^{-\sqrt{3}x} + c_3 e^{4x} + c_4 e^{-4x}$
$$+ e^{x/2}(c_5 \sin 2x + c_6 \cos 2x) + e^{-x}(c_7 \sin 3x + c_8 \cos 3x).$$

(j) $y = c_1 e^x + c_2 x e^x + c_3 x^2 e^x + c_4 + c_5 x + c_6 \sin x + c_7 \cos x$
$$+ x(c_8 \sin x + c_9 \cos x).$$

2. (a) $y = e^{-x/2}\left(c_1 \sin \dfrac{\sqrt{3}}{2}x + c_2 \cos \dfrac{\sqrt{3}}{2}x\right).$

(b) $y = c_1 e^x + c_2 e^{-x} + c_3 \sin x + c_4 \cos x$.

(c) $y = c_1 + c_2 x + c_3 \sin x + c_4 \cos x + x(c_5 \sin x + c_6 \cos x).$

(d) $y = c_1 + c_2 e^{2x} + c_3 x e^{2x}$.   (e) $y = c_1 + c_2 x + c_3 e^x$.

(f) $S = c_1 \sin 2t + c_2 \cos 2t + c_3 e^{\sqrt{2}t} + c_4 e^{-\sqrt{2}t}$.

B EXERCISES, p. 153

1. $a = 5$, $b = 24$, $c = 20$.

2. $(D^6 - 2D^5 + 7D^4 + 4D^3 - D^2 + 30D + 25)y = 0$,
$y = c_1 e^{-x} + c_2 x e^{-x} + e^x(c_3 \sin 2x + c_4 \cos 2x) + x e^x(c_5 \sin 2x + c_6 \cos 2x).$

C EXERCISES, p. 153

2. (a) $y = c_1 e^x + e^{-x/2}\left(c_2 \sin \dfrac{\sqrt{3}}{2}x + c_3 \cos \dfrac{\sqrt{3}}{2}x\right).$

(b) $y = c_1 e^x + e^{x \cos 4\pi/5}[c_2 \sin (x \sin 4\pi/5) + c_3 \cos (x \sin 4\pi/5)]$
$$+ e^{x \cos 2\pi/5}[c_4 \sin (x \sin 2\pi/5) + c_5 \cos (x \sin 2\pi/5)].$$

A EXERCISES, p. 158

1. l.d. denotes *linearly dependent*; l.i. denotes *linearly independent*. (a) l.i. (b) l.d. (c) l.i. (d) l.i. (e) l.d. (f) l.i. (g) l.d. (h) l.d.

3. (a) $y = c_1 e^x + c_2 e^{-3x}$. (b) $y = e^x(c_1 \cos 2x + c_2 \sin 2x)$.
   (c) $y = c_1 + c_2 x + c_3 e^{3x}$. (d) $y = (c_1 + c_2 x)e^{2x} + (c_3 + c_4 x)e^{-2x}$.

A EXERCISES, p. 162

1. (a) $y = c_1 \sin x + c_2 \cos x + \frac{1}{5}e^{3x}$.
   (b) $y = c_1 e^{-x} + c_2 x e^{-x} - \frac{12}{25} \sin 2x - \frac{16}{25} \cos 2x$.
   (c) $y = c_1 e^{2x} + c_2 e^{-2x} - 2x^2 - 1$.
   (d) $y = e^{-2x}(c_1 \sin x + c_2 \cos x) + \frac{1}{2}e^{-x} + 3x - \frac{12}{5}$.
   (e) $I = c_1 \sin \dfrac{t}{2} + c_2 \cos \dfrac{t}{2} + t^2 - 8 - \dfrac{2}{35} \cos 3t$.
   (f) $y = c_1 + c_2 \sin 2x + c_3 \cos 2x + \frac{1}{5}e^x - \frac{1}{3} \cos x$.

2. (a) $y = \frac{1}{3} \sin x - \frac{1}{12} \sin 4x$. (b) $s = 8e^{2t} - 24e^t + 4t^2 + 12t + 14 + 2e^{-t}$.

B EXERCISES, p. 162

1. $y = 3 - 4 \sin x - 2 \cos x - \cos 2x$.

C EXERCISES, p. 163

1. $y = c_1 e^x + c_2 e^{2x} + \frac{27}{130} \cos 3x - \frac{21}{130} \sin 3x + \frac{79}{6970} \sin 9x - \frac{27}{6970} \cos 9x$.

2. $y = \begin{cases} x - \sin x, \ 0 \leqq x \leqq \pi. \\ -\pi \cos x - 2 \sin x, \ x \geqq \pi. \end{cases}$

A EXERCISES, p. 165

1. (a) $y = c_1 e^x + c_2 e^{-3x} + \frac{1}{2}x e^x$.
   (b) $y = c_1 \sin x + c_2 \cos x + x^2 - 2 - \frac{1}{2}x \cos x$.
   (c) $y = c_1 + c_2 e^{-x} + \dfrac{x^3}{3} + \dfrac{x^2}{2} - x + \dfrac{1}{12} e^{3x}$.
   (d) $y = c_1 e^x + c_2 x e^x + \frac{1}{2}x^2 e^x$.
   (e) $y = c_1 \sin 2x + c_2 \cos 2x + 2x \sin 2x - x$.
   (f) $y = c_1 + c_2 \sin x + c_3 \cos x + \dfrac{x^2}{2} - \dfrac{x}{2}(\sin x + \cos x)$.

2. (a) $I = 4 \cos 3t + 2t \sin 3t$. (b) $s = 2 - 2e^{-t} + \dfrac{t^2}{2} - t - t e^{-t}$.

B EXERCISES, p. 165

1. $y = c_1 \sinh x + c_2 \cosh x + c_3 \sin x + c_4 \cos x + \dfrac{x}{4} \sinh x$.

2. $y = c_1 \sin x + c_2 \cos x + \frac{1}{4}(x \sin x - x^2 \cos x)$.

C EXERCISES, p. 165

2. $y = c_1 \sin 2x + c_2 \cos 2x + \frac{3}{32} - \frac{1}{96} \cos 4x - \frac{x}{8} \sin 2x.$

A EXERCISES, p. 167

1. (a) $c_1 \sin x + c_2 \cos x;\ (ax + b)e^{-x} + x(c \sin x + d \cos x).$

(b) $c_1 e^{-x} + c_2 e^{3x};\ (ax + b) \sin 2x + (cx + d) \cos 2x$
$$+ (fx^4 + gx^3 + hx^2 + kx)e^{3x}.$$

(c) $c_1 + c_2 x + c_3 \sin x + c_4 \cos x;\ ax^4 + bx^3 + cx^2 + de^x.$

(d) $c_1 e^x + c_2 x e^x;\ (ax^4 + bx^3 + cx^2)e^x.$

(e) $c_1 \sin x + c_2 \cos x;\ e^{-x}(a \sin x + b \cos x) + cx + d.$

(f) $c_1 e^x + c_2 e^{3x};\ axe^x + (bx^3 + cx^2 + dx + f)e^{-x}.$

2. (a) $y = c_1 e^x + c_2 e^{-x} + \dfrac{e^x}{4}(x^2 - x).$

(b) $y = c_1 \sin 2x + c_2 \cos 2x + \dfrac{x^2}{4} - \dfrac{1}{8} + \dfrac{3x^2}{8} \sin 2x + \dfrac{3x}{16} \cos 2x.$

(c) $y = c_1 e^{-x} + c_2 x e^{-x} + \frac{1}{6}x^3 e^{-x} - \frac{1}{50}(3 \cos 3x + 4 \sin 3x).$

(d) $Q = c_1 \sin t + c_2 \cos t + \frac{3}{4}t \sin t - \frac{1}{4}t^2 \cos t.$

B EXERCISES, p. 168

1. $y = c_1 e^{-2x} + c_2 e^{4x} - \left(\dfrac{x^3}{15} + \dfrac{4x^2}{25} + \dfrac{42x}{125} + c_3\right)e^{3x}.$

2. $y = \dfrac{t}{4\omega^2}(\sin \omega t + \cos \omega t) + \dfrac{t^2}{4\omega}(\sin \omega t - \cos \omega t) - \dfrac{1}{4\omega^3}\sin \omega t.$

3. $y = c_1 e^x + c_2 e^{2x} + \dfrac{1}{6}e^{-x} + \dfrac{e^{-x}}{52}(\cos 2x - 5 \sin 2x).$

C EXERCISES, p. 168

1. $y = c_1 \sin 2x + c_2 \cos 2x + \frac{1}{16} + \frac{1}{16}x \sin 2x - \frac{1}{48} \cos 4x - \frac{1}{128} \cos 6x.$

2. $y = c_1 e^{2x} + c_2 e^{-(3+\sqrt{3})x} + c_3 e^{-(3-\sqrt{3})x} + \dfrac{e^{4x}}{1472} - \dfrac{xe^{2x}}{88} - \dfrac{1}{32} - \dfrac{e^{-2x}}{32} + \dfrac{e^{-4x}}{192}.$

A EXERCISES, p. 170

1. $y = c_1 \sin x + c_2 \cos x + \sin x \ln (\csc x - \cot x).$

2. $y = c_1 \sin x + c_2 \cos x + x \sin x + \cos x \ln \cos x.$

3. $y = c_1 \sin 2x + c_2 \cos 2x + \frac{1}{4} \sin 2x \ln \sin 2x - (x/2) \cos 2x.$

4. $y = c_1 e^x + c_2 e^{-x} + \frac{1}{2}x e^x.$ **5.** $y = c_1 e^{-x} + c_2 e^{-2x} + \dfrac{x}{2} - \dfrac{3}{4} - 3xe^{-2x}.$

6. $y = c_1 e^{-2x} + c_2 e^x - \dfrac{1}{2} \ln x + \dfrac{e^x}{3} \displaystyle\int \dfrac{e^{-x}}{x}\, dx + \dfrac{e^{-2x}}{6} \int \dfrac{e^{2x}}{x}\, dx.$

7. $y = c_1 e^{-x} + c_2 e^{-x/2} + \frac{1}{10} e^{-3x}.$

8. $y = c_1 e^x + c_2 e^{-x} + \dfrac{e^x}{48}(8x^3 - 12x^2 + 12x).$

B EXERCISES, p. 170

3. $y = c_1 e^x + c_2 e^{-x} + c_3 e^{2x} - \frac{1}{2} x e^x.$

4. $y = c_1 x^2 + c_2 x - x e^{-x} - (x^2 + x) \displaystyle\int \dfrac{e^{-x}}{x}\, dx.$

A EXERCISES, p. 175

1. $y = c_1 + c_2 e^x - x.$ **2.** $y = c_1 e^x + c_2 x e^x + \frac{1}{2} x^2 e^x.$

3. $y = c_1 e^{-x} + c_2 e^{-2x} + \frac{1}{6} e^x - x e^{-x}.$

4. $y = c_1 e^x + c_2 e^{-x} - 2x^4 - 24x^2 + 3x - 49.$

5. $y = c_1 + c_2 e^{-x} + x^4 - 4x^3 + 12x^2 - 24x - \frac{1}{3} e^{2x}.$

6. $y = c_1 e^{-x} + c_2 x e^{-x} + \frac{1}{12} x^4 e^{-x} + 1.$ **7.** $y = c_1 e^{2x} + c_2 x e^{2x} - \frac{1}{9} e^{2x} \sin 3x.$

8. $y = c_1 + c_2 e^x + c_3 e^{-x} - \frac{1}{6} x^6 - 5x^4 - 60x^2 - x.$

B EXERCISES, p. 176

3. $\frac{1}{5} e^{4x},\ y = c_1 e^{3x} + c_2 e^{-x} + \frac{1}{5} e^{4x}.$

4. $\dfrac{e^{3x}}{15} + \dfrac{2e^{-5x}}{21},\ y = c_1 e^{2x} + c_2 e^{-2x} + c_3 e^{-3x} + \dfrac{e^{3x}}{15} + \dfrac{2e^{-5x}}{21}.$

9. (a) $-e^{2x}(x^3 + 6x).$ (b) $2e^{-2x}(x^2 + 4x + 6) + \frac{1}{3} e^{2x}.$

13. (a) $\frac{1}{130}(9 \cos 3x - 7 \sin 3x).$ (b) $\dfrac{8 \cos 2x - 19 \sin 2x}{85}.$

14. (a) $-\dfrac{e^{2x}}{50}(3 \cos 3x + \sin 3x).$ (b) $\dfrac{e^{-x}}{58}(2 \cos 2x - 5 \sin 2x).$

16. (a) $\dfrac{e^{3x}}{10}.$ (b) $-x^5 - 3x^4 + 2x^3 - 60x^2 - 72x + 12.$

     (c) $\dfrac{e^{2x}}{125}(25x^2 - 40x + 22).$ (d) $-\frac{2}{17}(\cos 4x + 4 \sin 4x).$

     (e) $\cos x.$ (f) $-\frac{1}{64} e^{3x} \sin 4x.$ (g) $\dfrac{e^x}{5}(4 \sin x + 7 \cos x).$

     (h) $e^{-x}\left(\dfrac{x^6}{120} - \dfrac{x^5}{10} + \dfrac{3x^4}{4} - 4x^3 + \dfrac{1}{2} \sin x\right).$

     (i) $-x^2 + 2x - 4 + \frac{3}{4}(\cos x - \sin x).$

     (j) $e^x(x^2 - 4x + 4) - \frac{4}{5} x^5 - 4x^4 + 48x^2 + 96x.$

C EXERCISES, p. 178

1. $\dfrac{e^{2x}}{60}\left(x^4 - \dfrac{4}{5}x^3 + \dfrac{12}{25}x^2 - \dfrac{24}{125}x + \dfrac{24}{125}\right)$.

4. (a) $\frac{1}{2}x^2e^x$. (b) $-2xe^x - xe^{2x}$. (c) $\frac{1}{24}x^4e^{-2x}$.

(d) $-\frac{1}{6}x\cos 3x$. (e) $-\dfrac{x}{2}(\sin x + \cos x)$.

(f) $-\dfrac{x}{4}\cos x - \dfrac{x^2}{8}\sin x$.

5. $y = \left(\dfrac{x^2}{4} - \dfrac{1}{8}\right)\cos x + \left(\dfrac{x^3}{6} - \dfrac{x}{4}\right)\sin x$.

A EXERCISES, p. 180

1. (a) $y = c_1 x^2 + \dfrac{c_2}{x} - \dfrac{x}{2}$.

(b) $y = x[c_1 \sin(\ln x) + c_2 \cos(\ln x)] + \frac{1}{2}\ln x + \frac{1}{2}$.

(c) $y = \dfrac{c_1}{x^2} + \dfrac{c_2 \ln x}{x^2} + \dfrac{x^2}{16} + 4(\ln x)^2 - 8\ln x + 6$.

2. $y = c_1 + \dfrac{c_2}{x} + c_3 x - \ln x + \dfrac{1}{2}x\ln x$.

B EXERCISES, p. 181

2. $m = -3, 1;\ y = c_1 x^{-3} + c_2 x$.

4. $y = \dfrac{c_1}{\sqrt{2x+3}} + c_2(2x+3) + \dfrac{3}{5}(2x+3)^2 - 6(2x+3)\ln(2x+3) - 27$.

5. $y = c_1(x+2)^{(1/2)(1+\sqrt{5})} + c_2(x+2)^{(1/2)(1-\sqrt{5})} - 4$.

C EXERCISES, p. 181

1. $y = c_1 \sin(\sin x) + c_2 \cos(\sin x)$. **2.** $y = c_1 e^{x^2} + c_2 e^{-x^2}$.

6. (a) $y = c_1 e^{\cos x} + c_2 e^{2\cos x}$. (b) $y = c_1 \sin\left(\dfrac{1}{x}\right) + c_2 \cos\left(\dfrac{1}{x}\right) + \dfrac{1}{x^2} - 2$.

7. $y = e^{-x^2}(c_1 \sin x + c_2 \cos x)$. **8.** $y = \dfrac{c_1 \sin x + c_2 \cos x}{x}$.

9. Eigenvalues are given by $\lambda = n^2,\ n = 1, 2, 3, \ldots$. Eigenfunctions are $B_n \sin nx$, $n = 1, 2, 3, \ldots$, where B_n, $n = 1, 2, 3, \ldots$ are constants.

11. $y = c_1 - c_1 x e^{-x}\displaystyle\int \dfrac{e^x}{x}\,dx + c_2 x e^{-x}$. **12.** $y = c_1 e^x + c_2 e^x\displaystyle\int \dfrac{e^{-x}}{x^2}\,dx$.

CHAPTER 5

A EXERCISES, p. 189

1. Take positive direction downward. Then

    (b) $x = \frac{1}{4} \cos 16t$ (ft), $v = -4 \sin 16t$ (ft/sec).

    (c) Amplitude $= \frac{1}{4}$ ft, period $= T = \pi/8$ sec, frequency $= f = 8/\pi$ cycles per sec.

    (d) $x = \sqrt{2}/8$ ft, $v = -2\sqrt{2}$ ft/sec, $a = -32\sqrt{2}$ ft/sec^2.

2. (a) $x = \frac{1}{4} \sin 8t$ (ft), $v = 2 \cos 8t$ (ft/sec).

    (b) Amplitude $= \frac{1}{4}$ ft, $T = \pi/4$ sec, $f = 4/\pi$ cycles per sec.

    (c) 1.89 ft/sec, 5.33 ft/sec^2.

3. $x = \frac{5}{12} \cos 4\sqrt{3}t$, amplitude $= \frac{5}{12}$ ft, $T = 2\pi/4\sqrt{3} = \pi\sqrt{3}/6$ sec, $f = 2\sqrt{3}/\pi$ cycles per sec.

4. $x = \dfrac{5}{12} \cos 4\sqrt{3}t + \dfrac{5\sqrt{3}}{12} \sin 4\sqrt{3}t = \dfrac{5}{6} \sin\left(4\sqrt{3}t + \dfrac{\pi}{6}\right)$.

    Amplitude $= \frac{5}{6}$ ft, $T = \pi\sqrt{3}/6$ sec, $f = 2\sqrt{3}/\pi$ cycles per sec.

5. (a) Amplitude $= 5$ cm, $T = \pi/\sqrt{5}$ sec, $f = \sqrt{5}/\pi$ cycles per sec.

    (b) $\pi/6\sqrt{5}, 5\pi/6\sqrt{5}, 7\pi/6\sqrt{5}, 11\pi/6\sqrt{5}, \ldots$ seconds.

6. (a) $x = 1.5$ in. above equilibrium position, $v = 5\sqrt{3}/8$ ft/sec moving upward.

    (b) Amplitude $= 3$ in., $T = 2\pi/5$ sec, $f = 5/2\pi$ cycles per sec.

    (c) $2\pi/15, 8\pi/15, 14\pi/15, \ldots$ seconds.

B EXERCISES, p. 190

3. 4.5 lb.

A EXERCISES, p. 194

1. (b) $x = \dfrac{e^{-8t}}{2} (\sin 8t + \cos 8t)$, taking downward as positive.

    (c) $x = \dfrac{\sqrt{2}}{2} e^{-8t} \sin\left(8t + \dfrac{\pi}{4}\right)$, $A(t) = \dfrac{\sqrt{2}}{2} e^{-8t}$, $\omega = 8$, $\phi = \dfrac{\pi}{4}$,

    quasi period $= 2\pi/8 = \pi/4$ sec.

2. (a) $x = -\frac{25}{32}e^{-4.8t} \sin 6.4t$, $v = e^{-4.8t} (3.75 \sin 6.4t - 5 \cos 6.4t)$, taking downward as positive.

    (b) $x = \frac{25}{32}e^{-4.8t} \sin (6.4t + \pi)$.

3. $x = 1.5e^{-3t}(3 \sin 4t + 4 \cos 4t) = 7.5e^{-3t} \sin (4t + \phi)$ where $\cos \phi = \frac{3}{5}$, $\sin \phi = \frac{4}{5}$ or $\phi = 0.927$ radians $= 53°$. Here, x is in inches.

A EXERCISES, p. 197

1. (a) $x = e^{-16t}(0.5 + 8t)$ (ft).   (b) Critically damped.

2. (a) $x = 10te^{-16t}$ (ft), $v = 10(1 - 16t)e^{-16t}$ (ft/sec).   (b) $5/8e = 0.23$ ft.

A EXERCISES, p. 200

1. (a) $x = 0.960e^{-1.56t} - 0.695e^{-6.45t} - 0.298 \sin 10t - 0.265 \cos 10t$.

(b) Steady-state part: $-0.298 \sin 10t - 0.265 \cos 10t = 0.397 \sin (10t + 3.87)$.

(c) Steady-state amplitude $= 0.397$ ft, period $= 2\pi/10 = \pi/5$ sec, frequency $= 5/\pi$ cycles per sec.

2. $x = \frac{2}{3} \cos 2t - 5 \sin 2t - \frac{2}{3} \cos 4t$, $v = \frac{8}{3} \sin 4t - \frac{4}{3} \sin 2t - 10 \cos 2t$.

A EXERCISES, p. 203

1. (b) $x = 2 \sin 2t - 4t \cos 2t$, $v = 8t \sin 2t$.

2. $x = \frac{1}{2} \cos 2t - 4t \cos 2t$, $v = 8t \sin 2t - \sin 2t - 4 \cos 2t$; yes.

A EXERCISES, p. 207

1. (a) $Q = 4 - 2e^{-5t/2}(2 \cos 5t + \sin 5t)$, $I = 25e^{-5t/2} \sin 5t$.

(b) Transient terms of Q and I are $-2e^{-5t/2}(2 \cos 5t + \sin 5t)$ and $25e^{-5t/2} \sin 5t$ respectively. Steady-state term of Q is 4.

(c) $Q = 4, I = 0$.

2. (a) Period $= 2\pi/50 = \pi/25$ sec, frequency $= 25/\pi$ cycles per sec. (b) 0.04 coulombs, 1 amp.

3. $Q = 2(\cos 40t - \cos 50t)$, $I = 20(5 \sin 50t - 4 \sin 40t)$.

4. $Q = 5.07e^{-5t} - 1.27e^{-20t} + 0.20$, $I = 25.4(e^{-20t} - e^{-5t})$ approximately.

A EXERCISES, p. 211

1. Period $= \pi/5$ sec, frequency $= 5/\pi$ cycles per sec.   **2.** 3.26 ft, 13.04 ft.

3. Frequency $= 1.6$ cycles per sec, period $= 0.625$ sec.

4. (a) $\theta = 5 \cos 4t$(degrees) or $(\pi/36) \cos 4t$ (radians).

(b) Frequency $= 2/\pi = 0.636$ cycles per sec. (c) $2\pi/9$ ft.

(d) Velocity $= 2\pi/9$ ft/sec, acceleration $= 2\pi^2/81$ ft/sec^2.

B EXERCISES, p. 211

2. 1/4 density of water $= 15.6$ lb/ft^3.

CHAPTER 6

A EXERCISES, p. 219

1. $x = \cos t, y = \sin t$.   **2.** $u = c_1 e^{2x} + c_2 e^{-2x} - \frac{1}{2}$, $v = c_1 e^{2x} - c_2 e^{-2x} + \frac{1}{2}$.

3. $x = c_1 e^{\sqrt{2}t} + c_2 e^{-\sqrt{2}t}$, $y = c_1(\sqrt{2} - 1)e^{\sqrt{2}t} - c_2(\sqrt{2} + 1)e^{-\sqrt{2}t}$.

4. $x = c_1 \sin t + c_2 \cos t,\ y = c_3 e^t + c_4 e^{-t}$.

5. $x = c_1 \sin t + c_2 \cos t + c_3 e^t + c_4 e^{-t} + 2$,
$y = -c_1 \sin t - c_2 \cos t + c_3 e^t + c_4 e^{-t} - 2$.

6. $x = 4e^{2t} - 2e^{-3t},\ y = e^{2t} + 2e^{-3t}$.

7. $x = \frac{3}{5} c_1 e^{-t/8} + \frac{2}{5} \sin t - \frac{1}{5} \cos t$,
$y = c_1 e^{-t/8} + \sin t + \cos t$.

B EXERCISES, p. 220

1. $x = 1 + t - 2t^2 + \frac{2}{3} t^3 - \frac{1}{6} t^4 + e^{-t} - \sin t$,
$y = -6 - 3t - 4t^2 - \frac{1}{6} t^4 + e^t + e^{-t} - \frac{1}{2} \sin t - \frac{1}{2} \cos t$.

2. (a) $x^2 - y^2 = c_1,\ y^2 - z^2 = c_2$.   (b) $x = c_1 \sqrt{y^2 + 1}$, $\arctan y = \ln z + c_2$.

3. $y = \frac{1}{4} (\ln x)^2 + \frac{1}{2} \ln x - \dfrac{x}{2} + c_1,\ z = \frac{1}{2} \ln x + \dfrac{x}{2} - \dfrac{1}{2}$.

4. $x = c_1 e^t + c_2 e^{\omega t} + c_3 e^{\omega^2 t}$,
$y = c_1 e^t + \omega c_2 e^{\omega t} + \omega^2 c_3 e^{\omega^2 t}$,
$z = c_1 e^t + \omega^2 c_2 e^{\omega t} + \omega c_3 e^{\omega^2 t}$,
where $1,\ \omega,\ \omega^2$ are the three cube roots of unity.

C EXERCISES, p. 220

1. $P_n(t) = \dfrac{(\lambda t)^n e^{-\lambda t}}{n!}$ where $n = 0, 1, 2, 3, \ldots$.

2. $c_1(z - y) = c_2(x - z) = \sqrt{c^3/(x + y + z)}$.

A EXERCISES, p. 223

1. (b) $x = 80t,\ y = 80\sqrt{3}\, t - 16t^2$.

(c) Range $= 400\sqrt{3} = 693$ ft, max. height $= 300$ ft, time of flight $= 8.66$ sec.

(d) Position after 2 sec (160, 213), position after 4 sec (320, 298), velocity after 2 sec has magnitude 109 ft/sec, velocity after 4 sec has magnitude 80.7 ft/sec.

2. Max. range $= 165$ miles, height $= 41\frac{1}{4}$ miles, time of flight $= 3$ min 53 sec.

3. (a) 4 sec.   (b) 200 ft.

B EXERCISES, p. 224

1. 283 ft/sec, 15.8 sec.

C EXERCISES, p. 232

3. Force is inversely proportional to r^5.

A EXERCISES, p. 235

1. (a) $x_1 = a(0.45 \cos 0.62\omega t - 0.45 \cos 1.62\omega t)$,
   $x_2 = a(0.72 \cos 0.62\omega t + 0.28 \cos 1.62\omega t)$.

   (b) $x_1 = a(0.72 \cos 0.62\omega t + 0.28 \cos 1.62\omega t)$,
   $x_2 = a(1.17 \cos 0.62\omega t - 0.17 \cos 1.62\omega t)$.

   (c) $x_1 = a(0.17 \cos 0.62\omega t - 1.17 \cos 1.62\omega t)$,
   $x_2 = a(0.28 \cos 0.62\omega t + 0.72 \cos 1.62\omega t)$.

A EXERCISES, p. 240

1. $I_1 = 3 - 2e^{-5t} - e^{-20t}$, $I_2 = 4e^{-5t} - e^{-20t} - 3$.

2. $I_1 = 2e^{-5t} + e^{-20t} + 3 \sin 10t - 3 \cos 10t$,
   $I_2 = 3 \cos 10t - 4e^{-5t} + e^{-20t}$.

3. Charge on capacitor $= 2 - e^{-t}$, current through capacitor $= e^{-t}$, current through inductor $= 20 - 20e^{-4t}$, current through battery $= 20 - 20e^{-4t} + e^{-t}$.

4. Charge on capacitor $= \sin 2t - 2 \cos 2t + 3e^{-t}$, current through capacitor $= 2 \cos 2t + 4 \sin 2t - 3e^{-t}$, current through inductor $= 40 \sin 2t - 20 \cos 2t + 20e^{-4t}$, current through battery $= 44 \sin 2t - 18 \cos 2t + 20e^{-4t} - 3e^{-t}$.

5. $I_1 = 500te^{-50t}$, $I_2 = 5e^{-50t} + 250te^{-50t} - 5 \cos 50t$,
   $I_3 = 5 \cos 50t - 5e^{-50t} + 250te^{-50t}$,
   $Q_3 = 0.1 \sin 50t - 5te^{-50t}$.

CHAPTER 7

A EXERCISES, p. 256

1. (a) $\dfrac{3}{s^2} - \dfrac{2}{s}$, $s > 0$. (b) $\dfrac{12}{s^2 + 9}$, $s > 0$. (c) $\dfrac{5s}{s^2 + 4}$, $s > 0$.

   (d) $\dfrac{10}{s + 5}$, $s > -5$. (e) $\dfrac{2}{s - 1} - \dfrac{3}{s + 1} + \dfrac{8}{s^3}$, $s > 1$.

   (f) $\dfrac{15 - 4s}{s^2 + 25}$, $s > 0$. (g) $\dfrac{6s}{s^2 - 9} - \dfrac{10}{s^2 - 25}$, $s > 5$.

   (h) $\dfrac{1}{(s + 3)^2} - \dfrac{6}{s^4} + \dfrac{1}{s^2}$, $s > 0$.

3. (a) $\dfrac{2}{(s - 3)^3}$. (b) $\dfrac{6 - 2s}{s^2 + 4s + 8}$. (c) $\dfrac{2s}{(s^2 + 1)^2} + \dfrac{1}{(s + 1)^2}$.

   (d) $\dfrac{s^4 + 4s^2 + 24}{s^5}$. (e) $\dfrac{s^2 + 4}{(s^2 - 4)^2} - \dfrac{4}{s^3}$. (f) $\dfrac{4s}{s^2 - 36} - \dfrac{4}{s}$.

4. (a) $\dfrac{3\sqrt{\pi}}{4s^{5/2}}$. (b) $\dfrac{\sqrt{\pi}}{2s^{3/2}} + \dfrac{2}{s} + \dfrac{\sqrt{\pi}}{s^{1/2}}$.

   (c) $\dfrac{2\Gamma(\frac{2}{3})}{3s^{5/3}}$. (d) $\dfrac{\sqrt{\pi}}{2(s - 1)^{3/2}}$.

5. (b) $\dfrac{1}{s^2} - \dfrac{e^{-4s}}{s^2} - \dfrac{4}{s}e^{-4s}$.

7. (a) $1 + H(t - 1)$.　(b) $2t + (t^2 - 2t)H(t - 3)$.

(c) $\cos t\{1 - H(t - 2\pi)\}$.

8. (a) $e^{-s}(s + 1)/s^2$.　(b) $\dfrac{e^{-2(s-1)}}{s - 1} - \dfrac{e^{-3(s+1)}}{s + 1}$.

B EXERCISES, p. 256

2. $\dfrac{2s + 2}{(s^2 + 2s + 2)^2}$.　**5.** $\dfrac{1}{s}\left(\dfrac{e^{as} - 1}{e^{as} + 1}\right) = \dfrac{1}{s}\tanh\dfrac{as}{2}$.

C EXERCISES, p. 258

5. (b) $\dfrac{\pi}{s^2 + \pi^2}\coth\dfrac{s}{2}$.

7. $3\sin t + (t^2 - 3\sin t)H(t - \pi) + (t - t^2 - \cos t)H(t - 2\pi)$.

A EXERCISES, p. 268

1. (a) $4e^{-2t}$.　(b) $3\cos 3t$.　(c) $3\sin 5t$.

(d) $6\cos 2t - 5\sin 2t - 3e^{4t}$.　(e) $\dfrac{2}{\sqrt{5}}\sin\sqrt{5}t - \cos\sqrt{5}t$.

(f) $t^2 + 3t - 1$.

2. (a) $\frac{1}{2}t^2e^{-2t}$.　(b) $\frac{1}{2}e^{2t}(4\cos 4t - 3\sin 4t)$.

(c) $\frac{1}{3}e^{-t/2}\left(3\cos\dfrac{\sqrt{3}}{2}t + \sqrt{3}\sin\dfrac{\sqrt{3}}{2}t\right)$.

(d) $\frac{1}{6}e^t(t^3 + 3t^2)$.　(e) $\frac{1}{2}e^{-t/2}(\cos t - \sin t)$.

3. (a) $\dfrac{9}{2}e^t - \dfrac{7}{2}e^{-3t}$.　(b) $\frac{1}{2}e^{4t} + \frac{5}{2}e^{-4t}$.

(c) $3e^{2t} - e^{-t} - 2e^{3t}$.　(d) $(2t - 3)e^{-t} + 5e^{2t}$.

(e) $2 - e^t(2\cos 2t - \sin 2t)$.　(f) $\frac{1}{6}(2\cos t - 2\cos 2t + 2\sin t - \sin 2t)$.

4. (a) $\frac{1}{4}(e^{2t} - e^{-2t}) = \frac{1}{2}\sinh 2t$.　(b) $(t + 2)e^{-t} + t - 2$.

(c) $\frac{1}{2}(\sin t - t\cos t)$.

5. (a) $Y = e^{3t} + 2e^t$.　(b) $Y = 3e^{-2t} + 2t - 2$.

(c) $Y = 2e^{-t} + \sin 3t - 2\cos 3t$.

(d) $Y = 24 + 12t + e^t(9t - 20)$.

(e) $Y = 4 - 2e^{-4t}(\cos 3t - 2\sin 3t)$.

6. (a) $X = 2\cos t - \sin t$, $Y = -2\sin t - \cos t$.

(b) $X = e^{-3t}(2\sin 4t - \cos 4t)$, $Y = 2e^{-3t}\cos 4t$.

B EXERCISES, p. 269

1. $\sin t - 2 \cos t + 2e^t(\cos 2t + 2 \sin 2t)$.

2. $(2t - 1)e^{-t} + (2 - 3t)e^{-2t}$.

3. $Y = e^{-t}(1 + t - t^2 + 2t^3)$.

4. $X = -2$, $Y = -1$, $Z = 3$.

5. (a) $\begin{cases} \frac{1}{2}(t - 2)^2, & t \geq 2 \\ 0, & t < 2 \end{cases}$.   (b) $\begin{cases} 2(t - 1)^{1/2}e^{-(t-1)}/\sqrt{\pi}, & t \geq 1 \\ 0, & t < 1 \end{cases}$.

6. $Y = 4 \sin t$.

C EXERCISES, p. 270

1. $Y = 1 - t$.   **2.** $Y = t$.

A EXERCISES, p. 273

1. $I = \dfrac{E}{R}(1 - e^{-Rt/L})$.   **2.** $X = v_0 t - \dfrac{1}{2} gt^2$, if $X = 0$ at $t = 0$.

3. (a) $\begin{cases} (E_0/R)(1 - e^{-Rt/L}), & t \leq T \\ (E_0/R)(e^{-R(t-T)/L} - e^{-Rt/L}), & t > T \end{cases}$.

(b) $\dfrac{E_0}{R^2 + \omega^2 L^2} (R \sin \omega t - \omega L \cos \omega t + \omega L e^{-Rt/L})$.

CHAPTER 8

A EXERCISES, p. 281

1. $y = 1 - x + \dfrac{x^2}{2!} - \dfrac{x^3}{3!} + \dfrac{x^4}{4!} - \cdots = e^{-x}$.

2. $y = 2\left(1 + \dfrac{x^2}{2} + \dfrac{x^4}{2^2 2!} + \dfrac{x^6}{2^3 3!} + \cdots\right) = 2e^{x^2/2}$.

3. $y = c + 1 + (c + 1)x + \dfrac{cx^2}{2!} + \dfrac{cx^3}{3!} + \dfrac{cx^4}{4!} + \cdots = ce^x + x + 1$.

4. $y = c - \dfrac{2}{9} + \left(\dfrac{2}{3} - 3c\right)x + c\left[\dfrac{(3x)^2}{2!} - \dfrac{(3x)^3}{3!} + \dfrac{(3x)^4}{4!} - \cdots\right]$

$$= ce^{-3x} + \dfrac{2}{3}x - \dfrac{2}{9}.$$

5. $y = c_1\left(1 - \dfrac{x^2}{2!} + \dfrac{x^4}{4!} - \dfrac{x^6}{6!} + \cdots\right) + c_2\left(x - \dfrac{x^3}{3!} + \dfrac{x^5}{5!} - \dfrac{x^7}{7!} + \cdots\right)$

$$= c_1 \cos x + c_2 \sin x.$$

6. $y = 1 + \dfrac{x^2}{2!} + \dfrac{x^4}{4!} + \dfrac{x^6}{6!} + \dfrac{x^8}{8!} + \cdots = \dfrac{e^x + e^{-x}}{2} = \cosh x$.

7. $y = c_1 + c_2\left(1 - x + \dfrac{x^2}{2!} - \dfrac{x^3}{3!} + \cdots\right) = c_1 + c_2 e^{-x}$.

8. $y = c_1\left[1 + 2x + \dfrac{(2x)^2}{2!} + \dfrac{(2x)^3}{3!} + \cdots\right] + c_2\left[1 - x + \dfrac{x^2}{2!} - \dfrac{x^3}{3!} + \cdots\right]$

$$= c_1 e^{2x} + c_2 e^{-x}.$$

9. $y = c\left(x - \dfrac{x^3}{2 \cdot 4} + \dfrac{x^5}{2 \cdot 4^2 \cdot 6} - \dfrac{x^7}{2 \cdot 4^2 \cdot 6^2 \cdot 8} + \cdots\right)$

$$= c\left(x - \dfrac{x^3}{(3^2 - 1)} + \dfrac{x^5}{(3^2 - 1)(5^2 - 1)} - \dfrac{x^7}{(3^2 - 1)(5^2 - 1)(7^2 - 1)} + \cdots\right).$$

(Note that this is not a general solution.)

10. $y = \dfrac{3x^2 - 1}{2}$.   **11.** $y = c(x^2 - 4x + 2)$ (not a general solution).

12. $y = x^2 - x + 1$.

B EXERCISES, p. 281

1. $y = 1 + x + x^2 + \tfrac{4}{3}x^3 + \tfrac{7}{6}x^4 + \tfrac{6}{5}x^5 + \dots$, $y(0.2) = 1.253$.

3. $y = a_0\left(1 - \dfrac{x^3}{3!} + \dfrac{x^6}{6!} - \dfrac{x^9}{9!} + \cdots\right) + a_1\left(x - \dfrac{x^4}{4!} + \dfrac{x^7}{7!} - \dfrac{x^{10}}{10!} + \cdots\right)$

$$+ a_2\left(\dfrac{x^2}{2!} - \dfrac{x^5}{5!} + \dfrac{x^8}{8!} - \dfrac{x^{11}}{11!} + \cdots\right).$$

5. $y = A\left(1 - \dfrac{x^3}{6} + \dfrac{x^6}{180} - \cdots\right) + B\left(x - \dfrac{x^4}{12} + \dfrac{x^7}{504} - \cdots\right)$

$$+ \dfrac{x^3}{6} - \dfrac{x^5}{120} - \dfrac{x^6}{180} + \dfrac{x^7}{5040} + \cdots.$$

6. $y = a_0 + a_1(x - 1) + \tfrac{1}{2}(x - 1)^2 - \tfrac{1}{2}(x - 1)^3 + \tfrac{1}{2}(x - 1)^4 - \dots$, $0 < x < 2$.

C EXERCISES, p. 282

3. $y = \dfrac{c_1 \sin x + c_2 \cos x}{x}$.   **7.** (a) $1, x, \dfrac{3x^2 - 1}{2}, \dfrac{5x^3 - 3x}{2}$.

A EXERCISES, p. 287

1. (a) $y = 4\left(1 + x + \dfrac{x^2}{2!} + \dfrac{x^3}{3!} + \cdots\right) = 4e^x$.

(b) $y = 1 - \dfrac{x^2}{2} + \dfrac{x^4}{2^2 2!} - \dfrac{x^6}{2^3 3!} + \cdots = e^{-x^2/2}$.

(c) $y = c - cx + (c + 2)\left(\dfrac{x^2}{2!} - \dfrac{x^3}{3!} + \dfrac{x^4}{4!} - \cdots\right) = 2x - 2 + (c + 2)e^{-x}$.

(d) $y = c_1\left(1 - \dfrac{x^2}{2!} + \dfrac{x^4}{4!} - \cdots\right) + c_2\left(x - \dfrac{x^3}{3!} + \dfrac{x^5}{5!} - \cdots\right) + x$

$$= c_1 \cos x + c_2 \sin x + x.$$

(e) $y = -\dfrac{1}{8} - \dfrac{x^2}{4} + \dfrac{1}{8}\left[1 + \dfrac{(2x)^2}{2!} + \dfrac{(2x)^4}{4!} + \dfrac{(2x)^6}{6!} + \cdots\right]$

$\quad = -\dfrac{1}{8} - \dfrac{x^2}{4} + \dfrac{1}{16}(e^{2x} + e^{-2x}) = -\dfrac{1}{8} - \dfrac{x^2}{4} + \dfrac{1}{8}\cosh 2x.$

(f) $y = c_1\left(1 - \dfrac{x^2}{2} + \dfrac{x^4}{2\cdot 4} - \dfrac{x^6}{2\cdot 4\cdot 6} + \cdots\right)$

$\qquad\qquad\qquad + c_2\left(x - \dfrac{x^3}{3} + \dfrac{x^5}{3\cdot 5} - \dfrac{x^7}{3\cdot 5\cdot 7} + \cdots\right).$

(g) $y = 1 + (x - 1) - (x - 1)^2 + (x - 1)^3 - \cdots = 2 - \dfrac{1}{x}, 0 < x < 2.$

(h) $y = (x - 1)^2 - \dfrac{(x - 1)^3}{2} + \dfrac{(x - 1)^4}{3} - \cdots = (x - 1)\ln x, 0 < x \leqq 2.$

2. (a) $y_4 = 1 - 3x + \dfrac{(3x)^2}{2!} - \dfrac{(3x)^3}{3!}$.

(b) $y_4 = 2\left(\dfrac{x^3}{3!} - \dfrac{x^4}{4!} + \dfrac{x^5}{5!}\right).$

(c) $y_4 = 3e^x - \dfrac{x^2}{2} - 2x - 3.$

(d) $y_4 = c\left(1 + \dfrac{x}{2} - \dfrac{x^2}{8} - \dfrac{5x^3}{48} + \dfrac{x^5}{64} - \dfrac{x^6}{384}\right).$

(e) $y_4 = 2 + 3(x - 1) + 2(x - 1)^2 + \dfrac{2(x - 1)^3}{3} + \dfrac{(x - 1)^4}{24}$.

B EXERCISES, p. 287

1. $y = \dfrac{x^3}{6} - \dfrac{x^5}{60} + \dfrac{x^7}{1680} - \cdots = \dfrac{1}{2}(\sin x - x\cos x), y(1) = 0.150.$

3. $y = 1 + x + x^2 + \frac{4}{3}x^3 + \frac{7}{6}x^4 + \frac{6}{5}x^5 + \cdots, y(0.2) = 1.253.$

4. $y = A\left(x - \dfrac{x^2}{1^2\cdot 2} + \dfrac{x^3}{2^2\cdot 3} - \dfrac{x^4}{2^2\cdot 3^2\cdot 4} + \cdots\right)$

$\quad = A\left(x - \dfrac{x^2}{1!\,2!} + \dfrac{x^3}{2!\,3!} - \dfrac{x^4}{3!\,4!} + \cdots\right)$ (not a general solution).

C EXERCISES, p. 287

1. $y_4 = 1 + x + x^2 + \frac{4}{3}x^3 + \frac{5}{6}x^4 + \frac{8}{15}x^5 + \frac{29}{90}x^6 + \cdots.$ Only the first four terms of this are actually correct.

A EXERCISES, p. 295

1. (a) $y = A\left(x - \dfrac{x^2}{1!\,2!} + \dfrac{x^3}{2!\,3!} - \dfrac{x^4}{3!\,4!} + \cdots\right)$ (not general solution).

(b) $y = A\left(x^{-1/2} - \dfrac{x^{3/2}}{2!} + \dfrac{x^{7/2}}{4!} - \cdots\right) + B\left(x^{1/2} - \dfrac{x^{5/2}}{3!} + \dfrac{x^{9/2}}{5!} - \cdots\right)$

$ = \dfrac{A \cos x + B \sin x}{\sqrt{x}}$

(c) $y = A\left(1 + \dfrac{x^2}{2 \cdot 3} + \dfrac{x^4}{(2 \cdot 4)(3 \cdot 7)} + \dfrac{x^6}{(2 \cdot 4 \cdot 6)(3 \cdot 7 \cdot 11)} + \cdots\right)$

$ + Bx^{1/2}\left(1 + \dfrac{x^2}{2 \cdot 5} + \dfrac{x^4}{(2 \cdot 4)(5 \cdot 9)} + \dfrac{x^6}{(2 \cdot 4 \cdot 6)(5 \cdot 9 \cdot 13)} + \cdots\right).$

(d) $y = A(x - \tfrac{5}{3}x^3) + B(1 - 6x^2 + 3x^4 + \tfrac{4}{5}x^6 + \tfrac{3}{7}x^8 + \tfrac{2}{7}x^{10} + \cdots).$

(e) $y = A\left(x^{-1} - \dfrac{x}{2!} + \dfrac{x^3}{4!} - \cdots\right) + B\left(1 - \dfrac{x^2}{3!} + \dfrac{x^4}{5!} - \cdots\right)$

$ = \dfrac{A \cos x + B \sin x}{x}.$

(f) $y = A\left(1 - \dfrac{x}{(1!)^2} + \dfrac{x^2}{(2!)^2} - \dfrac{x^3}{(3!)^2} + \cdots\right)$ (not general solution).

(g) $y = Ax^{-1} + B\left(1 - x + \dfrac{x^2}{3}\right).$

(h) $y = A\left(x^{1/2} + \dfrac{x^{5/2}}{2!} + \dfrac{x^{9/2}}{4!} + \cdots\right) + B\left(x^{3/2} + \dfrac{x^{7/2}}{3!} + \dfrac{x^{11/2}}{5!} + \cdots\right)$

$ = Ax^{1/2}\left(\dfrac{e^x + e^{-x}}{2}\right) + Bx^{1/2}\left(\dfrac{e^x - e^{-x}}{2}\right)$

$ = \sqrt{x}(A \cosh x + B \sinh x) = \sqrt{x}(c_1 e^x + c_2 e^{-x}).$

(i) $y = Ax^2\left(1 - \dfrac{x^2}{(2)(6)} + \dfrac{x^4}{(2 \cdot 4)(6 \cdot 8)} - \dfrac{x^6}{(2 \cdot 4 \cdot 6)(6 \cdot 8 \cdot 10)} + \cdots\right).$

(j) $y = A(1 - x)$ (not general solution).

(k) $y = A(1 - 2x^2) + B\left(x - \dfrac{x^3}{3} - \dfrac{x^5}{30} - \dfrac{x^7}{210} - \dfrac{x^9}{1512} - \cdots\right).$

(l) $y = A\left(1 - \dfrac{x^4}{2!} + \dfrac{x^8}{4!} - \dfrac{x^{12}}{6!} + \cdots\right) + B\left(x^2 - \dfrac{x^6}{3!} + \dfrac{x^{10}}{5!} - \dfrac{x^{14}}{7!} + \cdots\right)$

$ = A \cos x^2 + B \sin x^2.$

B EXERCISES, p. 295

2. (a) $y = A\left(x^{-1} + \dfrac{x}{2!} + \dfrac{x^3}{4!} + \dfrac{x^5}{6!} + \cdots\right) + B\left(1 + \dfrac{x^2}{3!} + \dfrac{x^4}{5!} + \dfrac{x^6}{7!} + \cdots\right)$

$ = \dfrac{A \cosh x + B \sinh x}{x} = \dfrac{c_1 e^x + c_2 e^{-x}}{x}.$

(b) $y = A\left(1 - \dfrac{x^3}{3!} + \dfrac{1 \cdot 4}{6!}x^6 - \dfrac{1 \cdot 4 \cdot 7}{9!}x^9 + \cdots\right)$

$ + B\left(x - \dfrac{2}{4!}x^4 + \dfrac{2 \cdot 5}{7!}x^7 - \dfrac{2 \cdot 5 \cdot 8}{10!}x^{10} + \cdots\right).$

4. $x = 0$ is an irregular singular point. The Frobenius solution

$$y = A\left(1 - \frac{x^2}{2} + \frac{x^3}{3} - \frac{3x^4}{8} + \frac{5x^5}{6} - \cdots\right) \text{ exists.}$$

5. $y = A\left(1 + \frac{x^2}{2} + \frac{x^4}{2 \cdot 4} + \frac{x^6}{2 \cdot 4 \cdot 6} + \cdots\right)$

$$+ B\left(x + \frac{x^3}{1 \cdot 3} + \frac{x^5}{1 \cdot 3 \cdot 5} + \cdots\right)$$

$$+ \frac{4}{3} x^{5/2}\left(1 + \frac{2x^2}{9} + \frac{4x^4}{9 \cdot 13} + \frac{8x^6}{9 \cdot 13 \cdot 17} + \cdots\right).$$

6. $y = A\left(x^{-1} - \frac{x}{2!} + \frac{x^3}{4!} - \frac{x^5}{6!} + \cdots\right) + B\left(1 - \frac{x^2}{3!} + \frac{x^4}{5!} - \cdots\right) + 2$

$$= \frac{A \cos x + B \sin x}{x} + 2.$$

C EXERCISES, p. 296

2. (a) $y = AU(x) + B\left\{U(x) \ln x + 2x\left[1 - \frac{x}{1^2 \cdot 2^2}\left(1 + \frac{1}{2}\right)\right.\right.$

$$\left.\left. + \frac{x^2}{1^2 \cdot 2^2 \cdot 3^2}\left(1 + \frac{1}{2} + \frac{1}{3}\right) - \cdots\right]\right\},$$

where $U(x) = 1 - \frac{x}{1^2} + \frac{x^2}{1^2 \cdot 2^2} - \frac{x^3}{1^2 \cdot 2^2 \cdot 3^2} + \cdots$.

(b) $y = Axe^{-x} + B\left\{1 - xe^{-x} \ln x - x^2\left[1 - \frac{x}{2!}\left(1 + \frac{1}{2}\right)\right.\right.$

$$\left.\left. + \frac{x^2}{3!}\left(1 + \frac{1}{2} + \frac{1}{3}\right) - \cdots\right]\right\}.$$

(c) $y = AV(x) + B\left\{V(x) \ln x + x^{-2}\left[1 + \frac{x^2}{2^2} + \frac{x^4}{2^24^2} - \frac{11x^6}{2^24^26^2} + \cdots\right]\right\},$

where $V(x) = -\frac{1}{16}\left(x^2 - \frac{x^4}{(2)(6)} + \frac{x^6}{(2 \cdot 4)(6 \cdot 8)}\right.$

$$\left. - \frac{x^8}{(2 \cdot 4 \cdot 6)(6 \cdot 8 \cdot 10)} + \cdots\right).$$

3. (b) $y = A\left(1 - \frac{x^{-2}}{2!} + \frac{x^{-4}}{4!} + \cdots\right) + B\left(x^{-1} - \frac{x^{-3}}{3!} + \frac{x^{-5}}{5!} + \cdots\right)$

$$= A \cos (1/x) + B \sin (1/x).$$

4. (a) $y = A\left(1 + x^{-1} + \frac{x^{-2}}{2!} + \frac{x^{-3}}{3!} + \cdots\right) + B\left(x^{-1} + x^{-2} + \frac{x^{-3}}{2!} + \frac{x^{-4}}{3!} + \cdots\right)$

$$= (A + Bx^{-1})e^{1/x}.$$

(b) $y = A\left(x^{-1} - \dfrac{x^{-2}}{3!} + \dfrac{x^{-3}}{5!} - \cdots\right) + B\left(x^{-1/2} - \dfrac{x^{-3/2}}{2!} + \dfrac{x^{-5/2}}{4!} - \cdots\right)$

$\qquad = x^{-1/2}[A \sin (x^{-1/2}) + B \cos (x^{-1/2})].$

5. (a) $y = Ax + B\left(1 - x^2 - \dfrac{x^4}{3} - \dfrac{x^6}{5} - \dfrac{x^8}{7} - \dfrac{x^{10}}{9} - \cdots\right).$

$\quad$ **(b)** $y = Cx + D(x^{-2} + \frac{3}{5}x^{-4} + \frac{3}{7}x^{-6} + \frac{3}{9}x^{-8} + \cdots).$

$\quad$ **(c)** $y = c_1 x + c_2\left[\dfrac{x}{2} \ln\left|\dfrac{1 + x}{1 - x}\right| - 1\right].$

CHAPTER 9

A EXERCISES, p. 305

1. 1.83; exact 1.95.   **2.** 0.78; exact 0.81.

3. $n = 4$ and $n = 8$ both yield 4.60; exact 4.60.

4. $n = 5$: 1.88; $n = 10$; 1.94; exact 2.00.   **5.** $n = 5$: 0.734; $n = 10$: 0.796.

6. $n = 5$: 1.28; $n = 10$: 1.31.   **7.** $n = 5$: 2.93; $n = 10$: 3.93.

B EXERCISES, p. 305

1. $n = 5$ gives $y(1) = 0.83$; $n = 10$ gives $y(1) = 0.81$. From $n = 10$, $\pi = 3.24$ approximately.

2. $n = 2$ gives $y(1) = 2.25$; $n = 5$ gives $y(1) = 2.49$; $n = 10$ gives $y(1) = 2.59$. From $n = 10$, $e = 2.59$ approximately.

4. 1.55.   **5.** $n = 5$ gives 0.723; $n = 20$ gives 0.754.

C EXERCISES, p. 306

2. $y(0.8) = 1.31$, $y'(0.8) = 0.95$.

A EXERCISES, p. 307

1. 1.946.   **2.** 0.811.   **3.** 4.6.   **4.** 2.80.

A EXERCISES, p. 311

1. 1.946.   **2.** 0.811.   **3.** 2.718.   **4.** $y(0) = 0.227$, $y(0.5) = 0.579$.

5. 1.05.   **6.** $y(1.9) = 2.946$, $y(2.1) = 5.376$.   **7.** 1.84.   **8.** 0.850.

B EXERCISES, p. 311

1. $y(0.8) = 1.31$, $y(1.2) = 3.77$.   **2.** 0.096.   **3.** $x = 0.766$, $dx/dt = 1.310$.

C EXERCISES, p. 311

4. 0.5.

CHAPTER 10

A EXERCISES, p. 316

1. (a) $x \dfrac{\partial z}{\partial x} + y \dfrac{\partial z}{\partial y} = 2z.$ (b) $(\tan x) \dfrac{\partial z}{\partial x} - (\cot y) \dfrac{\partial z}{\partial y} = z.$

(c) $y^2 \left(\dfrac{\partial z}{\partial x} \right)^2 + x^2 \left(\dfrac{\partial z}{\partial y} \right)^2 + 2x^2 y^2 \left(x \dfrac{\partial z}{\partial x} + y \dfrac{\partial z}{\partial y} \right) = 4x^2 y^2 z.$

(d) One possibility is $z \dfrac{\partial^2 z}{\partial x \, \partial y} + \left(\dfrac{\partial z}{\partial x} \right) \left(\dfrac{\partial z}{\partial y} \right) = 0.$ (e) $\left(\dfrac{\partial z}{\partial x} \right)^2 + \left(\dfrac{\partial z}{\partial y} \right)^2 = 1.$

(f) One possibility is $\dfrac{\partial^2 z}{\partial x \, \partial y} = 0,$ another is $x \dfrac{\partial^2 z}{\partial x^2} = \dfrac{\partial z}{\partial x}.$

(g) $\dfrac{\partial y}{\partial x} + (z \ln z) \dfrac{\partial y}{\partial z} = \cot y.$

2. (a) $2 \dfrac{\partial z}{\partial x} + \dfrac{\partial z}{\partial y} = 0.$ (b) $x \dfrac{\partial z}{\partial x} = y \dfrac{\partial z}{\partial y}.$ (c) $y \dfrac{\partial x}{\partial y} + z \dfrac{\partial x}{\partial z} = 0.$

(d) $y \dfrac{\partial z}{\partial x} + x \dfrac{\partial z}{\partial y} = 0.$ (e) $2 \dfrac{\partial z}{\partial x} + \dfrac{\partial z}{\partial y} = 3z.$ (f) $3 \dfrac{\partial^2 z}{\partial x^2} + 5 \dfrac{\partial^2 z}{\partial x \, \partial y} - 2 \dfrac{\partial^2 z}{\partial y^2} = 0.$

B EXERCISES, p. 317

3. $2x^2 \dfrac{\partial^2 z}{\partial x^2} - 5xy \dfrac{\partial^2 z}{\partial x \, \partial y} + 2y^2 \dfrac{\partial^2 z}{\partial y^2} + 2x \dfrac{\partial z}{\partial x} + 2y \dfrac{\partial z}{\partial y} = 0.$

6. $n = 3.$ 8. A differential equation obtained from each is $x \dfrac{\partial z}{\partial x} = 2y \dfrac{\partial z}{\partial y}.$

C EXERCISES, p. 317

3. (a) $6 \dfrac{\partial z}{\partial x} + 3 \dfrac{\partial z}{\partial y} = -4.$ (b) $y^2 \dfrac{\partial z}{\partial x} - xy \dfrac{\partial z}{\partial y} = xz.$

(c) $(\tan x) \dfrac{\partial z}{\partial x} - (\cot y) \dfrac{\partial z}{\partial y} + z = 0.$

(d) $x \dfrac{\partial z}{\partial x} + (x - y) \dfrac{\partial z}{\partial y} = y.$ (e) $xy^2 \dfrac{\partial z}{\partial x} + x^2 y \dfrac{\partial z}{\partial y} + (x^2 + y^2)z = 0.$

A EXERCISES, p. 325

2. $\dfrac{\partial^2 Y}{\partial t^2} + \beta \dfrac{\partial Y}{\partial t} = a^2 \dfrac{\partial^2 Y}{\partial x^2} + g.$

4. $U_x(0,t) = 0, \; U_x(L,t) = 0; \; U(x,t) = 100.$

CHAPTER II

A EXERCISES, p. 332

1. (a) $U = x \sin y$.   (b) $U = x^2(1 - \cos y) - 2x^2 y/\pi$.

    (c) $V = \frac{1}{3}x^3 + 3 \sin y$.   (d) $U = x^2 y^2 + ye^x + \frac{1}{2}y^2 - y + 2$.

    (e) $Z = \frac{1}{3}e^{3x}(y^3 - 2y^2) - \frac{1}{3}y^2 + x + 3e^{-x}$.

2. (a) $U = e^{2x+2y}$.   (b) $U = 4e^{-3x-2y}$.   (c) $U = 2e^{2x-y} + 3e^{3x-2y}$.

    (d) $Y = 4e^{-x+t} - e^{-5x+2t}$.   (e) $U = 5e^{-16\pi^2 t} \sin 2\pi x$.

    (f) $U = 2e^{-4.5t} \sin 3x - 5e^{-8t} \sin 4x$.   (g) $Y = 10 \sin \dfrac{\pi x}{2} \cos \dfrac{\pi t}{2}$.

    (h) $Y = 3 \sin 2\pi x \cos 4\pi t - 4 \sin \dfrac{5\pi x}{2} \cos 5\pi t$.

    (i) $Y = 6 \sin x \sin (t/3) - 4.5 \sin 2x \sin (2t/3)$.

    (j) $U = 5e^{(1-4\pi^2)t} \sin 2\pi x - e^{(1-16\pi^2)t} \sin 4\pi x$.

C EXERCISES, p. 334

2. (a) $U = F(y + x) + G(y + 2x)$.   (b) $U = F(x + iy) + G(x - iy)$.

    (c) $Y = F(x - at) + G(x + at)$.   (d) $U = F(y - 4x) + G(y)$.

    (e) $U = F(x) + G(3x + 2y)$.

3. (a) $U = F(y + 2x) + xG(y + 2x)$.   (b) $Y = F(2x + 3t) + xG(2x + 3t)$.

5. $Z = F(y - x) + G(y - 3x) + \frac{4}{55}e^{2x+3y}$.

6. $U = F(x - y) + xG(x - y) - \frac{1}{3}\sin (x - 4y) + \frac{1}{12}x^4$.

7. $U = F(x + y) + G(y - 2x) - \frac{3}{2}xe^{y-3x} + \frac{1}{15}\cos (x - 2y)$.

8. (a) $U = F(y + 2x) + G(y - x) + H(y + x)$.

    (b) $Z = F_1(x + iy) + F_2(x - iy) + xF_3(x + iy) + xF_4(x - iy)$.

    (c) $U = F(y) + G(2x + \sqrt{3}y) + H(2x - \sqrt{3}y) - \frac{3}{4}xe^y + \frac{2}{33}\cos (x + 3y)$.

9. (b) $F(x - y - z, x^2 - 2xy) = 0$.

10. (d) $U = 8c^{-4\pi^2 t} \sin 2\pi x$.

A EXERCISES, p. 348

1. (a) $f(x) = \displaystyle\sum_{n=1}^{\infty} \dfrac{-4}{n\pi} (1 - \cos n\pi) \sin nx$

$$= -\frac{8}{\pi}\left(\sin x + \frac{1}{3} \sin 3x + \frac{1}{5} \sin 5x + \cdots \right).$$

    (b) $f(x) = 1$.

    (c) $f(x) = 1 + \displaystyle\sum_{n=1}^{\infty} \dfrac{2}{n\pi} (1 - \cos n\pi) \sin \dfrac{n\pi x}{3}$

$$= 1 + \frac{4}{\pi}\left(\sin \frac{\pi x}{3} + \frac{1}{3} \sin \frac{3\pi x}{3} + \frac{1}{5} \sin \frac{5\pi x}{3} + \cdots \right).$$

(d) $f(x) = \dfrac{1}{4} + \displaystyle\sum_{n=1}^{\infty} \left\{ \left(\dfrac{\cos n\pi - 1}{n^2\pi^2} \right) \cos n\pi x - \dfrac{\cos n\pi}{n\pi} \sin n\pi x \right\}$

$\qquad = \dfrac{1}{4} - \dfrac{2}{\pi^2} \left(\cos \pi x + \dfrac{\cos 3\pi x}{3^2} + \dfrac{\cos 5\pi x}{5^2} + \cdots \right)$

$\qquad\qquad\qquad + \dfrac{1}{\pi} \left(\sin \pi x - \dfrac{\sin 2\pi x}{2} + \dfrac{\sin 3\pi x}{3} - \cdots \right).$

(e) $f(x) = \dfrac{\pi}{2} + \dfrac{2}{\pi} \displaystyle\sum_{n=1}^{\infty} \left(\dfrac{\cos n\pi - 1}{n^2} \right) \cos nx$

$\qquad = \dfrac{\pi}{2} - \dfrac{4}{\pi} \left(\cos x + \dfrac{\cos 3x}{3^2} + \dfrac{\cos 5x}{5^2} + \cdots \right).$

(f) $f(x) = \displaystyle\sum_{n=1}^{\infty} \dfrac{6}{n\pi} (1 - \cos n\pi) \sin \dfrac{n\pi x}{4}$

$\qquad = \dfrac{12}{\pi} \left(\sin \dfrac{\pi x}{4} + \dfrac{1}{3} \sin \dfrac{3\pi x}{4} + \dfrac{1}{5} \sin \dfrac{5\pi x}{4} + \cdots \right).$

(g) $f(x) = \dfrac{8}{3} - \displaystyle\sum_{n=1}^{\infty} \dfrac{16}{n^2\pi^2} \cos \dfrac{n\pi x}{2}$

$\qquad = \dfrac{8}{3} - \dfrac{16}{\pi^2} \left(\dfrac{1}{1^2} \cos \dfrac{\pi x}{2} + \dfrac{1}{2^2} \cos \dfrac{2\pi x}{2} + \dfrac{1}{3^2} \cos \dfrac{3\pi x}{2} + \cdots \right).$

(h) $f(x) = \displaystyle\sum_{n=1}^{\infty} \dfrac{1}{n\pi} \left(2 - \cos \dfrac{2n\pi}{3} - \cos \dfrac{4n\pi}{3} \right) \sin nx.$

2. (a) $f(x) = \displaystyle\sum_{n=1}^{\infty} \dfrac{10}{n\pi} (1 - \cos n\pi) \sin \dfrac{n\pi x}{3}$

$\qquad = \dfrac{20}{\pi} \left(\sin \dfrac{\pi x}{3} + \dfrac{1}{3} \sin \dfrac{3\pi x}{3} + \dfrac{1}{5} \sin \dfrac{5\pi x}{3} + \cdots \right).$

(b) $f(x) = \dfrac{1}{2} + \displaystyle\sum_{n=1}^{\infty} \left(\dfrac{2}{n\pi} \sin \dfrac{n\pi}{2} \right) \cos nx$

$\qquad = \dfrac{1}{2} + \dfrac{2}{\pi} \left(\cos x - \dfrac{1}{3} \cos 3x + \dfrac{1}{5} \cos 5x - \cdots \right).$

(c) $f(x) = \displaystyle\sum_{n=1}^{\infty} \left(\dfrac{20}{n^2\pi^2} \sin \dfrac{n\pi}{2} - \dfrac{10}{n\pi} \cos \dfrac{n\pi}{2} \right) \sin \dfrac{n\pi x}{10}.$

(d) $f(x) = 2.$

(e) $f(x) = \displaystyle\sum_{n=1}^{\infty} \dfrac{64}{n^3\pi^3} (1 - \cos n\pi) \sin \dfrac{n\pi x}{4}$

$\qquad = \dfrac{128}{\pi^3} \left(\sin \dfrac{\pi x}{4} + \dfrac{1}{3^3} \sin \dfrac{3\pi x}{4} + \dfrac{1}{5^3} \sin \dfrac{5\pi x}{4} + \cdots \right).$

(f) $f(x) = \displaystyle\sum_{n=1}^{\infty} -\dfrac{4}{n\pi} \sin \dfrac{n\pi}{2} \cos \dfrac{n\pi x}{4}$

$\qquad = -\dfrac{4}{\pi} \left(\cos \dfrac{\pi x}{4} - \dfrac{1}{3} \cos \dfrac{3\pi x}{4} + \dfrac{1}{5} \cos \dfrac{5\pi x}{4} - \cdots \right).$

B EXERCISES, p. 349

3. $f(x) = \sum\limits_{n=1}^{\infty} \dfrac{2L^2}{n^3\pi^3}\left[(2 - n^2\pi^2)\cos n\pi - 2\right]\sin\dfrac{n\pi x}{L}$

$\qquad = \dfrac{2L^2}{\pi^3}\left\{\left(\dfrac{\pi^2}{1} - \dfrac{4}{1^3}\right)\sin\dfrac{\pi x}{L} - \dfrac{\pi^2}{2}\sin\dfrac{2\pi x}{L}\right.$

$\qquad\qquad + \left(\dfrac{\pi^2}{3} - \dfrac{4}{3^3}\right)\sin\dfrac{3\pi x}{L} - \dfrac{\pi^2}{4}\sin\dfrac{4\pi x}{L}$

$\qquad\qquad \left.+ \left(\dfrac{\pi^2}{5} - \dfrac{4}{5^3}\right)\sin\dfrac{5\pi x}{L} - \dfrac{\pi^2}{6}\sin\dfrac{6\pi x}{L} + \cdots\right\}.$

A EXERCISES, p. 355

1. Assuming that initially the portion of the bar between $x = 0$ and $x = 50$ is at $80°C$, while the portion between $x = 50$ and $x = 100$ is at $0°C$ the temperature at place x at time t is given by

$$U(x,t) = \sum_{n=1}^{\infty}\frac{160}{n\pi}\left(1 - \cos\frac{n\pi}{2}\right)e^{-0.20(n\pi/100)^2 t}\sin\frac{n\pi x}{100}.$$

2. $U(x,t) = \sum\limits_{n=1}^{\infty}\dfrac{200}{n\pi}\left(\cos\dfrac{2n\pi}{5} - \cos\dfrac{3n\pi}{5}\right)e^{-0.20(n\pi/100)^2 t}\sin\dfrac{n\pi x}{100}.$

3. $U(x,t) = 20 + \sum\limits_{n=1}^{\infty}\dfrac{160}{n\pi}(1 - \cos n\pi)e^{-0.20(n\pi/40)^2 t}\sin\dfrac{n\pi x}{40}.$

4. (a) $Y(x,t) = 0.25\sin\dfrac{\pi x}{4}\cos 16\pi t.$

(b) $Y(x,t) = 0.1\sin\pi x\cos 64\pi t - 0.02\sin 3\pi x\cos 192\pi t.$

(c) $Y(x,t) = \sum\limits_{n=1}^{\infty}\dfrac{0.32}{n^2\pi^2}\sin\dfrac{n\pi}{2}\sin\dfrac{n\pi x}{4}\cos 16n\pi t.$

B EXERCISES, p. 355

1. $U(x,t) = \psi(x) + \sum\limits_{n=1}^{\infty}\left\{\dfrac{2}{L}\int_0^L [f(x) - \psi(x)]\sin\dfrac{n\pi x}{L}\,dx\right\}e^{-\kappa n^2\pi^2 t/L^2}\sin\dfrac{n\pi x}{L},$

where $\psi(x) = T_1 + (T_2 - T_1)x/L.$

2. $U(x,t) = 30 + x + \sum\limits_{n=1}^{\infty}\left(\dfrac{60 + 40\cos n\pi}{n\pi}\right)e^{-0.15(n\pi/50)^2 t}\sin\dfrac{n\pi x}{50}.$

3. (a) $U(x,t) = \dfrac{1}{L}\int_0^L f(x)\,dx + \sum\limits_{n=1}^{\infty}\left\{\dfrac{2}{L}\int_0^L f(x)\cos\dfrac{n\pi x}{L}\,dx\right\}e^{-\kappa n^2\pi^2 t/L^2}\cos\dfrac{n\pi x}{L}.$

(b) $U(x,t) = \dfrac{T}{2} + \sum\limits_{n=1}^{\infty}\left\{\dfrac{4T}{n^2\pi^2}\left(2\cos\dfrac{n\pi}{2} - 1 - \cos n\pi\right)\right\}e^{-\kappa n^2\pi^2 t/L^2}\cos\dfrac{n\pi x}{L}.$

4. $U(x,t) = T_0$
$$+ \sum_{n=1}^{\infty} \left\{ \frac{2}{L} \int_0^L [f(x) - T_0] \cos \frac{(2n-1)\pi x}{L} \, dx \right\} e^{-\kappa(2n-1)^2\pi^2 t/L^2} \cos \frac{(2n-1)\pi x}{L}.$$

5. $U(x,t) = e^{-ct} \sum_{n=1}^{\infty} \left\{ \frac{2}{L} \int_0^L f(x) \sin \frac{n\pi x}{L} \, dx \right\} e^{-\kappa n^2\pi^2 t/L^2} \frac{\sin n\pi x}{L}.$

6. $Y(x,t) = \psi(x) + \sum_{n=1}^{\infty} \left\{ \frac{2}{L} \int_0^L [f(x) - \psi(x)] \sin \frac{n\pi x}{L} \, dx \right\} \sin \frac{n\pi x}{L} \cos \frac{n\pi at}{L},$

where $\psi(x) = \dfrac{g}{2a^2} (Lx - x^2).$

C EXERCISES, p. 356

3. $U(r,\theta) = \dfrac{1}{2\pi} \int_0^{2\pi} f(\theta) \, d\theta + \sum_{n=1}^{\infty} r^n (A_n \cos n\theta + B_n \sin n\theta),$

where $A_n = \dfrac{1}{\pi a^n} \int_0^{2\pi} f(\theta) \cos n\theta \, d\theta, \; B_n = \dfrac{1}{\pi a^n} \int_0^{2\pi} f(\theta) \sin n\theta \, d\theta.$

A EXERCISES, p. 361

1. (a) $U(r,t) = 50 e^{-\kappa \lambda_1^2 t} J_0(\lambda_1 r).$

(b) $U(r,t) = 20 e^{-\kappa \lambda_1^2 t} J_0(\lambda_1 r) - 10 e^{-\kappa \lambda_2^2 t} J_0(\lambda_2 r).$

2. $Z(r,t) = \sum_{n=1}^{\infty} A_n J_0(\lambda_n r) \cos \lambda_n at$, where A_n is given by equation (9), p. 360.

3. (a) $Z(r,t) = 0.05 J_0(\lambda_1 r) \cos \lambda_1 at.$

(b) $Z(r,t) = 0.20 J_0(\lambda_1 r) \cos \lambda_1 at - 0.15 J_0(\lambda_3 r) \cos \lambda_3 at.$

4. $V(r,z) = \sum_{n=1}^{\infty} A_n J_0(\lambda_n r) \sinh \lambda_n z$, where $A_n = \dfrac{\displaystyle\int_0^1 r f(r) J_0(\lambda_n r) \, dr}{\sinh \lambda_n \displaystyle\int_0^1 r[J_0(\lambda_n r)]^2 \, dr}.$

5. $U(r,z) = \sum_{n=1}^{\infty} A_n e^{-\lambda_n z} J_0(\lambda_n r)$, where A_n is given by equation (9), p. 360.

B EXERCISES, p. 362

2. $U(r,t) = \sum_{n=1}^{\infty} A_n e^{-\kappa \lambda_n^2 t} J_0(\lambda_n r)$, where $\lambda_n, \; n = 1, 2, 3, \ldots$ are the positive roots of $J_0'(\lambda) = 0$ [or $J_1(\lambda) = 0$] and A_n is given by equation (9), p. 360.

6. (a) $U(r,t) = 200 \sum_{n=1}^{\infty} \dfrac{e^{-\kappa \lambda_n^2 t} J_0(\lambda_n r)}{\lambda_n J_1(\lambda_n)}.$

(b) $U(r,t) = 100 \sum_{n=1}^{\infty} \dfrac{e^{-\kappa \lambda_n^2 t} J_0(\lambda_n r)}{\lambda_n^3 J_1(\lambda_n)}.$

7. (a) $Z(r,t) = 0.1 \sum\limits_{n=1}^{\infty} \dfrac{(4 + \lambda_n - \lambda_n^2)}{\lambda_n^3 J_1(\lambda_n)} \cos \lambda_n at,$

    (b) $Z(r,t) = 0.4 \sum\limits_{n=1}^{\infty} \dfrac{J_0(\lambda_n r) \cos \lambda_n at}{\lambda_n^3 J_1(\lambda_n)}.$

C EXERCISES, p. 362

8. (a) $V(r,\theta) = \frac{3}{5} r P_1(\cos \theta) + \frac{2}{5} r^3 P_3(\cos \theta).$

    (b) $V(r,\theta) = \dfrac{3P_1(\cos \theta)}{5r^2} + \dfrac{2P_3(\cos \theta)}{5r^4}.$

INDEX